PREFACE

1.   This September 2014 Edition of The Admiralty Manual of Seamanship supersedes BR 67, Admiralty Manual of Seamanship October 2010 Edition.

2.   The purpose of this publication is to provide the Seaman Specialist with detailed information on all aspects of seamanship appertaining to the Royal Navy. It is also a source of information on seamanship matters for officers and ratings of other branches. Other publications referred to within this publication are not available outside the Ministry of Defence.

CONTENTS

Issued	September 2014
Superseding	2012 Edition
Dated	April 2012

BR 67

ADMIRALTY MANUAL OF SEAMANSHIP

By Command of the Defence Council
Fleet Commander & Deputy Chief of Naval Staff

ADMIRALTY MANUAL OF SEAMANSHIP

12th Edition dated September 2014 (superseding the 11th Edition dated October 2010)

© British Crown Copyright 2014 published with the permission of the
Controller of Her Majesty's Stationery Office
© The Nautical Institute

Authoring Authority: Officer in Charge (OIC),
Naval Staff Author: Vic Vance
Navy Publications and Graphics Organisation (NPGO),
Pepys Building, HMS COLLINGWOOD, Newgate Lane, Fareham,
Hampshire PO14 1AS, United Kingdom.

MoD Directorate of Intellectual Property Rights: DIPR (PL),
Ministry of Defence, Abbey Wood, Bristol, BS34 8JH, United Kingdom.

Publisher: The Nautical Institute
202 Lambeth Road, London SE1 7LQ, United Kingdom.
TEL: +44(0)20 7928 1351   FAX: +44(0)20 7401 2817
www.nautinst.org

Typeset by Phil McAllister Design

Book graphics and cover design by
Navy Graphics Studio, HMS EXCELLENT

Printed in England by Newnorth Print

ISBN : 978 1 906915 49 0

Cover Pictures: Courtesy the Royal Navy

FOREWORD

By Vice Admiral Sir Philip Jones KCB, Fleet Commander and Deputy Chief of Naval Staff.

I am honoured to follow in my predecessors' footsteps and write the Foreword to the 2014 revised edition of BR 67, *The Admiralty Manual of Seamanship*. Of great importance to the maritime community, this collaboration between the Royal Navy and The Nautical Institute contains a wealth of experience stretching back over one hundred years and, quite rightly, forms the basis for all of the Royal Navy's seamanship activity and training.

This revision comes at an exciting and evolutionary time for the Royal Navy. The introduction of the next generation of ships and submarines, including the DARING Class destroyers, QUEEN ELIZABETH Class carriers and ASTUTE Class submarines necessitates that the seamanship lessons already widely in use be extended to reflect new technology and procedures; many of the amendments in this edition reflect this. While technology offers welcome efficiency, it is no substitute for good seamanship. Respect for our hazardous environment, which is unforgiving of inadequate competence and preparation, remains the underpinning principle of this publication.

As an authority on its subject, this publication is of vital importance to all seafarers, both military and civilian, and I commend its content to all with a role to play in this challenging aspect of the conduct of maritime activity.

Sir Phillip Jones KCB
September 2014

THIS PAGE IS INTENTIONALLY BLANK

CHAPTER 1

GENERAL SEA TERMS

CONTENTS

CHAPTER 1

GENERAL SEA TERMS

01001. Introduction

Every profession and trade uses its own technical terms to describe the more specialised parts of its work; nowhere is this more evident than in the language of the seafarer. Many terms used by the British seafarer have, in the course of time, become part of the English language. This is because so many of the inhabitants of our small island kingdom have been born and bred near the sea, and because no other country has for so long been dependent for its existence and prosperity on its Royal and merchant navies. To learn seamanship the seaman must first understand the more general nautical terms and expressions, which are explained in this chapter. Others, more technical, are included in the chapters on the different aspects of seamanship to which they are applied.

01002. Terms relating to a ship - Parts of a ship

a. **The hull**

(1) The main body of a ship is called the hull. It is divided approximately into three - the **fore** part, the **midship** part and the **after** part. The fore part ends in the **stem**, the after part in the **stern** (Fig 1-1). When standing anywhere inside the hull a person is facing **forward** when facing the bow and facing **aft** when facing the stern.

Fig 1-1. Parts of the hull

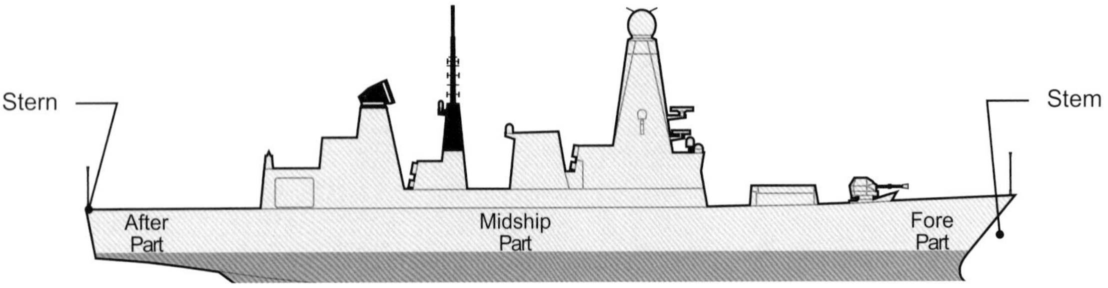

Stern —

Stem —

After
Part

Midship
Part

Fore
Part

(2) Any line which runs lengthways in the ship is said to run **fore-and-aft** and the line joining the middle of the bow to the middle of the stern is called the **fore-and-aft centre line** (middle line or centre line in ship's plans and drawings) (Fig 1-2).

Fig 1-2. Parts of the Hull

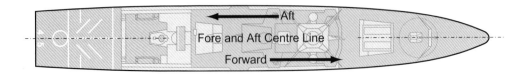

Aft

Fore and Aft Centre Line

Forward

Fig 1-3. Parts of the hull

(3)   The vertical plane (surface) passing through the fore-and-aft centre line divides the ship into two halves. When facing the bow, a ship's **starboard** side is on the right hand and the **port** side is on the left (Fig 1-3). It is customary to give equipment, such as ship's boats, odd numbers on the starboard side and even numbers on the port side.

b.   **Hull surfaces** (Fig 1-4)

(1)   The sides of a hull can be described generally as starboard or port, meeting under the bottom of the ship at the **keel**. The curved surface of the fore part is called the bow (port or starboard) and the curved surface of the after part is called the quarter (port or starboard); the centre part is referred to as **amidships**.

Fig 1-4. Hull surfaces

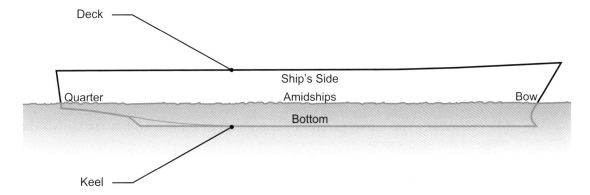

(2)   When a ship is **afloat** or **water-borne** the **waterline** divides the sides into **ship's side** above the waterline and **bottom** below it. These terms are used in a general sense, for example, when painting a ship's side or scraping her bottom. A more precise definition of an area can be achieved by referring to the side, the part and the waterline, for example: 'the ship was holed on the starboard bow two metres below the waterline'.

(3)   The continuous horizontal surfaces of a ship are called **decks**; if exposed they are called **weather decks**. Those that are not continuous are called **flats** or **platforms**.

c.   **Terms applied to the hull** (Fig 1-5)

(1)   *Freeboard.* The height of the highest continuous watertight deck (usually known as the upper deck) above the waterline at any point along the hull.

(2)   *Draught.* The depth of the keel below the waterline at any point along the hull.

Fig 1-5. Hull terms

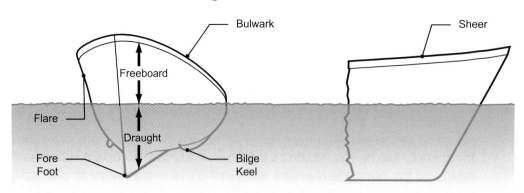

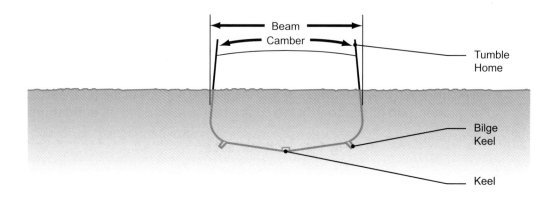

(3) *Beam.* The greatest width of the hull.

(4) *Camber.* The curve given to the surface of a deck so that water will drain away to the ship's side.

(5) *Sheer.* The upward sweep from amidships to forward and aft of the upper deck.

(6) *Bilge.* The nearly flat part of the bottom of the hull both inside and out. Bilge is also the foul water that collects inside the ship in the **bilges**.

(7) *Bilge keel.* A long projecting fin designed to decrease the rolling of a ship. It is normally secured to the hull at the **turn of the bilge**.

(8) *Tumble home.* When the ship's sides slope or curve inwards above the waterline they are said to tumble home.

(9) *Flare.* When the ship's side curve outwards above the waterline they are said to be flared.

(10) *Flush deck.* When the uppermost deck of a ship is continuous from stem to stern, unbroken by any raised or sunken portion (except upper works or superstructure), the ship is said to be flush-decked.

d. **Decks**. Whatever the arrangement of decks in different ships may be, it is useful and instructive to know their origin.

Fig 1-6. Arrangement of decks in a sailing man-of-war

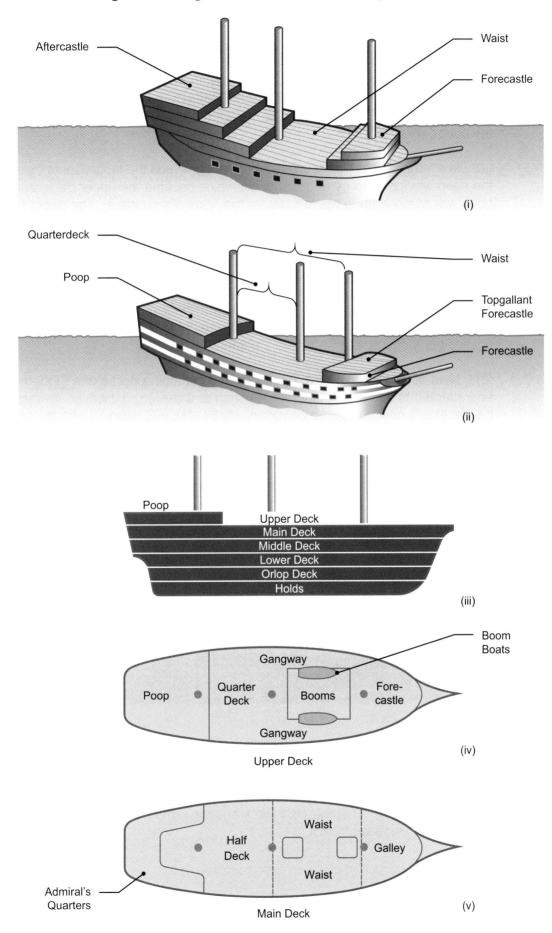

(1)   At the time of the Armada the ends of the upper deck were built up in tiers of decks to form castles from which the soldiers could fight. They were called the **fo'c'sle** and **aftercastle**. The lower part between the castles was called the **waist** (Fig 1-6(i)). By the end of the eighteenth century the level of the upper deck had been raised to make room for additional gun decks. Naval warfare had developed, but castles still existed. They were then called the **topgallant fo'c'sle** and the **poop**. The fo'c'sle was that part of the upper deck before the foremast, and the quarterdeck was that part of the upper deck between the mainmast and the poop (Fig 1-6(ii)).

(2)   In a large ship of Nelson's days the waist between the topgallant fo'c'sle and the poop was covered by an extra deck, which became the upper deck, and the poop was stepped up to make room for the Admiral's quarters. The decks below the upper deck were then named **main, middle, lower** and **orlop** and the space below the orlop deck was known as the **hold** (Fig 1-6(iii)). On the upper deck were the **booms** amidships over the **main hatch**; as the name implies, they constituted the stowage for spare spars and the ship's boats (Fig 1-6(iv)). Right aft on the main deck were the Admiral's cabin and cabins for his staff, and the space between them and the mainmast was called the **half deck**; the space between the mainmast and foremast was the waist, and the space between the foremast and the bows, which housed the kitchens, was known as the **galley** (Fig 1-6(v)).

(3)   Most of these terms have been retained in naming decks of a modern ship and adapted to suit changes in construction and design. However, in warships the decks are now numbered consecutively downwards, starting with the fo'c'sle deck as 1 deck. The decks above 1 deck are numbered 01, 02 and so on, consecutively upward (Fig 1-7).

Fig 1-7. Arrangement of decks in a warship

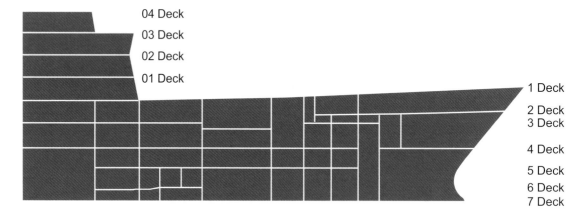

(4)   The highest complete deck (except in aircraft carriers) is known as the upper deck. Most modern warships are **flush-decked** and thus the upper and fo'c'sle decks are a common deck. In aircraft carriers, the flight deck extends for the full length of the ship and is constructed above the fo'c'sle deck, and so, in this case only, the flight deck is numbered 1 Deck and the remaining decks are numbered upward and downward from it.

(5) *Parts of decks.* Certain parts of any of these decks may also have special names. Below the upper deck a **flat** is a platform that does not run the length and breadth of a ship; a **lobby** is a space giving access to one or more compartments. These flats or lobbies may be named according to the principal adjacent compartments or equipment installed, eg wardroom flat, Captain's lobby, capstan machinery flat, or they may be referred to by deck numbers and positions in the ship relative to the bow and the centre line.

(6) The arrangement of the weather decks and superstructure of a ship is shown in Fig 1-8.

Fig 1-8. Arrangement of weather deck and superstructure of a ship

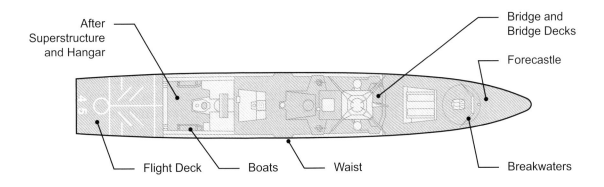

After
Superstructure
and Hangar

Bridge and
Bridge Decks

Forecastle

Flight Deck   Boats   Waist   Breakwaters

01003. Terms defining position and direction in a ship

a. **Position in general**

(1) A landsman lives **in** a house; therefore a seaman speaks of living **in** a ship – not **on** a ship. Let us now describe the movements of a seaman who is returning to the ship, the ship in which he/she is **borne**. If he/she arrives by boat and goes up an accommodation ladder or pilot/boarding ladder which is secured **outboard** (board is the old name for a ship's side), he/she comes over the **side** and is then **on board**. If the ship is lying against a dock wall it is **alongside** and the seaman crosses a **brow** from the dock to the ship and he/she is then on board and **on deck**, or on board and **between decks** if the brow leads into the ship below the weather deck; in either case he/she is **inboard** the moment he/she comes over the side.

(2) Having reported his return, the seaman then goes **below** by a **ladder** which gives access to the deck below through an opening in the deck called a **hatch**. The seaman then reaches the living quarters (**mess**), which is in a space of the ship called a **messdeck** of which the walls are called **bulkheads**, the ceiling is called the **deck head** and the floor is the **deck**.

b. **Position fore and aft**

(1) In Fig 1-9 the mast is **forward** (pronounced 'forrard') and the funnel is **aft**. The ensign staff is right aft and the jackstaff right forward. The hatch is **amidships**.

Fig 1-9. Position fore and aft

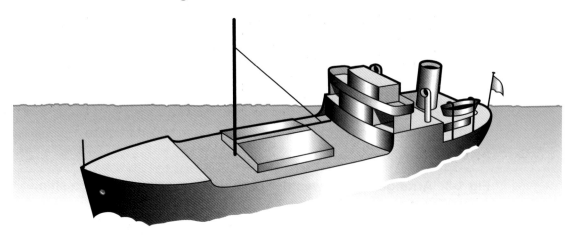

(2)   Amidships describes the position roughly in the middle of the ship; it also describes any position on the fore-and-aft line. **Midships** is used when defining an object: for example, the midship hatch is either the one that is in the middle of the ship or, if there are two or more hatches, that which is nearest the middle. Merchant Navy vessels invariably number their hatches 1, 2, 3 etc from forward.

(3)   Comparing positions of objects with one another, the funnel is **abaft** (aft of) the bridge, the bridge is abaft the hatch but **before** or **forward of** the funnel.

c.   **Position athwartships**

(1)   A position athwart or across the ship can be described relative to either the centre line or to the sides. The centre line divides the ship into port and starboard, while the ship's side gives an **inboard** and **outboard** position. In Fig 1-10, for example, a ship is carrying three boats; one is swung outboard to port, the other two are stowed inboard to starboard. When comparing the position of the two boats stowed on the starboard side, the black boat can be described as lying inboard of the white boat, or the white boat outboard of the black.

(2)   The position of an object can be clearly described by combining the two methods, as shown in Fig 1-11.

Fig 1-10. Position Athwartships

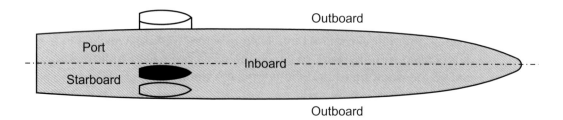

Fig 1-11. How positions are described

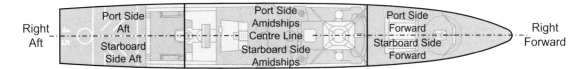

d.   **Movement of objects onboard.** A seaman speaks of going forward, aft, below, on deck and aloft (ie, anywhere in the rigging of a mast). The seaman uses the same expression for shifting an object; thus he/she may shift something aft, or farther forward, to port or starboard, or nearer the ship's side. (The terms inboard and outboard should not be used to describe the movement athwartships.) The following terms are used to describe how an object is moved:

(1)   To **launch** is to drag or heave an object along.

(2)   To **lift and launch** is to lift an object and then to heave it along.

(3)   To **fleet** is to shift an object a short distance.

(4)   To **ship** is to place an object in its proper position.

(5)   To **unship** is to remove an object from its proper position.

01004. Terms defining the movement of a ship

a.   A vessel is **under way** when she is neither anchored nor secured to a buoy, nor made fast to the shore, nor aground. When actually moving through the water, a vessel has **way** on her; if she is moving too fast she is said to have **too much way on**.

b.   When moving ahead a vessel is said to be **going ahead** or **making headway**; when moving astern a vessel is said to be **going astern** or **making sternway** or **making a stern board**. A vessel **gathers way** when she begins to move through the water, and she has **steerageway** when her speed is sufficient for steering (ie the rudder is effective).

c.   A vessel moving sideways is said to be moving **broadside on** (to port or starboard); if she is making headway and at the same time being blown sideways by the wind, she is said to be making **leeway**. When the wind is blowing from one side of the vessel, that side is called the **weather side**; the other, sheltered, side is called the **lee side**.

d.   A ship is said to be **adrift** when broken away from her moorings and without means of propulsion.

e.   A ship is steered by compass in a direction called the **compass course** or simply the **course**. The question **'how is the ship's head?'** means in what direction by the compass is the ship heading (pointing).

01005. Terms defining direction and position outside a ship

a. **Relative bearings** (Fig 1-12 and Fig 1-13)

(1)   **Ahead, astern** and **abeam** are relative bearings.   In addition, when an object is midway between ahead and abeam it is said to bear **on the bow**, and when midway between abeam and astern it is said to bear **on the quarter**.   The expressions **fine** and **broad** may also be used relative to ahead or astern; for example, an object may be fine on the port bow, broad on the starboard quarter (or abaft the starboard beam).

Fig 1-12. General relative bearings

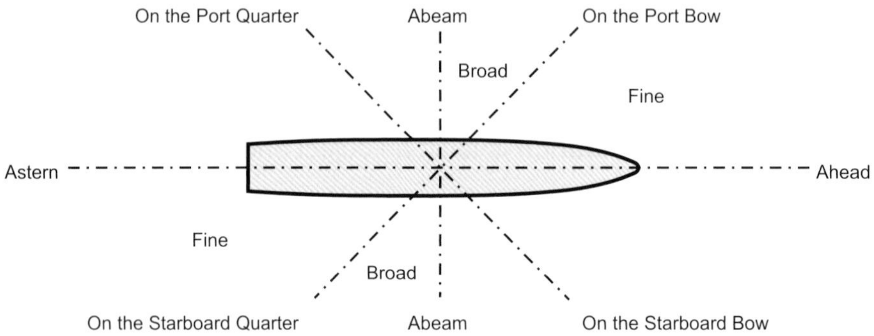

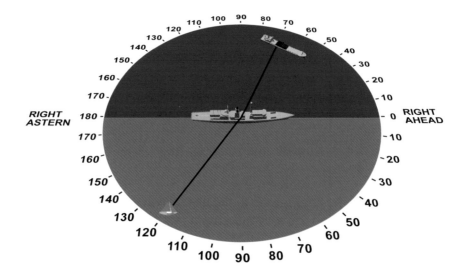

(2)   A greater degree of accuracy in relative bearings is obtained by expressing them in terms of degrees from ahead on each side of the ship.   The horizon is divided in degrees from zero (right ahead) to 180 (right astern).   Those on the starboard side are called green and those on the port side red.   Thus, in Fig 1-13, the sailing vessel bears **green** 120 and the steamship bears **red** 70 (the word 'degrees' is always omitted).

Fig 1-13. Red and green relative bearings

(3)   When one ship is lying next to another or on a dock wall it is said to be **alongside** the other ship or wall. When two ships are moving on the same course and level with each other they are said to be **abreast**.

b.   **Compass bearings**

(1)   The bearing of an object from the ship may be given relative to **true** or **magnetic** North. If it is a gyro-compass bearing the horizon is divided into 360 degrees from true North (the meridian). If it is a magnetic-compass bearing the horizon is divided into 360 degrees from magnetic North.

Fig 1-14. A compass card

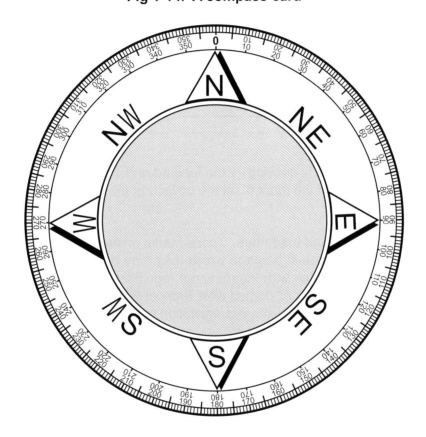

(2)   The **magnetic compass card** (Fig 1-14) is divided into 360° from North (0°), through East (090°), South (180°), West (270°), and so back to North. The card may be divided into 32 points of $11\frac{1}{4}$ degrees. The principal points, North, South, East and West are called **cardinal points**; the **intercardinal points** are North-east, South-east, South-west and North-west; and the **intermediate points** are North-north-east, East-north-east, East-south-east, South-south-east, South-south-west, West-south-west, West-north-west and North-north-west. The remaining 16 points are known as **by-points**.

c.   **Distances.** The distance of an object from the ship may be expressed in nautical miles (one nautical mile equals 1852 metres), in cables (one cable is one-tenth of a nautical mile) or in metres.

01006. Terms relating to shipping

a. Draught marks (surface ships)

(1) These show the draught of the ship, measured in decimetres, and are usually positioned at the bows, stern and amidships. The marks are Arabic numerals, one decimetre high and one decimetre apart, and only even numbers are used (Fig 1-15). Above the waterline they are generally engraved on plates welded to the hull and below the waterline they are painted in a contrasting colour.

Fig 1-15. Draught marks

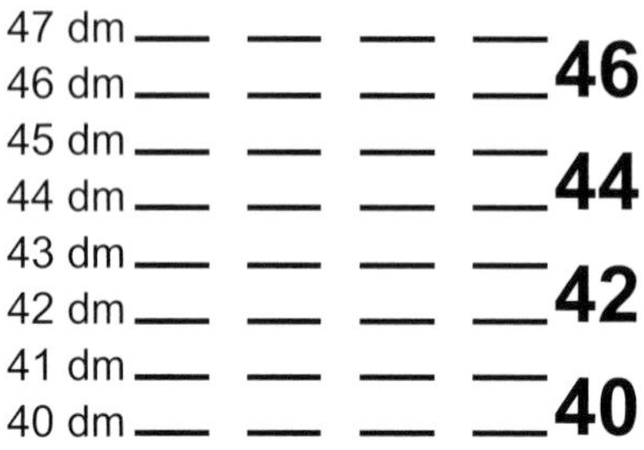

47 dm
46 dm
45 dm
44 dm
43 dm
42 dm
41 dm
40 dm
46
44
42
40

(2) When a ship is drawing 42 dm forward and 45 dm aft, the waterline touches the lower edge of the mark 42 at the bows and the upper edge of the mark 44 at the stern.

b. **Load line disc and load lines.** These marks on the sides of merchant ships (Fig 1-16) indicate the greatest depth to which they may be safely loaded under various conditions in accordance with international regulations. The marks were originally known as Plimsoll marks, so named after Samuel Plimsoll, MP, who rendered a great service to seamen by introducing this legislation which was ratified under the Merchant Shipping Acts of 1876 and 1890.

Fig 1-16. Load line disc and load lines

DECKLINE
SUMMER
=FREEBOARD
L
R
TF
F
T
S
W
WNA

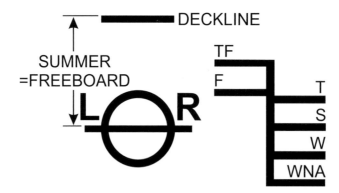

TF	Tropical fresh water	WNA	Winter, North Atlantic, for vessels under 100 metres in length
F	Fresh water		
T	Tropical sea water	LR	These letters indicate the classification society, in this case Lloyd's Register
S	Summer, sea water		
W	Winter, sea water		

c.   **Load waterline.** This is a term chiefly used in merchant ships to denote the position of the waterline when the ship is fully loaded with crew, stores, water, fuel, etc. The ship is then said to be in the **deep condition**.

d.   **Tonnage measurements.** The tonnage of a ship can be expressed in terms of weight or volume. When expressed by weight the unit of measurement is the tonne (one tonne equals 1000 kilograms), and when expressed by volume it is the ton of 2.83 cubic metres (previously 100 cubic feet). The tonnage of a ship can be measured in a variety of ways of which the following are the more usual:

(1)   *Displacement.* This is the actual weight of the vessel measured by the weight in tonnes of water she displaces when loaded with fuel, water, and stores and with the crew on board. It is seldom used for merchant ships because of the great difference in their displacement when fully and lightly loaded. It is, however, the usual method of describing the tonnage of warships.

(2)   *Gross tonnage.* This is a measure of the total internal volume of the ship, with certain exceptions such as wheelhouse, chartroom, radio room etc reckoned in tons of cubic capacity. It is the usual method of expressing the tonnage of passenger ships.

(3)   *Net register tonnage.* This represents the earning capacity of a passenger ship. It is a measure in tons of cubic capacity of the space, which can be used for carrying passengers and cargo. In other words, it is the gross tonnage less the capacity of spaces occupied by such items as machinery, equipment and crew. This measurement is usually employed when assessing costs such as harbour and port dues and canal tolls.

(4)   *Deadweight tonnage.* This is the measurement in weight of the cargo, passengers, crew, stores, fuel and water, which a ship can carry when floating at her summer load draught. It is the difference between the light and load displacements or, in other words, it is the weight of the removable or expendable items, which a ship can carry. This is the normal method of expressing the tonnage of cargo ships.

e. **Draught marks (submarines).** These show the depth of the submarine when immersed in the water. The marks are applied in 10cm high figures at 10cm intervals. The red draught marks show the depth being taken from the keel to the centre line at the bottom of a figure. The blue draught marks on the forward edge of the rudder (as seen from the casing) show the rudder depth.

Note. *Should a change of ± 5cm in one hour be noticed the officer on duty (OOD) is to be informed immediately.*

Fig 1-17. Reading submarine draught marks

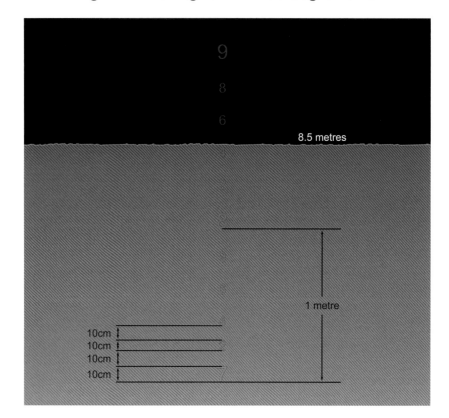

Fig 1-18. Submarine draught mark positions

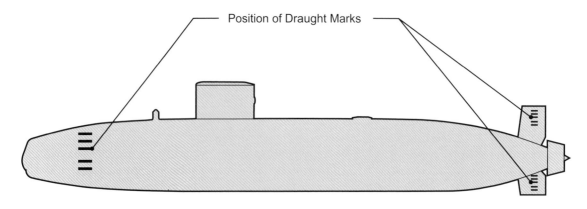

01007. Shipbuilding and launching

a.   A ship is built on a **slipway**, which is a sloping platform erected on the foreshore of a deep river or estuary and extending well beyond and below the water's edge. The ship is launched in a **cradle**, which slides down the slipway until the ship becomes waterborne (Fig 1-19). Usually the ship is launched stern first, but in some shipyards the tideway (river or canal) is not sufficiently broad to allow this and the ship has to be launched sideways.

b.   All the main structure of the hull up to the upper deck is completed before launching. In some cases the main machinery and other large equipment may be installed and some parts of the bridge and other superstructures may be erected.

c.   After launching the ship is taken to a **fitting-out** berth in a **basin** where machinery not already fitted, internal fittings, armament, radar equipment, funnels, masts and external fittings are secured in position and the rest of the superstructure is completed. Finally the ship is ready for equipment trials and then to proceed to sea for sea trials.

Fig 1-19. Launching a ship from a slipway

01008. Docks and slips
　　Periodically during a ship's life it is necessary to inspect her hull below the waterline to clean the bottom, change propellers, etc; for this special docks or slips are built and the process is called **docking** or **slipping**, followed by **undocking** or **unslipping**.

　a.　**Dry dock or graving dock** (Fig 1-20)

　　　(1)　This is an excavation faced with solid masonry, which lies adjacent to a harbour, river or basin.　The entrance is closed by a sliding **caisson** (pronounced 'cassoon'), a floating caisson, or **dock gates**.　Water is admitted through valves (**penstocks**) until the level in the dock is the same as that outside; the entrance is then opened and the ship floated in.　The entrance is then closed and the water pumped out, thus leaving the ship resting on **keel blocks** and supported by **breast shores** from the side of the dock to the ship's side, and by **bilge shores** to give additional support.　Side keel blocks and sometimes **cradles** in the wake of concentrated weights, are also used for heavier ships.

　　　(2)　Some small dry docks depend on the tide for flooding and draining.　The vessel is floated in at high water, the gates are closed and, as the tide falls, the water is drained out through valves, which are shut when the dock is dry.

Fig 1-20. Dry dock or graving dock

b.   **Floating dock.** This is a floating watertight structure, which can be submerged sufficiently to receive a ship by flooding the **pontoon tanks**, which form the bottom of the dock. When the ship has been floated into the dock and secured, the pontoon tanks are pumped out until the pontoon deck and the ship are dry. The ship rests on a line of blocks under the keel and in some cases blocks are positioned under the bilges. Because of the flexibility of a floating dock, it is essential that the ship be supported by breast shores between the ship and the dockside. This is necessary to prevent the sides of the dock deflecting inwards because of the weight of the ship resting on the blocks.

c.   **Patent slip.** (Fig1-21). This consists of a sloping runway of masonry or concrete, extending some distance below the low-water mark, on which rails are laid. A cradle, fitted with a wheeled carriage, is run out to receive the vessel when there is sufficient water. The vessel and cradle are hauled up the runway by winch or capstan until they are clear of the water.

Fig 1-21. Patent slip

d.   **Marine railway.** This is the term usually applied in Canada and the United States of America to a patent slip.

e.   **Gridiron (or grid).** This is a platform, usually sited against a tidal wall of a dockyard, on which a vessel is berthed at high water for underwater inspection at low water. The grid is normally constructed of parallel baulks of timber secured to the wall.

f.   **Hydraulic synchrolift.** (Fig 1-22). This is a platform on which a craft is positioned and is capable of being raised or lowered by hydraulic power. Its use is thus independent of the state of the tide and it permits work to progress continuously. These are now built to accommodate ships of more then 120 metres in length.

Fig 1-22. Hydraulic synchrolift

01009. Basins

When a ship is loading, unloading, being repaired or fitted out (after launching) it is safer and more convenient for her to be berthed in non-tidal waters.

    a.   **Basin or wet dock.** (Fig 1-23). This is an area of water, which, except for its entrance, is enclosed with walls of masonry and excavated to a depth sufficient to take floating ships. The water is shut in by caissons or gates, and is kept at a level sufficient to ensure that ships remain afloat.

Fig 1-23. Basin or wet dock

b.   **Locks.** (Fig 1-23). This is an excavated channel or approach to a basin or wet dock, faced with masonry and fitted at each end with a caisson or gates. Ships may then be moved to or from tidal waters at certain states of the tide without appreciably altering the level of the water in the basin or wet dock. Some locks are designed for use as dry docks.

c.   **Camber.** This is a made-up strip of sloping foreshore, from above high-water level to well below low-water level, used for hauling boats clear of the water. The term is also applied to a small **dock** or **tidal basin** that has an open entrance and may dry out at low water.

01010.   Jetties, piers and similar structures

a.   **Jetty.** A structure generally of wood, masonry, concrete or iron, which projects usually at right angles from the coast or some other structure. Vessels usually lie alongside parallel with the main axis of the structure.

b.   **Pier.** A structure generally of wood, masonry, concrete or iron, extending approximately at right angles from the coast into the sea. The head, alongside which vessels can lay with their fore-and-aft line at right-angles to the main structure, is frequently wider than the body of the pier. Some piers however, were built solely as promenades.

c.   **Pens.** These are bays, formed by a series of jetties or piers, for accommodating a number of small ships in berths alongside.

d.   **Mole or breakwater.** A long pier of heavy masonry built on the seaward side of a harbour for protection. It may be designed for berthing ships on its shoreward side, either alongside or with anchors down and wires from the stern to bollards (mooring posts) firmly embedded in it.

e.   **Groynes.** A sturdy timber and board construction between the high water and low-water mark projecting away from the shore line out to seaward to prevent drifting and coastal erosion caused by the scouring action of the sea.

01011.   Sea measures

a.   **International nautical mile.** This is a standard fixed length of 1852 metres.

b.   **Sea mile.** A sea mile is the distance equivalent to one minute of arc measured along the meridian at the latitude of measurement. Since the Earth is flattened at the poles and not a true sphere, this distance is not a fixed length; it varies between about 1843 metres at the equator and 1862 metres at the North and South poles. The sea mile is used for the scale of latitude on large-scale Admiralty charts because distances are measured using the latitude graduation on the chart borders.

c.   **Cable.** One tenth of a *sea mile* is known as a *cable*, which varies between 184.3 m (201.55yds) and 186.2 m (203.63 yds) according to *Latitude*. A *Cable* thus approximates to 200 yards, and this nominal distance is a convenient measure normally used at sea for short-range navigational purposes.

d. **Fathom.** The fathom was the traditional nautical linear measure for ropes, hawsers, depths of water and soundings and was based on the length of rope held between one's outstretched arms (dated from medieval times). It is now superseded for all these purposes by the metre. For conversion, if necessary:

1 fathom = 1.8288 metres
1 metre = 0.5468 fathoms.

e. **Knot.** A knot is a unit of speed equal to one nautical mile per hour (1.852 kilometres per hour or 1.15 statute miles per hour). For example, a ship may be **steaming at 15 knots**, meaning that she travels at a speed of 15 nautical miles per hour. (The expression 'knots per hour' is incorrect and should never be used to describe speed.) The term is derived from a method of measuring speed in the days of sail, when a piece of wood attached to a line was thrown overboard; the number of equally-spaced knots in the line that passed over the taffrail in a specified time gave the speed of the ship in **knots**.

01012. Miscellaneous

a. **Bridle or braidline bridle.** A bridle is referred to when using the ship's cable to secure to a buoy. A Braidline Bridle is referred to when using a designated Man-Made Fibre Cordage Bridle to secure to a buoy.

b. **Brow.** A narrow platform placed between ship and shore for embarkation and disembarkation, sometimes called a gangway.

c. **Between wind and water.** The term used to describe that part of a ship's side near the waterline, which is alternately submerged and exposed by the movement of the waves and the rolling of the ship. It is also used to describe that part of a sea wall, pile, etc which is uncovered between high and low water.

d. **Dolphins.** Mooring posts usually composed of groups of piles, driven into the bottom of a harbour.

e. **Dumb lighter.** A lighter without means of self-propulsion (see **Lighter**).

f. **Floating bridge.** A form of ferry, which is hauled from shore to shore by hauling on chains or wires, laid across the bed of a channel or river.

g. **Gangplank.** A narrow platform placed between one ship and another for embarkation and disembarkation.

h. **Gangway.** The opening in the bulwarks or position in the ship's side by which the ship is embarked or disembarked. The term is also used to describe a passageway in a ship, and sometimes used to describe the platform between ship and shore (see **Brow**).

i. **Hard.** A made-up strip of foreshore used as a landing place for boats at low water.

j. **Lighter.** A vessel used for transporting cargo or stores to or from a ship.

k. **Piles.** Baulks of steel-pointed timber or lengths of ferro-concrete, which are driven into the harbour bottom and used as the foundations for the platforms of piers and jetties. Some wooden piles are used for facing the sides of stones or concrete wharves. Some piles are made of steel sections, which are embedded in rock and reinforced concrete.

l. **Stream.** The 'stream' is a general term to describe the navigable channels and anchorages in the tidal waters of an estuary or river.

m. **Trot.** A line of moored buoys between which a number of small ships can be secured **head and stern**.

n. **Warp.** A rope extending between ship and shore, for moving (warping) the ship without using her engines.

o. **Winding.** The action of turning a ship the other way round in her berth (turning **end for end**).

THIS PAGE IS INTENTIONALLY BLANK

CHAPTER 2

ANCHORS, CABLE AND BUOYWORK

CONTENTS

ANNEXES

CHAPTER 2

ANCHORS, CABLES AND BUOYWORK

02001. Introduction

An anchor is a hook, attached to a length of chain or rope called a cable, by which a ship or boat can be held temporarily to the seabed in comparatively shallow water. The primitive anchor was a rock attached to a length of crude rope. Then, from about 400 BC until the days of Nelson, anchors made of iron and wood increased in size but changed little in design, whereas cable developed to the cable-laid hawsers that can be seen in HMS VICTORY. When iron and steel replaced wood in ship construction and sail gave way to steam, steel anchors of various designs were made, from which the modern anchor is derived, and iron and steel chain cable gradually developed into the very strong modern studded cable used today. This chapter describes anchor and cable arrangements and associated equipment fitted in HM ships, explains how a modern anchor holds and lists drills and procedures for anchoring and buoywork evolutions. Additional sources of information on the subject are: **BR 2, The Queen's Regulations for the Royal Navy**; **BR 367, Manual of Anchors, Chain Cables and Associated Equipment** for RN, Submarine and RFAs, and **BR 1637, Anchors for HM Service**. Details of anchor and cable outfits and associated equipment are also listed in individual ships 'As fitted drawings' and Rigging warrants. A full list of parts to the cable outfit, ancillary equipment and spare gear, complete with test/survey certificate and birth certificates are held within the Anchors and Cables Log. Navigational and shiphandling aspects of anchoring and buoywork are contained in **BR 45, Admiralty Manual of Navigation Volume 6**.

02002. Methods of securing to the seabed

a.   **Anchoring.** A ship can be secured to the seabed by means of her ground tackle, i.e. her anchors and cables, either with a single anchor (Fig 2-1) or with two anchors. Modern warships rarely use two anchors because the likelihood of the cables twisting as the ship swings with wind and tide, and the risk of damage to bow domes outweighs the advantages of the reduction in sea room and increased holding power that two anchors provide (see Note). However, ships with two anchors may on occasions use both to ride out a gale. In such circumstances the anchors are let go so that the ship lies with an angle between the cables of less than 20 degrees (Fig 2-2). In a single-anchor warship, provided there is sufficient sea room, veering more cable may check a dragging anchor. If this tactic is unsuccessful the main engines should be started and the ship manoeuvred slowly ahead to take the strain off the anchor and cable. As a final resort the ship must put to sea. Drills and procedures for anchoring are described later in the Chapter.

Note.   *In the past, to prevent turns forming in the cables of a ship riding at two anchors, a swivel, known as a mooring swivel, was inserted between the two cables. This procedure was discontinued because on occasions it strained and damaged the cables.*

Fig 2-1. A ship at single anchor

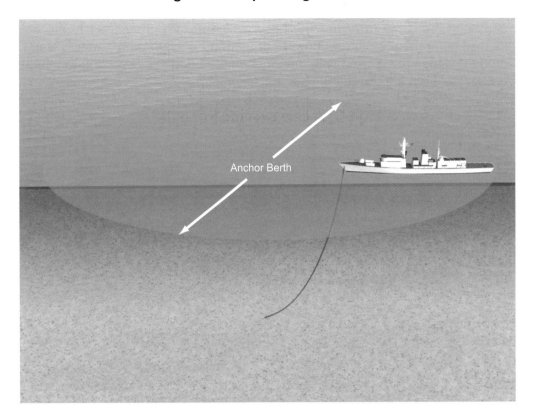

Fig 2-2. Putting down two ain a gale

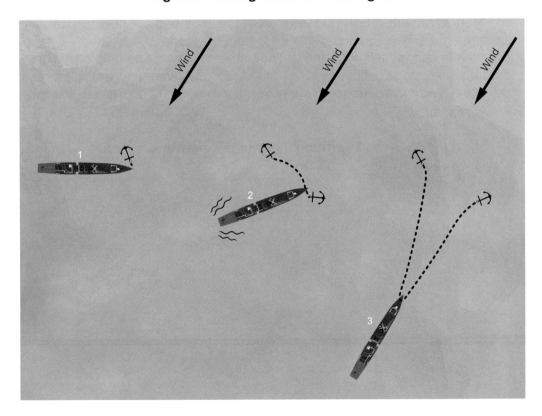

b. **Securing to a buoy.** (Fig 2-3). In ports and most large harbours a ship can also be secured to the bottom by unshackling one of her cables from its anchor and shackling the cable to a mooring buoy, which in turn is secured to the bottom by its own permanently laid groundwork of mooring anchors and mooring chain. Many modern ships are supplied with man-made fibre bridles for securing to a buoy. Drills and procedures are described later in this chapter.

Fig 2-3. A ship secured to a buoy

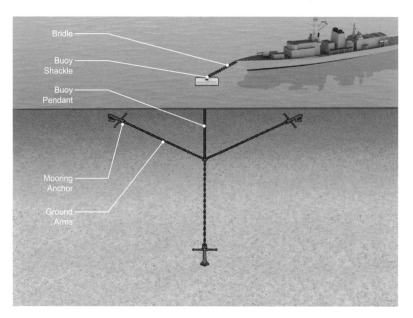

c. **Mediterranean moor.** (Fig 2-4). With this type of mooring ships are obliged to berth at right angles to a jetty, with their sterns secured to the jetty by berthing lines and their anchor(s) laid out ahead. The process can only be employed where there is a negligible range of tide, as is common in Mediterranean ports; for this reason it is called the **Mediterranean (or Med) moor**. Drills and procedures are described later in this chapter.

Fig 2-4. A ship berthing stern-to (Mediterranean moor)

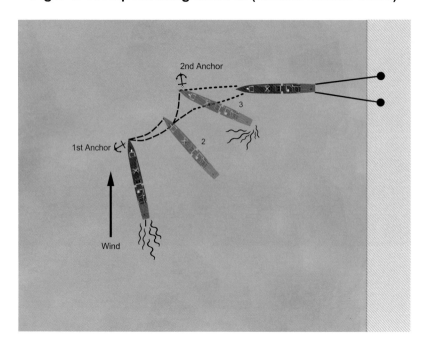

02003. Ship's anchors

a.   **Bower anchor.** A ship's main anchors are called her **bower anchors**. They are used for anchoring the ship and are stowed one on each bow, or one on the bow and one in a centreline hawsepipe. Certain ships carry only one bower anchor, which is stowed in a bow hawsepipe.

b.   **Sheet anchor.** A sheet anchor was traditionally an extra anchor carried for safety's sake to back up the main anchor or anchors. In ships fitted with a bow dome the main anchor is stowed in a centreline hawsepipe and the bow fitted anchor is referred to as the sheet anchor, for use only in an emergency because of the possibility of damage to the dome if it is deployed.

c.   **Stream anchor.** This anchor, which is used by some ships (principally RFAs) as a stern anchor, is stowed in a stern hawsepipe.

02004. Parts of an anchor
Fig 2-5 shows a modern anchor used in the Royal Navy. It should be noted that the flukes can move through an angle of 35 degrees each side of the shank.

Fig 2-5. Part of an anchor

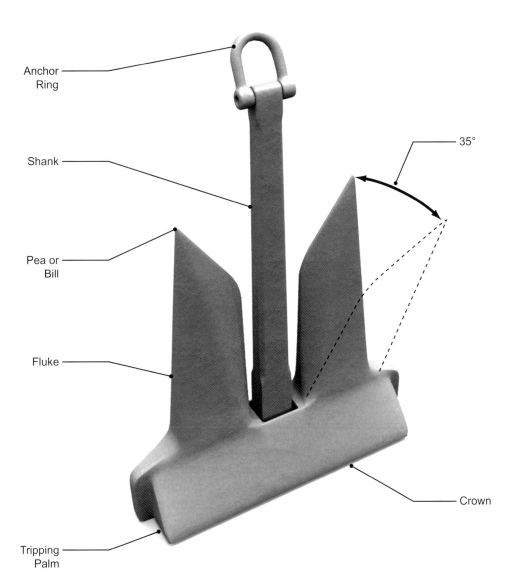

02005. How an anchor holds

Fig 2-6 shows how an anchor beds itself in the bottom after it has been let go and the strain comes on the cable. The anchor lies flat on the bottom until the pull of the ship on the cable drags the anchor along the bottom; the tripping palms then tilt the flukes, which then dig themselves in. After a further amount of dragging the anchor embeds itself completely until it holds. For the anchor to maintain its hold the pull of the cable must always be horizontal where the cable emerges from the seabed.

Fig 2-6. How a modern anchor holds

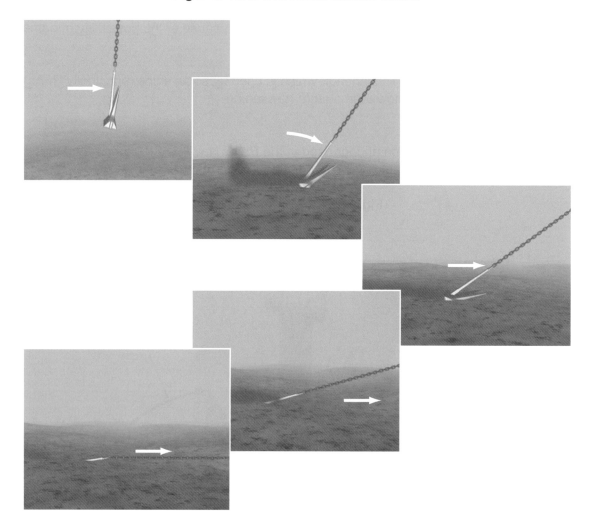

a.   **Amount of cable required.** The cable must be long enough to ensure that a part of it near the anchor always remains in the seabed. In firm ground, the anchor ring takes up a position just below the top of the seabed and therefore the cable lies almost on the seabed. The rest of the cable acts as a spring in preventing the anchor from being jerked when the ship is yawing from side to side or pitching. The amount of cable required therefore depends on the depth of water, weight of cable, length of stay, weather, and the nature of the bottom. An approximate formula for **forged steel cable** is: **Amount of cable to veer in shackles is one-and-a half times the square root of the depth of water in metres**, and for **copper based cable** (Aluminium bronze), which is heavier and larger than forged steel, the formula is: **Amount of cable to veer in shackles is equal to the square root of the depth of water in metres**.

b. **Nature of bottom and anchor design.** Older type anchors will hold satisfactorily in firm seabeds such as clay, soft chalk, sand, sand/shingle and heavy mud, but will drag in softer seabeds such as soft mud, shingle and shell. Improvements in the design of Admiralty anchors in recent years have resulted in obtaining satisfactory holds in any kind of seabed, because the improved anchors embed themselves deeper in the softer grounds during the final period of drag before they hold. No anchor, no matter how well designed, will hold on rock, except by a fluke; nor will it hold if fouled by some extraneous material, picked up on the sea bed, which prevents the anchor operating correctly.

c. **Breaking out an anchor.** When the anchor is weighed the upward pull of the cable should break the flukes out of the bottom. If the flukes are very firmly bedded the cable can be held at short stay and the anchor broken out using the main engines. If the flukes are caught in a rock it may be necessary to part the cable and buoy the end for recovery, if practical, by another vessel.

d. **Holding pof an anchor.** The holding pull of an anchor is expressed as a ratio of holding pull and anchor weight, and varies, depending on type of anchor, from 3:1 to 10:1. The holding pull for each type of anchor is given below.

02006. Types of anchor

The bigger the vessel, the heavier must be her anchors. Anchors also vary in design and performance as well as in size. The most common types in use in the fleet are illustrated in Fig 2-7. They are:

a. **Admiralty pattern anchor.** In spite of its name, this anchor is much older than the Admiralty itself and was long considered by seaman to afford the greatest holding pull, i.e. 3 to 3.5 times its own weight. It is used mainly for anchoring Danbuoys and markers, and occasionally as a boat's anchor. When the anchor is let go the stock comes to rest horizontally on the bottom, and as the flukes are set at right-angles to the stock, the lower fluke digs into the bottom and holds. Its disadvantage is that, because the upper fluke sticks up from the bottom, the anchor may well be dislodged through being fouled by the bight of its cable as the boat swings to wind and tide; it is also dangerous if let go in shallow water because a boat may impale herself on the upper fluke when the tide falls. It cannot be stowed in a hawsepipe, and so it must be stowed on deck or slung in some position from which it can be let go.

b. **Admiralty standard stockless (ASS) anchor.** This type of anchor will soon no longer be in use in the service; however, it is still fitted in a few of the older surface ships and submarines, and as a stream anchor in some RFAs. The maximum holding pull is about the same as that of the Admiralty Pattern. The flukes pivot about a pin, which passes through the crown. As the anchor is dragged along the bottom the weight of the flukes and the effect of the tripping palm tilt both flukes downwards so that they dig into the bottom.

c.   **AC (admiralty class) 14.** In 1943 the Admiralty instituted a series of tests aiMed at improving the ratio between the holding pull and anchor weight. These tests resulted in a major advance in anchor design and led to the development of AC anchors. The AC 14, fitted in the majority of surface warships in the Royal Navy has a ratio of holding pull to anchor weight of 10:1; it is designed to bite quickly and will achieve maximum holding power after dragging two shank lengths.

d.   **AC 16A and 17 anchors.** The stowage of an anchor in a submarine has always been difficult, and with the introduction of high speed, heavy, nuclear-powered vessels the requirement for an anchor which, when stowed, is flush with the hull and completely closes the hull opening has become important. A further requirement is for the anchor to be worked blind, by remote control. The AC 16A was designed for stowage in the bottom of the hull. To ensure correct entry of the anchor into its stowage, the shank on entering the hawsepipe rotates to line up the flukes with the hull opening. The rotation is effected by means of a guide pin in the upper end of the shank and a cam within the hawsepipe. The anchor will enter with the fluke's vertical and in line with the shank and the crown completely closes the opening. The remote controls include indicators, which allow the position of the anchor to be checked during the securing evolution. The ratio of holding pull to anchor weight is approximately the same as for the AC 14 anchor. The AC 17 anchor, also designed for stowage in the bottom of the hull of a submarine, has a holding pull of about seven times its own weight, but requires to be stowed with its shank vertical, or near vertical, and at right angles to the hull opening. The flukes are so balanced that they lie in line with the shank and can thus enter a comparatively narrow opening in the hull if the anchor is rotated to the correct position (normally fore and aft) prior to entry. Rotation is effected by a ball and pin inserted between the cable and the anchor shackle; the pin connects with a guide cam within the hawsepipe. The crown of the anchor when stowed lies flush with the hull and completely closes the hull opening. Remote control and warning devices are fitted as for the AC 16A anchor.

e.   **Stocked close-stowing (Danforth) anchor.** The stocked close-stowing anchor, fitted in some older minor war vessels, resembles a lightly built stockless anchor, both in appearance and method of operation, but it has a stock passing through the crown to prevent the anchor rolling when its flukes dig into the bottom. The ratio between holding power and anchor weight increases as the size decreases. It fits neatly into the hawsepipe and can be secured as efficiently as a stockless anchor.

f.   **CQR anchor.** The CQR anchor, so called because the letters sound like see-cu-re, is generally used only for small craft because it is difficult to stow in a hawsepipe. The shank can pivot about the flukes so that when dragging along the bottom the flukes will always turn over and dig in. Like the Danforth, the ratio between holding pull and anchor weight increases as the size decreases.

Fig 2-7. Types of anchor used in the fleet

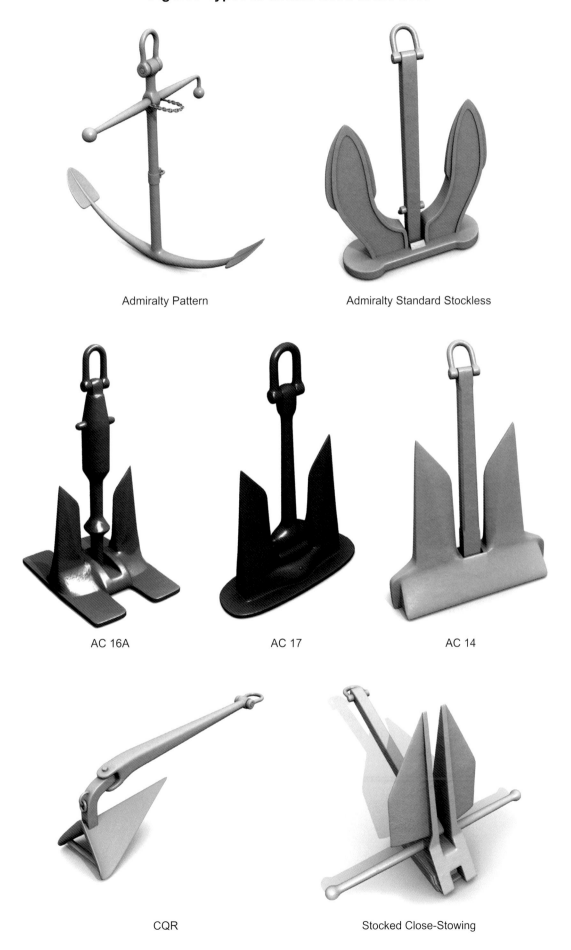

Admiralty Pattern

Admiralty Standard Stockless

AC 16A

AC 17

AC 14

CQR

Stocked Close-Stowing

02007. Chain cable

a. **Introduction.** A ship's anchor cable is generally assuMed to be made of chain although a *cable* is strictly speaking a strong thick rope. The bower cables of warships are made of studded chain; the studs are closed in the links by pressure and act to strengthen them and prevent the cable from kinking. Studded chain cable is supplied in lengths of 27.5 m and 13.75 m, called **shackles** and **half shackles** respectively. A ship's bower cable is usually made up of four half shackles and a number of shackles of cables. The half shackles are usually inserted in pairs, one at the outboard end next to the anchor and the other midway between the outboard and inboard ends. In the future a ship's cable will be made up of full shackles apart from two half shackles at the outboard end. The half shackles are required when working cable during operations described later in this chapter.

Note. *Precise details of the cable fit for individual ships will be found in the Anchors and Cables Log and 'As fitted' drawings.*

b. **Types of chain cable.** There are basically three types of ship's chain cable. Their composition and application in the Service is as follows:

(1) *Grade 2   Non-ferrous.* Manufactured from copper based material, usually referred to as aluminium bronze. It is supplied to mine countermeasure vessels, and the precise composition of the material is dictated by the magnetic signature constraint of the class of vessel.

(2) *Grade 2   Forged steel.* Supplied to various ships in the fleet.

(3) *Grade 3   Forged steel.* A higher grade steel, and consequently stronger than grade 2.

c. **Size of cable.** Size of cable is defined as the diameter of the metal in a common link (for 'common link' see below). The size always quoted for the anchor shackle, joining shackle or other cable gear is that of the cable with which the gear is intended to be used.

d. **Components of a shackle of chain cable.** The links forming each length of cable are of uniform size and are called **common links** (Fig 2-8). Shackles and half shackles of cable are usually joined with a lugless joining shackle (certain auxiliary vessels are fitted with lugged joining shackles). A length of chain cable will always contain an **odd** number of links to ensure that the joining shackle will pass around the cable holder or gypsy in the correct plane. Joining shackles, being slightly larger than the common links, should lie **vertically** as they pass round a cable holder or **horizontally** as they pass over the gypsy of a windlass. This will ensure they do not jam or strain.

Fig 2-8. Shackles of chain cable joined by a lugless joining shackle

e. **Marking of cable.** The shackles and joining shackles of a cable are numbered consecutively from its outer to its inner end, the first joining shackle being that which joins the first and second shackles together. To assist in identifying the joining shackles when it is being worked, the cable is marked. Every joining shackle, except the one between two half shackles, is painted white. One link on each side of a joining shackle is also painted white and marked with a number of turns of seizing wire around the stud corresponding to the number of the joining shackle. These marked links are separated from the joining shackle by a number of unmarked links, which serve to indicate the join between two particular shackles; for example, if the fourth link on each side of a joining shackle were so marked, it would indicate the join between the fourth and the fifth shackles. This marking system is illustrated in Fig 2-9, which shows the third joining shackle is on deck. Cable markings should be checked and remarked as necessary whenever weighing.

Fig 2-9. How cable is marked

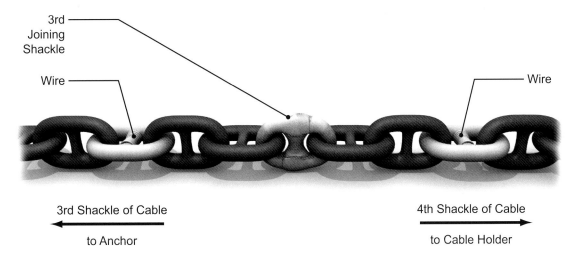

f.   **Cable lockers.**   The cable lockers, which are usually on the lowest deck and may be sited so that one is abreast of, or forward of the other, provide the stowage for the cables.   Modern warships have self-stowing cable lockers so the descending cable will automatically stow itself clear for running out; they are constructed either in the form of a circular trunk or a square or rectangular locker.   Drainage arrangements are provided for the removal of water.   Older warships have square lockers, with perforated steel plate sides to ventilate and drain the cable. If the locker is not self stowing it must be stowed by hand.   The inboard end of the cable is secured to a cable clench at the bottom of the locker by a lugged joining shackle. **The clench is tested to 20 % above the proof load of the cable**.   The Executive Officer or MEO is to witness the inboard ends of the cables being secured.   The Navigating Officer must know the length of each cable, where the half shackles appear and should, if available, check the securing of the inboard end of each cable.

02008.   Associated anchor and cable equipment

a.   **Joining shackles.**   The shackles which join lengths of cable together may be either lugless or lugged; all warships' cables are fitted with the lugless type, but some auxiliary vessels have the lugged type.   Joining shackles are also used in evolutions such as towing and buoywork.   Both types are described below.

(1)   *Lugless joining shackle.*   A lugless joining shackle (Fig 2-10(i)) is made of alloy steel and has three parts, one of which is the stud.   The two main parts are attached to the ends of the cable and then fitted together, and the stud then slides in place and locks the whole.   The stud is secured by hammering a tapered pin and lead pellet into the hole drilled diagonally through all three parts of the shackle.   The hole is tapered, and when the pin is driven right home a small conical recess called the **dovetail chamber** is left clear above its head. The lead pellet is hammered **broad end first** into this chamber so as to fill it completely and thereby keep the pin in place.   To avoid danger from pieces of lead flying from the shackle during hammering, goggles must be worn by personnel assembling the shackle.   Before inserting a new pellet the remains of the previous pellet must be scraped out of the chamber, otherwise the new pellet may work out; this is done by a small tool called a **reamer**.   When parting a lugless joining shackle a **top swage** must always be used between the hammer and shackle.   It is shaped to the curvature of the shackle so that the machined surfaces of the shackle are not damaged.

Fig 2-9a.   How a lugless joining shackle operates

CAUTION

The three main components of Lugless joining Shackles are not interchangeable, because each shackle is made as one unit.

---

(2) *Lugged joining shackle.* A lugged joining shackle (Fig 2-10(iii)) is a straight shackle whose bolt is secured by a tapered pin and a lead pellet. The pin fits into a tapered hole drilled through the bolt and one lug of the shackle. Except for the anchor shackle, all lugged shackles should be fitted into the cable with their lugs facing aft, so that they will not foul any projections on the deck as the cable runs out. Since the anchor shackle is already in the hawsepipe, there is no danger of fouling anything on the way out, but it may foul the stem or some projection on the ship's side as the anchor is being hove in, so it should be fitted with its lugs facing outboard.

b. **Securing-to-buoy shackle** (Fig 2-10(iv)). The securing-to-buoy shackle is supplied for securing the ship's bridle(s) to the buoy shackle or reducing link of a mooring buoy, and is therefore especially wide in the clear. It can be used with either lugless or lugged joining shackles, and is tested to the **proof load of its largest associated cable**. The width of the shackle in the clear for cable of all sizes is given below in Table 2-1:

Table 2-1. Securing-to-buoy shackles. Width in the clear for given sizes.

Size of cable (mm)	Width of shackle in the clear (mm)
28 and below	95
From above 28 to 38	115
From above 38 to 48	145
From above 48 to 58	185
Above 58	210

c. **Lugged anchor shackle** (Fig 2-10(v)). A lugged anchor shackle is used to join the swivel piece at the outboard end of the cable to the ring of the anchor. It is wider in the clear than the lugged joining shackle and its bolt is oval in cross-section whereas the bolt of the lugged joining shackle is egg-shaped in cross section.

d. **Towing shackle.** Similar to, but longer than, the lugged anchor shackle, the towing shackle is designed to take the tongue of a towing slip. It is fitted between the Steel Wire Rope towing pendant and the chafing piece in the 'bollard and clench' towing method.

e. **Joggle shackle** (Fig 2-10(vi)). The joggle shackle is long and slightly curved, and shaped to fit across a link of cable; it is used for attaching a wire rope to a bight of cable, or for securing the top two turns of a cable that has been turned up around bollards. The bolt fits easily in the lugs and is held in place by 'feathers' protruding from it. To remove or insert the bolt it must first be turned until the feathers are in line with the featherways cut in the lugs of the shackle. Table 2-2 gives the size of shackle supplied for different sizes of cable:

Table 2-2. Size of joggle shackle supplied for different sizes of cable

Size of cable (mm)	Diameter of bolt (mm)
19 to below 28	32
28 to 36	42
38 to 52	48
54 to 60	58
62 and above	60

f.   **Adaptor piece** (Fig 2-11(i)). An adaptor piece consists of an interMediate link and an end link together and is used to adapt the end of the cable to accept a lugged shackle, which will not pass through a common link. Its principal use is for adapting the cable to accept the towing hawser.

g.   **Swivel and link assemblies (box and cup)** (Fig 2-11(ii) and Fig 2-11(iii)). Swivel and link assemblies are fitted to prevent the chain cable from twisting when the ship is at anchor. A swivel piece is fitted at the outboard end of the chain cable for attachment to the anchor and inboard between the end of the chain cable and the cable locker. The inboard swivel piece is always secured to the cable clench with a lugged joining shackle.

h.   **Stoppers.** Cable stoppers, usually known as **slips**, are provided to hold the cable prior to letting go an anchor, or to act as preventers when the ship is riding on the brake of the cable holder, or to hold the cable temporarily so that the inboard part of the cable can be handled, or to house the anchor securely in the hawsepipe.

(1)   *Blake slip.* A Blake slip (Fig 2-11(iv)) is a general purpose slip. Its primary use is holding the cable prior to letting go an anchor (in the RN an anchor is always let go from the Blake slip). It can also be used as a preventer, or to hang the cable whilst working on its inboard part. **It is tested to half the proof load of the cable. The clench plate to which the Blake slip is secured is tested to 60 % of the proof load of the cable**.

(2)   *Blake bottle screw slip.* A Blake bottle screw slip (Fig 2-11(v)) differs from the Blake slip only in that a bottle screw is incorporated in the chain between the slip and the deck clench. The bottle screw enables the anchor to be hove close home in its hawsepipe when secured for sea. **Test details are as for the Blake slip**.

(3)   *Riding slip.* A riding slip is a Blake slip, normally shackled to a deck clench on the upper deck between the navel pipe and cable holder. It is put on the cable when the ship is at anchor or secured to a buoy, and acts as a preventer should the brake of the cable holder fail to hold the pull of the anchor. **Test details are as for the Blake slip**.

Note.   *In some ships the riding slip is replaced with a compressor or guillotine.*

(4)   *Devil's claw.* In many merchant ships the cable is stoppered by a devil's claw, as shown in Fig 2-11(vi).

Fig 2-10. Associated anchor and cable gear

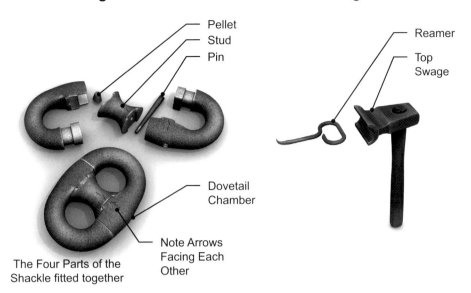

Pellet
Stud
Pin

Reamer

Top
Swage

Dovetail
Chamber

Note Arrows
Facing Each
Other

The Four Parts of the
Shackle fitted together

(i) A Lugless Joining Shackle

(ii) Top Swage and Reamer

(iii) A Lugged Joining Shackle

(iv) Securing-to-Buoy Shackle

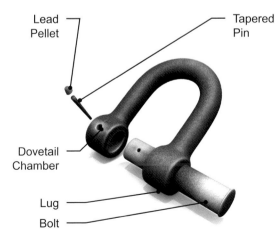

Lead
Pellet

Tapered
Pin

Dovetail
Chamber

Lug

Bolt

(v) A Lugged Anchor Shackle

(vi) Joggle Shackle

Fig 2-11. Associated anchor and cable gear

(i) Adapter Piece

(ii) Box Swivel

(iii) Cup Swivel

(iv) Blake Slip

(v) Blake Bottle Screw Slip

(vi) Devil's Claw

02009. Cable deck fittings

The fittings described below are used in conjunction with anchors and cables and associated gear.

a.   **Navel pipes.** Navel pipes are fitted forward of the cable holder, or incorporated in the base of a windlass, for the passage of the anchor cables to and from the cable lockers. Their upper ends stand proud of the deck to ensure smooth-working of the cable and prevent wash deck water finding its way below.

b.   **Bonnets.** (Fig 2-12(i)). A bonnet is a fixed or portable cover for a Navel pipe or compressor, to stop water from flooding the cable locker. The opening, which faces aft, is made reasonably watertight by a portable steel cover, slotted to slide down over one link of the cable.

Note.   *In ships fitted with a windlass, the opening of the Navel pipe at deck level should be fitted with a steel plate or PVC cover.*

c.   **Compressor.** (Fig 2-12(i)). Some ships with fixed bonnets have compressors fitted into the bonnets to take the place of riding slips. A compressor consists of a wedge of steel operated by a lever or handwheel; the wedge can be moved down across the mouth of the Navel pipe until it nips a link of cable against the lip. A portable cover fits over the mouth of the bonnet.

d.   **Guillotine.** The guillotine, which can take the place of a riding slip or compressor in vessels fitted with a windlass, is commonly found in Merchant Navy ships, but is relatively rare in Royal Navy ships.

e.   **Bullring.** (Fig 2-12(ii)). In most destroyers and below, a bullring is fitted to give a fair lead for the headrope, picking-up rope and ship-to-buoy bridle.

f.   **Hawsepipes.** (Fig 2-12(iii)). A hawsepipe is a steel tube, which houses the anchor in its stowed position or gives a lead for the cable during anchor work. Most ships are fitted with port and starboard hawsepipes to house their bower anchors, but some have a third hawsepipe in the stem called a stem hawsepipe for giving a fairlead to the cable when the ship is secured to a buoy, or being towed. Ships fitted with a bow dome have a stem hawsepipe for the main anchor and a starboard bow hawsepipe for the sheet anchor. Cable washing sprayers are fitted in the hawsepipes of modern warships and grills are provided at the inboard end for the safety of personnel.

Note.   *Hawsepipe grills must be fitted and secured at all times unless cable is being worked.*

Fig 2-12. Typical cable deck fittings

(i) Compressor with Bonnet Fitted

(ii) Bullring

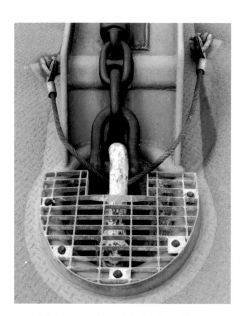

(iii) Hawsepipe with Anchor Strop
Fitted to Anchor Ring

02010. Capstans, combined capstan and cableh, and windlasses

a.   **Capstans**. Fig 2-13 shows a typical after capstan. A capstan in its simpler form has a **barrel** or **rundle** mounted on a vertical shaft which is driven by a hydraulic or electric motor and is used for working berthing lines and other ropes. The barrel is waisted, i.e. made smaller in diameter at its middle than at its top or bottom, with the object of checking the tendency of the turns of rope to work up or down and so form a riding turn as the capstan revolves. Standing out at intervals from the barrel, and extending from top to bottom, are slight projections called **whelps**, which are cast with the barrel and help it to grip the rope. The same rules apply for a riding turn on a capstan as for a warping drum. If the turns of rope are reluctant to slip towards the middle of the barrel, slight surging of the rope will usually induce them to do so. If surging has no effect upon the turns building up towards the top or bottom of the barrel then it is likely that too many turns have been taken round the barrel. Onboard documentation must be checked to ascertain performance details of individual capstans.

Fig 2-13. Typical after capstan with handle control

b.   **Combined capstan and cable holder** (Fig 2-14).

(1)   A cable holder is designed solely for working cable and is an integral part of the capstan, which is mounted above the cable holder on the same shaft and is therefore driven by the same motor, which can be either electric or hydraulic. The cable holder consists of a sprocket with **snugs** to carry the links of cable. The sprocket can revolve freely on the shaft or be connected to its shaft by a **dog clutch** situated in the head of the sprocket. When it is disconnected the rotation of the sprocket can be controlled by a band brake operated by a handwheel; when connected the sprocket will hold the cable and can be made to heave in or veer the cable by turning the motor in the required direction. The capstan is mounted on a square-section shaft on which it can slide up or down.

(2)   The head of the shaft is cut with a screw head, which works in a nut fixed to the centre of an engaging/disengaging handwheel secured to the crown of the capstan, so that when the handwheel is revolved the capstan is raised or lowered on its shaft. A number of dogs project at intervals round the bottom of the capstan barrel, and when the capstan is lowered on to the cable holder they engage in slots cut in the head of the cable holder sprocket, thereby locking the cable holder to the capstan. When the capstan is raised by turning the handwheel, the dogs are disengaged from their slots thereby freeing the cable holder. To connect the cable holder to the capstan, the capstan motor is turned until the indicating mark on the bottom of the capstan barrel is in line with a corresponding mark on the head of the cable holder. The capstan is then lowered onto the cable holder by turning the handwheel on the crown of the capstan in the required direction, and the dogs then engage in their slots and lock the capstan and cable holder together. Each cable holder is fitted with a simple band brake, which bears on the skirt of the sprocket and is operated by a handwheel. Rotation of the handwheel in a clockwise or counter-clockwise direction applies or releases the brake at the cable holder sprocket. The motor of the combined capstan and cable holder is usually controlled either by a T-handle or a hand wheel. An emergency stop button is located close to the controls.

Fig 2-14. Typical combined capstan and cable holder

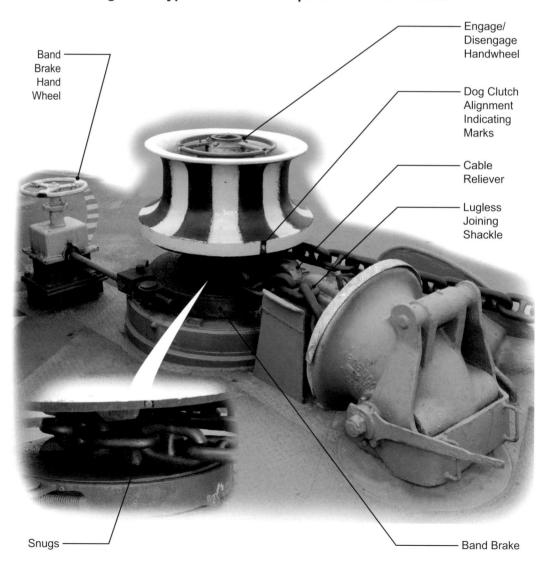

c.   **Submarine capstans.** There are two capstans fitted, one forward and one aft on the centre line. The capstans are retractable and are wound up when required for use. A capstan key (NSN F203 526 7019) and a control point adjacent to the capstan, controls the capstan which is powered by the external hydraulic system. Checks must be made that the system is online when the capstan is required. The capstan operating recess is faired off with a brass plate when the capstan is not in operation and the capstan is in the lowered position.

Fig 2-15. Cable holder band-brake

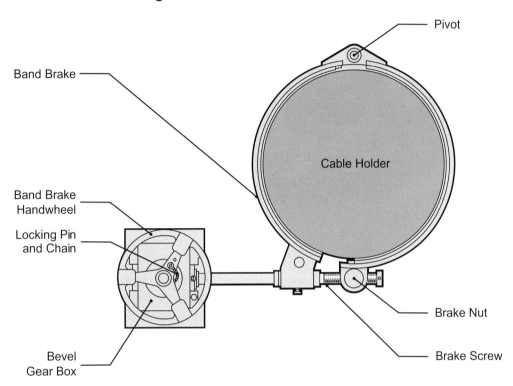

d.   **Windlasses.** (Fig 2-16) The chief difference between a windlass and a combined capstan and cable holder is that the windlass is mounted on a horizontal shaft whereas the other is mounted on a vertical shaft. Although its primary function is to work the bower cables, the windlass is also fitted with warping drums for working hawsers. The motor of a windlass is usually situated directly abaft the windlass on the fo'c'sle deck, and for the normal requirement of anchor work one man can operate both motor and windlass. The motor, through gearing, drives the shaft and warping drums. The two sprockets for taking the bower cables are mounted on the shaft outside the gear wheel, and are called **gypsies**; they are exactly similar to the sprocket of a cable holder, and the joining shackles must pass over them in the correct slew. Each gypsy can revolve freely on the shaft, or be clutched to the shaft. To connect the gypsy to the shaft, the motor is turned until the slots in the gypsy are in line with the dogs, and the wheel inside the warping drum is turned until the dogs engage in the gypsy, and the wheel is then locked. To disengage the gypsy the brake is applied and the wheel turned in the other direction until the warping drum dogs are clear of the gypsy slots, and the wheel is then locked. Each gypsy has a simple hand brake, operated by a handle. The windlass is operated either by a hand lever, or a T-handle inserted in a deck fitting. An emergency stop is provided situated adjacent to the T handle on an electric windlass.

Note.   *The motors of windlasses and combined capstan and cable holders are designed to heave in both bower anchors simultaneously.*

Fig 2-16. A typical electric windlass

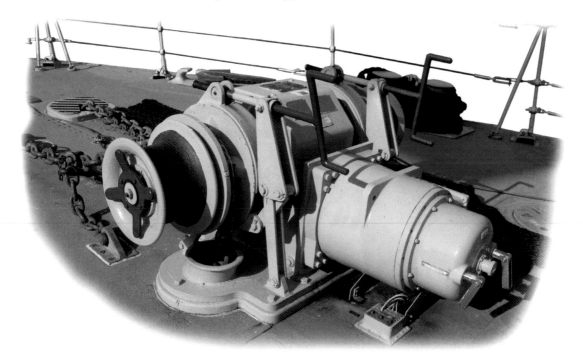

02011. Cable deck layouts

In recent years the arrangement of anchor and cable equipment on the fo'c'sle of certain warships has been influenced by the introduction of bow dome sonars, and, in some cases, the need to reduce topweight. The various arrangements found throughout the Fleet are as follows:

a. **Traditional layout of frigates and above**

(1) Fig 2-19 shows the traditional arrangement of equipment on the fo'c'sle of frigates and above for working the anchors and cables. From each hawsepipe each cable leads aft to its **cable holder**, then forward to its **Navel pipe**, and down this pipe to the **cable locker**. The cable holders each have a capstan drum fitted above them and these are driven in either direction by the capstan engine, which is fitted in the compartment below. The capstan drums are permanently connected to the capstan engine but each cable holder can be mechanically connected to or disconnected from its capstan drum. Cable can be hove in or veered under power by connecting up its cable holder and setting the capstan engine in motion in the required direction; or cable can be allowed to run out freely by disconnecting its cable holder. When both cables are being worked, this arrangement enables both of them to be hove in or veered simultaneously; it also allows either cable to run out freely while the other is hove in or veered under power. Each cable holder is fitted with a band brake, operated by a handwheel just abaft the cable holder. This brake controls the speed at which the cable is allowed to run out when the cable holder is disconnected; it also holds the cable holder fast when the ship is riding at anchor or made fast to a buoy. The cable can be stoppered (i.e. held temporarily) or secured by means of the slips.

(2)   Abaft each hawsepipe is the Blake screw slip, used for heaving the anchor close home in its hawsepipe. Abaft each screw slip is the Blake slip, used for holding the cable temporarily and 'letting go' when coming to an anchor or when handling the inboard part of the cable. It may also be used as a preventer. Between the cable holder and the Navel pipe is the riding slip, which is put on the cable when the ship is at anchor, or secured to a buoy, and acts as a preventer should the brake of the cable holder fail to hold the pull of the cable. A removable bonnet is clamped over each Navel pipe to prevent water running down to the cable locker. Each cable is provided with two swivel pieces, one next to the anchor and one on the inboard end, which is shackled to a cable clench at the bottom of the cable locker. The fo'c'sle deck is strengthened and protected beneath the cable run by a strip of steel plating called a Scotchman. In the stem is a centreline or stem hawsepipe through which the bridles are led when the ship makes fast to a buoy. Centre-line bollards are provided for use with tugs and for securing a second bridle when the ship is made fast to a buoy. Eyeplates are fitted at each side of the port and starboard hawsepipes. The anchor strop, which acts as a preventer when the anchor is home in the hawsepipe and secured by the screw slip, is shackled to these eyeplates. In some ships the Navel pipe bonnets are fixed and have compressors fitted to them. When screwed down, the compressor nips a link of cable and acts as a preventer. This obviates the need for riding slips. When anchoring or secured to a buoy, the ship rides by the cable-holder brake with the riding slip or compressor acting as a preventer. The Blake slip is put on slack as an additional preventer.

Note.   *When ships are operating tugs close to berth, it is at the CO's discretion when to have the anchors fully A'cockbill. As soon as tug operations are complete both anchors are to be made ready for letting go.*

Fig 2-17. Fo'c'sle arrangements of a type 45 destroyer looking forward

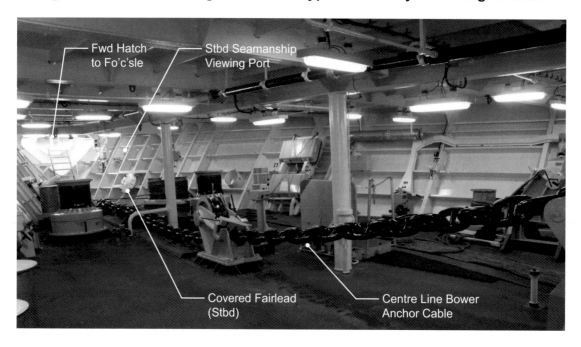

Fig 2-18. Fo'c'sle arrangements of a type 45 destroyer looking aft

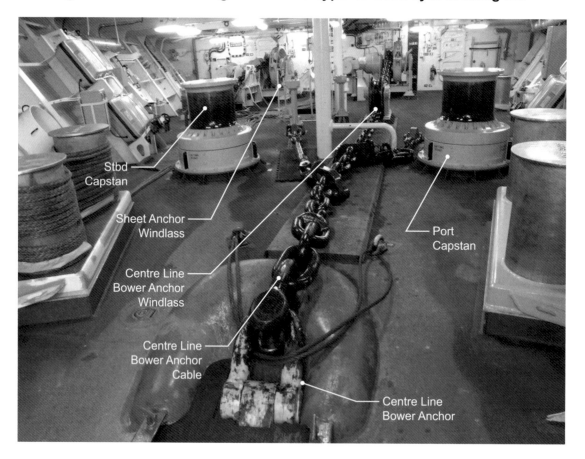

b   **Type 23 frigates and type 45 destroyers.** These ships are fitted with two bower anchors, one stowed in a centreline hawsepipe, and the other, known as the sheet anchor, on the starboard side (Fig 2-19). Because of the position of the bow dome in Type 23 frigates the sheet anchor is only used in emergencies. Other arrangements are generally as described for the traditional layout, although a single cruciform bollard (staghorn) replaces the centreline bollards, compressors are fitted in lieu of riding slips, and a bullring is fitted in addition to the centreline hawsepipe.

Fig 2-19. Anchor and cable arrangements of a type 23 frigate

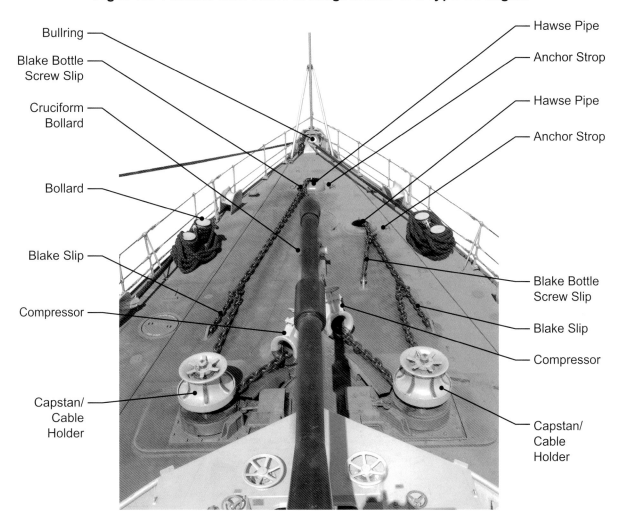

c   **Minor war vessels.** The fo'c'sle arrangement in these vessels is shown in Fig 2-20. The capstans and cable holders are replaced by a **windlass**, which revolves on a horizontal shaft driven by a reversible electric motor (Sandown Class) situated just abaft the windlass on the fo'c'sle deck.   (Hunt Class are fitted with hydraulic windlasses). Two **gypsies**, which take the place of cable holders, are mounted on the shaft and each is provided with a band brake. As with a cable holder, each gypsy can be connected to, or disconnected from, the shaft by a clutch. **Warping drums**, which take the place of a capstan, are keyed and usually clutched, one to each end of the shaft and revolve with it. A Blake slip is fitted as in the traditional fo'c'sle layout, and the anchor is hove hard home in the hawsepipe by a Blake bottle screw slip. The ship rides on the windlass brake, with the Blake slip on as a preventer, when anchored or secured to a buoy.

Fig 2-20. Typical fo'c'sle layout in a minor war vessel

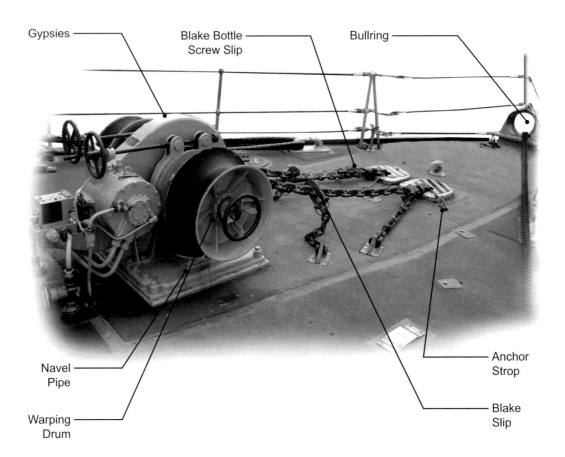

d   **Submarine anchors and cable arrangement.** The cable is secured and housed in the cable locker as shown in Fig 2-21, which is situated in the forward ballast tanks. The anchor slip at the bottom of the locker is connected to the first half shackle by a swivel piece and joining shackle. The cable runs up the "Navel Pipe" which guides the cable from the cable locker to the windlass. The cable lies over the gypsy of the windlass and then leads through the "Hawse Pipe" to where the anchor is stowed at the bottom. The final half shackle is connected to the anchor by a swivel piece and the anchor shackle. The anchor slip is mechanically operated from within the submarine via rod gearing with the operating hand wheel located in the Fwd Escape compartment. When cable is connected to the anchor slip it is the responsibility of the Navigating Officer to ensure that the cable is connected to the submarine correctly and that the slip is secured. The clench is tested to 20% above the proof load of the cable.

Note.   *The submarine should always sail with the Blake Slip off to ensure that the anchor is available for use, unless for operational reasons the CO judges that the consequences of counter detection from anchor radiated noise outweigh the risk of being unable to save the submarine from going aground or requiring a tow. The state of the anchor/Blake slip must be briefed at the leaving/entering harbour brief.*

Fig 2-21. Submarine anchor and cable arrangements

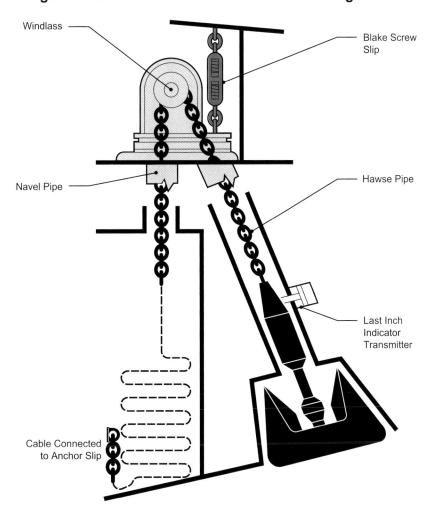

e   **Merchant ships.**   A merchant ship's anchor and cable arrangements are generally very similar to those of a minor war vessel equipped with a windlass, except **guillotines** replace the Blake slips.

02012. Miscellaneous cable deck equipment

a.   **Anchor strop.** An anchor strop (Fig 2-12(iii)) is used as an additional preventer when securing the anchor for sea; it consists of a wire strop rove through the ring of the anchor and shackled to an eyeplate on each side of, and just abaft, the hawsepipe. It has to be a snug fit.

b.   **Anchor buoy.** An anchor buoy is used when it is necessary to mark the position of the anchor on the seabed; on such occasions it is streaMed just before the anchor is let go. It is particularly useful in crowded anchorages to enable other vessels to keep clear of your anchors and cables. A danbuoy float pellet, bearing the ship's name in 50mm black lettering, is suitable for the purpose, although any similar float may be used. One end of the buoy rope (4mm-8mm polyester or polyamide is suitable) is bent to the float and the other end secured to the anchor ring. A floating line must not be used for a buoy rope, as it may become a hazard to boats during low water. The length of buoy rope must be sufficient to ensure the buoy will continue to **watch** at high water. (A buoy is said to watch when it floats, and is not watching when carried under the surface by the stream or the rise of the tide).

c.   **Deck tackle.** In the past all surface warships carried a large tackle, known as the deck tackle, as a means of weighing anchor if the combined capstan and cable holder broke down. Modern warships are no longer provided with this equipment, and an alternative method of weighing the anchor using other available winches or forms of power must be devised by individual ships. In extreme circumstances the cable can be broken (parted) and slipped, having first attached an anchor buoy to the end. The emergency means of recovery is to be recorded in the Seamanship Data Book (form S2676).

d.   **Bullrope.** A bullrope (sometimes called a heaving-out rope) is a multi-purpose rope used in large ships for ranging cable, lighting cable through a stem hawsepipe or bullring, and adjusting the height and position of the end of a ship's bridle to enable it to be shackled to a buoy. The bullrope is fitted at one end with a grommet strop and a spring hook.

e.   **Cable jack.** A cable jack (Fig 2-22) is supplied to capital ships only. It is a handspike mounted on a pedestal which functions as a fulcrum. It is used as a lever to lift up heavy cable so that, for example, the tongue of a slip can be passed under it.

Fig 2-22. Cable jack

Fig 2-23. Picking-up rope

f.   **HPMT Picking-up Rope.** (Fig 2-23 and Fig 2-24) HPMT (Q12) Picking up Rope is manufactured in Lime Green colour enabling high visibility to the operator. It is constructed from a length to suit of Quantum 12. It is fitted with a 10m chafe protection piece for use when deployed as the slip rope (positioned and spliced on by ship's staff approx 15m from the Picking up Rope Pendant). The PUR is attached to the Picking up Rope Pendant fitted with chafe protection pieces, a hook and shackle. Ships outfits are shown in Table 2-3, Table 2-4 and Table 2-5.

Table 2-3. HPMT picking-up ropes

	HMPE picking up rope	**Picking up rope pendant**	**Hook and shackle**
HPMT 1	22mm x 109m F227-99-667-5586	22mm x 3.0m F227-99-813-1436	1.5m Size B F227-99-151-6871
HPMT 2	24mm x 142m F227-99-865-9147	24mm x 3.0m F227-99-693-1091	1.5m Size B F227-99-151-6871
HPMT 3	30mm x 152m F227-99-670-5380	24mm x 6.0m F227-99-471-5118	1.5m Size C F227-99-361-3086
Capital Ships	32mm x 155m F227-99-498-9325	24mm x 6.0m F227-99-471-5118	1.5m Size C F227-99-361-3086

Note.   *Ensure that chafing pieces are fitted to all points of contact on all occasions of use.*

Fig 2-24. HPMT picking up rope

Table 2-4. Ship-to-buoy securing bridles

Securing to buoy shackle	Class of ship
0263/901424 (see Note 1)	Type 23
4030-663-9865	SVHO
0263/901421	River Class OPV

Table 2-5. Quantum 12 HMPE ship-to-buoy securing bridles NSNs

Q12 HMPE bridle	HMPE bridle	Fairlead shackle	Shock mitigation strop (SMS)
HPMT 1	28mm x 65m F227-99-707-5400	M90 F227-99-958-4133 Buffers Toothbrush F227-99-316-9347	32mm x 13m F227-99-273-0329
HPMT 2	30mm x 85m F227-99-246-1912	M90 F227-99-958-4133 Buffers Toothbrush F227-99-316-9347	44mm x 20m F227-99-373-9951
HPMT 3	40mm x 97m F227-99-246-6443	M120 F227-99-151-5477 Buffers Toothbrush F227-99-813-1451	48mm x 22m F227-99-379-2057
Capital ships	44mm x 122m F227-99-151-5454	M120 F227-99-151-5477 Buffers Toothbrush F227-99-813-1451	56mm x 22m F227-99-958-4205

Notes:

1.   Bridles supplied to Type 23 frigates and Type 45 destroyers are fitted with an adaptor piece Pattern No 0222/571-6162. This allows the attachment of a Bow Dome Anchoring Pendant when the bridle is used for bow dome anchoring.

2.   Bridles should not be dragged over non-skid decks. They must be checked for damage before and after use, and the leather gaiter is to be in place to protect the bridle during use. Braidline ship-to-buoy bridles are generally not to be used when compass swinging except in ships which are unable to break their cable.

3.   RFAs that secure to a Buoy using Braidline Bridles are to follow the procedures laid down in Annex 2F.

4.   Q12 HMPE Bridles are also used as designated tug lines.

g.   **Quantum 12 HMPE braidline bridle.** (Fig 2-25) The Q12 braidline bridle is fitted with 2 x fairlead shackles, shock mitigation strop (SMS) and a securing to buoy shackle.

Fig 2-25. Quantum 12 HMPE braidline bridle

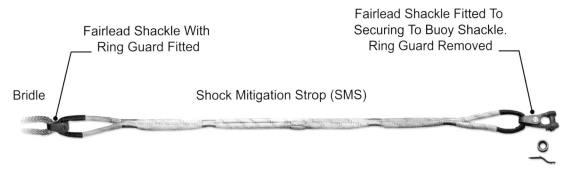

h.   **Braidline ship-to-buoy securing bridle.** (Fig 2-26). These bridles enable ships fitted with a single anchor, and ships with bow domes, to secure to a buoy and still have the bower anchor available for letting go. The bridles are made of double-braided polyamide, one end of which is fitted with a soft eye incorporating an adaptor piece to which a buoy securing shackle can be attached using a lugless joining shackle; the other end of the bridle is whipped and heat-fused. A sliding gaiter is fitted to protect the bridle from chafing at the bullring or fairlead. Two bridles are supplied to eligible ships as shown in Table 2-4.

Fig 2-26. Braidline securing to buoy bridle

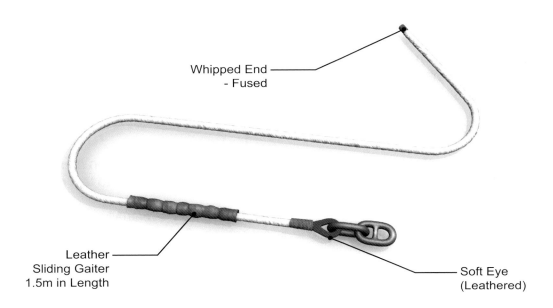

i.   **Braidline anchoring bridle.** This bridle (Fig 2-27) is used to enable ships with a fixed bow dome to avoid damaging the dome with the cable when the ship is at anchor. It consists of the braidline ship-to-buoy securing bridle, modified with a 28 mm x 7 m SWR pendant with a hard eye in each end, one end of which is shackled to the braidline bridle via a lugless joining shackle, and the other end, after the ship has anchored, to a bight of the cable using a joggle shackle. Cable is then veered, and weight transferred to the bridle. Detailed drill procedures are given later in this chapter.

Fig 2-27. Braidline anchoring bridle

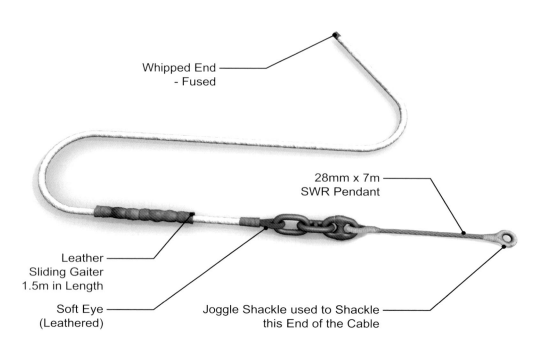

Whipped End
- Fused

28mm x 7m
SWR Pendant

Leather
Sliding Gaiter
1.5m in Length

Soft Eye
(Leathered)

Joggle Shackle used to Shackle
this End of the Cable

02013. Testing, survey, marking and maintenance of anchors, cables and associated fittings

BR 367, Manual of anchors, chain cables and associated equipment, is the authoritative publication regarding the testing, survey and marking of anchors, cables and associated equipment; the Maintenance Management in Ships system (MMS) is also a source of information. It gives details of cable bag equipment, including Naval Stores numbers for all classes of ship, submarine and RFA vessels. The following data provides a broad outline of the rules for ships in commission.

    a. **Requirement to test.** Equipment is tested to a proof load on manufacture, or after repair, or as the result of a survey. **There is no requirement to test periodically**.

    b. **Survey periodicity.** The strength of cables may eventually decrease through wear, corrosion or fatigue. Fatigue is caused chiefly by the battering to which the cable is subjected when running out through the hawsepipe and the Navel pipe, and when being hove in under strain. Equipment is therefore surveyed periodically. The survey should bring to light any deterioration caused by wear or corrosion, and should detect any flaw or crack in a link. The survey also provides an opportunity for rectifying minor defects, cleaning and overhauling joining shackles, and transposing the harder worked lengths with others so that the whole cable will wear evenly. The periodicity of survey is laid down in **BR 367, Manual of Anchors, Chain Cables and Associated Equipment.** Ships built to class will be surveyed in accordance with Lloyd's requirements.

    c. **Markings**

        (1) *Anchors.* Anchors are marked (stamped) by the manufacturer with details that include the weight, the material, the initials of the Supervisor of Tests and the date of test.

(2) *Chain cable.* Chain cable is marked on the end links with letters indicating the certifying authority, the certificate number, the year and the initials of the Supervisor of Tests. The penultimate links are stamped with the grade and size of the chain cable.

(3) *Shackles and other associated cable equipment.* All shackles and other associated cable equipment are stamped with letters indicating the certifying authority, the certificate number, the year, the initials of the Supervisor of Tests, the grade and the size of chain cable with which it will be used.

d. **Procedure for survey.** Surveys on anchors, cables and associated equipment can only be undertaken by a suitably qualified competent person. When a survey falls due, contact should be made with the surveying organisation in good time to discuss arrangements. To prepare for a survey the cable locker must first be cleared and the cable ranged (i.e. laid out in fleets). Depending on the requirements of the surveyors the cable may be ranged on deck, in a lighter, in a dock bottom, or possibly transported to the chain house for survey there. If desired to range the cable along the bottom of the dry dock, permission must first be sought from the General Manager of the dockyard. As part of the survey every joining shackle is examined to ensure the pin does not project, and is then broken (i.e. parted). The machined surfaces are cleaned and greased with XG286 before reassembly, and the dovetail chamber of each shackle reaMed to remove every particle of the old lead pellet before inserting the pin and new pellet. New pins may be required for joining shackles that have been regularly broken. (They are coated with tin to prevent corrosion and the tin tends to wear off). Every link and stud of chain cable is tapped with a hammer by the surveyor, to test it for flaws, and carefully examined. Should any link be found to have lost more than a tenth of its original size (or one-eighth if the cable is smaller than 70mm) from wear, corrosion or any other cause, the length of cable which includes the link is unfit for sea service and is to be returned to the dockyard, where the link will be replaced, or the whole length condemned. A serviceable length is to be demanded, to replace any length that is condemned. (Swivels are examined); the box-types are greased with a grease gun and the cups of the cup-type are filled with soft grease. All slips, adaptor pieces and associated or spare gear is surveyed at the same time as the cable. The shackles of cable are then transposed as required to avoid undue wear on any one length, joined up together and re-marked. Finally the entire cable is coated with a lubricant rust preventative (NSN 9150-225-1556) before or as it is re-stowed.

e. **Restowing cable**

CAUTION
The cable must never be lowered directly down the Navel Pipe

With or without the assistance of a dockside crane, the cable should never be lowered directly down the Navel pipe because it may acquire several unnoticed turns which will result in severe kinking and jamming of the cable when it is run out on the next occasion of anchoring. It must first be passed round the cable holder. If a crane is used, the cable is lowered onto the fo'c'sle first. If no power is available the cable must still be passed round the cable holder and eased into the cable locker, using a tackle and joggle shackle. Whenever the movement of the cable is halted, for example to connect the next length of cable, the brake should be applied and a pinch bar inserted through the link of cable nearest to the top of the Navel pipe; the compressor (or riding slip) need not be used unless the work is halted for a long period. The inboard end of the cable is secured to a cable clench at the bottom of the locker by a lugged joining shackle.

The Executive Officer or MEO is to witness the inboard ends of the cables being secured. The Navigating Officer must know the length of each cable, where the half shackles appear and should, if available, check the securing of the inboard end of each cable.

f.   **Certification.** On completion of a survey a **Form S194** is issued by the surveying authority, listing all equipment surveyed, and the outcome. A test certificate is issued for items that have been retested as a result of repair. The original Lloyds certification (red-stamped) is to be inserted into the Anchors and Cables Log which is to be made up as explained in BR 367.

g.   **Maintenance procedures.** Maintenance routines for anchors, cables and associated equipment are laid down in the ship's MMS system. They are devised to reduce the risk of equipment failure.

h.   **Cable bag, cable tools and miscellaneous equipment.** A cable bag (Fig 2-28) and cable tools should be readily to hand whenever cable is being worked. Other equipment may be required, depending on the nature of the task; it is listed below as miscellaneous equipment.

Fig 2-28. Cable bag and contents

Cable bag contents	Cable tools	Misc. equipment
1. Topswage 2. Hammer 3. Punches 4. Reamer 5. Spare Pins 6. Lead Pellets 7. Goggles 8. Seizing wire 9. Pliers 10.Eyewash bottle (in plastic bag to prevent contamination) 11.Buffers Tooth Brush	Maul Tommy Bar Cable Jack Bottlescrew Spanner Capstan Bar	Brooms Hoses White Paint and Brush Rags

02014. Safety precautions when handling and working cable

Handling or working cable safely requires observation of certain safety precautions. They are as follows:

a.   DMS boots must be worn by all personnel.

b.   Rope hangers (2 m lengths of suitable cordage) must be used when manhandling cable. They should be rove behind the link stud to avoid jamming.

c.   Personnel must never straddle the cable.

d.   A topswage must be used when connecting or parting a lugless joining shackle.

e.   Goggles must be worn by personnel operating the brake of a cable holder or gypsy windlass to avoid the risk of eye injuries caused from debris being thrown off as the cable is let go. Personnel in close proximity when lead pellet plugs are being hammered into joining shackles must also wear goggles.

f.   All personnel in the enclosed FX on T45 Destroyers during anchoring operations are to wear ear defenders and goggles, those operating and those in close proximity to the Gypsy windlass are also to wear Safety Helmets.

g.   Personnel detailed to let go the Blake slip during anchoring must stand as far aft as possible on the side of the slip when letting go.

h.   Because of their different diameters, the heaving and veering rates of the capstan and cable holder differ. This fact must be borne in mind, particularly when ranging cable using a bullrope.

02015. Accident prevention

a.   **Anchoring.** The efficiency of a ship's cable is of such importance that rapidity in anchoring must give place to a method by which the strain on the cables, and in consequence the incident of failure, is reduced to a minimum by ensuring that:

(1)   The speed of a ship is reduced to a minimum before releasing the anchor.

(2)   Anchoring in deep water is avoided as far as possible.

(3)   When anchoring in deep water (over 27 m) is unavoidable, the cable is veered to within approximately 18 m of the bottom before anchoring.

b.   **Weighing anchor.** To avoid straining the cable when shortening-in, care must be exercised to prevent:

(1)   The cable drawing under the forefoot or across the stem.

(2)   The anchor swinging under the forefoot and becoming fouled.

02016. Loss or accident

When ships fracture or part their cable the administrative authority will convene a ships investigation to determine the cause. The loss or breakage of anchors or cables must be reported by signal. The report should include details of any associated gear lost, e.g. anchor and joining shackles and swivel pieces. The broken link or part should be recovered if possible and the fracture covered with tinfoil or other suitable material to prevent rusting. It should then be sent to a Naval Base for onward dispatch to a metallurgical laboratory.

02017. Terminology and expressions used in anchor work

Terms and expressions used in anchor work are as follows:

a. **A'cockbill.** An anchor is said to be a'cockbill when it has been eased just clear of the hawsepipe and its weight is taken by the Blake slip in readiness for letting go.

b. **Anchor coming home** means that the anchor is dragging towards the ship as the cable is hove in. When weighing her anchor, the ship should always move towards it, using her engines if necessary, and the anchor should not break out of the bottom until the cable is up and down,

c. **Anchor aweigh.** The anchor is said to be aweigh imMediately it is clear of the bottom.

d. **Clear hawse.** This term means that the cables are clear of one another when a ship is riding to two anchors.

e. **Foul hawse.** A ship has a foul hawse if the cables are crossed or otherwise foul of each other when she is riding to two anchors. If the ship swings 180 degrees she will have a foul hawse, and the cables are then said to have a cross in them: another 180 degrees more in the same direction would cause an elbow in the cables; a further 180 degrees would cause an elbow and a cross, and yet another 180 degrees would cause a round turn.

f. **Clear or foul anchor.** The anchor is reported clear or foul as soon as it is entirely sighted. To be clear the anchor must be hanging from its ring and clear of its own cable and of any obstruction such as a bight of rope or chain picked up from the bottom. This visual sighting does not apply to the modern submarine's anchor.

g. **To come to**. A ship is said to come to an anchor at the moment of letting go. The entry in the ship's log would read: '0900. Came to with port anchor. etc'. A ship has got her cable when she has dropped back on her cable and is riding to it.

h. **Dragging.** An anchor is said to be dragging when, instead of holding the ship, the ship drags it along the bottom; this may occur in heavy weather, in a strong current, or when insufficient cable has been paid out. A small amount of dragging on anchoring is necessary, in order to bury the anchor in the seabed.

i. **To grow**. A cable is said to grow in the direction in which it leads outside the hawsepipe. When asked 'How does the cable grow?' the reply is given by pointing the arm in that direction, unless it grows vertically, when the report 'Up and down' should be given.

j. **To hang cable** is to hold it temporarily with a stopper.

k. **A hanger** is usually a rope, which is passed through a link of chain cable or round the bight of a rope to hang it.

l. **Long stay.** The cable is said to be at long stay when it is taut, and reaches out well away from the hawsepipe and enters the water at an acute angle.

m. **Short stay.** The cable is said to be at short stay when it is taut and leads down to the anchor at a steep angle, and a bridle is said to be at short stay when the mooring buoy is hove close under the hawsepipe.

n.   **Shortening-in cable.** A ship lying at anchor is said to shorten-in her cable when she heaves in part of it; for example, a ship riding to eight shackles of cable might shorten it to three shackles of cable before weighing anchor, or temporarily to reduce her swinging radius.

o.   **To snub** a cable is to restrain it suddenly when running out by applying the brake. This is damaging to the cable, so it should only be carried out in an emergency.

p.   **Up-and-down.** The cable is said to be up-and-down when it is vertical. When weighing anchor the cable will be up-and-down just before the anchor is broken out of the bottom, and this usually occurs soon after it is at short stay.

q.   **To veer cable** is to pay out or ease out cable from the combined capstan and cable holder or windlass when these are connected to and controlled by their motors; the brake should be in the 'off' position. It also means to allow the cable to run out by its own weight or strain on the outboard end under control by the cable holder or windlass brake.

Note.   The person in charge (I/C) must qualify the order 'Veer' by stating whether the cable holder is to be connected or disconnected i.e., whether the cable is to be veered under power or controlled by the brake. If the cable is to be veered under power, the order would be 'Connect up' (port cable holder), 'Off brake', 'Veer port'.

r.   **Weighing anchor** is the operation of heaving in cable until the anchor is broken out of the bottom. (**Weigh** must not be confused with **way**, which refers to the motion of a ship through the water).

02018. Anchoring and weighing

Before a ship anchors, the Captain studies the selected or allocated berth and decides which anchor to use and the amount of cable, taking into consideration the direction of the wind, the tidal stream, the depth of water and the nature of the bottom. When possible the weather anchor is used so the ship will swing clear of her cable. The Navigating Officer must prepare an anchoring plan so that the ship's speed may be reduced and then the engines stopped in sufficient time. HM ships, except those with underwater fittings vertically below the hawsepipe, usually let the anchor go with slight headway so that the anchor is dropped in the exact position and the cable is laid out on the seabed clear of the anchor. This method is called a **running anchorage**. Ships with underwater fittings that preclude this method should use the **dropping anchorage**. For this method the ship stops in the anchorage position and the anchor is let go as the ship gathers sternway. The ship continues making slight sternway to ensure the cable is laid out ahead of the ship. HM ships with two anchors always prepare both bower anchors and cables for imMediate use when preparing to come to single anchor. If one anchor hangs (e.g. fails to move) when the Blake slip is released, the other anchor can be let go instead. See also the Notes at the end of sub para b.

a.   **The cable party.** The composition of the cable party depends on the type and size of the ship, her fo'c'sle, the design of the cable lockers and the type and motive power of her combined capstan and cable holder or windlass. Personnel detailed for the task should dress appropriately for the prevailing weather conditions, including the wearing of lifejackets and full body harness/restraint belt if deeMed necessary by the OIC. All must wear DMS boots. A typical cable party consists of:

1   Safety officer (warfare branch PO)
1   I/C Leading seaman specialist
1   Capstan driver
2   Able seaman specialists
2   AB any

b.   **Clearing away anchors and cables.** The operation of preparing the anchors for letting go is called **clearing away anchors and cables**, and this is carried out, as explained in Annex 2A, when approaching the land, whether it is intended to enter a harbour or not.

Notes:

*1.   **Anchoring drills in ships not fitted with a Blake Slip**. Ships not fitted with a Blake slip let go the anchor from the brake. As far as practicable the preparations are as described in Annex 2A. When the anchor has been veered a'cockbill the brake and compressor are put on and the cable holder disconnected. The bridge is then inforMed that both anchors are ready for letting go. With half a cable to run the compressor is removed. At the order 'Let go' the brake is released as quickly as possible*

2.   When berthing and unberthing, ships are to have both anchors ready for letting go (one anchor in some patrol vessels). The offshore bower anchor, (centreline anchor in Type 23s) is to be prepared so that it is at the a'cockbill position and clear of the hawsepipe. The inshore bower anchor, (sheet anchor on Type 23s) is to be prepared so that it is eased down the hawsepipe sufficiently to ensure free running of the anchor if let go but not to the extent that it will foul any jetty/berth obstruction. The weight of the anchor is to be on the Blake slip with the brake applied to the cable holder and the cable holder disconnected.

c.   **Letting go.** The ship approaches the anchorage at slow speed and usually heads into the wind or tidal stream. When anchoring in deep water (over 27m) the anchor is veered under power to within about 18m of the bottom before it is let go, otherwise the anchor may be damaged on hitting the bottom and the cable may become brittle as it runs out. The procedure for letting go is explained in Annex 2A.

d.   **Securing the cable.** It is customary to secure the cable with the ordered joining shackle just abaft the Blake slip. Having the joining shackle in this position makes it easy in an emergency to part the cable and slip the anchor. The procedure for securing the cable is explained in Annex 2A.

Notes:

1.   The depth of water at the anchorage must be known by the I/C to enable him to assess, by the number of shackles veered, whether or not the cable is piling up on itself, and also to alleviate the possibility of inadvertently snubbing the cable.

2.   If the depth of water requires more shackles of cable than are available, it must be remembered should the weather deteriorate that the anchor is not providing its maximum holding pull.

3.   HM ships fitted with a windlass ride by the brake of the windlass with the Blake slip and guillotine (if fitted) acting as a preventer. In ships with no Blake slip fitted the Blake bottlescrew slip, fully shortened on its screw thread, must be put on as a preventer, positioned as described above for the Blake slip.

4.   Because of the length of the fo'c'sle, Type 23 Frigates should use the Blake bottle screw slip rather than the Blake slip as a preventer when riding at a single anchor. The Blake bottle screw slip must be fully shortened on its screw thread before it is attached to the cable forward of the required joining shackle. This arrangement reduces the amount of cable passing over the deck in the event of it being necessary in an emergency to break the cable at the joining shackle.

e.   **Amount of cable to be used.** The minimum amount of cable to be used with a single anchor, which will ensure that the maximum holding pull of the anchor can be developed, is that which is needed to give a horizontal pull on the ring of the anchor in all conditions of wind and stream. It depends upon the magnitude of the holding pull, the depth of water, and whether the cable is forged steel or a copper based material. Given that the cable size is selected to provide a working load equal to the maximum anchor pull, then the variation in the amount of cable required over a range of anchor pulls from 0 to 100 tonnes is quite small, and it can be assuMed that the variants are only depth of water and type of cable. The formula for **forged steel cable** is: **Amount of cable to veer in shackles is one-and-a half times the square root of the depth of water in metres.** The formula for **copper based cable** is: **Amount of cable to veer in shackles is equal to the square root of the depth of water in metres**.

f.   **Effect of the cable.** The cable acts as a shock absorber between the anchor and the ship. The weight of the cable causes it to lie in a catenary between the hawsepipe and the seabed. The greater the force (from wind and stream) acting on a ship, the greater will be the distance between the hawsepipe and the anchor, so that the amount of cable lying on the bottom will vary. This cable on the bottom provides a holding pull of two thirds of the actual weight of the length of cable on the bottom, and this is added to the pull of the anchor. In conditions where there is a likelihood of the anchor dragging, there is unlikely to be any cable lying on the seabed and it is therefore safer to consider only the holding pull of the anchor.

g.   **Precautions in bad weather.** If the ship is lying at single anchor and if there is sufficient sea room to leeward, more cable may be veered. The cable holder must be connected while veering, because if the cable were allowed to run out on the brake, the snatch on the cable, caused by the weight of the ship suddenly coming on it after drifting astern and taking up the slack, might weaken the hold of the anchor.

h.   **Yawing.** A ship, especially one with a high fo'c'sle, usually yaws considerably to each side of the wind when lying at single anchor in bad weather (Fig 2-29). At the end of each yaw the ship is liable to drag her anchor, because she first surges ahead and then falls back on her cable, thereby imparting a jerk to the anchor. The situation may be eased by veering more cable. The more cable, the heavier the catenary, and the greater the tension before the cable is 'straightened out'. The tension is a measure of the force being applied to the ship by the cable, and if sufficient tension can be obtained to stop the motion of the ship before the cable is straightened out, there will be no jerk. As link after link is picked up from the bottom, weight is added to the catenary. With enough chain, the ship will usually be brought about from one tack to the other steadily, without a jerk. A large scope of cable also exerts a damping effect on the yawing by its resistance to being dragged sideways across the bottom. This adds to the catenary effect of the weight of the cable, but is more effective in pulling the bow through the wind because it causes the cable to lead more to the side as the ship sails across the wind. If the yaw becomes serious, the situation can be relieved by letting go a second anchor at the end of the yaw away from the first anchor. Both cables are then veered so that the ship rides with one anchor at long stay and the other at short stay.

Fig 2-29. Yaw of ship in strong wind

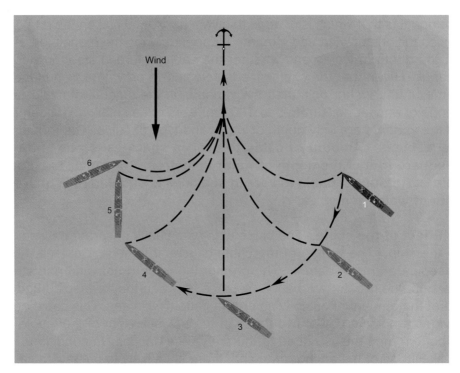

i.   **Anchoring in a gale.** If it is expected that a ship fitted with two anchors will have to ride out a strong and prolonged gale both anchors should be used. The procedure for this is fully explained in **BR 45 Admiralty Manual of Navigation Volume 6.** However, the basic method used is illustrated in Fig 2-2.

j.   **Anchor watch.** An anchor watch should always be set in bad weather. This watch consists of an officer on the bridge and a special party on or near the fo'c'sle ready to watch and work the cable. Power should be on the capstan and main engines, and sea duty men should be closed up.

k.   **Dragging an anchor.** Dragging of the anchor can be detected by taking frequent compass bearings on shore objects, or by taking soundings with a hand lead line, or by the behaviour of the cable. When the anchor is dragging, the cable usually tautens and slackens alternately in a marked manner and vibration can be felt in it as the anchor is dragged along the bottom.

l.   **Shortening-in and weighing anchor**. (See Annex 2A)

m.   **Clearing a Foul Anchor.** An anchor may come up foul of its own cable or of a bight of rope or chain picked up from the bottom. If foul of its own cable and the ship is stopped, it is best to let go the anchor as it will then usually clear itself. If foul of a bight of rope or chain it is usually best to pass a hanger round the fouled bight, lead the hanger aft, secure it and then veer the cable until the hanger takes the weight of the obstruction and the anchor comes clear. The anchor can then be hove up and the hanger slipped or cut.

n.   **Clearing a foul hawse.** (Fig 2-30)

(1)   To clear a foul hawse the non-riding cable is hung outboard below the foul, then broken inboard, and the foul is cleared by passing the free end of the non-riding cable in the reverse direction to that of the turns; only half a turn, however, should be taken out at a time.

The procedure will usually entail the use of a boat, and safety aspects as described for mooring to a buoy will apply. A detailed description of this operation is given below, in which it is assuMed that the ship is riding by the starboard cable and that there is a round turn to be cleared. If the turn is submerged the starboard cable is hove in to bring the turn to a convenient height above the water, and the two cables are lashed together just below the turn to prevent the turn slipping down the cables. With heavy cable there is a danger that when the lashing is cut after the hawse has been cleared the two cables will spring back and injure whoever cuts the lashing. To prevent this possibility it is best to lash the cable by reeving a length of and appropriate length and diameter cordage through the links, as shown in the inset in Fig 2-30 and then to belay the two ends inboard, ensuring that the rope does not take the weight of the cable while the hawse is being cleared. The cables can then be unlashed from inboard by unreeving the rope. The picking-up rope is led outboard through the port hawsepipe or a convenient fairlead and attached with a joggle shackle to the port cable below the turn (Fig 2-30(i)). It is then brought to the capstan and hove in to take the weight of the cable. The port cable is hung inboard or put on the screw slip, and then broken. A suitable **messenger** (a berthing rope will suffice) is now passed out through the port hawsepipe, dipped round the starboard cable in the opposite direction to the turn to be cleared, brought up again through the hawsepipe, and tailed on to the end of the outboard part of the port cable (Fig 2-30(ii)).

(2) The slip is knocked off and the messenger hove in; if necessary, the picking-up rope can be stoppered and the capstan used. If the cable is heavy (above 60mm) it is advisable not to let the end run out through the hawsepipe, but to ease it out on a rope fitted with a slipping arrangement. When half a turn in the cables has been cleared the messenger is stoppered, its end dipped again round the riding cable, and again hove in; this will clear the remaining half-turn (Fig 2-30(iii). The end of the port cable is now hove back into the hawsepipe and the cable is joined up again. The picking-up rope is eased up and cast off, and the lashing is cut or slipped from inboard.

Fig 2-30. Clearing a foul hawse

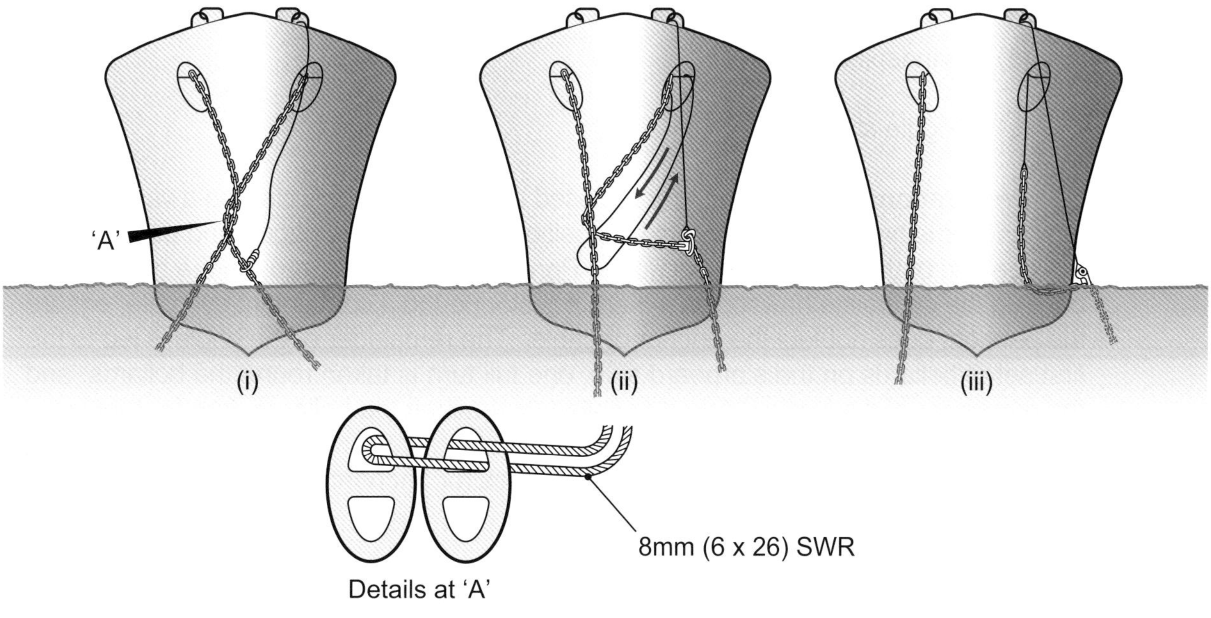

'A'

(i)   (ii)   (iii)

8mm (6 x 26) SWR

Details at 'A'

o.   **Securing anchors and cables for sea.** The anchors must not be secured for sea until ordered by the Captain who, under normal conditions, will require both anchors (where fitted) ready for letting go until the ship is clear of the harbour. Then it must be done thoroughly or the anchors will work loose in a heavy sea; and it must be done quickly as explained in Annex 2A.

Notes:

1.   *To prevent damage, the anchor must not be brought fully home under power.*

2.   *'Post Heavy Weather' Shackle pins and leads must be checked for movement and security post heavy weather. In the event of movement they are to be re-leaded and consideration must be given for backing up with an additional preventer i.e. Roundsling.*

02019. Anchoring with a MMFC bridle

Ships fitted with bow domes are currently supplied with MMFC bridles. There are two types in service. These are secured to the cable to act as a chafing piece against the dome when the ship is at anchor (Fig 2-31, Fig 2-32 and Fig 2-33). The bridle is described in para 02012 sub para g. MMFC bridles are to be used at all times when anchoring unless the Captain is confident the cable will remain clear of the dome whilst the ship is at anchor.

a.   **Equipment required.** The following equipment is required in addition to that needed for going to single anchor:

(1)   *MMFC bridle with Bow Dome Anchoring pendant attached.* (One end of the pendant is attached to the adaptor piece on the bridle using a lugless joining shackle). On the first occasion of use, and after the Bow Dome Pendant has been attached to the braidline bridle, a measurement is taken from the free end of the pendant, and the point marked on the bridle by the insertion of a strip of red bunting or similar easily visible marking. This mark indicates the position at which the bridle will be turned up on the bollards.

(2)   Shepherd's crook or boat hook.

(3)   Strayline.

(4)   Handspikes.

(5)   Joggle shackle.

b.   **Preparations.** The cable party is closed up, the cables are cleared away, and the bow anchor is brought to the a'cockbill position. A strayline is rigged and used to haul the free end of the Bow Dome Anchoring Pendant (BDAP) out through the bullring and back up the centreline hawsepipe, where it is stopped to a convenient eyeplate; ensure the pendant does not foul the anchor or cable. The remainder of the bridle is led to the first set of bollards on the starboard side, one full turn is taken round the bollards, and the remainder of the bridle is faked or coiled down abaft the bollards, free for running.

c.   **Execution.** Standard anchoring procedures for anchoring with a MMFC Bridle is explained in Annex 2B.

d.   **Recovering the MMFC bridle.** (In accordance with Annex 2B).

e.   For ships fitted with HPMT the bow dome anchoring pendant is supplied length to suit of Turbo 75 HMPE with a polyethylene coating.

Fig 2-31. HMPE bow dome anchoring pendant

M90 Fairlead Shackle
MBL: 90 tonne (HPMT2)
or
M120 Fairlead Shackle
MBL: 120 tonne (HPMT3)

Joggle Shackle
NSN 0222/1939 - 54-60mm
NSN 0222/1938 - 38-48mm
NSN 0222/1936 - 28-36mm

Anchoring Pendant - 9m x 34mm Turbo -75 (HPMT3)
Anchoring Pendant - 7m x 34mm Turbo -75 (HPMT2)
With PU Coating, Soft Eye One End,
Encapsulated Blue Line
HMPE Thimble Eye Other End.
MBL: 83.9 Tonne

HPMT Bridle
or
HPMT 2 = 73m x 30m 59.4t
HPMT 3 = 85m x 40m 108.9t

Stainless Steel
Tubular HMPE
Thimble

Fig 2-32. Joggle shackle attached to cable and SWR pendant

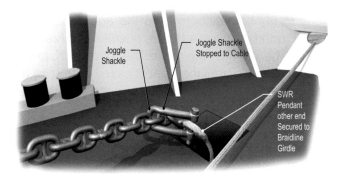

Joggle
Shackle

Joggle Shackle
Stopped to Cable

SWR
Pendant
other end
Secured to
Braidline
Girdle

Fig 2-33. Ship anchored with MMFC bridle attached to the cable

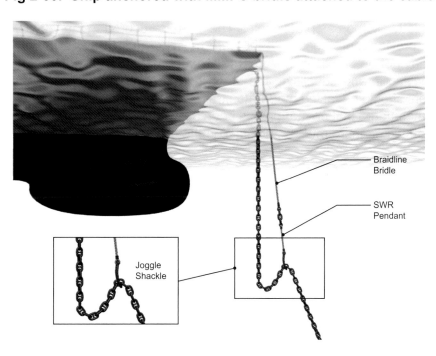

Braidline
Bridle

SWR
Pendant

Joggle
Shackle

02020. Stern-to berths (Mediterranean moor)

In some harbours where there is insufficient room to berth many ships alongside, ships may be obliged to berth at right-angles to a jetty, with their sterns secured to it by berthing lines and their anchor(s) laid out ahead. This type of mooring can only be employed where there is a negligible range of tide, and it is commonly used in Mediterranean ports; for this reason it is often called the **Mediterranean (or Med) moor**. Navigation and shiphandling aspects of this evolution are covered in **BR 45 Admiralty Manual of Navigation Volume 6**. The major considerations are to veer sufficient cable so that the ship can swing clear of other ships at the berth when leaving, to lay the anchors sufficiently far apart to make the ship secure in a wind, and to ensure the anchors do not foul those of other ships. In a shallow harbour it is recommended that a frigate veers about four shackles of cable on each anchor, and that cables are spanned with an included angle of about 50 degrees, so as to make the ship more secure in a wind. It is obvious, however, that the berth will not be safe if a gale blows from abeam. If such weather is forecast it is advisable to put to sea or seek a sheltered anchor berth. Ships fitted with a single anchor can, in theory, carry out a Mediterranean moor; however, the single anchor will hold the bows steady only in benign weather conditions.

    a.   **Preparations.** All personnel involved in the evolution must be briefed on the task. The cable party is closed up and both anchors are cleared away and made ready for letting go; heaving lines, berthing hawsers and a 12mm polypropylene towing messenger are prepared on the quarter deck by a berthing party; the towing messenger will be used to pass the first line. The Commanding Officer decides how far from the jetty to lay the anchors, and the approach the ship will make; this will usually be parallel to the jetty towards the position the first anchor will be let go. The seaboat is deployed before the ship makes her approach, and the coxswain is ordered to stay well clear of the ship until the boat is called in to take the towing messenger to the jetty. Clear instructions from the bridge to the fo'c'sle, quarterdeck and seaboat are important throughout the process.

    b.   **Procedure.** The ship makes her approach and the first anchor is let go. (Fig 2-34 position 1); the bow is turned to port to prevent the cable running under the ship and to bring the starboard hawsepipe to the correct position for letting go the second anchor (position 2). When both anchors are down, the boat is called in to take the first line clear of the water to the jetty. The ship is manoeuvred into her berth, veering cable as necessary during the process, and the hawsers are passed from the quarterdeck to the jetty as soon as practicable. The stern is secured to the jetty by two hawsers, which provide more security if they are crossed under the stern, but in some ships this may not be practicable. After the stern has been secured, the moor is tautened by heaving in and equalising the strain on the anchor cables. When secured, both anchors should be taking moderate strain and standing well out of the water. It must be remembered that no margin has been allowed for safety astern in the case of wind from ahead so there must be no slack in the cables.

Notes:

1.   There are alternative methods of approach available to the Commanding Officer depending on the prevailing weather conditions and the geographical position of the berth; however, the seaman's task remains fundamentally as described above.

2.   It is important that anchor buoys are used to mark anchors in congested berths.

Fig 2-34. Berthing stern-to in calm weather

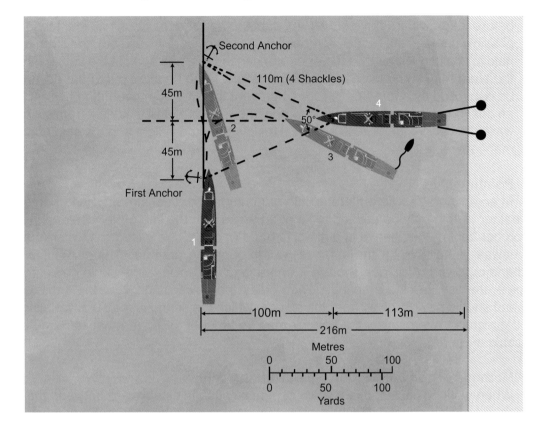

c.   **Leaving a stern-to berth.**   Opinion is divided, when slipping from a stern-to berth, on whether to keep a stern rope rove while the cables are hove in. The ship does not have to move very far forward before a stern rope loses its effect in checking a stern swing, and it might foul a propeller or hamper use of the engines if required. Nevertheless, some ship handlers prefer to retain the windward hawser rove as a slip rope until the ship has moved forward sufficiently for the stern rope to have no further use in manoeuvring. Anchor positions should be plotted and considered in relation to the likely direction of swing as the ship leaves the berth.

02021. Use of an anchor at an alongside berth

In some harbours it may be necessary to let go an anchor before going alongside, so that, when the ship subsequently casts off, her bows can be hauled clear of her berth by her cable. She can then weigh her anchor and go ahead into the fairway. The anchor should be let go in such a position that, when the ship is secured alongside, the cable grows abeam, and with sufficient scope to ensure the anchor holding when the bows of the ship are hauled off; the shallower the water, the closer to the jetty can the anchor be let go. When using an anchor at an alongside berth the anchor must be buoyed.

a.   **Procedure**.   In calm weather the ship approaches at right-angles to the jetty and pointing to the head of her berth; and as the anchor is let go at the required distance from the jetty the rudder is put over to swing the bows in the required direction. As the way of the ship is reduced the cable is braked to assist the swing of the bows, and a headline is passed ashore and used to prevent the bows swinging out too far. The ship is eventually stopped a little more than half a ship's length ahead of her berth, when a stern line is passed ashore and the ship is backed stern first into the berth. The use of an anchor may also be dictated by a stiff onshore wind (or stream) when berthing. Details of this procedure are in **BR 45, Admiralty Manual of Navigation Volume 6.**

b.   **Slipping from alongside with an anchor down**. When slipping from alongside with an anchor down, the stern must be cast out on a spring or hauled out by a tug before the bows are hove out by the cable, otherwise the stern will foul the jetty and possibly damage the rudder or propeller. As the bows are hove out, the stern must be held in position, either by a tug or by working the engines against the cable, otherwise the stern may swing in again and foul the jetty. The heaving out of the bows should be controlled by a fore breast rope to prevent the ship from overriding her anchor. In an onshore wind the help of a tug to haul the stern out, and to keep it from swinging in while the cable is hove in, is essential unless the wind is light and the ship particularly manoeuvrable.

02022. Pointing ship

In an anchorage where there is little or no current or tidal stream, and in reasonably calm weather, a ship may be pointed to lie at an angle with the line of her cable by putting a spring on her cable. First heave in a shackle or so of cable. Now lead a hawser (the ship's towing hawser is suitable for the purpose) out through the aftermost quarter fairlead, then forward and outboard of all, and shackle it with a joggle shackle to the cable outboard of the hawsepipe, thereby forming a spring. Then belay the hawser and veer the cable and the ship's head should pay off, away from the side on which the spring is rove until pointing in the required direction. Alternatively the hawser may be brought to an after capstan and hove in as the cable is veered.

02023. Methods of communication when working cables

When working cables, direct voice communication is established between the bridge and the fo'c'sle using either The Rationalised Integrated Communication Equipment (RICE) telephone system or a sound powered telephone. Portable radios may be used subject to the Emission Control (EMCON) policy in force at the time. To indicate progress in working cables to other ships in the vicinity 'Uniform' is hoisted at the yardarm on the appropriate side and used as shown in Table 2-6:

Table 2-6. 'Uniform' flag hoists when working cable

Operation	Progress	Signal
Anchoring	'Anchor let go'	At the dip on appropriate side
	'Cable veered correct amount'	Close - up
	'Cable secured'	Hauled down
Weighing	'Am heaving in' (when lying to two anchors 'port' or 'starboard' may be used to indicate side)	At the dip on appropriate side
	'Anchor aweigh'	Close - up
	'Ready to proceed'	Hauled down

Note.   *By night, the information is either signalled by light or passed by voice.*

a.   **Captain's anchor flags**. These consist of two small hand flags, one red and one green, which may be used by the Commanding Officer to indicate the exact instant at which to let go the port and starboard anchors respectively. By night, red and green wands are used instead of the Captain's anchor flags. For ships with enclosed forecastles, where fitted, Stop Go lights can be used.

b.   **Example of use of anchor flags**. The following example shows the cable signals used by a ship in daylight when coming to with a single anchor. The Commanding Officer shows the red anchor flag from the bridge, meaning 'Stand by to let go port anchor', and this is repeated by the Cable Officer. 'Uniform', made up ready for breaking, is hoisted at the dip at the port yardarm. The Commanding Officer lowers the red anchor flag, whereupon the slip is knocked off the port cable and the anchor let go. 'Uniform' is broken at the dip at the port yardarm. 'Uniform' is hoisted close up when cable is veered the correct amount, and hauled down when the cable is secured.

02024. Moorings

a.   Permanent moorings may be laid for the following purposes:

(1)   To make the most of the usually limited space of a harbour anchorage.

(2)   To berth ships as near as possible to the landing places so as to facilitate embarking and disembarking stores, cargo, crew or passengers.

(3)   To provide secure moorings for ships in crowded waters, especially for those laid up and others unable to move under their own power.

(4)   To ensure that ships are berthed precisely, and in the most suitable positions for each other's safety and for the preservation of lanes for harbour traffic.

(5)   To reduce the possibility of ships dragging in heavy weather. (A ship is more secure at a permanent swinging mooring than at anchor.)

b.   **Types of mooring**. The two main types of permanent mooring are the swinging mooring, where a ship secures head to buoy and is free to swing to the wind and tidal stream; and the head-and-stern mooring, where a ship secures head-and-stern between two buoys. Swinging moorings are always laid if space permits, because ships can make fast to them and slip from them with the minimum of help. Where space is limited, however, ships must be secured to head-and-stern moorings, which have the following disadvantages:

(1)   A ship usually requires tugs when securing to, and slipping from them.

(2)   When a ship is secured to them in a strong beam wind they are subjected to a very great load and so they have to be particularly strong and secure.

(3)   A mooring intended for a long ship is not suitable for a short ship.

Note.   *Remarks on shiphandling while securing to head buoys or between head-and-stern buoys appear in **BR 45, Admiralty of Navigation Volume 6**.*

02025. Parts of a mooring

The three main parts of a mooring comprise the **ground tackle**, the **riser pendant** and the **buoy**. These are illustrated in Fig 2-35, which shows a first-class three-leg swinging mooring.

Fig 2-35. A first-class three-leg swinging mooring showing the principle parts

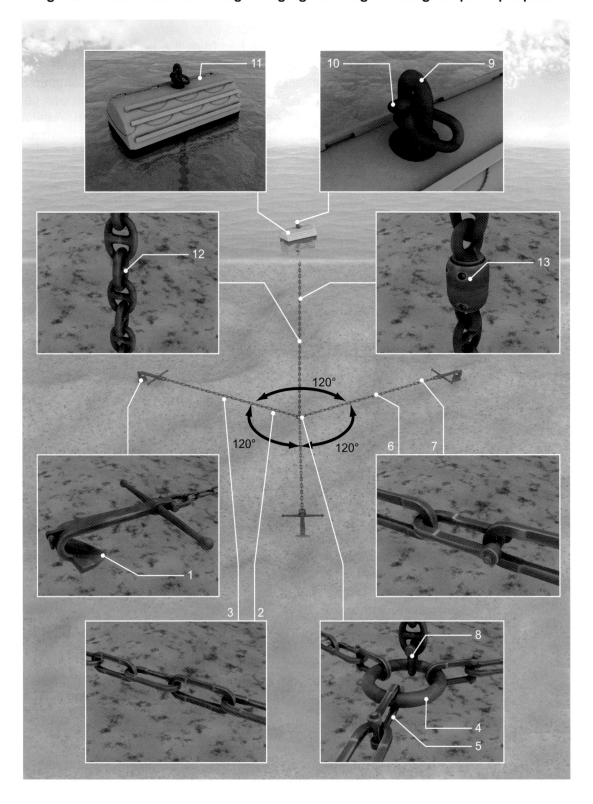

Reference	Description	Size	QTY
1	Anchor Mooring (C/W) Stock	9.75 Tonnes	3
2	Chain Mooring – Square Link	102 mm	165 m
3	Chain Mooring – Square Link	95 mm	220 m
4	Ring Mooring – Pattern 'A'	102 mm	1
5	Shackle – Square Link – Clench	102 mm	3
6	Shackle – Square Link – Forelock	102 mm	6
7	Shackle – Square Link – Forelock	95 mm	15
8	Shackle Anchor – Clench	102 mm	1
9	Shackle – Buoy Ring	102 mm	1
10	Reducing Link for Buoy Ring Shackle	103 mm	2
11	Buoy – Cylindrical – With trunk	first class	1
12	Riser Pendant – Grade 2 Steel Chain cable	102 mm	1
13	Swivel	102 mm(4in)	1

a.   **Ground tackle.** This consists of two or more anchors, with a **ground arm** of mooring chain shackled to each and led to a **central mooring ring**, to which is shackled the **riser pendant**.

(1)   *Mooring anchors and clumps.* (Fig 2-36). These are usually stocked single-fluke anchors, and they are usually heavier than the bower anchors of the ships for which the mooring is designed. They are carefully placed and embedded to ensure that the mooring and its buoy are in the correct position. Because they are never dropped and embedded by dragging like a ship's anchor they have only one fluke, and a stock is incorporated to prevent the anchor from rolling out of its bed. Cast-iron sinkers are sometimes used in minor moorings instead of fluked anchors.

(2)   *Legs of ground tackle.* These are made up of 18 m lengths of special square-link mooring chain, each link being approximately 1 m long and of square section. The lengths are joined by special *forelock mooring shackles* (Fig 2-35). *Clenched or welded mooring shackles* are used where the inner ends of the arms are shackled to the *central mooring ring* (Fig 2-35), as most wear occurs in this position.

Note.   *The special square-link mooring chain is gradually being superseded by studded chain cable.*

b.   **Riser pendants.** Pendants are made up from lengths of Grade 2 steel studded chain cable and are fitted with a swivel provided there is sufficient swinging room at the mooring. Pendants of head-and-stern moorings may be fitted with swivels so that, if necessary, they can be used as swinging moorings. The swivel is inserted at one-third of the length of the pendant from its upper end. The lower end of the riser is made of open end-link cable for a length equal to the maximum range of the tide. For any size of cable the open end links are made of the same grade steel but the diameter of the metal is 20% greater than that of the common studded links. This additional thickness compensates for the absence of the stud, and provides a greater margin for wear at the position where most movement and abrasion occurs. The length of the pendant of a standard mooring is equal to the depth of water at Mean High Water Springs plus two metres and the freeboard of the buoy. In exposed positions where heavy seas and swell are likely to be experienced the length is increased accordingly.

Fig 2-36. Mooring anchors, clumps and types of ground tackle

Admiralty Mooring Anchor AM7

Admiralty Mooring Anchor
(AM12-6 tonne)

Clump Mooring (Stockless) Anchors

Heavy Cast Iron Clump

Feather

Shackle

Link

Washer

Forelock Pin

Bolt

Square Link and Forelock
Mooring Shackle

Cast Iron Buoy Sinker

c. **Buoys**

(1) *Mooring buoys.* Most modern Admiralty mooring buoys are built on the trunk principle and are cylindrical in shape (Fig 2-37). The larger sizes are divided into watertight compartments by longitudinal and transverse bulkheads. The riser pendant is led up through a central trunk in the buoy, and the bolt of the buoy shackle is passed through the end link of the riser pendant. The ships cables are shackled directly to the buoy shackle using the securing-to-buoy shackle. If this is not possible because the buoy shackle is too large for the securing-to-buoy shackle, then both cables are shackled to the reducing links, using one link for each cable. The size of a buoy depends on the size and length of the pendant, which it supports, and also the reserve of buoyancy required for the buoy. A reserve of buoyancy of 35% is usually allowed, but this may be reduced to 25% if necessary. Table 2-8 shows the various classes of mooring buoy size and maximum length of pendant with which each is designed to be used in normal circumstances. There are five classes of mooring buoy but in deep water a higher classification of buoy may be used because it has to support a longer riser pendant. Two further buoys, the **X-class** and the **Monster**, are provided to permit moorings to be laid at depths greater than those for which a first-class buoy is suitable.

Fig 2-37. A cylindrical steel mooring buoy, first class

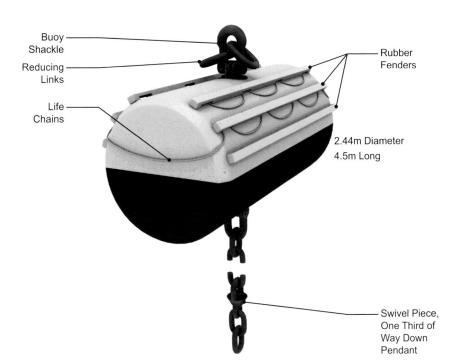

Buoy Shackle

Reducing Links

Life Chains

Rubber Fenders

2.44m Diameter
4.5m Long

Swivel Piece, One Third of Way Down Pendant

(2) *Mark buoys* (Fig 2-38). These are used to provide permanent navigational indications, e.g., to mark a safe channel or a particular hazard. There are five basic buoy shapes, which are fitted to the buoy body, namely; can, conical, spherical, pillar and spar. Details are given in **NP 735, IALA Maritime Buoyage System 'A'.**

Fig 2-38. Mark buoy mooring

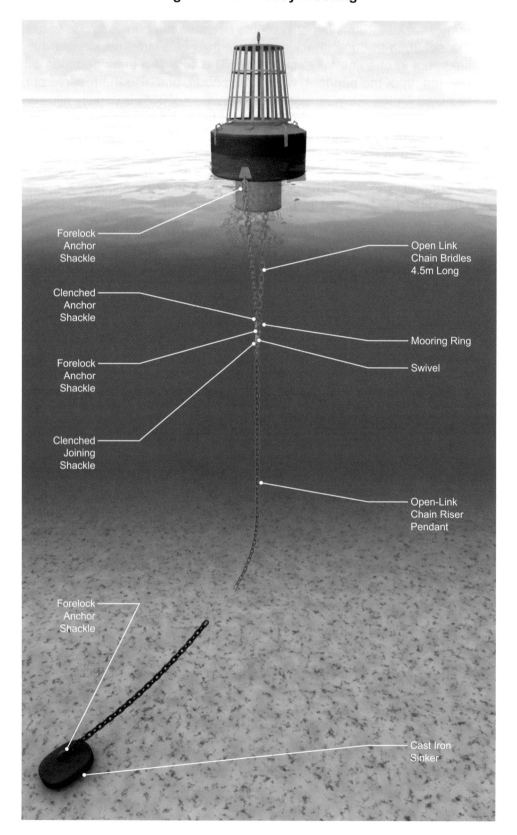

02026. Types of mooring for ships

a. **Single-clump mooring.** The simplest form of mooring (Fig 2-39) consists of a buoy, a riser pendant and a sinker or clump. It is generally used for small craft such as harbour launches.

Fig 2-39. Single mooring – fifth class swinging mooring for sheltered sites

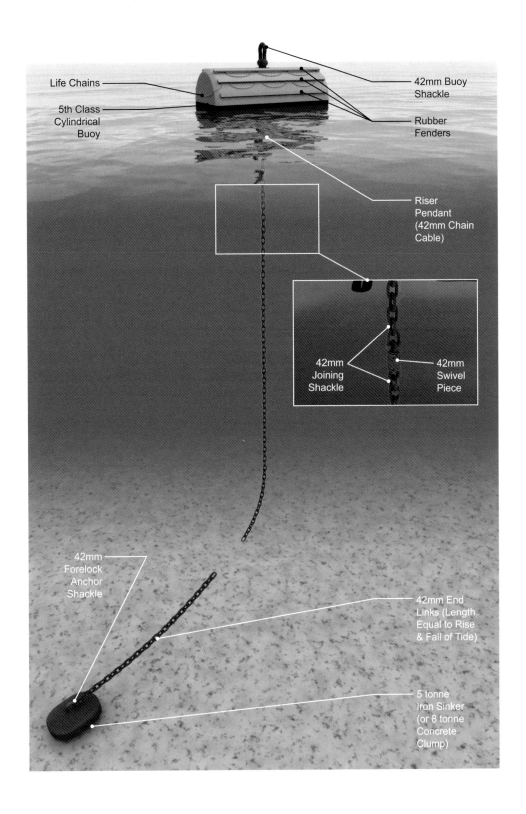

b. **Two-legged swinging mooring.** The lighter swinging moorings in restricted waterways may be of the two-legged type. (Fig 2-40(i)), one anchor being laid on a leg of chain cable upstream, and the other on a similar leg downstream. The type illustrated is **resilient mooring**, often referred to as an anti-snatch mooring in which the mooring ring is always suspended above the sea bottom, and the catenaries of the two legs are weighted with lengths of chain which acts as dampers during surge loads.

c. **Three-legged swinging mooring.** The three-legged swinging mooring (Fig 2-40(ii)) has greater holding power than the two-legged mooring. Its resistance to dragging is nearly constant with the wind from any direction, but it occupies a wider area than the two-legged mooring.

d. **Four-legged swinging mooring.** A four-legged swinging mooring (Fig 2-40(iii)) is used for the heaviest types of ship. It has all the advantages of the three-legged mooring, and its four legs provide greater holding power.

e. **Head-and-stern mooring.** The type of mooring shown in Fig 2-40(iv) is that generally used for mooring a ship head and stern. The mooring is usually laid along the direction of the tidal stream and the splayed legs are laid at an angle of 60 degrees to the fore-and-aft line of the mooring.

f. **Trot mooring.** A trot mooring (Fig 2-40(v)) is laid for securing a number of vessels in line, head to stern, and is economical in terms of space and material. As with the head and stern mooring, it is usually laid along the direction of the tidal stream and the splayed legs are laid at an angle of 60 degrees to the fore-and-aft line of the mooring.

g. **Hauling off moorings.** Hauling off moorings are usually provided in a harbour, which is subject to swell conditions, for holding a ship clear of a jetty against her berthing hawsers. If the weather deteriorates and the ship is in danger of bumping heavily against the jetty or catamarans, the **off-fasts** (wires from the moorings) should be used to haul her off until the wind moderates.

Fig 2-40. Types of moorings for ships

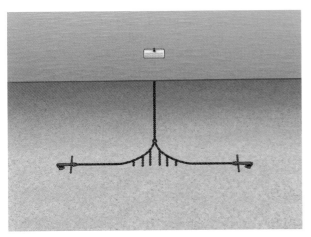

(i) Two-Legged Swinging Mooring

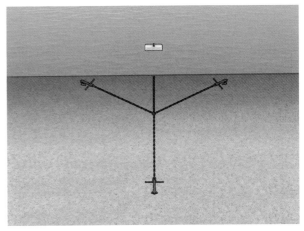

(ii) Three-Legged Swinging Mooring

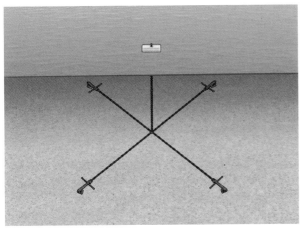

(iii) Four-Legged Swinging Mooring

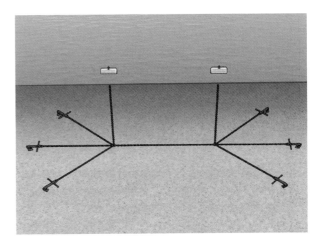

(iv) Head-and-Stern Mooring

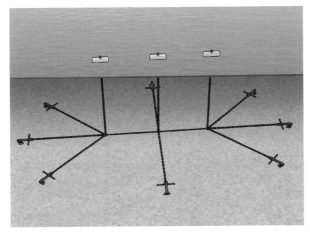

(v) Trot Mooring

02027. Classification of moorings

Because of the great differences in length and displacement of ships, several **classes** of moorings are provided. Moorings are classified according to the proof load of the cable or the displacement tonnage of the ships, which may safely use them. Generally speaking, **first-class** moorings are suitable for the largest vessels including large auxiliaries, **second-class** for vessels of cruiser size and small auxiliaries, **third-class** and **fourth-class** for destroyers or frigates, and **fifth-class** for other small ships and craft.

```
CAUTION

A ship should not secure to a lighter class of mooring
than that designed for her.
```

A ship may use heavier swinging moorings than those designed for her, and also heavier head-and-stern moorings if the length between the head and stern buoys is not too great. For this purpose one or two special **reducing links** (Fig 2-37) are fitted to each buoy shackle of the heavier moorings to enable the securing-to-buoy shackle of a smaller ship to be joined to the buoy. (Table 2-7 gives a list of the different classes of mooring, together with the size and material of ship's cable for which each class of mooring is suitable). The proof load of cable, which is related to its size and material, should always be the standard used when deciding whether a mooring is suitable for a particular ship, because it takes into account the maximum stresses involved at all states of loading, these usually being highest when the ship is at light-load draught owing to the large windage area she then presents. The last column of Table 2-7 sets out the displacement of the largest ship for which each class of mooring is suitable. In determining the number of small craft that may lie abreast at any mooring, the aggregate proof load of the several cables should be the deciding factor. In sheltered waters, the number of ships permitted to lie abreast in a head-and-stern mooring may be calculated on a displacement basis, by adding to the displacement of the largest ship one-half the displacement of each of the other ships. This rule is to be applied at the discretion of the local mooring officer, who should bear in mind that, at reduced displacements, ships present increased windage area. Proof load of a ship's cable is more reliable than her displacement tonnage when determining the class of mooring to be used because the proof load of a ship's cable is selected with due regard to her windage area. Dimensions and reserve buoyancy of mooring buoys are given in Table 2-8.

Table 2-7. Classes of mooring

Class of mooring	Cable size of largest acceptable ship			Maximum acceptable fully-loaded displacement
	Grade 1	Grade 2	Grade 3	
1st (4-leg) 1st (4-leg, telephone)	mm 95	mm 78	mm 66	tonnes 50,800
1st (3-leg) 1st (3-leg, resilient)	89	73	62	40,650
2nd (3-leg)	70	58	48	16,260
3rd (3-leg) 3rd (3-leg, resilient)	60	50	42	8,250
4th (3-leg) 4th (3-leg, resilient)	54	44	38	4,500
5th (3-leg)	34	28	24	400
5th (Sinker)	Small craft only			150

Notes:

1.   *First-class swinging moorings cannot accept any ship fitted with cable of size 28 mm and below, and the non-rotating telephone buoy mooring cannot accept any ship fitted with cable of size 38 mm and below, because the securing-to-buoy shackles are too small to pass over the reducing links.*

2.   *Nuclear submarines must not be secured to any mooring below third class.*

Table 2-8. Dimensions and reserve buoyancy of mooring buoys

Buoy (cylindrical)				Chain cable riser pendant		
Class (Note 1)	Length	Diameter	Class of mooring	Size	Reserve buoyancy	
					35%	25%
X-Class (4)	m 5.18	m 2.82	1st 2nd	mm 102 90	m 61.87 84.43	m 72.24 98.15
Monster (4) (Note 2 below)	4.88	2.44	1st 2nd	102 90	41.45 57.61	48.77 67.06
First (4)	4.47	2.44	1st 2nd	102 90	37.49 52.12	43.89 57.91
Second (4)	4.01	2.29	1st 2nd 3rd	102 90 76	28.04 39.62 56.08	32.92 46.33 65.53
Third (4)	3.51	1.98	3rd 4th	76 66	31.03 48.77	36.58 56.69
Fourth (4)	2.90	1.68	4th 5th (Exposed sites)	66 42	25.30 69.80	29.57 81.08
Fifth (2)	2.13	1.22	5th	42	21.03	24.38

Notes:

1.   *The number of compartments in each class of cylindrical buoy is shown in brackets.*

2.   *The Monster class buoy is obsolescent and will be replaced, in due course, with X-class.*

02028. Telephone cables at moorings
       Certain mooring berths may be provided with telephone or teleprinter cables. For head and stern moorings the telephone cables are led from the shore along the bottom, clear of the ground tackle, to a separate buoy, sufficient scope being allowed in the cables for tidal range. The ship's telephone cables are then joined to the shore telephone cables on this buoy.

a. **Non-rotating telephone buoy mooring.** The provision of telephone cables for a swinging mooring is complicated by the fact that the cables are liable to foul the riser pendant as the ship swings round the buoy. In some ports this difficulty is overcome by mooring the buoy with a three- or four-leg bridle to ground arms as shown in Fig 2-40, thus preventing rotation of the buoy. The ship's cable is then shackled to links on a spectacle lug, which revolves around a collar fitted to the upper end of the buoy trunk. The shore telephone cable is led up through the buoy trunk and thus is clear of the mooring. The ship's telephone cable is tensioned, either as shown in Fig 2-41 or by a patent tensioning reel fitted to the buoy, to avoid chafe by the anchor cables as the ship swings. The connection between ship and shore telephone cables is made at a connection box on the buoy, which also incorporates a slip-ring unit to prevent twisting of the telephone cables. Where provision is not made to prevent a telephone cable fouling the mooring, a watch must be set to keep it clear as it swings.

Fig 2-41. Non-rotating buoy mooring

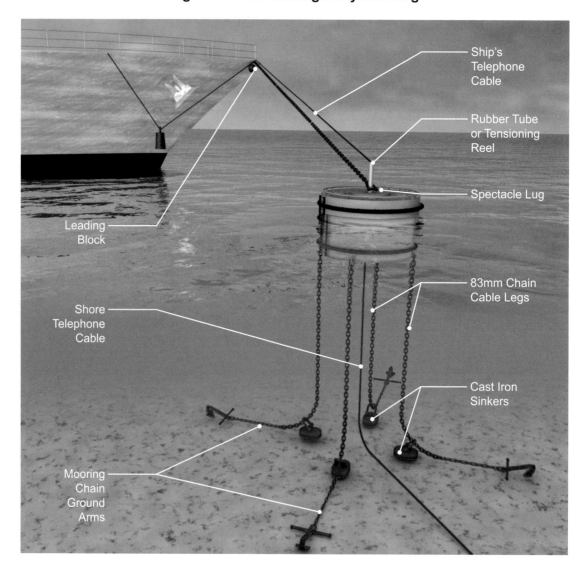

02029. Securing to a buoy using ship's cable

a.   A ship is usually secured to a buoy with two bridles of cable (see Note), both of which are provided from one of her two bower anchors, thereby leaving the other anchor and cable ready for letting go if required. The standing bridle consists of a convenient length of cable detached from the bower anchor, its inboard end held by bitts or bollards and a Blake slip, or by means of a joggle shackle on ships not fitted with Blake slips and according to the layout of the fo'c'sle. The working bridle is the remainder of the bower cable left rove around the cable holder or windlass and held by the brake, with the Blake slip and riding slip/compressor acting as preventers. The ship approaches the buoy with her bridles and picking-up rope ready for use. The bridles lead through the stem hawsepipe or bullring. The picking-up rope can be taken through a separate fairlead, but the best lead is usually through the hawsepipe or bullring, with the bridles. As far as possible neither bridles nor picking-up rope should be allowed to show outboard until just before reaching the buoy. On arrival at the buoy a boat is used to make fast the picking-up rope to the buoy shackle, buoy jumpers being carried in the boat for this purpose. The buoy jumpers are then taken off the buoy before the ship heaves in the picking-up rope. When the buoy has been hauled underfoot, the ends of the bridles are lowered to the buoy, then the buoy jumpers man the buoy and secure the ends of the bridles to the buoy shackle or its reducing links. When the bridles are shackled on, the buoy jumpers are taken off the buoy; the picking-up rope is veered until slack, then cast off, hauled inboard and stowed away.

WARNING

BUOY JUMPERS MUST NOT BE ON THE BUOY WHILE THE PICKING-UP ROPE OR CABLE IS BEING WORKED.

---

b.   Certain classes of ship whose anchoring arrangements preclude or restrict the use of ships cable for securing to a buoy are provided with braidline bridles for the purpose; the procedure for this method is explained later. Shiphandling aspects of buoywork are in BR 45 Admiralty Manual of Navigation Volume 6.

c.   RFAs normally secure to a buoy when there is a requirement to load/discharge ammunition, or because of a lack of alongside berthing facilities. The harbours of Rosyth and Devonport are both equipped with class 1 buoys, to which RFAs secure. Between 1 October and 31 April, RFA ships are required to secure two cables to a buoy. At all other times of the year this requirement is reduced to one unless weather conditions dictate otherwise.

Note.   In Northern European waters, unless otherwise stated in Fleet Operating Orders Vol 2 and/or local orders, ships are normally to use two bridles when at a buoy berth between October - May inclusive, and otherwise whenever a gale warning is in force. From June - September inclusive a single bridle may be used provided the ship is at no more than four hours Notice for Sea and there is assessed to be less than 50% probability of a gale within the Notice for Sea period. Elsewhere, unless otherwise stated in Fleet Operating Orders Vol 2 and/or local orders, the decision to forgo the added safety provided by a second bridle in order to expedite securing/ slipping rests with the CO. However, a ship at more than four hours Notice for Sea should always use a second bridle, and if opting to rely upon a single bridle the CO should be satisfied that there is less than 50% probability of a gale within the Notice for Sea period.

d. **Preparations for securing with a single bridle**. (See Annex 2C).

Dress	Equipment
DMS boots	Tapered pins for securing to buoy
Overalls	shackle
Immersion suit (If necessary)	Lead pellets
Marine Safety helmet	Punches
(Earplugs removed)	Hammer
Hazardous Duty Lifejacket	Reamer
Sharp seaman's knife	Goggles
	Rope hangers/tails (2 m lengths of suitable cordage).

e. **Preparations for securing with a double bridle**. (See Annex 2D)

Note. The end of the working bridle can be veered down to the buoy and adjusted for height as necessary using the cable holder. The end of the standing bridle must be lowered by a bullrope secured a few links from the end. Its height can then be adjusted to aid the task of the buoy jumpers in connecting the cable to the buoy.

f **Sending the picking-up rope to the buoy.** There are various methods of sending the picking-up rope to the buoy; the main points in the two usual methods are described below. Whichever method is used the boat must be lowered in plenty of time to ensure that she gets to the buoy well in advance of the ship.

> **WARNING**
>
> THE COXSWAIN MUST BE CAREFUL NEVER TO LET HIS BOAT GET BETWEEN THE SHIP AND THE BUOY OR ACROSS A TAUTENING PICKING-UP ROPE. WHEN LYING OFF HE MUST ALWAYS KEEP HIS BOAT POINTED AT THE BUOY, READY TO GO ALONGSIDE IT IMMedIATELY WHEN REQUIRED.

(1) *First method.* The boat is deployed as the ship approaches the buoy, and the bridle(s) are lowered. The boat is called in under the fo'c'sle, a heaving line is bent to the picking-up rope and taken in the boat to the buoy; the picking-up rope is then hove out by the buoy jumpers and made fast to the buoy shackle; it is important not to pay out more than the buoy jumpers can comfortably handle. This method is very quick, but requires the ship being brought close to the buoy.

(2) *Second method.* The boat takes all of a 12 mm polypropylene rope coiled in the stern. (A 12 mm towing messenger is suitable for the task.) As the boat passes under the fo'c'sle, one end is passed inboard and secured below the spring hook of the picking-up rope and the strop is stopped to the rope. The boat approaches the buoy, paying out the rope; places the jumpers on the buoy; passes the end of the rope through the buoy shackle and secures it in the stern. The boat then moves away from the buoy, hauling the picking-up rope towards the buoy while the ship pays it out. When the strop passes through the buoy shackle the stops are cut and the strop is placed on the hook. The boat then recovers the rope and buoy jumpers before the picking-up rope is hove in.

Notes:

1.   *Method 2 alleviates ship-handling problems in poor weather conditions but is reliant on competent boat handling.*

2.   *In certain circumstances RFAs will be provided with a boat by local authorities.*

g   **Scope of bridles.** Bridles should be matched (of equal scope) to ensure a fair division of stress between them. The working bridle is adjusted to match the scope of the standing bridle, then the Brake is applied, the cable holder disconnected, and the Blake slip and riding slip/compressor put on slack as preventers. The standing bridle is secured as described earlier. Shackle pins must be regularly checked, particularly in bad weather.

02030. Securing to a buoy using ship's cable (RFA Specific)

Preparations for securing to a buoy from an RFA are as laid down in Annex 2C. However due to the size of cable fitted to certain classes of RFA this evolution can be awkward, therefore the following additional equipment and procedures are required by RFAs when securing to and slipping from a Buoy.

a.   **Additional equipment when securing to a buoy**

(1)   *Heaving-out wire (Fig 2-42).* 16 mm (minimum) SWR. Length to suit. One end whipped. 0.5T SWL spring hook and 1m SWR spliced into opposite end.

Fig 2-42. Heaving-out wire

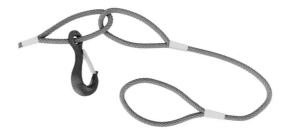

(2)   *Hanging-off rope (Fig 2-43).* 24 mm Manila, length to suit. One end is whipped, the opposite end is a soft eye spliced through a 2T SWL spring hook. A 1 m Round Sling is attached.

Fig 2-43. Hanging-off rope

(3)   *Mooring rope (Fig 2-44).* 2 x Mooring rope with 24 mm polyamide (doubled) pendants fitted.

Fig 2-44. Mooring rope with polyamide pendant

Note.   *Polyamide pendants should be taken in the boat to the buoy along with the buoy bag.*

(4)   *Steel snatch block (see Fig 2-47).* A 1 x 2 ton SWL snatch block is to be supplied for use with the heaving-out wire for ranging the cable as follows.

(5)   *Handy Billy* (plus two small round slings).

b.   **Preparing the cable.** When Command approval has been given to break the cable, the following procedure is to be carried out:

(1)   Ensure windlass/capstan is out of gear, and guillotine or cable slip is secured over cable. Fit additional securing wires/chain/pendants to the anchor shackle.

Fig 2-45. Anchor properly secured before cable is broken (if bottlescrew slip fitted)

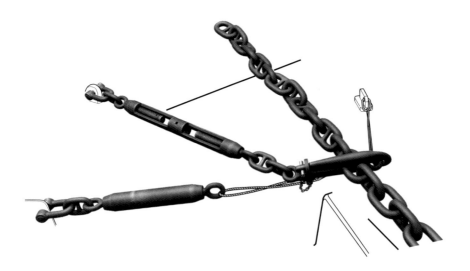

(2)   Engage windlass/capstan gear and veer until sufficient cable is ranged on the deck. (Ships with a half shackle of cable at the outboard end should range and detach this length as part of their preparations).

Fig 2-46. Cable ready to be broken

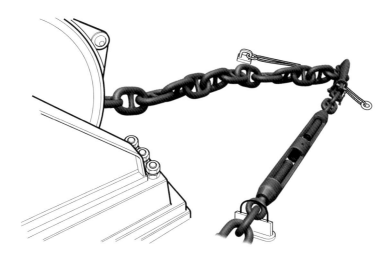

(3)   Align the lugless joining shackle athwartships, then, using a punch, knock out the lead and cable pin. The lead will be ejected first, followed by the pin.

(4)   Remove the shackle stud and lay to one side. Use a topswage and maul to separate the two remaining parts of the lugless joining shackle. When broken, take the parts of the shackle and stud fwd, ready to connect the Munroe shackle to the cable.

(5)   Take the bight of the heaving out wire fwd and snatch it into the snatch block (Fig 2-47). Ensure the gate of the block is properly secured and the securing pin is correctly located.

Fig 2-47. Rigging the steel snatch block and reeving the heaving-out wire

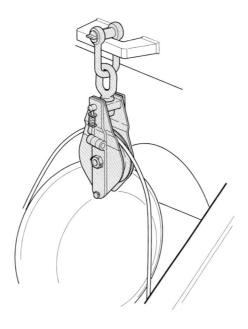

(6)   Secure the hook and eye end of the heaving out wire to the broken cable, passing the wire behind the stud of the first link.

(7)   Take two turns around the drum end/capstan, having first taken up all the slack by hand. Veer away on the windlass and at the same time heave and surge on the heaving-out wire. Continue heaving until the end of the cable is in the eyes of the ship, then apply a thin coat of oil to the machined surfaces and connect the Munroe shackle/lugless joining shackle as explained in Annex 2C.

c.   **Rigging the hanging-off rope.** The hanging-off rope is used to lower (cm by cm if necessary) the Munroe shackle down to the buoy jumpers to enable them to position it precisely over the buoy link. The procedure is as follows:

(1)   Lead the hook end of the hanging-off rope out through the fwd fairlead and back in through the bullring. Count off a minimum of 6 links back from the Munroe shackle and insert one end of the strop through the link, forward of the cable stud (Fig 2-48). Take the working end of the rope to the most suitably placed set of bitts, and take a dry turn.

Fig 2-48. Hanging-off rope rigged

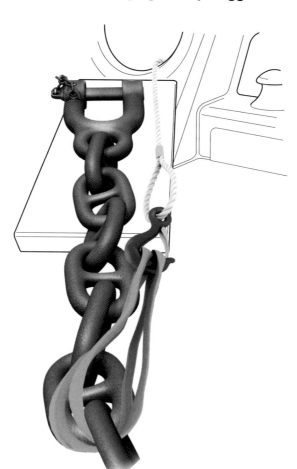

(2)   Range on deck a length of cable, sufficient to allow the Munroe shackle to be manhandled through the bullring. When doing this, observe the standard precautions when hauling cable from the gypsy. Now secure the heaving-out wire pendant abaft of the link stud (Fig 2-49).

Fig 2-49. Heaving-out wire pendant secured abaft link stud

(3)   Continue heaving out additional cable. The Bosun must indicate to the tender of the hanging-off rope when to make the rope fast. More cable is then heaved out until the overall length of the cable, hanging in a bight, is sufficient to reach the buoy comfortably (See Fig 2-51). The brake is then applied and the windlass/capstan taken out of gear.

(4)   Lower the outboard ends of the mooring ropes from their port and starboard leads, to approximately 1m above the water. Take the inboard ends to a warping drum/capstan. The ship can now approach the buoy, tended by two tugs and with one cable 'hanging off' over the bow ready for lowering to the buoy.

Note.   *Mooring lines are to be led from leads that will best achieve positioning of the buoy beneath the hanging off cable.*

d.   **Making fast to the buoy**

(1)   When the ship is at a distance of 75 m – 100 m from the buoy, the mooring boat moves in and picks up one mooring line at a time and secures it to the mooring links of the buoy, using the polyamide pendants. Once both lines are secure (Fig 2-50 and Fig 2-52), heaving in on the mooring ropes can commence until the buoy is directly under, or, in the case of bulbous bow ships, to one side of the bow (Fig 2-51).

Fig 2-50. Mooring lines secured to the buoy

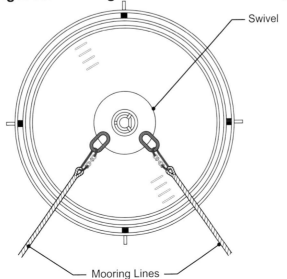

WARNING

A MINIMUM OF THREE TURNS SHOULD BE USED WHEN HEAVING THE SHIP TO THE BUOY. PERSONNEL TENDING DRUM END/CAPSTAN ARE TO BE BACKED UP.

Fig 2-51. Buoy positioned beneath the cable

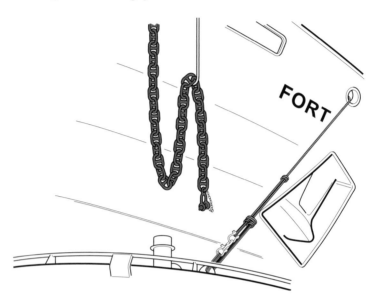

(2)   When the I/C of the fo'c'sle is satisfied that the buoy is in the correct position, the mooring boat, carrying the buoy jumpers, can be called in. The hanging-off rope is slackened away, lowering the Munroe shackle into position directly above the buoy link. The buoy jumpers should use a rope tail to assist in positioning the Munroe shackle. The seizing wire is removed from the Munroe shackle, and the second buoy jumper withdraws the pin. The fo'c'sle team slacks away on the hanging-off rope until the Munroe shackle is in the correct position to be secured to the buoy link by the pin and lead pellet. Once this has been completed (Fig 2-52), the buoy jumpers leave the buoy, then mooring line tenders surge their lines until the weight is transferred to the cable.

Fig 2-52. Buoy jumpers securing the Munroe shackle to the buoy

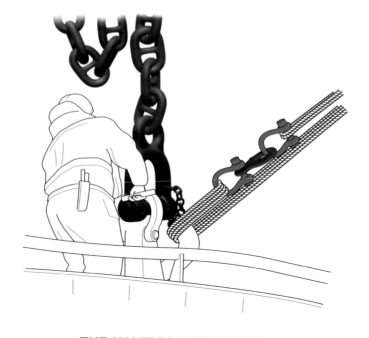

(3)   When the weight is on the cable, the buoy jumpers return and remove the slackened mooring lines and hanging-off rope. The buoy jumpers now leave the buoy, taking all equipment with them (Fig 2-53).

Fig 2-53. Ready to adjust the length of the cable

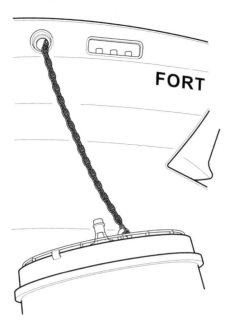

e.   **Securing a single cable to a buoy**. The usual procedure is to veer the cable to a length of one shackle, sufficient for the ship to ride to the buoy. At the desired distance the Blake slip is secured to the cable just forward of the joining shackle, then the cable is veered until the Blake slip just has the weight. The winch/windlass is then taken out of gear.

f.   **Securing two cables to a buoy**. When the first cable is secured to the buoy the second cable is ranged on deck, broken, and a Munroe shackle connected. The buoy is kept underfoot on the first cable until the second cable has been connected. Once the second cable has been connected, both cables are veered to a length of one shackle, and then secured. As one anchor is always to be available for letting go, one of the cables must be broken **aft** of the Blake slip and reconnected to the hung-off anchor. The cable broken aft of the Blake slip is now referred to as the Standing Bridle and the other cable which remains secured between the buoy and winch/windlass is known as the Working Bridle.

02031. Securing to head and stern buoys
Trots of mooring buoys for securing a number of ships head-and-stern are usually laid along the line of the tidal stream or prevailing current; consequently when securing a ship between two buoys difficulty is more likely to be caused by the wind than by the stream. Much will depend on prevailing weather conditions, and tugs will usually be required to position the ship during the initial stages of the evolution. The ship is secured to the head buoy in the manner already described, but a second picking-up rope must be sent from aft to the stern buoy. After shackling on the bridles forward they are veered as necessary so the ship can be dropped astern and the stern hawsers secured to the after buoy. (Most head and stern moorings have wire pendants permanently attached to the stern buoy for securing the stern of the ship; otherwise the ship's berthing hawsers are used). The method usually adopted for veering the bridles is to break the cable on the anchor kept ready for letting go and tail it on to the standing bridle, the slack then being taken down and both bridles veered together. Once the stern is secured to the after buoy the bridles are hove in and the stern hawsers paid out until the ship is middled between the buoys. The after hawsers are then turned up around bollards and racked, and the bridles secured as described earlier.

02032. Slipping from a buoy (See Annex 2C and Annex 2D)

a. **Pointing ship before slipping from a buoy.** In a crowded anchorage where there is little room for manoeuvring it may be necessary before slipping from a buoy to point the vessel in a direction other than that in which she is lying. This is done by reeving an additional sliprope, from the quarter fairlead, outboard of all, through the buoy shackle and then back through an adjacent fairlead on the same quarter. The ship is then given an initial cast using the engines, the head slip rope is surged as necessary and any slack is taken down in the after slip rope. The head slip rope is then slipped and run in, and when the ship is pointing in the required direction the after slip rope is slipped and run in.

Note.   When singling up to one bridle or shortening in on a single bridle to pass a slip rope, strain will be put on the buoy shackle and pendant. As a precaution against the mooring parting and the ship breaking adrift, the main engines should be at imMediate notice.

02033. Slipping from a buoy (RFA specific)

a. **Method 1.** The working bridle is shortened in. A slip rope is rove through the ring of the buoy. The soft eye of the slip rope is secured to a Blake slip. As much weight as possible is taken in by hand on the slip rope before it is turned up to a set of bitts. The working bridle is then veered until the slip rope has the weight. The working bridle is now disconnected from the buoy, heaved inboard and reconnected to its anchor. The standing bridle is now reconnected to its cable and the slack hove in until just before the weight is taken off the slip rope. This bridle is now disconnected from the buoy, hove in and reconnected to its anchor. When ordered the slip is knocked off the slip rope and the slip rope recovered inboard.

b. **Method 2.** The standing bridle is reconnected to its cable; the bridle is hove in until the weight is taken off the slip. The slip is then knocked off. Both cables are shortened in, and then one cable is slackened back sufficiently to allow removal of the Munroe shackle. This cable is then recovered and reconnected to its anchor. The slip rope is then rove through the ring of the buoy, and the soft eye of the slip rope is secured to a Blake slip. As much slack as possible is taken down before the slip rope is turned up on a set of bitts. The remaining bridle is now veered until the weight is on the slip rope. The bridle is now disconnected from the buoy, recovered and reconnected to its anchor. When ordered the Blake slip is knocked off and the slip rope recovered.

02034. Securing to a buoy using MMFC bridles (See Annex 2E)

a. **Introduction**. MMFC bridles for securing to a buoy (Fig 2-25, Fig 2-26 and Fig 2-27) are supplied to all ships. Using MMFC bridles allows the Buoy to be secured and rigged prior to the ship's arrival. The bridles are connected to the SMS's in the boat and the whole evolution has significantly reduced downtimes. Rather that hauling the buoy underfoot, the ship can lay back on the Picking-up-Rope due to the lightweight bridles. There is no restriction of operation due to weather, time of year or areas of operation – it is a Command decision to use MMFC or Cable. Two MMFC bridles must be used when securing to a buoy. **A mix of MMFC and chain cable bridles is not to be used.**

Notes:

1.   Before serial start-time all equipment is to be examined fit for purpose and reported to the Command. This is to include Locking Stitching on Quantum 12 ropes.

2.   There is no requirement to bring the buoy underfoot due to the lightweight bridles and ease of connection within the boat.

3.   If the required scope of the bridles is known beforehand, the bridles can be brought to the bollards and fully turned up and racked as part of the preparations for the procedure.

4.   Ensure that chafing pieces are fitted to all points of contact on all occasions of use.

5.   Ensure that two dry turns are taken on the lead bollard when securing Bridles iaw 03014.

b.   **Gear required**

    (1)   Bridles x 2 (Ice protection coloured blue)

    (2)   Shock mitigation strops x 2

    (3)   Stainless steel fairlead shackle x 4

    (4)   Picking up rope x 1 (coloured lime green)

    (5)   Ship to buoy shackle x 2

    (6)   Bollard strop and slip x 1

c.   **Preparations**

    (1)   *FX*

        (a) Picking up rope passed through the bull-ring and back inboard and faked on deck

        (b) Bridles faked on deck adjacent to the bollard and fairlead from which they will be passed through

        (c) Bollard strop and slip rigged for slip rope

    (2)   *Boat*

        (a) 2 x SMS's with fairlead shackle (ring guard removed) and Ship to Buoy Shackles secured one end

        (b) 2 x further fairlead shackles carried in the boat to attach to the Bridles

d.   **Sequence of events.** For securing to the buoy and slipping from the buoy the sequence of events is to be carried out in accordance with Annex 2E

Fig 2-54. Picking up rope attached to main ring of the buoy, bridles passed

Fig 2-55. Ship secured to the buoy

Fig 2-56. Slip rope rigged

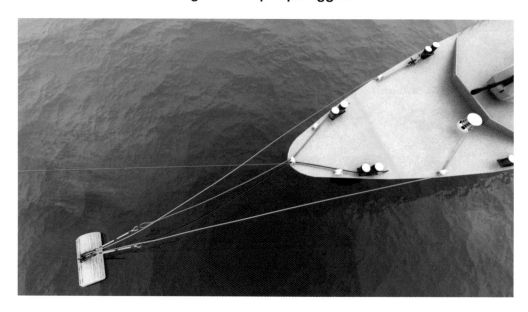

02035. Submarine coming to and slipping from a buoy

Fig 2-57. Vanguard class at delta buoy - Plymouth

a. **Personnel.** The minimum number of personnel required for mooring to a buoy is:

   (1)   Casing officer I/c.

   (2)   Second coxswain.

   (3)   Buoy jumper.

   (4)   4 x casing party.

b. **Equipment.** The basic equipment is:

   (1)   Fwd casing to be rigged.

      (a) Fwd fairlead; capstan; 1's & 2's bollards raised.

      (b) 2 x berthing ropes faked down on the opposite side of the casing to which the buoy will be secured.

      (c) Boat transfer equipment rigged.

      (d) Bollard and casing keys.

   (2)   Buoy jumper prepared and suitably dressed.

      (a) DMS safety boots.
      (b) Overalls.
      (c) Musto gear/multi-fab.
      (d) In-date industrial safety helmet.
      (e) Hazardous duty lifejacket.
      (f) Seaman's rigging set

c.   **Routine.** As submarines are not normally equipped with a boat it is necessary that a boat be provided to get the buoy jumper from the submarine to the buoy and back again. Having prepared the casing equipment, arranged a buoy jumper and boat, the routine is as shown on the following grid.

Serial	Casing party	Buoy jumper	Tug
1	Boat transfer Buoy Jumper From S/M to Buoy.	Board Boat	
2	Secure tug to S/M on the opposite side to which it is intended to place the buoy.	Embark on to the Buoy.	
3		Embark on the buoy.	
4	Pass heaving line attached to berthing hawser out through the fairlead to the Buoy jumper.	Haul in the heaving line and berthing hawser. Led the eye of the hawser up through the buoy shackle then pass the heaving line and berthing hawser back to the casing party.	
5	Haul in the heaving line end berthing rope to the submarine, placing the eye over No. 1's inboard.		
6		Transfer from the buoy to the boat.	
7	Using the capstan, haul in on the berthing hawser to bring the S/M alongside the buoy.		As required by the CO, assist in manoeuvring the S/M towards the buoy to a suitable position.
8		Return to the buoy.	
9	Pass the 2nd berthing hawser from No. 2 bollard to the buoy.	Pass the eye of the 2nd berthing hawser up through the eye of the buoy shackle and back to the S/M.	
10	Pass the eye of the 2nd berthing hawser onto No. 2's bollard. Down slack and turn up		
When CO is satisfied with the position of the buoy relative to the submarine			
11	Double up on both hawsers using the other ends of the berthing hawsers.	Pass the eyes of the doubling up hawsers through the buoy shackle and back to the S/M.	
12		Transfer from the buoy onto the boat.	
13	Slip the tug.		Slip from submarine.
14	Recover the buoy jumper.	Return to the S/M using boat transfer routine.	

02036. Securing to Z mooring in Portsmouth

a. **Preparations**

(1)   4 x 70 m x 43 mm HMPE mooring hawsers will be delivered to the ship by road if the ship is alongside. If the ship is coming from sea or at very short notice they will be delivered by SERCO launch. Once embarked, the mooring ropes are to be inspected by the CBM to ensure they are fit for purpose. If there are any concerns regarding the mooring ropes' serviceability, Harbour Movements are to be inforMed. The ship is not to proceed to 'Z' mooring until any concerns have been resolved.

(2)   All preparations, including the placing of the two mooring ropes both forward and aft are to be in place prior to the ship cold moving. The ship may be required to provide two buoy jumpers who will work from the SERCO mooring boat. Ships boats will not be used.

b. **Securing to the buoys**

(1)   The two forward bridles (marked 30 m) are to be turned up on the forward set of bollards port and starboard making sure that both of the markings are at the forward end of the bollards. Both bridles are then to be racked. As the ship stems the buoy, both bridles are to be passed out of the bullring to the SERCO mooring boat by use of a heaving line. When the OIC of the fo'c'sle and the Pilot are content that the ship is in position, the boat is to be called in and the buoy jumpers are to alight to the buoy. The soft eyes of the bridles are to be snatched into the rams hook (Port/Starboard) making sure that they are not crossed or snagged on the safety gate. Once secure the buoy jumpers are to clear the buoy allowing the ship to be moved aft.

(2)   The two bridles aft are to be used as a working bridle and a standing bridle. As the stern approaches the stern buoy the boat is to be called in to receive a heaving line with the after bridles attached. When the pilot is content that the ship is in position and the weight is on the fwd bridles, the buoy jumpers will be called onto the buoy. The buoy jumpers will then snatch the soft eyes of both stern bridles into the rams hook making sure that they are not crossed or snagged on the safety gate.

(3)   When the buoy jumpers are clear of the buoy the Working Bridle is to be brought to the quarterdeck capstan and heaved in. When the Working Bridle is holding the stern in position, the slack is to be taken down by hand on the Standing Bridle then turned up on a free set of bollards and racked. The Working Bridle is then veered until the standing bridle has the weight. Once the Working Bridle is transferred to a free set of bollards the scope of the bridles are matched.

c. **Slipping from the buoys**

(1)   The aft Working Bridle is to be transferred from the bollards to the capstan and heaved in to take the weight off the Standing Bridle. The Standing Bridle is then taken off the bollards and kept in hand and the Working Bridle is veered. When all weight is off the Working Bridle, the boat is then called in and the buoy jumpers are ordered back onto the buoy. Both bridles are then un-snatched from the rams hook and recovered inboard. The buoy jumpers are then recovered to the boat to proceed forward to work the head buoy.

(2)   Once the bridles are clear of the aft buoy the ship will be moved forward by tugs to take the weight off the forward bridles. When the pilot is content with the position of the ship and the OIC of the fo'c'sle confirms that the weight is off the bridles, both bridles can then be removed from the bollards and kept in hand. The boat is then called in and the buoy jumpers are ordered back onto the buoy. Both bridles are then un-snatched from the rams hook and recovered inboard. The ship is now clear to cold-move back to her berth.

(3)   On return alongside the HMPE hawsers will be collected by SERCO. Ships proceeding to sea on completion of ammunitioning will transfer the ropes to SERCO tugs.

ANNEX 2A

PROCEDURE FOR ANCHORING

1.   **CLEARING AWAY ANCHORS AND CABLES**

ORDER	ACTION
Cable party close up (piped from bridge)	Muster and brief cable party (including safety -see Para 02014), check power to capstans, check comms with bridge (primary and secondary), provide cable bag and all other associated equipment. Obtain permission from bridge to prepare anchors.
Clear away anchors and cables (OIC)	Remove PVC covers, tackles and lashings, tommy bars from bottle screw slips, bonnet covers, hawse pipe covers and anchor strops. Remove riding slip/guillotine/compressor. The compressor must be fully eased off to prevent damage from the cable running out of the naval pipe.
Connect up (OIC) (port/stbd)	Connect the capstan to the cable holder by lining up the marks on the capstan with those on the cable holder, then engage the dog clutch by winding down on the hand wheel.
Ease back the bottle screw slip (OIC)	Start the bottle screw slip with a tommy bar or similar tool, and ease back on it until the cable becomes taut to the cable holder. (This process must be carried out to transfer the line of pull from the slip to the cable holder; otherwise the slip or cable might be unduly strained.)
Reposition Blake slip (OIC)	Knock off the Blake slip then re-attach it to the cable at a position that will allow the anchor to assume the a'cockbill position once the cable has been veered to the slip. Remouse the slip. *Note. The precise positioning of the slip will vary ship to ship. Ships with long hawsepipes may require to veer sufficient cable to enable the anchor to reach a'cockbill before repositioning the Blake Slip.*
Off bottle screw slip (OIC)	Knock off the bottle screw slip and move it clear of the cable.
Off brake (OIC) (port/stbd)	Take off the brake.
Stand clear of the cable (OIC)	This warning is given to personnel to inform them the cable is about to be worked.
Veer (OIC) (port/stbd)	Veer the cable until the weight of the anchor is transferred to the Blake slip (check the anchor is now a'cockbill).
Avast veering, on brake (OIC) (port/stbd)	Avast veering and apply the brake
Disconnect (OIC) (port/stbd)	Disconnect the capstan from the cable holder by using the hand wheel.
	The above procedure is repeated to prepare the second anchor ready for letting go. The bridge is inforMed when both anchors are ready for letting go and the brakes are applied.

2.   LETTING GO THE ANCHOR AND SECURING THE CABLE DECK

ORDER	ACTION
	On the run in to the anchorage the bridge should give regular distances to run, all personnel other than the OIC and the person detailed to slip the cable should be positioned clear of the cable deck.
Two cables to run (info from bridge) **off brake** (OIC) (port/stbd)	Take off the brake.
One cable to run (info from bridge) o**ff mousing** (OIC)	Remove the mousing from the Blake slip and ensure the pin is free to rotate in its hole.
Half a cable to run (info from bridge) **out pin** (OIC)	Place the maul against the buckler link of the Blake slip to prevent it slipping and remove the pin.
Let go (from bridge)	The bridge will signal this by using red or green flags during daytime and wands at night. They are initially held aloft and when brought down indicate Let Go. (Red for port/bower anchor and green for stbd/sheet/ anchor).
Slip (OIC)	Knock off the Blake slip. Use the brake to control the running out of the cable.
On brake, off brake (OIC) As required	The OIC should watch the cable outboard and order the brake to be applied as necessary in order that the cable is laid out straight and clear along the seabed without causing undue strain or allowing it to pile up on itself. (The way of the ship must be stopped by her engines and not by the cable). Regular reports must be made to the bridge regarding the number of shackles on deck and the direction the cable grows.
On brake (OIC)	Once the required amount of cable has been paid out apply the brake. When the OIC is satisfied that the ship has her cable (ie the ship has fallen back and is held by her anchor and cable) he reports to the bridge 'Ship has her cable'.
Secure the cable (from the bridge, specifying the number of shackles on deck)	This is the order to secure the Blake slip (or fully shortened bottle screw slip in the case of Type 23s) to the cable just for'ard of the specified joining shackle. Secured in this manner makes it easy to part the cable and slip the anchor in an emergency.
Connect up (OIC) (port/stbd)	Connect up.
Off brake, veer/heave in (OIC)	Take off the brake, veer or heave into position the joining shackle abaft of the Blake slip (or fully shortened bottle screw slip Type 23s).
Avast, on brake (OIC)	Avast veering/heaving, apply the brake.
On Blake slip (OIC) (Fully shortened bottle screw slip Type 23s)	Attach the Blake slip (or the fully shortened bottle screw slip for Type 23s) to the cable.

ORDER	ACTION
Off brake, veer (OIC)	Take off the brake; veer the cable until just before the slip takes the weight.
On brake, disconnect (OIC)	Apply the brake hard disconnect the capstan. Then on riding slip (slack) or guillotine (Blake slip Type 23s) or fully shortened bottle screw slip as an extra preventer. The second anchor is left ready for letting go, with an extra preventer applied. Report to the bridge that the cable deck is secured. **_Note_**. *A compressor is not to be used as an additional preventer.*

3.   SHORTENING IN AND WEIGHING

ORDER	ACTION
Cable party close up (piped from bridge)	Muster and fully brief the team. Check power to the capstan and comms with bridge (primary and secondary). Provide cable bag and associated equipment. Rig hoses and provide brooms ready to wash down cable as it comes in through the hawse pipe. Remove extra preventers from both cables.
Shorten-in (info from bridge)	The order to shorten-in may be given by the bridge to reduce the amount of cable on deck and therefore the time taken to weigh anchor when the ship requires to get underway. (ie a ship riding to eight shackles on deck might shorten in to three on deck.) As the cable comes in any remaining mud on it is washed and scrubbed off by the cable party. The joining shackles and appropriate links are repainted and the wire strands marking the outer painted links are renewed where necessary.
Connect up (port/stbd), **off Blake slip** (OIC)	Connect up, take off the Blake slip.
On hawse pipe sprays, off brake, heave in (OIC) (ports/stbd)	Turn on hawse pipe sprays to clean the cable as it comes in. Take off the brake and commence heaving in the cable to the number of shackles ordered by the bridge. During this period the OIC must give frequent reports on how the cable grows and how many shackles are on deck so the bridge can use ship's engines to assist if required. Once shortened-in to the required joining shackle the OIC reports to the bridge. The bridge will either answer 'Hold at three' or 'Carry on and weigh'.
Avast heaving, on brake (OIC)	Avast heaving in and apply the brake.

ORDER	ACTION
Carry on and weigh (from bridge)	This is the order given by the bridge to weigh anchor.
Off brake, heave in (OIC)	Take off the brake and commence heaving in. Continue reporting how the cable grows to the bridge as the cable is hove in.
Cable up and down (OIC)	This report is made to the bridge when the cable is up and down just prior to the anchor breaking free from the seabed.
Anchor's aweigh	This report is made to the bridge when the anchor has broken clear of the seabed. Knowing the depth of water at the anchorage will assist the OIC in determining this.
Clear anchor or foul anchor (OIC)	Once the anchor is fully visible the appropriate report is made to the bridge to indicate if it is clear or foul. To be clear the anchor must be clear of its own cable and any obstructions such as a bight of rope or chain picked up from the bottom, otherwise it is reported as foul. *Note. At night a red/blue filtered torch should be available to aid the OIC in sighting the anchor.*
Avast, on brake (OIC)	Avast heaving in and apply the brake. Prepare the anchor ready for letting go again. Once the anchor has been made ready this is reported to the bridge. The bridge will order the cable deck to be secured once the ship is in open water and clear of navigational hazards.

4.   SECURING THE CABLE DECK FOR SEA

ORDER	ACTION
Secure the cable deck (from bridge)	The order to secure the anchors and cable deck for sea.
Connect up (OIC) (port/stbd)	Connect up. Off Blake Slip.
Off brake, heave in (OIC)	Take off the brake and heave in, bringing the anchor into the hawse pipe, the final stages of this must be done carefully to prevent damage. *Note. When heaving in the bow anchor the OIC must ensure that in the final stages of recovery the flukes trip to prevent damaging the stem of the ship.*
Avast heaving, on brake (OIC)	Avast heaving, then apply the brake.
On bottle screw slip (OIC)	Put on the bottle screw slip and tighten up by hand.
Off brake, veer (OIC)	Veer the cable to the bottle screw slip.

ORDER	ACTION
Avast veering, on brake (OIC)	Avast veering once the weight is transferred to the bottle screw slip, then apply the brake. Fully tighten the slip using a tommy bar or bottle screw spanner.
On Blake slip (OIC)	Put the Blake slip onto the cable (slack).
Disconnect (OIC)	Disengage the capstan drum from the cable holder.
On compressor (OIC)	Wind down the compressor hand tight. Follow the same procedure to secure the second anchor.
Secure anchors and cables for sea (OIC)	On anchor strops (these are passed through the anchor ring) On bonnet covers, lash them to the deck/cable. Lash the Blake slip links to the cable. Place a tommy bar through the bottle screw slips and the cable and lash in place. This will prevent the bottle screw easing back on its thread. On hawse pipe covers and secure them. Lash the two cables together using strops and tackles, to prevent banging and chaffing on the deck. Fit all PVC covers and secure in place. Take power off the capstan. Secure Comms Stow away all loose gear and clear all personnel from the fo'c'sle. On completion of above inform the bridge that the fo'c'sle is secured for sea.

ANNEX 2B

ANCHORING WITH A MMFC BRIDLE

1. **ANCHORING WITH A MMFC BRIDLE.**

ORDER	ACTION
Cable party close up (piped from bridge)	Muster and fully brief cable party (including safety - see para 02014), check power to capstans, check comms with bridge (primary and secondary), provide cable bag and all other associated equipment. Provide one MMFC bridle and attach to it the bow dome pendant using a lugless joining shackle (Fig 2-24). Provide a Joggle shackle, handspikes and shepherd's crook or boat hook.
Clear away anchors and cables (OIC)	Prepare both anchors ready for letting go as described in annex 2A to this chapter and inform the bridge.
	Attach a strayline to the free end of the pendant and use it to haul the end of the pendant out through the bullring and back through the centreline hawse pipe. Stop the pendant to a convenient eyeplate and ensure it does not foul the anchor or cable. The braidline bridle is led from the bullring down the starboard side to the first set of bollards, and the remainder faked down abaft the bollards free for running. ***Note***. *From this point until attaching the bridle to the cable the anchoring procedures are precisely as described in Annex 2A to this Chapter. It is assuMed that the ship intends to anchor with six shackles on deck.*
On brake (OIC)	The brake is applied once the fifth shackle is on deck. When satisfied that the ship has her cable, the OIC reports to the bridge that the ship has her cable and requests permission to insert the bridle.
Insert the bridle (from bridge)	This order is the authority to attach the pendant to the cable and veer to six shackles on deck.
Connect up port (OIC)	Connect up.
Off brake, veer/heave in (OIC)	Take off the brake and veer or heave in until the fifth joining shackle is positioned between the compressor and capstan.
On brake, attach pendant to the cable (OIC)	Apply the brake, then attach the pendant to the cable by the joggle shackle, as close as possible to the lip of the hawse, in the configuration shown in Fig 2-29. Mouse the joggle shackle. Take two full turns of the bridle around the starboard bollards, and stand-bye to surge.
Off brake, veer the cable - surge the bridle (OIC)	Take off the brake, veer the cable and surge the bridle at the same rate until the red mark is at the front of the bollards (the measurement for the red mark in the bridle is described in Para 02019). OIC is to ensure the joggle shackle runs out freely through the hawse pipe.

ORDER	ACTION
Avast veering, on brake, turn up (OIC)	Avast veering, apply the brake; turn up the bridle on the bollards with two dry turns on the lead bollard. Apply a racking and wrap the remainder of the braidline around the bollards.
Off brake, veer (OIC)	Take off the brake and veer until the sixth shackle is just abaft the Blake slip (fully shortened bottle screw slip for Type 23s). The bridle now has the weight.
Avast veering, On brake (OIC)	Avast veering, apply the brake. Report to the bridge that the bridle is attached, the sixth shackle is on deck and the ship has her bridle/cable.
Secure the cable (from bridge)	Secure the cable at six on deck. Once secured the pivotal point of the anchorage will be from the bridle pendant with a bight of cable paid out to protect the bow dome, see Fig 2-33.
On Blake slip (OIC) (Fully done up bottle screw slip Type 23s)	Attach the Blake slip to the cable forward of the joining shackle. (Or use fully done-up bottle screw slip for Type 23s.)
Off brake, veer (OIC)	Take the brake off; veer the cable until just before the Blake slip has the weight (fully shortened bottle screw slip Type 23s).
On brake, disconnect (OIC)	From this point the cable and fo'c'sle are secured as described in Annex 2A to this Chapter when going to single anchor.

2.   **SHORTENING-IN AND WEIGHING ANCHOR WHEN ANCHORED WITH A MMFC BRIDLE**

ORDER	ACTION
Cable party close up (piped from bridge)	Muster and fully brief the team. Check power to the capstan and comms with bridge (primary and secondary). Provide cable bag and associated equipment. Rig hoses and provide brooms ready to wash down cable as it comes in through the hawse pipe. Remove extra preventers from both cables.
Connect up (OIC) (port/stbd)	Connect up.
Off Blake slip (OIC)	Knock off the Blake slip (bottle screw slip for Type 23s). OIC reports to the bridge that the cable party is closed up, port/stbd (second) anchor is ready for letting go, the brake is on and all is ready to commence shortening-in to remove the bridle.

ORDER	ACTION
Shorten-in, remove the bridle (from bridge)	OIC acknowledges order.
Off brake, heave in (port/stbd)	Take off the brake and heave in until there is no weight on the bridle.
Avast, on brake, off turns (OIC)	Avast heaving in and apply the brake. Take off the turns of the bridle from the bollards and take it in hand.
Off brake, heave in, haul in the bridle (OIC)	Take off the brake, commence heaving in on the cable and hauling in on the bridle until the joggle shackle comes inboard and is on deck. **Note.** *The OIC must ensure the joggle shackle does not snag, as it is heaved up the hawse pipe because it can strain the cable and damage the joggle shackle.*
Avast, on brake, on Blake slip, off joggle shackle (OIC)	Avast heaving, apply the brake, on Blake slip. Remove the joggle shackle from the cable and pendant.
Haul in bridle (OIC)	The bridle and bow dome pendant are recovered through the centreline hawse pipe and moved clear. OIC reports to the bridge that the bridle and pendant are detached and clear of the cable and the number of shackles on deck and how the cable grows.
Shorten-in (from bridge)	From this point on the procedures for weighing anchor are as laid down in Annex 2A to this Chapter.

Annex 2C

SECURING TO A BUOY USING A SINGLE BRIDLE (CABLE)

ORDER	ACTION
Cable party close up (piped from bridge)	Muster and brief cable party (including safety - see Para 02014), check power to capstans, check comms (the same system is to be used by bridge, fo'c'sle and boat), provide cable bag and all other associated equipment. Make up two heaving lines ready for throwing and provide shot mats to protect deck area as required. Fake down the picking up rope abaft the capstan and lead the hook end out through the bullring/centreline hawse, then back inboard.
Boat's crew and buoy jumpers to muster (piped from bridge)	Muster the boat's crew and the buoy jumpers and brief them on the task. Ensure all safety aspects are covered and personnel are aware of the method being used to pass the picking-up rope (see para 02029 of this chapter). Provide heaving line and cable bag for buoy jumpers.
Clear away anchors and cables (OIC)	Clear away anchors and cables and prepare one anchor ready for letting go as described in annex 2A to this chapter. Report to the bridge when the anchor is ready for letting go. **Note**. *Do not remove the bottle screw slip and the anchor strop from the cable that is to be used to provide the bridle.*
Prepare the bridle (OIC)	Prepare the bridle by breaking the cable at the first joining shackle, leaving the anchor secured in the hawse pipe. Attach a Securing to Buoy (STB) shackle to the end of the bridle.
Off brake, veer (OIC)	Take off the brake and veer the bridle. Use rope ends to assist in leading the cable towards the centreline hawsepipe/bullring. Ensure there is sufficient slack to enable the end of the bridle to be passed through the bullring.
Avast veering, on brake, disconnect (OIC)	Avast veering, apply the brake, disconnect. Report to bridge that the fo'c'sle is ready to come to a single bridle. The ship now approaches the buoy and at an appropriate moment the bridge orders the seaboat away.
Off brake, veer (OIC)	As the ship makes her approach to the buoy the bridle is passed out of the hawsepipe/bullring and veered until it is approximately 2m above the waterline. A bullrope may be used if required.
Avast veering, on brake (OIC)	Avast veering, apply the brake. (Ships fitted with a windlass must apply the Blake slip prior to disconnecting).
Pass the picking up rope (from bridge)	The bridge gives the fo'c'sle permission to take control of the boat. The boat is called in to receive a heaving line (or messenger), which is passed from the fo'c'sle to the boat. The inboard end of the heaving line is bent to the hard eye of the picking-up rope.

ORDER	ACTION
Proceed to the buoy (OIC)	Boat proceeds to the buoy; buoy jumpers man the buoy taking heaving line with them.
Check away picking-up rope	Check away the picking-up rope as it is hauled onto the buoy and secured to the main ring of the buoy by the buoy jumpers. Once the picking-up rope has been attached the heaving line is removed. (See Fig 2-23.)
Buoy jumpers clear the buoy (OIC)	Buoy jumpers clear the buoy, boat lays off well clear. OIC reports to the bridge that the picking up rope is secured, and requests permission to bring the buoy underfoot.
Down slack, bring to on the picking up rope (OIC)	Take down the slack on the picking up rope and bring to on to the capstan.
Heave in (OIC)	Heave in on the picking up rope until the buoy is underfoot. The bridge is to be kept inforMed of the position of the buoy at all times.
Avast heaving (OIC)	Once the buoy is underfoot, avast heaving, report to the bridge that the buoy is underfoot, request permission to connect the bridle.
Secure the bridle (from bridge)	Call the boat in to the buoy.
Buoy jumpers on the buoy (OIC)	Instruct the buoy jumpers to go onto the buoy and secure the bridle to the buoy. When the bridle is secured, buoy jumpers clear the buoy and the boat lays off. Report to the bridge that the bridle is secured.
Veer (OIC)	Veer on the picking up rope to transfer the weight to the bridle.
Avast veering (OIC)	Avast veering.
Buoy jumpers on the buoy (OIC)	Call the boat in, buoy jumpers man the buoy and remove the picking up rope. Buoy jumpers then clear the buoy, boat stands by for recovery.
Haul in picking up rope (OIC)	Recover the picking up rope on deck.
Off brake, veer the bridle (OIC)	Take off the brake and veer the bridle to the required scope.
Avast veering, on brake (OIC)	Avast veering, apply the brake, report to the bridge that the ship is secured to the buoy at the required scope.
Secure the fo'c'sle (from bridge)	Secure the bridle and cable deck. The bridle cable is secured as if at anchor and the second anchor is secured as described in annex 2A to this chapter. On completion the boat is recovered.

SLIPPING FROM A BUOY USING A SINGLE BRIDLE (CABLE)

ORDER	ACTION
Cable party close up (piped from bridge)	Muster and brief cable party (including safety - see Para 02014), check power to capstans, check comms (the same system is to be used by bridge, fo'c'sle and boat), provide cable bag and all other associated equipment. Make up two heaving lines ready for throwing and provide shot mats to protect deck area as required. Fake down the slip rope ready for passing; rig a bollard strop and slip with anti-twist bar available. Prepare the anchor ready for letting go. When ready report to bridge.
Boat's crew and buoy jumpers to muster (piped from bridge)	Muster the boat's crew and the buoy jumpers and brief them on the task. Ensure all safety aspects are covered (see Para 02029 of this Chapter). Provide heaving line and cable bag for buoy jumpers. OIC requests permission from the bridge to shorten-in the bridle. Boat is deployed when ordered by the bridge.
Rig the sliprope	OIC requests permission to take control of the boat. Once permission is granted the OIC calls in the boat and passes a heaving line to it.
Buoy jumpers on the buoy (OIC)	Buoy jumpers man the buoy and commence hauling in on the slip rope as it is checked away on the fo'c'sle. When the sliprope is to hand it is passed through the main ring of the buoy. The free end of the heaving line is then passed back to the fo'c'sle; the other end remains bent to the sliprope.
Buoy jumpers off the buoy (OIC)	Buoy jumpers vacate the buoy and man the boat; the boat then lays off. The eye end of the sliprope is hauled inboard and attached to the bollard strop and slip. It is secured and moused, and an anti-twist bar is inserted through the slip. The free end of the sliprope is turned up on bollards or brought to the capstan; the heaving line is removed. OIC reports to the bridge that the sliprope is rigged.
Shorten in the bridle (from bridge)	
Connect up, off Blake slip (OIC)	Connect up the capstan ready to recover the bridle, take off the Blake slip and other preventors.
Off brake, heave in (OIC)	Take off the brake; heave in until the buoy is underfoot, keeping the bridge inforMed on the position of the buoy.
Heave in/down slack on the sliprope (OIC)	As the buoy is brought underfoot the slack in the sliprope is either hove in or taken down by hand.
Avast heaving, on brake (OIC)	Avast heaving, apply the brake when the buoy is underfoot, turn up the sliprope on the bollards, then inform the bridge. Permission is now sought from the command to transfer the weight from the working bridle to the sliprope.

ORDER	ACTION
Off brake, veer. OIC	Take off the brake and veer the bridle to transfer the weight onto the sliprope.
Avast veering, on brake (OIC)	Avast veering, apply the brake.
Buoy jumpers on the buoy (OIC)	Call in the boat, buoy jumpers man the buoy and remove the securing to buoy (STB) shackle. The bridle is now free to be recovered.
Buoy jumpers off the buoy (OIC)	Buoy jumpers vacate the buoy and the boat lays off.
Off brake, heave in (OIC)	Take off the brake, heave in the bridle until the end is on deck adjacent to the swivel piece.
Avast heaving, on brake (OIC)	Avast heaving, apply the brake. Detach the STB shackle and reattach the cable to the anchor. The anchor is then made ready for letting go. Report to bridge that the anchor is ready for letting go, ready to slip the sliprope.
Stand-bye to slip (from bridge)	OIC nominates a person to knock off the slip. Turns on the bollards are reduced to two turns ready to surge the sliprope.
Surge the slip rope, off mousing out pin (OIC)	Commence surging the slip rope, take off the mousing on the slip, place the maul against the buckler link and remove the pin from the slip.
Slip (from bridge)	Knock off the slip. When the eye is clear of the buoy remove the turns and run in or if required heave in until the sliprope is inboard. Inform the bridge that the sliprope is inboard. Recover the seaboat.
Secure the Fx for sea (from bridge)	Secure the cable deck as described in annex 2A of this chapter then report to the bridge.

Annex 2D

SECURING TO A BUOY - DOUBLE BRIDLE USING SHIP'S CABLE

ORDER	ACTION
Cable party close up (piped from bridge)	Muster and brief cable party (including safety - see para 02014), check power to capstans, check comms (the same system is to be used by bridge, fo'c'sle and boat), provide cable bag, handspikes and all other associated equipment. Make up two heaving lines ready for throwing and provide shot mats to protect deck area as required. Fake down the picking up rope abaft the capstan and lead the hook end out through the bullring/centreline hawse, then back inboard. Provide a spare Blake bottlescrew slip attached to the deck clench for'ard of the bollards that are to be used to secure the standing bridle. Provide two securing to buoy (STB) shackles, one joggle shackle and a bullrope.
Clear away anchors and cables (OIC)	Clear away anchors and cables and prepare one anchor ready for letting go as described in annex 2A to this chapter. Report to the bridge when the anchor is ready for letting go. *Note. Do not remove the bottle screw slip and the anchor strop from the cable that is to be used to provide the bridles.*
Boat's crew and buoy jumpers to muster (piped from bridge)	Muster the boat's crew and the buoy jumpers and brief them on the task. Ensure all safety aspects are covered and personnel are aware of the method being used to pass the picking-up rope (see para 02029 of this chapter). Provide heaving line and cable bag for buoy jumpers.
Prepare the bridles (OIC)	Prepare the standing bridle by breaking the cable at the first joining shackle, leaving the anchor secured in the hawse pipe.
Connect up, off Blake slip, off brake, veer (OIC)	Connect up the capstan, knock off the Blake slip, take off the brake and veer the cable. Use rope ends to assist leading the cable towards the centreline hawsepipe/bullring. Continue veering until a full shackle of cable has been ranged on deck.
Avast veering, on brake (OIC)	Avast veering, apply the brake. Break the cable at the second joining shackle and secure the inboard end of the standing bridle by turning it up in Figures of eight (two turns) around bollards or bitts and fasten together the two parts of the final turn with a joggle shackle.
Off brake, veer (OIC)	Take off the brake and veer the cable. Use rope ends to assist in leading the cable towards the centreline hawsepipe/bullring. Ensure there is sufficient slack to enable the end of the working bridle to be passed through the centreline hawsepipe/bullring. *Note. Setting up for a double bridle is time-consuming and preparations should be made well in advance.*

ORDER	ACTION
Avast veering, on brake (OIC)	Avast veering and apply the brake. Attach a STB shackle to the outboard end of both bridles.
Rig the bullrope, attach the bottlescrew slip (OIC)	Attach the bullrope to the standing bridle two or three links above the STB shackle. Take the free end of the bullrope to the bollards to which the standing bridle is secured and bring to with two turns ready to be backed up. Secure by means of a robust lashing or Blake bottle screw slip (if fitted) the standing bridle at a position that will allow the bridle, when hung outboard on the lashing/slip to be connected to the buoy. Report to the bridge that the fo'c'sle is ready to come to the buoy. The ship now approaches the buoy and at an appropriate moment the bridge orders the seaboat away.
Pass out the standing bridle (OIC)	As the ship makes her approach to the buoy the bridles are passed out; first the standing bridle followed by the working bridle. Manoeuvre the end of the standing bridle out through the hawsepipe/bullring (assist with handspikes if necessary). When the end of the bridle is outboard continue to ease out the bight of the bridle until the weight is held by the bottlescrew slip. Surge the bullrope (it may be necessary to reduce to one turn) until the STB shackle is in a position to be connected to the buoy.
Off brake, veer (OIC)	Pass the end of the working bridle out of the hawsepipe/bullring, off brake and veer on the working bridle (assist with rope ends if necessary) until the STB is in a position to be connected to the buoy.
Avast veering, on brake (OIC)	Avast veering and apply the brake.
Pass the picking up rope (from bridge)	The bridge gives the fo'c'sle permission to take control of the boat. The boat is called in to receive a heaving line, which is passed from the fo'c'sle to the boat. The inboard end of the heaving line is bent to the eye of the picking-up rope.
Proceed to the buoy (OIC)	Boat proceeds to the buoy; buoy jumpers man the buoy taking a heaving line with them.
Check away picking-up rope (OIC)	Check away the picking-up rope as it is hauled onto the buoy and secured to the main ring of the buoy by the buoy jumpers. Once the picking-up rope has been attached the heaving line is removed. (See Fig 2-23.)
Buoy jumpers clear the buoy (OIC)	Buoy jumpers clear the buoy, boat lays off well clear. OIC reports to the bridge that the picking up rope is secured, and requests permission to bring the buoy underfoot.
Down slack, bring to on the picking up rope (OIC)	Take down the slack on the picking up rope and bring to on the capstan.

ORDER	ACTION
Heave in (OIC)	Heave in on the picking up rope until the buoy is underfoot. The bridge is to be kept inforMed of the position of the buoy at all times.
Avast heaving, on brake (OIC)	When the buoy is underfoot, avast heaving, report to the bridge that the buoy is underfoot, request permission to connect the bridles. OIC checks bridles are in position to be secured and adjusts them as required.
Buoy jumpers on the buoy (OIC)	Call in the boat, buoy jumpers man the buoy and secure the bridles to the buoy (working bridle first). Once the bridles are secured, buoy jumpers clear the buoy and the boat lays off. *Note. To assist the buoy jumpers in connecting the bridles the height of the standing bridle can be adjusted using the bullrope.*
Veer (OIC)	Veer on the picking up rope to transfer the weight to the working bridle. Surge on the bullrope until it is slack.
Avast veering (OIC)	Avast veering on the picking-up rope once the working bridle has the weight and the picking-up is slack enough to be removed.
Buoy jumpers on the buoy (OIC)	Call the boat in, buoy jumpers man the buoy and remove the picking up rope and the bullrope. Buoy jumpers then clear the buoy, boat stands by for recovery.
Haul/heave in picking-up rope (OIC)	Recover the picking up rope and bullrope on deck.
Off bottlescrew slip (OIC)	Cut robust lashing/slip the Blake/bottle screw slip to allow the remainder of the standing bridle to run outboard.
Off brake, veer the working bridle (OIC)	Take off the brake and veer the working bridle to the approximate scope of the standing bridle. *Note. Do not exactly marry the scope of the two bridles because they may bang and chafe together.*
Avast veering, on brake, on Blake slip, disconnect (OIC)	Avast veering and apply the brake. On Blake slip and disconnect. Report to the bridge that the bridles are secured at the required scope.
Secure the fo'c'sle (from bridge)	Secure the bridles and cable deck. The working bridle cable is secured as if at anchor and the fully shortened bottlescrew slip is put back onto the standing bridle to act as a preventer. On completion the boat is recovered and fo'c'sle secured as described in annex 2A to this chapter.

SLIPPING FROM THE BUOY - DOUBLE BRIDLE SHIP'S CABLE

ORDER	ACTION
Cable party close up (piped from bridge)	Muster and brief cable party (including safety - see para 02014), check power to capstans, check comms (the same system is to be used by bridge, fo'c'sle and boat), provide cable bag, handspikes and all other associated equipment. Make up two heaving lines ready for throwing and provide shot mats to protect deck area as required. Fake down the slip rope ready for passing; rig a bollard strop and slip with anti-twist bar available. Prepare the anchor ready for letting go. When ready report to bridge.
Boat's crew and buoy jumpers to muster (piped from bridge)	Muster the boat's crew and the buoy jumpers and brief them on the task. Ensure all safety aspects are covered (see para 02029 of this chapter). Provide heaving line and cable bag for buoy jumpers. Boat is deployed when ordered by the bridge.
Pass the sliprope (from bridge)	The bridge gives the fo'c'sle permission to take control of the boat and rig the slip rope. The OIC calls in the boat and passes a heaving line to it.
Buoy jumpers on the buoy (OIC)	Buoy jumpers man the buoy and commence hauling in on the slip rope as the fo'c'sle checks away. When the eye of the slip rope is to hand it is passed through the main ring of the buoy. The free end of the heaving line is then passed back to the fo'c'sle, the other end remains bent to the sliprope.
Buoy jumpers off the buoy (OIC)	Buoy jumpers vacate the buoy and the boat lays off. The eye end of the slip rope is hauled inboard and attached to the bollard strop and slip. It is secured and moused, and an anti-twist bar is inserted through the slip. The free end of the sliprope is turned up on bollards or brought to on the capstan; the heaving line is removed. OIC reports to the bridge that the sliprope is rigged and requests permission to shorten in the working bridle.
Shorten in the bridle (from bridge)	
Connect up, off Blake slip (OIC)	Connect up the capstan ready to recover the bridle, take off the Blake slip and other preventers.
Off brake, heave in (OIC)	Take off the brake, heave in working bridle until the buoy is underfoot. Keep the bridge inforMed on the position of the buoy.
Heave in/down slack on the sliprope (OIC)	As the buoy is brought underfoot the slack in the slip rope is either heaved in or taken down by hand.
Avast heaving, on brake (OIC)	Avast heaving, apply the brake when the buoy is underfoot. Either turn up the slip rope onto bollards or back it up on the capstan. Permission must now be sought to transfer the weight from the working bridle to the slip rope.

ORDER	ACTION
Off brake, veer (OIC)	Take off the brake and veer on the working bridle to transfer the weight onto the slip rope.
Avast veering, on brake (OIC)	Avast veering, apply the brake.
Buoy jumpers on the buoy (OIC)	Call in the boat, buoy jumpers man the buoy and remove the STB shackle from the working bridle. The bridle is now free to be recovered.
Buoy jumpers off the buoy (OIC)	Buoy jumpers vacate the buoy and the boat lays off.
Off brake, heave in (OIC)	Take off the brake, heave in the working bridle until the end is on deck adjacent to the joggle shackle on the standing bridle. Remove the STB shackle.
Avast heaving, on brake (OIC)	Avast heaving, apply the brake.
Reposition the bottlescrew slip (OIC)	Take off the bottlescrew slip from the standing bridle and fully open it before repositioning it back on the standing bridle. Now tighten up the bottlescrew to transfer the weight of the standing bridle from the joggle shackle to the bottlescrew slip.
Off Joggle shackle, reconnect the cable (OIC)	Take off the joggle shackle, remove the turns from the bollards and reconnect the end of the standing bridle to the cable.
Off brake, heave in (OIC)	Take off the brake and heave in to transfer the weight from the bottlescrew slip to the cable.
Avast heaving, on brake (OIC)	Avast heaving, apply the brake. Take off the bottlescrew slip and move it clear.
Off brake, heave in (OIC)	Take off the brake and heave in until all the slack of the standing bridle has been taken up.
Avast heaving, on brake (OIC)	Avast heaving, apply the brake.
Buoy jumpers on the buoy (OIC)	Call in the boat, buoy jumpers man the buoy and remove the standing bridle STB shackle from the buoy. The bridle is now free to be recovered.
Buoy jumpers off the buoy (OIC)	Buoy jumpers vacate the buoy and the boat lays off.
Off brake, heave in (OIC)	Take off the brake, heave in the bridle until the end is on deck adjacent to the swivel piece.

ORDER	ACTION
Avast heaving, on brake (OIC)	Avast heaving, apply the brake. Detach the STB shackle and re-attach the cable to the anchor. The anchor is then made ready for letting go. Report to bridge that the anchor is ready for letting go and the sliprope is ready for slipping.
Stand-by to slip (from bridge)	OIC nominates a person to knock off the slip. Reduce to two turns on the bollards ready to surge the slip rope (or veer on the capstan).
Surge/veer the sliprope, off mousing out pin (OIC)	Commence surging/veering the slip rope, take off the mousing on the slip, place the maul against the buckler link and remove the pin from the slip. Stand by to slip the slip rope.
Slip (from bridge)	Knock off the slip. When the eye is clear of the buoy remove the turns and run in or if required heave in until the slip rope is inboard. Inform the bridge that the slip rope is inboard. Recover the seaboat.
Secure the fo'c'sle for sea (from bridge)	Secure the cable deck as described in Annex 2A of this Chapter then report to the bridge.

Annex 2E

SECURING TO A BUOY USING MMFC BRIDLES

When using MMFC Bridles the following rules apply:

1. The ship must always go to a double bridle.
2. MMFC bridles must not be used for a compass swing.
3. A mix of MMFC and cable bridles must not be used.

ORDER	ACTION
Cable party close up (piped from bridge)	Muster and brief cable party (including safety - see Para 02014), check power to capstans, check comms (the same comms for bridge, fo'c'sle and boat), provide cable bag and all other associated equipment. Bring up both bridles and attach a securing to buoy shackle to the end of each. Fake down the bridles in the eyes of the ship, clear of each other, and then bring to with two turns on the port and stbd bollards respectively. Place a bollard strop and slip on the bollards prior to turning up the Bridles. Fake out the picking up rope, ensure locking stitches are correct ready for passing, reeve the hook end through the bullring and back inboard. Make up two heaving lines ready for throwing. Prepare both anchors ready for letting go in accordance with Annex 2A. Report to the bridge when ready.
Boat's crew and buoy jumpers to muster (piped from bridge)	Muster the boat's crew and the buoy jumpers and brief them on the task. Ensure all safety aspects are covered and personnel are aware of the method being used to pass the picking-up rope (see Para 02029 of this Chapter). Provide heaving line, cable bag, Shock Mitigation Strop (SMS) fitted with fairlead shackles and Securing to Buoy Shackle (HPMT fitted ships).
	The ship now approaches the buoy and at an appropriate moment the bridge orders the seaboat away. During the final approach to the buoy the bridles are lowered out of the bullring. Buoy jumpers inspect the buoy and attach HPMT ancillary equipment in preparation.
Pass the picking up rope (from bridge)	As the ship closes the buoy the bridge gives the Fo'c'sle permission for to take control of the boat and pass the picking-up rope. The boat is called in to receive a heaving line, which is passed from the Fo'c'sle to the boat. The inboard end of the heaving line is bent to the eye of the picking-up rope.
Proceed to the buoy (OIC)	The boat proceeds to the buoy, buoy jumpers man the buoy taking the heaving line with them.
Check away picking up rope (OIC)	Check away the picking-up rope as it is hauled onto the buoy and secured to the main ring of the buoy by the buoy jumpers. Once the picking-up rope has been attached the heaving line is removed. (See Fig 2-23).

ORDER	ACTION
Buoy jumpers clear the buoy (OIC)	Buoy jumpers clear the buoy, boat lays off well clear. OIC reports to the bridge that the picking up rope is secured, and requests permission to bring the buoy underfoot if required.
Down slack, Bring to on the picking up rope (OIC)	When permission has been obtained, take down the slack on the picking up rope and bring to on to the capstan with a minimum of 5 turns.
Heave in (OIC)	Heave in on the picking-up rope. The bridge is to be kept inforMed of the position of the buoy at all times.
Avast heaving (OIC)	Once the buoy is in position, avast heaving. Report to the bridge that the buoy is in position, request permission to connect the bridles.
Secure the bridles (from bridge)	Lower the bridles to the buoy.
Buoy jumpers on the buoy (OIC)	Instruct the buoy jumpers to go onto the buoy and secure the bridles. When the bridles are secured, buoy jumpers clear the buoy and the boat lays off well clear. Report to the bridge that the bridles are secured. (If possible the bridles should be secured to the main ring of the buoy. If this is not possible each bridle should be secured to a separate reducing link).
Hold on both bridles, veer on the picking up rope (OIC)	Back up both bridles round the bollards with two full turns around the leading bit. Veer the picking up rope until the weight is transferred to the bridles. When there is sufficient slack in the picking up rope for it to be removed.
Buoy jumpers on the buoy, remove the picking up rope (OIC)	Call the boat in, buoy jumpers man the buoy and remove the picking up rope. Buoy jumpers then clear the buoy, boat stands by for recovery.
Haul/heave in picking up rope (OIC)	Recover the picking up rope on deck.
Surge on both bridles (OIC)	Surge both bridles to the required scope. Ensure they are middled and the chafing pieces are correctly positioned.
Secure bridles	Fully turn up and rack both bridles. Report to the bridge that the ship is secured to the buoy.
Secure the fo'c'sle (from bridge)	Secure the cable deck as described in annex 2A to this chapter. Report to bridge once secured.
	Note. *If the required scope of the bridles is known beforehand the bridles can be brought to the bollards and fully turned up and racked as part of the preparations for the evolution.*

SLIPPING FROM THE BUOY WHEN SECURED WITH BRAIDLINE/HMPE BRIDLES

ORDER	ACTION
Cable party close up (piped from bridge)	Muster and brief cable party (including safety - see Para 02014), check power to capstans, check comms (the same system is to be used by bridge, Fo'c'sle and boat), provide cable bag and all other associated equipment. Make up two heaving lines ready for throwing and provide shot mats to protect deck area as required. Fake down the slip rope ready for passing; rig a bollard strop and slip with anti-twist bar available. Prepare the anchor ready for letting go. When ready report to bridge.
Boat's crew and buoy jumpers to muster (piped from bridge)	Muster the boat's crew and the buoy jumpers and brief them on the task. Ensure all safety aspects are covered (see Para 02029). Provide heaving line and cable bag for buoy jumpers. Boat is deployed when ordered by the bridge.
Rig the sliprope (from bridge)	OIC requests permission to take control of the boat. Once permission is granted the OIC calls in the boat and passes a heaving line to it.
Buoy jumpers on the buoy (OIC)	Buoy jumpers man the buoy and commence hauling in on the slip rope as it is checked away on the Fo'c'sle. When the slip rope is to hand it is passed through the main ring of the buoy. The free end of the heaving line is then passed back to the Fo'c'sle; the other end remains bent to the sliprope.
Buoy jumpers off the buoy (OIC)	Buoy jumpers vacate the buoy and man the boat, the boat then lies off. The eye end of the sliprope is hauled inboard and attached to the bollard strop and slip. It is secured and moused, and an anti-twist bar is inserted through the slip. The free end of the sliprope is turned up on bollards or brought to on the capstan; the heaving line is removed. OIC reports to the bridge that the sliprope is rigged.
Recover the bridles (from the bridge)	Transfer one of the bridles from the bollards to the capstan (use the bridle on the opposite side to where the slip rope is being worked) this will become the working bridle.
Heave in on the working bridle (OIC)	Heave in on the working bridle, keeping the bridge inforMed on the position of the buoy.
Heave in/down slack on the slip rope (OIC)	As the buoy is brought underfoot the slack in the sliprope is either heaved in or taken down by hand.
Avast heaving (OIC)	Avast heaving when the buoy is underfoot, then turn up the sliprope on the bollards and inform the bridge. Permission must now be sought from the command to transfer the weight from the working bridle to the sliprope.

ORDER	ACTION
Veer working bridle (OIC)	Veer the working bridle to transfer the weight to the slip rope.
Buoy jumpers on the buoy (OIC)	Call in the boat, buoy jumpers man the buoy and disconnect both bridles from the reducing Link. Inform the bridge when bridles have been removed.
Buoy jumpers off the buoy (OIC)	Buoy jumpers vacate the buoy and the boat lays off.
Heave in/haul in both bridles (OIC)	Recover both bridles on to the fo'c'sle. Report to the bridge that the bridles are inboard. Stand-bye to surge on the sliprope, and have a nominated person ready to slip the slip rope.
Stand by to slip (from bridge)	OIC nominates a person to knock off the slip. Reduce to two turns on the bollards to surge the sliprope, or if sliprope is brought to on the capstan stand by to veer.
Surge the slip rope, off mousing out pin (OIC)	Commence surging/veering the sliprope, take off the mousing on the slip, place the maul against the buckler link and remove the pin from the slip. Stand by to slip the sliprope.
Slip (from bridge)	Knock off the slip. When the eye is clear of the buoy remove the turns and run the sliprope inboard. Inform the bridge that the sliprope is inboard.
Secure the focsle for sea (from bridge)	Secure the cable deck as described in annex 2A of this chapter then report to the bridge.

Annex 2F

RFA BUOY SECURING ARRANGEMENTS USING THE SMIT BRACKET

1.   **RFA buoy securing arrangements using the SMIT bracket**

a. **Introduction.** RFAs that are fitted with the SMIT bracket system (Fig 2F-1) for mooring to buoys use 2 x 76 mm Steelite ropes which enables them to moor to the Admiralty buoys at Plymouth Sound without the need for breaking the ships cable and using all the associated equipment required for that system. This ensures a safer and speedier mode of operation, both in securing to and slipping from a buoy. Each Steelite rope has a breaking load of approximately 210 tons which can dampen the effect of a possible combined shock load of 420 tons on the vessel's scantlings. A 30 m Tensioning Line (as shown in Fig 2F-9) is secured at the midway point of the longer Steelite (42 m). Once both Steelite ropes are secured to the buoy, the weight is taken on the messenger, thus bringing the catenary of the longer Steelite rope to that of the shorter. In the unlikely event of extreme weather causing the Steelite ropes to part, the sequence would be:

(1) Tensioning line parts.

(2) 40m Steelite rope parts. (Stb'd Steelite).

(3) 42m Steelite rope parts. (Port Steelite).

b.   The Steelite ropes and monroe shackles are held by SALMO, and are fitted to the buoy prior to the ship's arrival. A mooring boat manned by shore staff will also be on standby.

c.   A steel collar is provided for each bracket. This collar, when fitted over the horizontal pin, enlarges the circumference of the Steelite rope eye thus ensuring an acceptable safe working load (SWL).

d.   A threaded "T" bar can be used to hold the collar in position whilst pin "A" is closed. If the "T" bar is not held then a round sling can be used as shown in Fig 2F-6).

Note.   *It is not permissible at any time to secure to the buoy using just one Steelite Rope.*

Fig 2F-1. SMIT bracket and collar

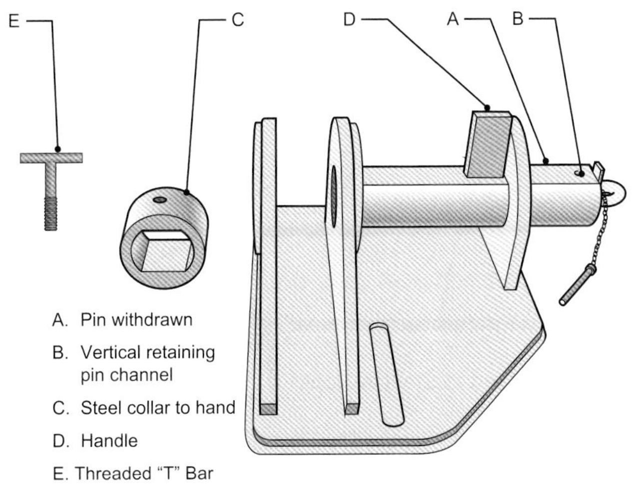

A. Pin withdrawn

B. Vertical retaining
    pin channel

C. Steel collar to hand

D. Handle

E. Threaded "T" Bar

e. **Securing to the buoy.** The ship approaches the buoy with head into wind and tide, whichever is the strongest (Fig 2F-2). At approximately 60-70 m from the buoy, the rope's end of a 100 m x 21 mm Braidline messenger is lowered to the mooring boat through the starboard centreline Panama lead. Once the messenger has been secured with a double sheetbend to the pennant attached to the Steelite rope (Fig 2F-3), heaving commences via leads to the windlass with a minimum of three turns (Fig 2F-4). As the ship closes the buoy, the eye of the Steelite rope is heaved inboard whilst maintaining a safe catenary in the rope.

Fig 2F-2. Ship approaching the buoy

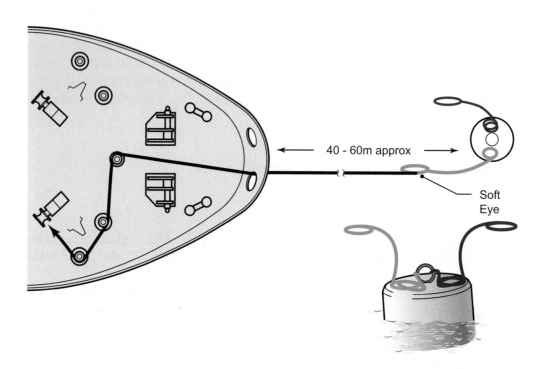

Fig 2F-3. 2m pendant stopped to Steelite rope

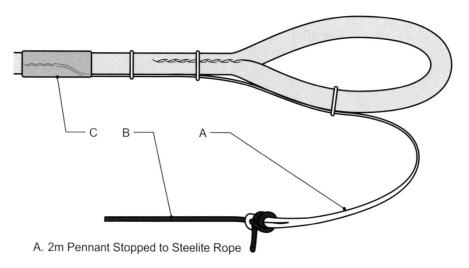

A. 2m Pennant Stopped to Steelite Rope

B. Ships 100m Messenger Secured to Pennant by Double Sheetbend

C. Protective Sleeve

Fig 2F-4. Leads for heaving in mooring lines

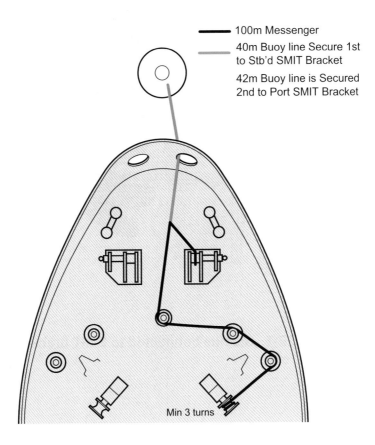

— 100m Messenger
40m Buoy line Secure 1st
to Stb'd SMIT Bracket

42m Buoy line is Secured
2nd to Port SMIT Bracket

Min 3 turns

f.   When the eye of the Steelite rope is adjacent to the SMIT bracket, the stops are cut, and the eye placed over the inboard upright of the bracket (Fig 2F-5 and Fig 2F-6). The steel collar is then fitted to line up with the horizontal pin of the bracket. The pin is then slid home and the eye of the Steelite rope is placed over the collar on the pin (Fig 2F-7). The vertical pin is dropped in place. The messenger is then disconnected. (The 2 m pennant is to remain attached to the Steelite rope). This completes the procedure for securing the first Steelite rope to the Stb'd SMIT bracket. Follow the same procedure for securing the 2nd Steelite rope to the port SMIT bracket.

Fig 2F-5. Steelite over upright

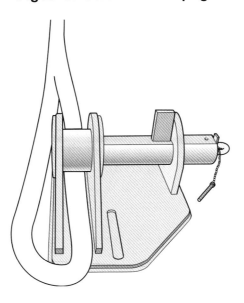

Fig 2F-6. Collar lined up to pin

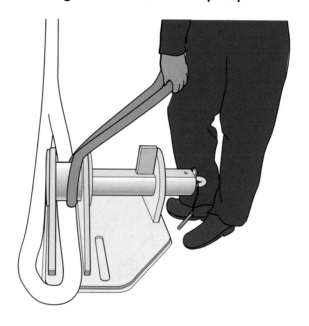

Fig 2F-7. Steelite connected to SMIT bracket

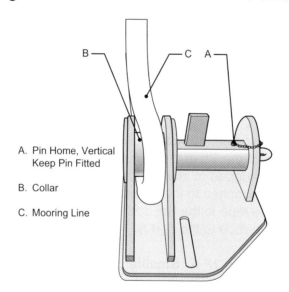

A. Pin Home, Vertical
   Keep Pin Fitted

B. Collar

C. Mooring Line

g. The second Steelite rope is then hauled inboard using the same messenger. Once the eye is secured to the bracket, the 30 m x 30 mm tensioning line iaw Fig 2F-9 is led to the Port windlass, where it is heaved in until the catenary of the Steelite rope matches that of the starboard rope. The tensioning line is then stoppered off and secured to the bollard bitts adjacent to the SMIT bracket (Fig 2F-8). The ship will now ride to the buoy as shown in Fig 2F-9.

Fig 2F-8. Tensioning line stopped off to bollards

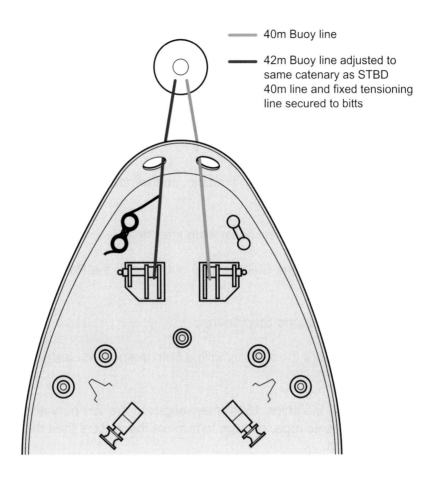

— 40m Buoy line

— 42m Buoy line adjusted to same catenary as STBD 40m line and fixed tensioning line secured to bitts

Fig 2F-9. Ship secured to buoy using Steelite rope

STBD 76mm x 40m Buoy Rope

30mm x 30m Tensioning Line

PORT 76mm x 42m Buoy Rope

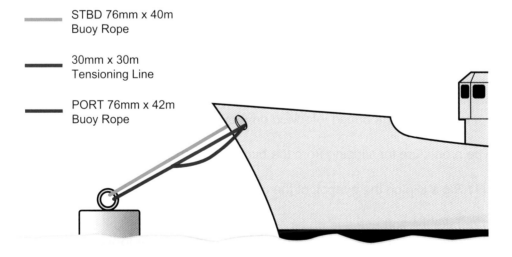

h. **Slipping from the buoy**. Because of the light weight of the Steelite rope it is possible for the weight to be taken off the short Steelite rope by hand. However, prevailing weather conditions should dictate whether a messenger should be used instead. The procedure for slipping from the buoy in ideal weather conditions is as follows:

(1) *Longest Steelite rope to be slipped first*

(a) Request command to give a slight push ahead on main engines.

(b) Attach the ships 100m messenger to the 2m Pennant and take the weight off the Steelite rope.

(c) Remove vertical retaining pin, and withdraw the main horizontal pin from the bracket.

(d) Remove the steel collar from the bracket.

(e) Veer/surge the Steelite rope out through the Panama lead into the mooring boat.

(2) *Slipping the second Steelite rope*

(a) Ease back the tensioning line from the bollard bitts and stop it to the Steelite rope.

(b) Attach the ships 100m messenger to the 2m pennant and take the weight off the Steelite rope, enough to remove the vertical then the horizontal pins from the bracket.

(c) Remove the steel collar from the bracket.

(d) Veer/surge the messenger allowing the Steelite rope to feed out through the Panama lead.

(e) Once the Steelite rope is in the mooring boat, remove the messenger from the windlass and pay out sufficient slack to allow the mooring boat's crew to remove the messenger from the 2 m pennant and recover inboard.

(f) Keep the bridge inforMed on movement and distance from the buoy.

i. The procedure for slipping from the buoy in less than ideal conditions is as follows:

(1) Rig a slip on the eyebolt of the centreline old man.

(2) Take the soft eye end of the 100 m messenger and lead it through the eye of the 2 m pennant attached to the Steelite rope and secure it to the slip on the centreline single roller lead/old man. Take a minimum of three turns of the rope's end of the messenger on the windlass.

(3) When sufficient weight is off the Steelite rope, heave in on the messenger. When enough slack is evident, remove the vertical and horizontal pins from the bracket.

(4) Remove the steel collar from the bracket.

(5) Walk, or ease back the messenger allowing the Steelite rope to feed out through the Panama lead.

(6) Once the Steelite rope is in the water slip the messenger and recover inboard.

THIS PAGE IS INTENTIONALLY BLANK

THE NAUTICAL INSTITUTE

CHAPTER 3

RIGGING AND DECK GEAR

CONTENTS

CONTENTS (Continued)

ANNEXES

CHAPTER 3

RIGGING AND DECK GEAR

03001. Introduction to types of rope

a.   Most ropes can be described as belonging to one of three main types:

Cordage made of natural fibres (NFC)
Class I - Man-made fibre cordage (MMFC) consists of traditional fibres such as olefin, nylon and polyester.
Class II – MMFC rope constructions consist of high modulus fibres such as, Dyneema (HMPE) Technora and Vectran.

b.   In the Royal Navy, ropes are described by reference to the diameter of the rope measured in millimetres (mm), the type of construction and the material from which it is made - for example, 36 mm Quantum 12. However, certain proprietary brand ropes contain a mixture of materials, either from two of the three main types, or from a mix of materials from one type, e.g. a combination of man-made fibres. These ropes are usually referred to by their proprietary name.

03002. Construction, characteristics and details of supply of natural fibre cordage

a.   Use in the Royal Navy of natural fibre cordage has dwindled in recent years, primarily because man-made fibre cordage is stronger, harder wearing, more cost effective, and in most circumstances, more functional than natural fibre cordage. However, natural fibre cordage is still required for certain tasks, and this requirement is likely to continue for the foreseeable future. All cordage supplied to the Royal Navy is supplied with a certificate of conformity, on which are listed the date of manufacture, the British standard to which the rope has been manufactured, and the guaranteed minimum breaking strength of the rope.

b.   **Construction**

(1)   Natural fibre ropes are made from fibres of varying length dependent upon their source, and the first process is to comb out these fibres into a long, even ribbon shown in Fig 3-1.

Fig 3-1. Fibres of a natural fibre cordage rope

(2)   The ribbons are then twisted up into yarns, and the twist given binds the fibres firmly together so that they hold by friction when the yarn is subjected to strain. This process is known as 'spinning', and the yarns are said to be spun left-handed or right-handed according to the direction of the twist. Next, a certain number of yarns are twisted together to form strands. The number and size of yarn to make each strand depends on the size of the rope to be made. This stage is known as 'twisting the strands', and again, the twist can be left-handed or right-handed. Three or four strands are now made up into a left-handed or right-handed rope. This process is called 'laying' or 'closing', and is always carried out in the direction opposite to that used in the previous stage of twisting the strands; it is, moreover, distinct from the simple spin or twist and is two-fold, in that:

(a) The strands are twisted up together to form the rope.

(b) At the same time the strands are rotated individually in the direction of the original twist.

i. Were this not done, laying the strands up together would tend to untwist the yarns in each strand.

ii. As the rope is laid up, its length contracts like a coiled spring, giving it certain elasticity. The harder the twist given to the strands in laying, the shorter will be the resultant rope and thus a rope is said to be **hard-laid, ordinary laid** or **soft-laid**. In practice, three strands of 275 metres lay up into a rope of about 220 metres in length. Three strands so laid up constitute a *hawser-laid* rope (Fig 3-2). Right-handed hawser-laid rope is the only type of natural fibre cordage now used in the Royal Navy.

Fig 3-2. Component parts of a natural fibre right-handed hawser-laid rope

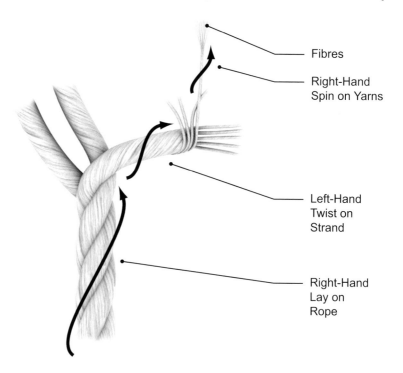

Fibres

Right-Hand
Spin on Yarns

Left-Hand
Twist on
Strand

Right-Hand
Lay on
Rope

c. **General characteristics.** The strands tend to unlay unless the end of the rope is whipped (ie firmly bound) with twine. The rope will stretch under load and will not completely recover when the load is removed. The rope acquires a permanent and irreversible **set**; the higher the load in relation to the breaking strength, the greater the set. The set may be observed by the extension in length and reduction in diameter when the rope is slack and will eventually render the rope unfit for service. The older and more worn the rope, the less elasticity it will possess and the weaker it will become. Rope under load will tend to twist in the opposite direction to that of its lay and thereby tend to unlay itself, but it should regain its normal form when slack. When wet, natural fibre cordage will usually shrink in length in proportion to the amount by which it swells in diameter, but it will recover its original length when dry and after use. Rope which is continually subjected to heat and damp - when in the tropics, for example - will lose its elasticity and strength sooner than rope used under normal conditions of temperature and humidity.

d. **Materials used**. There are now only two natural fibre ropes supplied to the Royal Navy, **Manila** and **Sisal**. The fibres of the rope are treated with a water proofing solution during the first stage of rope-making when the fibres are combed into ribbons.

(1) *Manila rope*. This rope is made from the leaf fibre of the **Abaca** plant, which is grown in the Philippines and shipped from the port of Manila (whence its name), and also Sumatra and Borneo. When new and untreated, it is a deep golden-brown in colour. The rope is flexible, durable, and strong when compared with other natural fibre ropes, impervious to salt water and stands up well to wear and tear. However, its advantages over man fibre cordage are that it stretches less, will surge more readily around a winch or capstan, and does not fuse when heated (ie when being surged under strain or used as a check stopper). It is currently used as a check stopper for towing operations. Manila rope is marked with one black yarn in each of two strands, and supplied in coils of 220 metres.

(2) *Sisal rope*. This rope is made from the **Agave Sisalana** plant, which is a member of the cactus plant. It is grown in Brazil, Madagascar, Kenya, Tanzania, Haiti and Java; when new and untreated it is hairy, and of a pale straw colour. New sisal is as strong as manila, but is not as flexible, durable or resistant to wear and weather. Its principle use is as a slip rope during replenishment at sea, and its advantages over man-made fibre ropes are similar to those outlined for manila. Sisal rope is marked with one red yarn in one strand, and supplied in coils of 220 metres.

e. **Strength**. A method of finding the approximate breaking strength of manila and sisal cordage is to divide the square of the diameter of the cordage in millimetres by 200, the answer being in tonnes. This allows for a good margin of safety. To estimate the strength of a rope which is well worn but in good condition, apply the formula as for new rope, but use the **actual** and not the **nominal** diameter. However, the only really reliable method by which the strength of a rope may be determined is to test a sample of the worst part of the rope to destruction. This will not be achievable onboard.

f. **Details of natural fibre cordage supplied to the Royal Navy**. Table 3-1 gives details of natural fibre cordage supplied to the Royal Navy.

Table 3-1. Details of natural fibre cordage supplied to the Royal Navy

Type	Size	Naval stores No	Minimum breaking load	Supply denomination
Manila	8 mm	0350/571-3074	0.45 tonnes	220 m
	12 mm	0350/125-0228	1.06 tonnes	220 m
	16 mm	0350/942-5025	2.03 tonnes	220 m
	20 mm	0350/571-3077	3.25 tonnes	220 m
	24 mm	0350/942-5026	4.57 tonnes	220 m
Sisal	12 mm	0350/942-5042	0.95 tonnes	220 m
	16 mm	0350/942-5044	1.80 tonnes	220 m
	20 mm	0350/942-5046	2.85 tonnes	220 m
	24 mm	0350/942-5048	4.07 tonnes	220 m
	28 mm	0350/942-5050	5.33 tonnes	220 m
	72 mm	0350/942-5060	32.7 tonnes	220 m

g. **Care and maintenance of natural fibre rope**. Natural fibre rope does not have a permanent elastic limit. The life of a rope depends on the amount it is used under strain, because the fibres tend to slip a small amount under each load in spite of the twist given during manufacture. NFC should not be stowed away while it is wet; if this is unavoidable the rope must be brought out and dried at the first opportunity. Although any rope in good condition can be confidently expected to bear its full working load with ease, allowance for wear must be made in assessing the full strength of used rope, particularly when it has been subjected to hard conditions. Before estimating the strength of such a rope it should be examined for damage, chafe, rot and fatigue. Serious damage can be seen when the strands are distorted and bear unequal strain, or when the rope becomes opened. Rot can be detected by the smell of the rope and by opening out the strands and examining their inner surfaces. Should they be healthy and strong, all is well; if they are powdery, discoloured, and weak or can be plucked out, rot exists and the rope should be condemned. Rope may also be subject to chemical attack. Many rust-removal compounds are based on phosphoric acid which has a disastrous effect on natural fibre, and for this reason cordage should always be protected from contamination. If doubt exists as to the serviceability of a rope, the rope should be condemned.

03003. Construction, characteristics and details of supply of man-made fibre cordage

a. Prior to 1939, natural fibres were the only materials available for cordage manufacture. In 1939 a new man-made yarn known as **Nylon**, invented earlier, became available to the cordage industry. From the outset it was evident that this synthetic fibre possessed such remarkable qualities that a great advance had been made in the cordage industry. The technical name for Nylon is **Polyamide**. Both names are interchangeable but the latter is preferred in the Royal Navy to distinguish it from other synthetic materials, which were subsequently developed and are used for cordage manufacture. These latter materials are **Polyester, Polypropylene, Polyethylene**, and the three most recently developed, **Aramid**, a derivative of **polyamide, polyolefin**, a derivative of polypropylene, and **High Modulus Polyethylene** (HMPE). The various man-made fibre ropes have different characteristics which make them especially suitable for specific tasks. For example, polyamide has greater elasticity than polyester and is therefore very suitable for use as Shock Mitigation Strops (SMS) and boat anti-shock strops. Polyester, because of its relatively low elasticity and excellent weather and abrasion resistance, is suitable for berthing ropes and replenishment lines, and staple spun polypropylene is appropriate when light, floating, easily handled ropes such as towing hawser messengers and swimmer recovery lines are required. Polyethylene in its basic form is used principally in ships' diving operations as a swim-line, because it is orange in colour and therefore easily visible. It has similar characteristics to, but is weaker than, polypropylene. Aramid is at present used only for dressing lines as it is strong, non-inductive and has little elasticity. Cordage made from man-made fibre is naturally rot-proof and almost impervious to water. Unless specially treated, this type of rope, except Aramid and HMPE, will stretch far more than natural fibre cordage. This stretch ranges from 25-30% for film-fibre polypropylene to 45-50% for polyamide at breaking load. All man-made fibre ropes can be considered non-flammable in that they do not readily ignite or burn with a flame. In the molten state these materials will burn but only at a temperature approximately twice that of their melting point.

b. **Construction**. Polyamide, polyester, polypropylene and polyethylene all fall into the **polymer** group. Polyamide is produced from coal whereas the remainder are produced from oil. Most man-made fibres are made from either continuous filaments, or yarns of staple fibres, but polypropylene ropes can be manufactured from **multifilament, monofilament, staple or film-fibre**. Details are as follows:

(1) *Staple*. These fibres vary in length and the processing machine on which they are to be used determines this length. For rope-making the staple length varies between 150mm and 1300mm. Although weaker than continuous filament cordage of equivalent size and material, staple spun cordage is ideal in applications where a good grip is required.

(2) *Multifilament*. These yarns are composed of a number of very fine filaments of circular cross-section twisted together, each filament being continuous throughout the yarn length.

(3) *Monofilament*. These are usually circular in cross-section and are continuous throughout their length. Micrometer-type gauges are used to measure their diameter, which, for rope-making, can range from 0.125mm upwards.

(4) *Film-fibre*. Film-fibre is composed of **fibrils** produced by longitudinal splitting when an extruded tape or ribbon is twisted into a yarn.

(5) *3 Strand hawser-laid*. Hawser-laid man-made fibre ropes are manufactured in the same manner as natural fibre ropes, with three strands laid up and a right-hand twist (Fig 3-2). Each strand is composed of a sufficient number of uniform filaments of specified polymer to give a rope the required strength. A higher twist is imparted to the strands than to those of natural fibre, and the ropes are subjected to a form of heat treatment to stabilise the lay and thereby reduce the tendency of the strands to separate in service. It is important that the twist and balance of the lay should be undisturbed, especially when being spliced.

(6) *Plaited rope*. The rope is constructed of eight strands arranged in four pairs (Fig 3-3), two pairs of left-hand lay and two pairs of right-hand lay. This arrangement is known commercially as 'Squareline' but in naval use is commonly referred to as multi-plait. Its properties are very similar to hawser-laid except that it is a softer rope and does not kink.

Fig 3-3. Construction of plaited rope

(7) *Braided rope*. This rope, known commercially as core/cover rope, is constructed by crossing and re-crossing the yarns or strands in 'maypole' fashion such that each yarn or strand passes alternatively over and under one or more of the others to form a circular tubular sheath, which may contain a core. The use of braided cordage in the Royal Navy is limited to certain specific applications. Braided construction gives the following advantages over hawser laid ropes; good flexibility and easy handling when wet or dry, new or worn; non-rotating

and will not kink; more grip on capstans or warping drums because of the greater contact area. At present the only categories of braidline in use in the Fleet are a braided sheath around a core of either parallel strands, or a three-strand rope, or a multiplicity of three strand rope core members. All braided ropes fall into one of the following categories:

(a) A braided sheath around a braided core having a heart of parallel strands (Fig 3-4).

(b) A braided sheath around a hollow braided core (Fig 3-5).

(c) A braided sheath around a core of either parallel strands, or a three-strand rope, or a multiplicity of three strand rope core members. (Fig 3-6).

(d) A braided sheath with no core (hollow-centred rope).

(8) *Guardwire.* This type of rope is constructed of a load bearing core of densely packed parallel filaments, generally polyester, and encased within a tough durable polyethylene sheath. An example of this type of rope is parafil.

(9) *Aramid.* This type of rope has a braided polyester sheath around a three-stranded Aramid multifilament core. 95% of the strength of this rope comes from the Aramid core.

Note.   *Unlike other MMF cordage the Aramid core cannot be heat-sealed.*

Fig 3-4. A braided rope with braided core and heart of parallel strands

Fig 3-5. A braided rope with hollow braided core

Fig 3-6. A braided rope with a multiplicity of three strand rope core members

c. **Characteristics**

(1) *Polyamide.* This multifilament cordage is approximately two-and-a-half times as strong as manila of equivalent size. It stretches by almost half its length before parting and gives little, if any, warning that it is about to reach the limit of its stretch. Used within its safe working load it will stretch approximately 25% of its length and has excellent recovery. It does not float and it loses approximately 10% of its strength when wet. The melting point is 240-260°C and it is virtually unaffected by 80°C of frost. The working temperature range is -40°C to +100°C. Polyamide has a good weather and abrasion resistance and a high resistance to alkalis but low resistance to certain acids. Strong sulphuric acid, for example, will dissolve the fibres. The energy absorption qualities are excellent and are retained to a significant degree during repeat loading.

(2) *Polyester.* This multifilament cordage is nearly twice as strong as manila of equivalent size. It stretches approximately 36% before parting. Used within its safe working load it will stretch 14% of its length and has excellent recovery. The strength is virtually unchanged when wet, it does not float, the melting point is 240-260°C and it is virtually unaffected by 80°C of frost. The working temperature range is -40° to +100°C. Polyester has excellent weather and abrasion resistance and high resistance to acids but not alkalis.

(3) *Polypropylene.* This cordage is nearly twice as strong as manila of equivalent size and is the lightest in weight of the man-made fibres. It stretches up to 44% before parting. Used within its safe working load it will stretch 17% of its length. It retains its strength when wet and has a low water absorption. It will float indefinitely in water. The melting point is 160-170°C. The working temperature range is -40° to +80°C. Polypropylene has high resistance to acids and alkalis. Multifilament and monofilament polypropylene is not normally used for load-bearing ropes.

(4) *Polyethylene.* This cordage is about one-and-a-half times as strong as manila of equivalent size. It stretches 33% before parting, but used within its safe working load will stretch 14%. It floats, retains its strength when wet and has low water absorption. The melting point is 120-135°C. Because of its low softening temperature it is not recommended for load bearing application. High Modulus Polyethylene, a derivative of polyethylene, is size for size as strong as conventional steel wire rope.

(5) *Parallel polyester covered with polyethylene sheath (guardwire).* These ropes are light, thin and strong, require little maintenance and are resistant to creep and stretch. Tensile properties of parafil are close to those of steel wire rope, with the added advantage of electrical insulation and ultra-violet resistance. The dimensional and tensile properties are determined directly by the core yarn. As the polyethylene sheath is not a load-bearing component it follows that, provided the core yarn is undamaged, any damage to the sheath will not result in a loss of rope strength. These ropes are not affected by water, will not corrode or rot, and have an energy absorption two-and-a-half to three-and-a-half times that of steel wire rope of equivalent breaking load. These ropes are not suitable for winching or running through blocks because of the likelihood of sheath stripping, thereby exposing the core yarn to damage from abrasion. The smooth sheathing has excellent ice-shedding properties under severe conditions.

> ***Note.*** *Because of the requirement accurately to test new guardwires manufactured from parallel polyester covered with a polyethylene sheath, they can only be produced by shoreside authorities. Damaged or broken guardwires onboard ship must be temporarily replaced with a spliced 12 mm Polyester rope Patt No 0350/923-7143. Whenever possible the polyester rope should form the lower guardrail, if necessary by swapping guardrails.*

(6) *Aramid.* These ropes are nearly six times as strong as manila of equivalent size. They require no maintenance and are highly resistant to stretch. However, Aramid has poor ultraviolet and abrasion resistance so the Aramid core is sheathed for protection in a braided polyester cover. Aramid ropes are very susceptible to damage if run through block sheaves or around winches that have a diameter less than thirty times that of the Aramid core of the rope.

(7) *AmSteel-blue lime green.* This is a HPME 12 strand constructed rope. It is torque free, very flexible and easy to handle. This floating line has a similar elastic elongation to wire rope but is 1/7th of the weight. It can be easily spliced. It is used along with the shock mitigation strops and fairlead shackles as the emergency tow.

(8) *Turbo-75.* This is a braid on braid constructed HMPE line. It is used as the bow dome anchoring pennant as it retains its hard round shape during use and resists wear.

(9) *Parallay nylon.* This is a double braided constructed nylon rope. It has a high energy and shock mitigation properties and excellent wear resistance. It is used for shock mitigation in a ship's tow, braidline bridles and spring hawsers.

(10) *Quantum 12 (Q12).* This is a unique 12 strand construction Polyester Hybrid Class II HMPE Fibre Rope. This rope has a higher coefficient of friction (CoF) basically 'grip' than all other non-jacketed HPMT fibres. This rope can be easily spliced and works as well on winch-based mooring systems and standing fittings. Chafing pieces are to be fitted to all points of contact on all occasions that Q12 is in use. For general description see para 03004.

Fig 3-7. Quantum 12 HMPE fibre rope

> ***Note.*** *The above graphic depicts the rope as grey in colour for illustration purposes only.*

d. **Identification**. Like Natural Fibre Cordage, all Man-made Fibre cordage supplied to the Royal Navy comes with a certificate of conformity, on which are listed the date of manufacture, the BSEN Standard to which the rope has been manufactured, and the guaranteed minimum breaking strength of the rope when new.

To prevent confusion, particularly between polyamide and polyester ropes the external appearance of which is identical, identification yarns, where possible, are incorporated in man-made fibre ropes, in accordance with BSEN Standards; Table 3-2 gives the details. However, with certain smaller ropes it is not possible for the manufacturer to include an identification mark, and in the most recently developed type of ropes and in certain ropes that contain a mixture of fibre types, no common standard of identification exists; therefore the test certificate and certificate of conformity supplied with the rope should be regarded as the only reliable guide to the breaking strength of the rope.

Table 3-2. Identification yarns in man-made fibre cordage

Material	Identifying colour	Identification marking
Polyamide	Green	One green yarn in one strand
Polyester	Blue	One blue yarn in one strand
Polypropylene	Brown	One brown yarn in one strand or rope wholly coloured brown
Polyethylene	Orange	One orange yarn in one strand or rope wholly coloured orange

e. **Strength**. The rule-of-thumb method of calculating the breaking strain of man-made fibre rope is to divide the square of the diameter by a known factor. Table 3-3 gives the approximate strength of new cordage according to its diameter, d, in millimetres.

Table 3-3. Calculation for approximate breaking strength of man-made fibre cordage

Cordage	Formula for calculating breaking strength
High Modulus Polyethylene	$d^2/18$ tonnes
Aramid	$d^2/40$ tonnes
Polyamide (under 32 mm)	$d^2/50$ tonnes
Polyamide (32 mm and over)	$d^2/60$ tonnes
Polyester (under 32 mm)	$d^2/64$ tonnes
Polyester (32 mm and over)	$d^2/66$ tonnes

f. **Uses**. The principle service uses of man-made fibre ropes are as follows:

(1) *Polyamide*. Because of its elastic properties it is used for Anti-shock and Shock Mitigation Strops.

(2) *Polyester*. Because of its low stretch, high strength, and excellent weather and abrasion resistance, these ropes are used as replenishment lines, safety nets, signal halyards and small boat berthing lines.

(3) *Polypropylene*. Being a floating rope it is used in its staple form for messengers associated with towing hawsers. It is also used for boat ropes, ammunition resupply whips, lifelines, and as the recovery line in Swimmer of the Watch rigs.

(4) *Polyolefin*. Used for berthing lines on P2000s.

(5) *Polyethylene*. This cordage, also a floating line and easily visible, is used principally in ships' diving operations.

(6) *Aramid*. This cordage is at present used only for dressing lines.

(7) *Parallel polyester core with polyethylene sheath*. This cordage is used for standing rigging, principally guardrails.

(8) HMPE used extensively in the HPMT system (Quantum 12 and Amsteel Lime Green) for all Mooring and Emergency Tow lines. It provides floating lines with enhanced capability. These ropes are designed to perform numerous tasks while achieving excellent wear and abrasion properties and are un-jacketed to allow visual inspection and survey by the user.

g. **Details of man-made fibre cordage supplied to the Royal Navy**. Table 3-4 to Table 3-10 give details of most man-made fibre cordage available through Naval stores.

Table 3-4. Polyamide ropes and lines supplied to the Royal Navy

Type	Size	Naval stores No	Minimum breaking load	Supply denom-ination
Polyamide 3 strand	24 mm	0350/923-7129	12.0 tonnes	220 m
Polyamide 3 strand	28 mm	0350/923-7130	15.8 tonnes	220 m
Polyamide 3 strand	32 mm	0350/923-7131	20.0 tonnes	220 m
Polyamide 3 strand	36 mm	0350/923-7132	24.8 tonnes	220 m
Polyamide 3 strand	40 mm	0350/923-7133	30.0 tonnes	220 m
Polyamide 3 strand	44 mm	0350/923-7134	35.8 tonnes	220 m
Polyamide 3 strand	64 mm	0350/923-7137	72.0 tonnes	220 m
Polyamide braided	21 mm	0350/549-1143	8.70 tonnes	220 m
Polyamide braided	64 mm	0350/251-4431	90.0 tonnes	65 m*
Polyamide multi-plait	48 mm	0350/794-8239	42.0 tonnes	220 m
Polyamide multi-plait	64 mm	0350/543-0143	72.0 tonnes	220 m
Polyamide multi-plait	80 mm	0350/543-0149	110.0 tonnes	220 m
Polyamide cord gunline	1.5mm	0350/571-3024	64 kg	860 m

* Braidline Bridle

Table 3-5. Polyester ropes and lines supplied to the Royal Navy

Type	Size	Naval stores No	Minimum breaking load	Supply denom- ination
Polyester 3 strand	6 mm	0350/923-7140	0.56 tonnes	220 m
Polyester 3 strand	8 mm	0350/923-7142	1.02 tonnes	220 m
Polyester 3 strand	10 mm	0350/879/5226	1.60 tonnes	220 m
Polyester 3 strand	12 mm	0350/923-7143	2.27 tonnes	220 m
Polyester 3 strand	16 mm	0350/923-7144	4.1 tonnes	220 m
Polyester 3 strand	20 mm	0350/923-7145	6.3 tonnes	220 m
Polyester 8 plait blue	8 mm	0350/529-7387	0.39 tonnes	220 m
Polyester 16 plait blue	10 mm	0350/529-7388	2.25 tonnes	220 m
Polyester 16 plait blue	12 mm	0350/529-7389	3.20 tonnes	220 m
Polyester 16 plait blue	14 mm	0350/529-7390	4.40 tonnes	220 m
Polyester 16 plait blue	20 mm	0350/529-7391	8.10 tonnes	220 m
Polyester 8 plait red	6 mm	0350/529-7392	0.30 tonnes	220 m
Polyester 8 plait red	8 mm	0350/529-7393	0.39 tonnes	220 m
Polyester 16 plait red	10 mm	0350/529-7394	2.25 tonnes	220 m
Polyester 16 plait red	12 mm	0350/529-7395	3.20 tonnes	220 m
Polyester 16 plait red	14 mm	0350/529-7396	4.40 tonnes	220 m
Polyester 16 plait gold	12 mm	0350/529-7397	3.20 tonnes	220 m
Polyester 16 plait gold	14 mm	0350/529-7398	4.40 tonnes	220 m
Polyester 8 plait white	6 mm	0350/529-7399	0.47 tonnes	220 m
Polyester 8 plait white	8 mm	0350/529-7400	0.56 tonnes	220 m
Polyester 16 plait white	10 mm	0350/529-7401	2.25 tonnes	220 m
Polyester 16 plait white	12 mm	0350/529-7402	3.20 tonnes	220 m
Polyester 16 plait white	14 mm	0350/529-7404	4.40 tonnes	220 m
Polyester braided	5 mm	0350/120-8768	0.40 tonnes	220 m
Polyester braided	7 mm	0350/571-3167	0.70 tonnes	220 m
Polyester braided	9 mm	0350/120-8692	0.79 tonnes	220 m
Polyester cord	1.5 mm	0350/520-9610	0.14 tonnes	500 m

Table 3-6. Polypropylene ropes supplied to the Royal Navy

Type	Size	Naval stores No	Minimum breaking load	Supply denom- ination
Polypropylene 3 strand	24 mm	0350/375-2994	7.6 tonnes	220 m
Polypropylene 3 strand	8 mm	0350/529-9737	0.96 tonnes	220 m
Polypropylene 3 strand	10 mm	0350/447-1147	1.42 tonnes	220 m
Polypropylene 3 strand	12 mm	0350/525-6204	2.03 tonnes	220 m
Polypropylene 3 strand	16 mm	0350/571-3172	3.5 tonnes	220 m

Table 3-7. Polyethylene lines supplied to the Royal Navy

Type	Size	Naval stores No	Minimum breaking load	Supply denom- ination
Polyethylene H/L Orange	4 mm	0350/571/3169	0.20 tonnes	220 m
Polyethylene H/L Orange	8 mm	0350/543-0141	0.70 tonnes	220 m
Polyethylene H/L Orange	10 mm	0350/571-3171	1.08 tonnes	220 m

Table 3-8. Polyester/polypropylene blend multiplait rope supplied to the Royal Navy

Type	Size	Naval stores No	Minimum breaking load	Supply denom- ination
Polyester/polypropylene blend	24 mm	0350/605-7959	9.92 tonnes	220 m
	28 mm	0350/807-3997	13.3 tonnes	220 m
	32 mm	0350/168-9190	17.1 tonnes	220 m
	36 mm	0350/810-3975	21.0 tonnes	220 m
	40 mm	0350/396-0753	26.1 tonnes	220 m
	44 mm	0350/244-7033	31.0 tonnes	220 m
	48 mm	0350/083-3184	36.5 tonnes	220 m
	64 mm	0350/513-8184	63.1 tonnes	220 m

Table 3-9. Aramid (Kevlar) ropes supplied to the Royal Navy

Type	Size	Naval Stores No	Minimum Breaking Load	Supply Denomination
Aramid (Kevlar)	10 mm	0350/801-0503	2.5 tonnes	500 m

Table 3-10. Guardwire ropes supplied to the Royal Navy

Type	Size	Naval stores No	Minimum breaking load	Supply denomination
Guardwire rope	13.5 mm	0350/635-1268	3.5 tonnes	300 m

h. **Care and maintenance of man-made fibre rope**. The following advice is given for the care and maintenance of man-made fibre ropes.

(1) *Exposure to sunlight*. Although earlier experience of deterioration through exposure to sunlight, especially with polypropylene, has been mainly overcome by the use of inhibitors in the manufacturing process, man-made fibre ropes should not be exposed unnecessarily to sunlight.

(2) *Exposure to chemicals.* Avoid contamination by chemicals or fumes. Ropes that are inadvertently contaminated must be washed in cold running water.

(3) *Handling.* Do not drag ropes over sharp or rough edges. Avoid penetration of abrading particles.

(4) *Stowage.* Man-made fibre ropes are resistant to bacteriological attack, so they can be stowed for long periods without deterioration and may be stowed wet; however, when coiled, man-made fibre ropes should be stowed in bins or on raised boards in such a way as to allow free circulation of air beneath as well as around the rope. Ropes that are to be stowed on reels must be allowed up to six hours to recover their normal length before stowing if they have been under tension.

(5) *Wear.* The presence of a fibre nap or whiskering fuzz distributed uniformly on strand surfaces is an indication of normal wear. Some disarrangement or breaking of the outside fibre is normally unavoidable, and, if it is not excessive, harmless.

(6) *Crowsfooting.* Localised distortion of a strand by a back twist is known as 'crowsfooting' or 'cockling'. It occurs when the tension in a hawser laid rope is suddenly released and the balance of the twist does not recover in time, or when kinks are forced out of the line by pulling on the rope. The distortion is often so great that the strand is unable to return to its original lay thereby weakening the rope. Any section of rope with two or more strands 'cockled' must be cut out and the rope can either be rejoined with a short splice in natural fibre rope or a cut splice in man-made fibre rope or both parts of the rope can be made up to two shorter ropes for general use.

(7) *Chafing.* Chafing appears as a longitudinal line of heavy wear along the rope's surface and can be recognised by the tufted appearance of the rope. Avoid unnecessary chafing by protecting the parts concerned.

(8) *Stretching.* The resistance of man-made fibre rope to repeated loading is good, but localised temporary elongation may occur. Measurement of the distance between regularly spaced indelible marks will indicate temporary elongation, and a reduction in diameter may be observed after loading.

(9) *Rust.* Rope that has been in contact with corroding steel shows signs of yellow or brownish black. Stains that can be removed with soapy water have no adverse effect and those that persist only detract from the rope's appearance.

(10) *Heat.* Ropes must not be stowed where there is excessive heat.

(11) *Icing.* Although man-made fire ropes are virtually unaffected by very low temperatures (-80ºC for polyamide and polyester) when a rope is iced it must be thawed at a **moderate** temperature before stowing.

(12) *Oil and grease.* Oil and grease may be removed with a mild solution of soap and water, followed by thorough rinsing in fresh water; strong detergent should not be used.

03004. High performance mooring and towing equipment (HPMT)

a. **Introduction.** HPMT is introduced to address the manpower intensive Seamanship evolutions carried out onboard HM Ships. With Platforms, both legacy and future concept ships, introducing leaner manning HPMT has become fundamental in the overall operational effectiveness and safety of both platform and personnel. HPMT works by introducing smaller size ropes which have replaced all Steel Wire Ropes (SWR's) and large, heavy and often cumbersome synthetic ropes. These ropes are 'multi-tasked' to perform a range of evolutions, thereby reducing the number of ropes carried by each platform. HPMT reduces the manpower required for seamanship evolutions, for example: a typical towing evolution reduces the manpower requirement from 40+ personnel to 5-7 personnel on a legacy platforms. This manpower reduction includes for the preparing, rigging, towing, recovery and stowage. HPMT also reduces the 'down-time' for this evolution from approximately 2-3 hours to 30 minutes and elastic elongation stowage of the main tow line is reduced from 24 hours to 30 minutes.

b. **HMPE Rope.** HPMT relies on an innovative and unique HMPE fibre rope at its core. This rope, Quantum-12 (Q-12) forms the 'backbone' to the fleet's ropes. Q-12 is the only floating HMPE line in the world that is specifically designed to increase the 'grip', increase the heat resistance and can be surged or rendered on a multitude of static marine fittings (bollards, capstans, bitts etc.) Q-12 is also suitable for winch-based operations.

c. **Towing evolutions.** HPMT also employs a standard 12 strand HMPE rope, Task Specific for towing evolutions. This HMPE rope, AmSteel-Lime (ASL), is stronger than Q-12, size for size. ASL is not rendered on static fittings.

d. **Shock mitigation strop (SMS).** The third rope used extensively within HPMT is a super strong 2 in 1 Parallay Nylon. This is used for shock absorption for Towing, Ship-to-Buoy and where exposed berths/severe weather berthing is encountered.

e. **Bow dome anchoring pendants.** Finally, the last rope within HPMT is again, a task specific rope designed to replace steel wire rope – bow dome anchoring pendants. This line, Turbo-75 (T-75), is specially made and coated for each platform class that are bow-domed. This line is a triple braided, 100% HMPE rope that retains a firm cross-section even under load. This rope replaces the last running rigging steel wire rope onboard HM Ships. This rope has the hardest task of all due to its vulnerability to being 'trapped' and 'worked' under the ships cable whilst bow-dome anchoring.

f. **Securing to buoy strop.** A Quantum 12 pendant fitted with heavy duty chafe protection used in conjunction with HPMT bridles. These strops remove the requirement for heavy manpower, intensive securing to buoy shackles and they attach directly from the buoy's reducing links to the SMS. Securing to buoy shackles are retained onboard for use with chain cable as and when required.

g. **Rope stopper.** This is included in the HPMT system as the Tech 12 rope stopper and is used with HPMT ropes during evolutions as and when required.

h. **Legacy ropes.** These four ropes replace a minimum of eight legacy ropes and, are generally half the diameter in size, a fifth to a seventh of the weight and most importantly, are rated for compatibility with a ship's existing fittings. For instance, a Capital Ship Towing outfit now becomes approximately the same in weight than that of an MCMV's legacy Towing outfit.

Note. *Chafing pieces are fitted to all points of contact on all occasions of use of the above equipment.*

i.   **Training.** Periodic onboard training is to continue to maintain seamanship capabilities. Duty SRs and OODs are to be fully briefed on the ships berthing/mooring arrangements. This training should highlight the importance of line tending during periods alongside and the use of foul weather pendants in the mooring plan.

j.   Each HPMT Class Outfit has an allowance which has been pre-determined to offer platforms full operational capability. Each item has been NATO codified and is a demand controlled issue. Some items are multi-tasked and some are task-specific.

k.   **Ship's outfit.** A full listing of RN and RFA ship's outfit of HPMT is at Annex 3D.

l.   HPMT has flexibility for certain platforms to inter-change between categories due to strength of existing fittings or, for operational requirements.

m.   HPMT can be incorporated into all future concept ships and submarines from the original design concept, through the build programme and through the whole life of the ship.

03005. Twines, lines and spunyarn

a.   **Twines** consist of a number of yarns twisted or laid to produce a balanced twisted structure of continuous length. Chalk line, used for marking material that is to be cut or stitched, is made from cotton. Seaming twine is made from flax and is used for whippings and sewing canvas gear; roping twine is also made from flax but is sturdier than seaming twine, and is used for whippings and sewing canvas and other heavy cloths where seaming twine is insufficiently robust.

b.   **Spunyarn** consists of a number of yarns twisted (spun) together. Originally it was made from any type of vegetable fibre or from yarns unlaid from any kind of old natural fibre rope; nowadays only three and six strand sisal spunyarn is available. It is used for servings, seizings, stops or any small work, and it has no specific strength.

c.   Details of twines, lines, and spunyarn supplied to the Royal Navy are in Table 3-11.

Table 3-11. Twines lines and spunyarn supplied to the Royal Navy

Type and Size	Naval stores No	Minimum breaking load	Supply denomination
Chalk line (cotton)	0350/571-3260	N/A	250gm Cops
Flax seaming twine	0350/571-3267	N/A	250gm Cops
Flax seaming twine	0350/571-3269	N/A	250gm Cops
Flax roping twine	0350/571-3270	N/A	250gm Cops
Sisal spunyarn 3 strand	0350/722-2646	N/A	4kg Spools
Sisal spunyarn 6 strand	0350/722-2649	N/A	4kg Spools

03006. Junk and rounding
Junk consists of condemned cordage of 32 mm size and above; Rounding is condemned cordage under 32 mm in size. Junk and Rounding are used for lashings and other securing where the use of good rope is not necessary.

03007. Construction, characteristics and details of supply of steel wire rope (SWR)

a. Improvements in the design and characteristics of man-made fibre cordage and slings, and the need in ships to reduce topweight and limit noise, has resulted in a reduction in recent years in the use of SWR throughout the fleet. However, steel wire rope still has various applications aboard warships.

b. **Construction**

(1) A wire rope is constructed of a number of small wires, which extend continuously throughout the entire length; these wires are laid up into strands, and the strands themselves are laid up to form the rope. With the exception of certain special types described later, all wire rope used at sea is preformed, has a galvanised finish, and consists of six strands. The wires forming a strand are laid up left-handed round a fibre or wire core and the strands forming the rope are laid up right-handed round a fibre main core.

c. **Uses**

(1) *Steel wire rope, 7X7 and 7X19 construction.* Suitable for standing rigging such as shrouds or guys, where it is not required to be as flexible as the wire rope used for running rigging. Its strands are made up of a small number of large-gauge wires wound round a wire core and the strands themselves are made up around a main core of similar construction to the strands.

(2) *Steel wire rope, 6X12 construction.* Suitable for lashings, or temporary guardrails on a ship in refit or Docking Period (DP). To make it flexible necessitates sacrificing a certain proportion of its strength and each strand consists of a certain number of medium-gauge wires wound round a large fibre core, the strands themselves being made up around a fibre main core.

(3) *Steel wirer, 6X19, 6X24, 6X26, 6X36 and 6X41 construction.* This range of ropes has greater strength and flexibility, and is used for running rigging, mooring, slinging, and towing in certain auxiliary craft. The strands are constructed of a number of small-gauge wires made up around a fibre core.

d. **Details of conventional steel wire rope supplied to the Royal Navy.** Details of conventional steel wire rope (SWR) supplied to the Royal Navy are given in Table 3-12 and Table 3-13.

Table 3-12. Details of conventional SWR 6X12 to 6X36 available through Naval stores

Construction	Size	Naval stores No.	Minimum breaking load	Supply denomination
6X12	8 mm	0235/523-8624	1.91 tonnes	250 metres(m)*
6X12	12 mm	0235/523-8625	4.28 tonnes	250 m*
6X12	16 mm	0235/523-8626	7.62 tonnes	250 m*
6X19	3 mm	0235/523-8627	0.49 tonnes	200 m*
6X19	4 mm	0235/523-8628	0.87 tonnes	200 m*
6X19	5 mm	0235/523-8629	1.36 tonnes	200 m*
6X19	6 mm	0235/523-8630	1.96 tonnes	450 m*
6X19	8 mm	0235/523-8631	3.75 tonnes	550 m*
6X24	12 mm	0235/523-8633	5.76 tonnes	550 m*
6X24	14 mm	0235/523-8634	7.83 tonnes	550 m*
6X24	16 mm	0235/523-8635	10.2 tonnes	550 m*
6x24	18 mm	0235/523-8636	13.0 tonnes	550 m*
6X24	21 mm	0235/523-8637	17.6 tonnes	550 m*
6X24	22 mm	0235/523-8638	19.4 tonnes	550 m*
6X24	24 mm	0235/523-8639	23.0 tonnes	660 m*
6X24	28 mm	0235/523-8640	31.3 tonnes	660 m*
6X24	32 mm	0235/523-8641	40.9 tonnes	660 m*
6X24	36 mm	0235/523-8642	51.8 tonnes	280 m*
6X26	10 mm	0235/523-8643	5.85 tonnes	550 m*
6X26	12 mm	0235/523-8644	8.41 tonnes	550 m*
6X36	14 mm	0235/523-8645	11.4 tonnes	550 m*
6X36	16 mm	0235/523-8646	15.0 tonnes	550 m*
6X36	16 mm	0235/523-8647	15.0 tonnes	1100 m*
6X36	18 mm	0235/523-8648	18.9 tonnes	550 m*
6X36	20 mm	0235/523-8649	23.4 tonnes	550 m*
6X36	22 mm	0235/523-7095	28.2 tonnes	310 m*
6X36	24 mm	0235/523-8650	33.7 tonnes	280 m*
6X36	26 mm	0235/537-0235	39.6 tonnes	280 m*
6X36	28 mm	0235/523-8651	45.9 tonnes	280 m*

* Refers to length of full coil. Ropes can be demanded to length required in metres

Table 3-13. Details of conventional SWR 6X41 to 7X19 available through naval stores

Construction	Size	Naval stores No.	Minimum breaking load	Supply denomination
6X41	32 mm	0235/523-8652	59.8 tonnes	280 metres (m)*
6X41	32 mm	0235/523-8653	59.8 tonnes	430 m*
6X41	32 mm	0235/523-8654	59.8 tonnes	920 m*
6X41	32 mm	0235/523-8655	59.8 tonnes	1010 m*
6X41	36 mm	0235/523-8656	75.8 tonnes	280 m*
6X41	36 mm	0235/523-8657	75.8 tonnes	450 m*
6X41	36 mm	0235/523-8658	75.8 tonnes	550 m*
6X41	36 mm	0235/523-8659	75.8 tonnes	1010 m*
6X41	40 mm	0235/523-8660	93.5 tonnes	280 m*
6X41	40 mm	0235/523-8661	93.5 tonnes	450 m*
6X41	40 mm	0235/523-8662	93.5 tonnes	650 m*
6X41	44 mm	0235/523-8663	113.0 tonnes	280 m*
6X41	48 mm	0235/523-8664	135.0 tonnes	280 m*
6X41	52 mm	0235/523-8665	158.0 tonnes	280 m*
7X7	5 mm	0235/523-8616	1.72 tonnes	350 m*
7X7	7 mm	0235/523-8617	3.38 tonnes	350 m*
7X7	12 mm	0235/523-8618	7.92 tonnes	350 m*
7X7	16 mm	0235/523-8619	14.2 tonnes	350 m*
7X7	20 mm	0235/523-8620	22.0 tonnes	350 m*
7X7	24 mm	0235/523-8621	31.8 tonnes	350 m*
7X7	28 mm	0235/523-8622	43.3 tonnes	250 m*
7X19	32 mm	0235/523-8623	53.0 tonnes	250 m*

* Refers to length of full coil. Ropes can be demanded to length required in metres.

e.   **Special types of steel wire rope.**   In addition to conventional SWR, there are certain special types of wire ropes that are supplied to the fleet. They are:

(1)   *Non-rotating wire.* This type of wire rope (Fig 3-8) has its strands laid up in the same direction as that in which their constituent wires are twisted. All the wires and strands are small, and the inner strands are arranged so that the tendency of the rope to rotate under load is reduced to a minimum. It is very flexible and is particularly suitable as a whip for cranes and single point davits, where strength and non-unlaying action are essential. The wire requires very careful handling before and during installation. It has no tendency to twist either way but it is so pliable that turns either way can be imparted. When making fast the plain end to the side of the drum or crane structure, ensure that the entire cross-section of the rope is firmly secured. At present, non-rotating wire rope whips are supplied as made-up items, details of which can be found in the ship's Rigging Warrant/LARR or spares documentation on board.

Fig 3-8. Non-rotating wire rope

(2) *Malleable Stainless Steel Wire.* This wire, Pattern No 0258-361-7273, is 1mm in diameter and supplied in 2 kilogram coils approximately 320 metres in length. It is used for mousing stainless steel shackles and slips.

03008. Handling of natural and man-made fibre cordage

a. **Elementary rules**. The lessons which a seaman must learn before handling a rope are explained below:

(1) *The seaman's pocketknife.* The seaman's pocketknife is for issue to the Seaman Specialists and other personnel that carry out seamanship evolutions in their normal course of duty. It is supplied with a lanyard to enable the knife to be attached to a belt or belt loop and placed in the side or back pocket. The pocketknife is a tool and not a weapon and the edge of the blade should be sharpened like a chisel to avoid wearing away the thickness and strength of the blade, and the hinge should be kept lightly oiled.

(2) All hands working POS are to wear rigging sets (NSN F1-5180-433/4293) with belt. Knives are to be sharp at all times.

(3) *Safety of tools.* Whenever seaman work aloft, or over the side, they must secure whatever tools they may be using with a lanyard secured to a part of the rigging or passed round their body. This is a common-sense precaution for avoiding possible injury to personnel working below or loss of the tools over the side.

(4) When working ropes during seamanship evolutions a sharp seaman's knife is to be available to cut away ropes in an emergency.

(5) *Rope ends.* Before a rope is cut a whipping should be applied either side of the point at which the cut is to be made to prevent the rope unlaying. The different methods of whipping are described later in this chapter.

(6) *Coiling down ropes.* A heaving-line, or any line or rope (with the exception of HPMT ropes), which is being hauled in, should be coiled either in the hand or on the deck as it is hauled inboard. This is an elementary precaution to ensure that the line or rope is immediately ready for further use.

(7) Class 2 ropes are to be faked and not coiled.

b. **Special precautions when handling man-made fibre cordage**. Although the rules for handling natural fibre cordage and man-made fibre cordage are generally similar, no standard exists for recoil properties. Stretch, construction, length and a host of other properties/scenarios will have an impact on the recoil of any rope. The lower the stretch, the lower the recoil and the lower the melting point, the lower the recoil. The amount of twist within each yarn within each strand and the amount of twist within each strand within the fibre rope would also affect snap back/recoil and minimum break load of the rope. Therefore, the properties and characteristics of man-made fibre necessitate greater care in its handling. Many of the advantages of using man-made fibre ropes can become serious liabilities if the seaman is not familiar with certain characteristics of these ropes. When a man-made fibre rope parts, it immediately tends to regain its original length. Polyamide when stretched over 40% is liable to part **suddenly without audible warning** and it then whips back along the line of tension and can kill or seriously injure anyone in its path. The following rules must be observed when handling man-made fibre ropes:

(1)   Personnel backing-up a man-made fibre rope under tension on a capstan drum or any other holding surface must stand well back and out of the line of recoil of the rope. Fig 3-9 shows the ideal position of personnel backing-up (B) a man-made fibre rope under tension (A), and the approximate angle of the Snap Back Zone (C), which is the ideal with respect to the line of recoil.

Fig 3-9. Backing-up a man-made fibre rope under tension

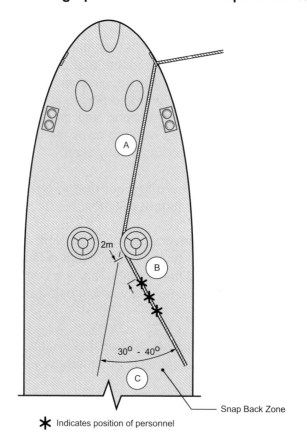

✳ Indicates position of personnel

(2)   Theoretically HMPE fibre ropes will have a lower snap back velocity compared to nylon fibre ropes of the same strength. Due to the low elongation properties of HMPE fibre based ropes, a much smaller amount of energy is stored in the rope at break point, which results in a less violent snap back. Also at break point HMPE fibres melt which removes energy from the system and reduces the amount of energy that is released through the snap back. In general all 12-strand and, to a lesser extent, 8-strand HMPE based ropes will have a similar snap back behaviour. However, please note that recoil danger still exists no matter what rope is used so proper training and caution is essential.

(3)   When a man-made fibre rope is turned up on any holding surface, and is in tension, a certain amount of heat is generated by friction between the rope and the holding surface. Should this heat approach the melting point of the fibres of the rope, the outer fibre will melt and create a lubricant, whereupon the rope in tension **may surge violently**. It is essential therefore those personnel backing-up a man-made fibre rope in tension on a capstan drum, bollards or any holding surface must stand well back. The minimum distance between the first person backing-up the rope in tension and the holding surface should be two metres (Fig 3-13). Should the rope surge violently, this distance of two metres means that the first person backing-up will have some warning before being drawn dangerously close to the holding surface.

(4)   SMSs that have been subject to local permanent elongation should be given time to recover to achieve its natural length if it is to be reeled up.

(5)   Do not pass man-made fibre and steel wire ropes through the same fairlead. The stretch is incompatible and the resultant chafing of the man-made fibre will seriously weaken it.

(6)   Users should be aware that wherever possible twists in lines are to be removed before they come under load as they greatly reduce the MBL. Twists should also be removed when stowing ropes.

c.   **Handling all cordage.** From the precautions listed above for the safe handling of man-made fibre cordage, the following points should always be practised when handling any ropes or lines:

(1)   Avoid bad leads and sharp edges. Ensure thimbles or such fittings do not chafe or cut a rope.

(2)   As a general rule rope should be veered rather than surged on a capstan or winch drum because surging induces friction and damages the surface of the rope. However, surging the slip rope during the final stages of a replenishment is accepted practice as it enables the receiving ship to readily match the speed at which the delivering ship is recovering the replenishment rig. **A rope should never be surged on a capstan or drum which is rotating in the same direction (turning to veer).** This is a dangerous practice.

(3)   A minimum of five turns are to be used when hawsers are being hove in on capstans or drum ends.

(4)   If surging around bollards is necessary, it should be done before the strain on the rope is heavy. Great care must be taken when easing out a rope around bollards if it is heavily loaded.

03009. Preparing natural fibre and man-made fibre ropes for use

a.   **Coiling and uncoiling.** A Class 1 and NFC rope laid out straight will have no tendency to twist or turn either way, whether its lay is left- or right-handed, and from this position it can be stowed on a reel or coiled down. When stowed on a reel, or hauled off a reel, a rope will not develop any twists or turns in its length. When coiling down a rope however, the part of the rope remaining uncoiled will be given one twist or turn as each loop in the coil is formed. When coiling down a rope the end should be kept free to allow the uncoiled length to rotate and thus keep it free from becoming snarled up with kinks or turns. Similarly, a rope which is run off a coil will acquire a twist or turn for every loop in the coil, but if the end is kept free the rope will usually free itself of these turns when hauled out straight. One method of avoiding these turns, should the end of the rope not be free, is to turn the coil round while coiling down the rope, thus turning the coil into a reel. Another method, as when coiling direct from a reel, is to allow as long a length as possible between reel and coil; this length will absorb the turns until the end of the rope is free from the reel, and so can be freed of its turns. Similarly, when coiling down a rope which is led through a block, the coil should not be made too near the block; otherwise a slight check may cause a kink to develop in the rope as it is running through and thus choke the luff (Fig 3-10).

b.   **Coiling down** (Fig 3-10). Cordage is very resilient and will absorb a number of turns in its length without becoming snarled if the length is sufficient and the turns correspond with the lay of the rope; if the turns are against the lay, however, it will quickly become snarled. For this reason, rope of right-hand lay is always coiled down right handed, and rope of left-hand lay is always coiled down left-handed.

Fig 3-10. Mistakes in coiling down

c.   **To coil a rope for running** (Fig 3-11). Lay the rope as straight as possible along the deck; begin coiling it down close to where the standing part is made fast, and lay each loop flat upon the other below it until the bare end is reached. The size of the loops should be as large as stowage space permits. The running part is now underneath the coil, so turn the coil over and the rope should then run out freely when required. Remember that the running part or end part should always be on top of any coil.

Fig 3-11. To coil a rope for running

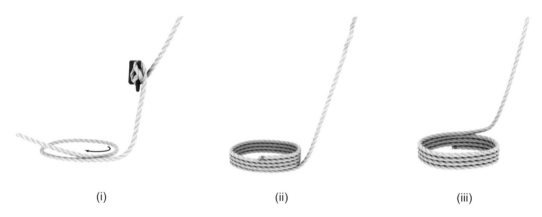

(i)   (ii)   (iii)

d. **To coil a small line in the hand** (Fig 3-12). When coiling in the right hand the rope should be held with the right thumb pointing towards the end; and when coiling in the left hand the thumb should point towards the bight. The coil will then form correctly.

Fig 3-12. Coiling a line

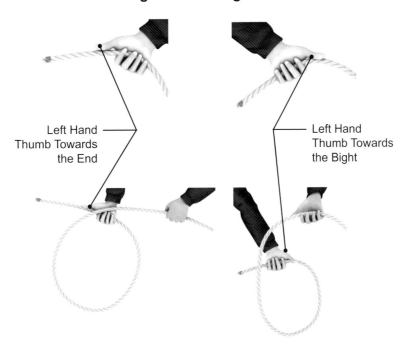

Left Hand
Thumb Towards
the End

Left Hand
Thumb Towards
the Bight

e. **To thoroughfoot a rope**. This is the most effective way of taking a large number of turns out of a rope. First determine whether the turns to be removed are left- or right-handed. Then, to remove left-hand turns, coil down left-handed, dip the end through the coil and haul the coil out straight. To remove right-hand turns, coil down right-handed, dip the end through the coil and haul the coil out straight. If the bight of the rope is badly snarled, thoroughfoot the end for only a few metres at a time, repeating this operation as often as necessary. Thoroughfooting also describes the method of joining two ropes by their soft eyes (Fig 3-13). The eye of rope A is passed through the eye of rope B, and the bight of B is then hauled through the eye of A, thus joining the ropes by their eyes. This method is not used for joining two ropes temporarily, because it may take some time to unhitch them.

Fig 3-13. Thoroughfooting

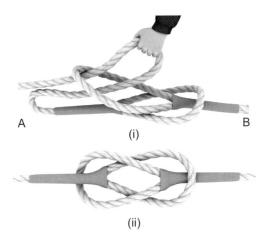

A   B
(i)

(ii)

f.   **To fake down a rope** (Fig 3-14). A rope that may have to be paid out quickly should be faked down in as long fakes as space allows. When faked, a rope does not acquire as many turns as when coiled and it will, therefore, run out with less chance of becoming snarled. Care should be taken that each bight at the end of a fake is laid under that immediately preceding it to ensure a clear run. All Class II ropes are to be faked.

Fig 3-14. Faking down a rope

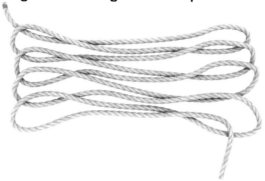

g.   **To cheese down a rope** (Fig 3-15). When a neat stow is required for a short end of rope, it may be cheesed down. This method should never be used when the rope will be required to render quickly through a block.

Fig 3-15. Cheesing down a rope

| The Coil | Beginning to Cheese | Cheese Complete |

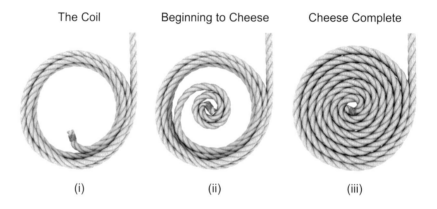

(i)   (ii)   (iii)

h.   **Belaying.** When a rope will have to be cast off while still under strain it cannot be secured with a bend or a hitch, except perhaps a slipping one. It is therefore belayed to a fitting made for the purpose, such as a cleat, staghorn or bollard. The action of belaying consists of taking sufficient turns round the fitting to hold the rope by friction when it takes the strain. Generally speaking, four complete turns should be sufficient, but the number of turns may have to be increased according to the degree of friction existing between rope and fitting. A wet and slippery rope or bollard, or a smooth cleat or staghorn and a well-worn rope may require extra turns.

i.   **To belay a rope to a cleat or staghorn**. Take initial turns as shown in Fig 3-16, then continue with figure-of-eight turns round the horns of the cleat or staghorn as many times as required. It will be seen that when the figure-of-eight turns are removed the rope is ready to be checked under control. A rope belayed to a cleat or a staghorn must be ready for casting off at a moment's notice; therefore the turns should not be completed with a half hitch, because this may jam them. Cleats are not suitable for belaying wire rope.

Fig 3-16. Belaying a rope to a cleat or staghorn

j.   **To hang a coil on a belaying pin or cleat.** (Fig 3-17 and Fig 3-18). Whenever possible a coil of rope should be hung up clear of the deck so as to keep the deck clear and the rope dry.

Fig 3-17. Hanging a small coil on a belaying pin

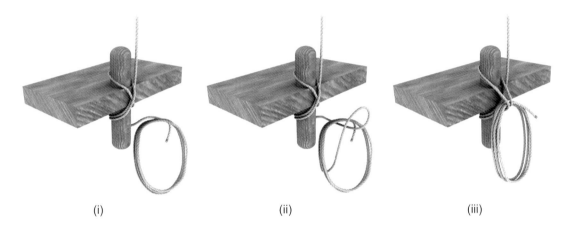

(i)   (ii)   (iii)

Fig 3-18. Hanging a large coil on a cleat

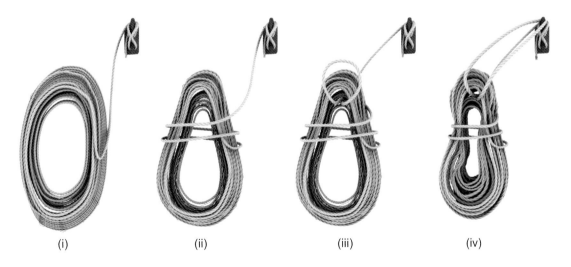

(i)   (ii)   (iii)   (iv)

k.   **Making and throwing a heaving line** (Fig 3-19).

(1)   As its name implies, a heaving line is a light flexible line that can be thrown. It is used as a messenger to pass hawsers from ship to shore, or vice versa. Braidline of 8 mm is very flexible and makes excellent heaving lines, although any similar size cordage can be used. A heaving line consists of approximately 30 metres of 8 mm cordage. One end should be whipped and the other end weighted with a monkey's fist (Fig 3-68), a small sandbag or a heaving line knot.

WARNING

HEAVING LINES MUST NOT BE WEIGHTED BY INSERTING A STEEL NUT OR LEAD WEIGHT INTO THE MONKEY'S FIST. NEITHER SHOULD THE MONKEY'S FIST BE PAINTED.

---

(2)   To prepare a heaving line for throwing, it should be wetted and between 22 and 24 metres should be coiled carefully in the non-throwing hand, using small coils. One third of the line is taken in the throwing hand; the line is then thrown with the throwing arm straight, and it must be allowed to run out freely from the coil in the non-throwing hand. The most frequent cause of bad casts is failure to have this coil properly clear for running. There is more than one method of heaving a line and most good throwers have their own variations. Some take rather less than half the coil in the throwing hand and throw both halves together, letting go with the throwing hand before the non-throwing hand. This method is very effective but harder to learn. Before heaving a line the standing end must be anchored between the thumb and index finger of the non-throwing hand. Never secure the standing end to the wrist or any other part of the body; the turning propellers make this a dangerous practice. As soon as the heaving line has been caught, the standing end or a bight of the line should be bent with a bowline to the eye of the hawser and not before. Every effort should be made to keep the line out of the water.

Fig 3-19. Throwing a heaving line

(i)   (ii)

I.   **Handling new cordage**

(1)   *Opening a new coil (Fig 3-20).*   A length of rope is supplied to a ship in a compact, machine-wound coil, bound with yarns or strands. To open up a new coil of rope of less than 48 mm diameter, a seaman should roll it over until the outside end of the rope is at the top and pointing directly at him. The user should then turn the coil over towards their left and lay it flat on its side. The lashings are now cut and the inner end of the rope is pulled out from the centre (Fig 3-20(i)). The rope will then leave the coil correctly and can then be coiled down. With rope of 48 mm diameter or larger, the twisting involved in the preceding method is not acceptable and the coil must be unreeled in the opposite way to that in which it was made up. The coil should be placed on a turntable, or slung so that it can be revolved (Fig 3-20(ii)). Cut the lashings and haul the rope off from the outside. If this method is not possible, stand the coil on its end, and lap the rope off the top of the coil, turn by turn. As each turn is removed, revolve the end of the rope to take out twists.

(2)   *Cutting off a length of rope from a new coil.*   The required amount of rope is hauled from the coil, as previously described, and then the rope is whipped or taped at each side of the position at which it is to be cut. Whenever a length of rope is cut off a coil, a label, on which should be clearly stated either the length cut off or the length remaining should be attached to the coil.

Fig 3-20. Opening a new coil

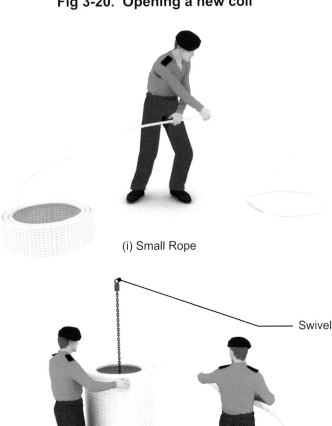

(i) Small Rope

Swivel

(ii) Large Rope

m. **Storage of cordage.** Coils of new rope should be stowed clear of the deck, in a cool, well-ventilated, dry place, to allow the air to circulate freely around them. Used rope should be hung in loose coils if this is practicable. No cordage should be stowed in contact with bare steelwork. If cordage has to be stowed in the open it should be protected from sunlight because man-made fibres are susceptible to deterioration caused by the sun's rays.

03010. Handling wire rope

a. **Care and maintenance of steel wire rope**. Wire ropes have a lubricant incorporated during manufacture. This serves a dual purpose; it provides corrosion protection and also minimises internal friction. The protection provided by this manufacturing lubricant is normally adequate to prevent deterioration due to corrosion during the early part of a rope's life. However, the lubricant applied during manufacture must be supplemented by lubrication in service. This lubrication is termed the 'dressing'. The kind of dressing used and the frequency of application vary with the type of rope and its usage.

b. **Inspecting steel wire rope**. Steel wires ropes carried or fitted in HM ships must be inspected periodically in accordance with the MMS system. When inspecting, the indications described below should be sought:

(1) *Distortion of strands*. This is the result of damage by kinking, crushing, serious crippling round a bad nip, or other mistreatment. If likely to cause the strands to bear unequal stresses, they must be considered as reducing the strength of the rope by 30%; and should they be sufficiently serious to cause the heart to protrude, the rope must be discarded. A crushed rope may be restored to some extent by the careful use of a mallet.

(2) *Flattening of some of the outer wires by abrasion*. These flats are easily seen because the abrasion gives the flattened wires a bright and polished appearance, but they do not affect the strength of the rope unless they are very pronounced. Flats, which extend to three-quarters of the diameter of the wires, will reduce their cross-sections – and therefore their individual strengths – by 10%, and as only a limited number of wires will be affected the loss in strength of the whole rope will be very small. (These flats must not be confused with flattening of the whole rope, which indicates distortion of the strands and is therefore much more serious).

(3) *Broken wires*. These are usually the result of fatigue and wear, and mostly occur in crane wires. It is generally accepted that a wire rope is coming to the end of its useful life when one wire of any strand breaks. To deal with a broken wire, grip the broken end with a pair of pliers and bend the wire backwards and forwards until the wire breaks inside the rope between the strands, where it can do no harm. A rope should be discarded if more than 5% of its wires are broken in a length equal to ten times the diameter of the rope; for example a 24 mm diameter, 6 X 24 wire rope should be discarded if seven broken wires are found in a length of 240 mm. Because of the danger to handlers, berthing wires should be discarded if any broken wires are discovered.

(4) *Corrosion*. Wire rope can be corroded by:

(a) The action of damp on the wires from which the galvanising has worn off; if this occurs to the inner wires first it causes rust to fall out of the rope and is therefore easily detected.

(b) The action of fumes and funnel gases, which attack the outside wires, the effect then becomes visible on inspection.

(c) Contact with acid, which soaks into the heart and attacks the inside wires; this is not necessarily noticeable on the outside of the rope, and can be the cause of parting without warning.

(5) Lack of lubrication is a frequent cause of corrosion. When a wire rope is under tension it stretches and becomes thinner, and during this process the individual wires are compressed and friction is set up; the fibre heart and cores are also compressed, releasing oil to overcome the friction. A wire rope of outwardly good appearance, but with a dry powdery heart or core, has not been properly maintained and should be treated with caution.

(6) *Effect of extreme cold.* When subjected to extreme cold a wire rope may become brittle and lose its flexibility, and an apparently sound rope may part without warning. The brittleness is not permanent and the rope will regain its resilience in a normal temperature, but the potential danger should be remembered when working wires in very cold climates.

c. **Testing of steel wire rope**. The wire from which the rope is to be made is tested before manufacture of the rope to ensure it complies with the relevant British Standards Specification with regard to tensile strength, torsion and galvanising properties. After manufacture of each production length of rope, test samples are cut from the finished rope and strand. These samples are used for a tensile test to destruction, tests of preforming of the rope, and tests on a mixture of the individual wires with regard to diameter, tensile strength, torsion and quality of galvanising. A certificate of conformity and a test certificate showing the guaranteed minimum breaking strength of the wire when new accompany each coil of wire.

03011. End terminals on wire rope

a. Besides the soft, thimble and hawser eyes, other kinds of terminals are used for the ends of wire rope and some of them are explained below.

b. **Sockets**. There are several types of socket (Fig 3-21(i)) but a standard method of attaching them to the end of a wire. The wires at one end of the rope are fluffed out like a shaving brush to fill the hollow conical head of the socket, the ends of the wire are then hooked over towards the centre and molten white metal is poured in to make the whole head solid. This skilled work is normally done by qualified dockyard personnel. A well-made socket should have the strength of the rope but the rope is subject to fatigue where it enters the socket because of the abrupt loss of flexibility. Frequent examination is essential and if a single broken wire is seen near the socket the rope should be recapped without delay.

c. Swaged Terminals are a modern alternative to the sockets described above, and as with the socket there are various types. (See Fig 3-21). The end of the wire is inserted in the terminal and both are placed in a special swaging machine in which the terminal is hydraulically compacted on to the rope. This process, which is carried out cold, does not affect the temper or strength of the rope.

Fig 3-21. Example of terminals for wirer

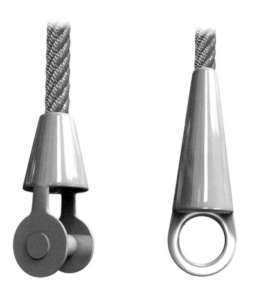

03012. Factors of safety, safe working loads and proof loads

a.   All lifting equipment fitted in, and carried by HM ships is of a proven and tested design and has a designated safe working load, which is the maximum load the equipment is designed to bear in practice. The required size and strength of all the components of the equipment has been calculated by the design authority, and the seaman will rarely be called upon to exercise his judgement on the subject. However, knowledge of the principles involved will give a greater understanding of equipment limitations, and assist in making accurate calculations should extempore rigging of lifting equipment be necessary. To determine the size of cordage or wire rope to be used for any working load a factor of safety is laid down for different conditions of working; it applies to the rope only, as other components within the rig, such as shackles, hooks and blocks are unlikely to be subjected to the same stresses as the rope, and in any case such items are marked with their safe working load and this information can be taken as reliable regardless of the application of the equipment. For SWR, MMFC and NFC the following formula is employed:

$$\textit{Safe working load} \; = \; \frac{\textit{breaking strength of rope}}{\textit{factor of safety}}$$

b.   The following factors of safety for rope are used generally in the Royal Navy:

(1)   Lifts and hoists   12

(2)   Running rigging and slings   8

(3)   Other purposes   6

c.   **Proof load.** The proof load of lifting equipment is normally twice its safe working load and this information is required when equipment is tested. For example, a shackle with a safe working load of two tonnes is tested to a proof load of four tonnes. In the past it was usual to mark equipment with details of the proof load, but current practice is for the safe working load to be shown.

03013. Orders and terms used in handling hawsers, ropes and cables

The various orders and terms used by the seaman when handling hawsers, ropes and cables are listed below:

Order or term	Definition
Heaving	
A heave	A pull on a rope or cable; a throw or cast with a rope
To heave	To throw a rope, or to pull on a rope or cable either by hand or power
Heave	The order to give a strong pull together
Heave in	The order to heave in on a capstan or winch
Two six, heave	An order to men hauling on a rope to make them heave together, repeated as necessary
Hauling	
A haul	A pull on a rope by hand
To haul	To pull by hand
To haul hand over hand	To haul a rope in quickly with alternate hands
Haul taut	An order to take down the slack and take the strain
Haul away	An order to haul in steadily
Avast hauling! and Avast	Order to stop hauling
STOP	**THE WORD 'STOP' CAN BE USED AT ANY TIME DURING A SEAMANSHIP EVOLUTION. IT IS MADE TO INDICATE A SAFETY ISSUE. ON HEARING 'STOP' ALL PERSONNEL ARE TO STOP WHAT THEY ARE DOING IMMEDIATELY AND AWAIT FURTHER INSTRUCTIONS. NOT TO BE CONFUSED WITH AVAST.**
Hold fast	An order to hold a rope under strain so as to keep it from moving
Hoisting	
A hoist	A system designed for lifting, or the load which is lifted
To hoist	To lift
Hoist away	The order to haul away on a rope when hoisting something with it
High enough	The order to stop hoisting
Marry	The order to bring two ropes together side by side and handle them as one. Also a term used in splicing, meaning to butt two ropes' ends together with their respective strands interlocking.
Lowering	
Lower away	The order to lower steadily
Avast lowering	The order to stop lowering

Order or term	Definition
General	
Avast!	Stop immediately, especially heaving/hauling/veering.
Handsomely!	Slowly, with care (e.g. 'lower handsomely')
Roundly!	Smartly, rapidly
Walk back!	An order to ease a rope back or out while keeping it in hand
Light to!	The order to fleet a rope back along the deck so as to provide slack.
Belay	Make fast a rope by turning it up on a cleat/staghorn/bollard.
Bring to	Pass turns of a hawser or rope round a capstan or winch. (It is usual to specify the number of turns to be taken).
To veer	To pay or ease out a cable or hawser from the cable holder or capstan when these are connected to and controlled by their engines (veer on power); or to allow a cable to run out by its own weight or strain on the outboard end under control by the cable-holder brake (veer on the brake).
Check away!	The order to ease a rope steadily by hand while keeping a strain on it
To snub	Suddenly to restrain a rope or cable when it is running out. This may cause damage to a rope or cable and should be avoided if possible.
To surge	To allow a hawser to ease out by its own weight, or by the strain on the outboard end. A hawser slipping round the barrel of a capstan or winch is said to surge, whether the barrel is stopped or turning to heave in. **Surging when the barrel is veering is dangerous**.
To render	A rope is said to render when it surges under strain round a rotating drum.
Well! or *Enough!*	Orders to stop heaving, veering, hauling, lowering checking, etc. *Enough!* is usually applied only to hoisting and lowering, and is preceded by *High* or *Low*, respectively.
To back up	To haul on the hauling part of a rope when passed round a bollard or similar fitting so that you assist the bollard to hold it. Also, to reinforce men already handling a rope.

03014. Handling hawsers

a.   As the name implies, a hawser was originally a heavy, natural fibre rope, which was led through a hawse-pipe for use in connection with the ship's anchors or for towing. Nowadays the term hawser is applied to any long length of heavy cordage or wire which is specially fitted and supplied to a ship as part of her outfit and used for heavy duties such as towing, berthing and working ship.

b.   **Summary of safety rules for handling man-made fibre, natural fibre and steel wire hawsers**. Before working hawsers, the user should learn the simple rules for safety, which are illustrated in Fig 3-22 and Fig 3-23 and described briefly below.

(1)   Look at the end of the rope or hawser and determine which is the running end, the standing part, the hauling part, and which part forms a bight or a coil.

(2)   The wearing of finger rings is strongly discouraged. Serious injury, including amputation, may result if a ring snags on a broken strand of a wire hawser. The practice of taping over the ring does little to reduce the chance of injury.

(3)   Don't turn up SWR and Cordage on the same bollard or cleat.

(4)   Always keep a good lookout aloft and remain alert to what is happening above you. If avoidable never stand below an object that is being hoisted or lowered. The warning cry to those below if something above them is about to be let fall is 'Stand from under!' or 'Under below!'

(5)   When working hawsers round equipment such as bollards, warping drums or capstans ensure there is a distance of at least two metres between the equipment and the first person manning the hawser. Other personnel manning the hawser should be spaced at least one metre apart.

(6)   Always look out for chafe, and take steps to prevent or minimise it.

(7)   Be aware that man-made fibre ropes and hawsers may surge round capstans and bollards without warning when in tension.

(8)   Never stand within a bight or coil. Never stand directly in the line of recoil/snap back of a hawser under tension.

(9)   Wearing gloves whilst handling wires and ropes carries certain risks, ie if they snag on a broken strand in a wire, or become trapped in turns on a capstan or winch. However, in certain circumstances these risks are outweighed by other dangers, eg, frost bite in very cold weather, or the inability to grip with bare hands a greasy wire hawser. Therefore the wearing of gloves is left to the discretion of the OIC, who must take account of the prevailing conditions.

(10) Whenever possible lines are to be tended from forward, this is particularly important during underway evolutions.

Fig 3-22. Never stand underneath a hoisted load –
(animated Graphic – see CD for demonstration)

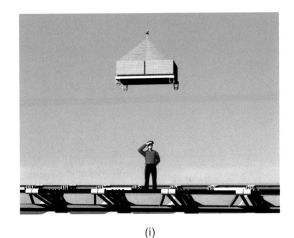

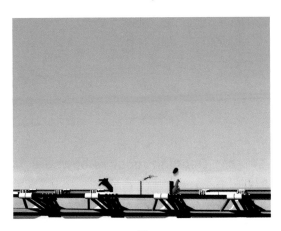

(i)   (ii)

Fig 3-23. Never stand within a bight or coil

c. **Bending ropes to hawsers**

(1) *To bend a heaving line to a berthing hawser* Secure the heaving-line to the eye of the hawser with a long bowline. This will give personnel hauling it a better grip as the bollard eye of the hawser comes to fairlead or bollard and will enable the line to be slid clear as the eye is placed over the bollards.

(2)   *To bend a mto a heavy hawser* (Fig 3-24). A messenger is used instead of a heaving-line to pass the heavier hawsers between ships, or ship and shore, as it is made of heavier cordage. It should be bent to the neck of the eye of the hawser with a rolling hitch, and firmly stopped to the crown of the eye. The eye of the hawser can then be hauled through a fairlead and the stop cut, leaving the eye free for shackling on or putting on to a slip. The rolling hitch should be well secured and stopped, and the stop on the eye should be firmly secured to prevent the hitch sliding over the shoulders of the eye (Fig 3-24).

Fig 3-24. Bending a messenger to a heavy hawser

d.   **Belaying hawsers to bollards**

(1)   *A fibre rope to a single bollard* (Fig 3-25). Bring the rope to the bollard and belay it as shown in the illustration. The first turn round the bollard must be as low down as possible and overlapping or riding turns should be avoided.

(2)   *Racking.* The method of racking the end of a rope belayed to a single bollard is as follows:

(a) Middle the racking underneath the rope; pass both parts of the racking over the end and under the rope; take a turn round the end. Pass the racking under the rope, and repeat the process as often as required. To finish, separate the parts of the racking, bring them up each side of the cross, and secure them with a reef knot on the top.

Note.   *Cordage of at least 4 mm size should be used for racking; Spunyarn is not strong enough.*

Fig 3-25. Belaying a fibre rope to a single bollard

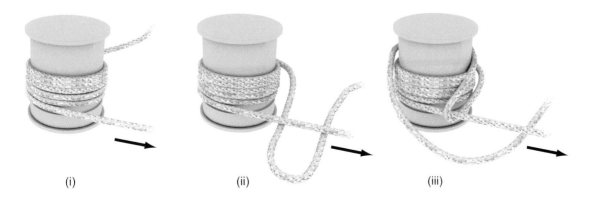

(i)   (ii)   (iii)

(3)   *Two or more berthing hawsers over a single bollard* (Fig 3-26). When two or more berthing hawsers have to be secured to the same bollard eye, the eye of the second hawser must be passed up through the eye of the first before it is placed over the bollard. Similarly, the eye of a third hawser must be passed up through the eyes of the first two; this enables the hawsers to be cast off the bollard in any order. The term used for this procedure is called 'dipping the eye'.

Fig 3-26. Placing the eyes of two berthing hawsers on a single bollard (dipping the eye)

e. **Typical bollard construction and in-use working loads**. There are a number of different standards for the manufacture and fit of bollards. The most common fitted to warships is the BSMA-12 Type 'A' Bollard as shown in Fig 3-27.

Fig 3-27. Bollard construction and in-use working loads

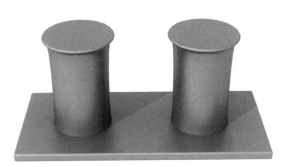

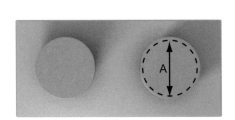
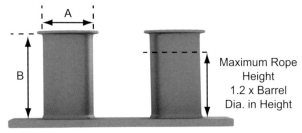

Type	A	B	M tonne	T tonne
250	250mm	380mm	13.2t	30t
315	315mm	480mm	19.7t	50t
400	400mm	600mm	33.5t	100t
500	500mm	750mm	55.4t	130t
630	630mm	940mm	82.8t	160t

(1)   *Maximum permissible load on bollard in tonnes*
       M = Mooring Mode
       T = Towing Mode

(a) **M** – The Bollard can be loaded with two ropes, belayed in figure of eights, each with a breaking strength not exceeding the values of the table.

(b) **T** – The Bollard can be loaded with one towing rope with a single eye placed on one of the Barrels/Bitts and with a breaking strength not exceeding the values of the table.

(c) **HPMT** – The Bollard can be loaded with a single rope, belayed in figure of eights, with a breaking strength of not more than twice the figure of **M** – Mooring Mode value.

(d) **When** Cross-Belaying in Figure of Eights always catch one full dry-turn around the leading Barrel/Bitt when using two ropes on the Bollards.

(E) **When** cross-belaying in figure of eights always catch two full dry turns around the leading barrel/bitt when using a single rope on the bollards.

(f) **Always** ensure that turned-up ropes never exceed 1.2 x the barrel diameter in height.

(g) **Racking** is to be applied to all ropes belayed in figure of eights as shown in Fig 3-30.

Fig 3-28. Belaying a hawser to twin bollards

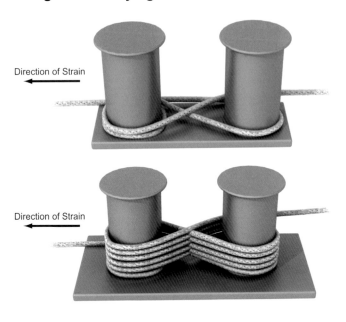

Fig 3-29. Twin bollards showing snap back zone

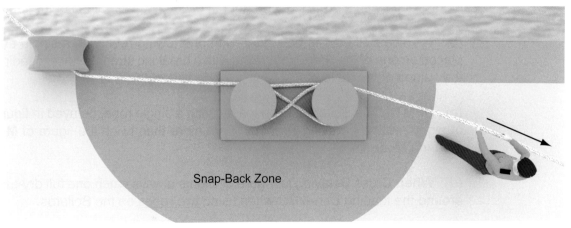

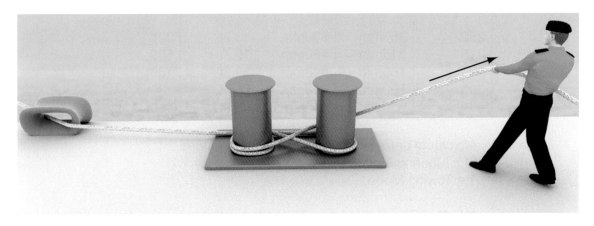

Snap-Back Zone

> **WARNING**
>
> **ADDITIONAL LINES ARE NOT TO BE PLACED ON BOLLARDS WITH TWO FULLY TURNED UP HAWSERS.**

(2)   *A hawser to twin bollards.* A ship's twin bollard may take up to a maximum of two lines (one doubled up) belayed in figure of eights. If the diameter of the rope allows there should be one full turn taken on the lead bollard before going into figure of eights which will greatly increase the safe working load of the bollards. Securing to bollards in this manner puts the user in the best possible position in relation to snap back and facilitates full control and ease to catch/remove turns and surge. It also eases the stress on the bollards.

(3)   *Racking a hawser.* Middle the racking and make an overhand knot round the cross of the two upper turns of the hawser; with each part of the racking, pass racking turns round both parts of the upper turns, working outward from the cross; when sufficient racking turns have been taken, knot both parts of the racking over the cross with an overhand knot. To finish off, pass the ends in opposite directions down and round all the turns of the hawser, haul the ends taut, and finish them off with a reef knot on the top (see Fig 3-30).

Fig 3-30. Racking a hawser at twin bollards

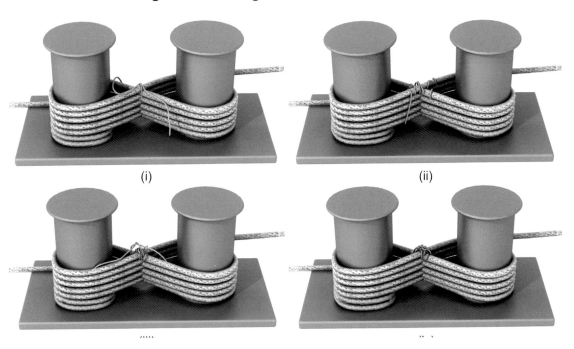

(i)   (ii)

Fig 3-31. Bringing to a capstan/windlass/drum end

"BRINGING TO"
CAPSTAN - Min. 5 turns

"BRINGING TO"
WINDLASS / DRUM END
Min. 5 turns

Note*.   Never surge on a rotating capstan/windlass or drum End.*

Fig 3-32. Bringing to on a split drum winch

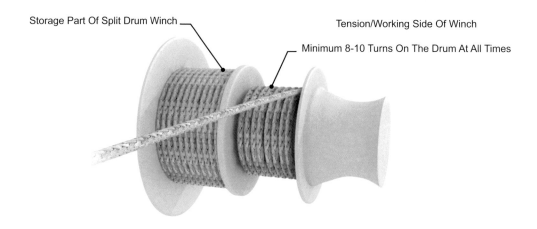

Storage Part Of Split Drum Winch

Tension/Working Side Of Winch

Minimum 8-10 Turns On The Drum At All Times

(4)   *To catch a turn on a single bollard* (Fig 3-33). When a rope is under strain, catching an extra turn round a single bollard is difficult unless done correctly. Careful attention should be paid to the position of the hands and fingers to prevent them being nipped, especially if the hawser should render.

Fig 3-33. Catching a turn on a single bollard

(5) *To catch a turn round twin bollards.* Fig 3-34 shows how to catch turns with a hawser under strain round twin bollards. Note that the lead is first to the bollard farthest from the source of strain, and from outboard to inboard. Belaying turns of a hawser leading forward are taken right-handed on the starboard side of a ship and left-handed on the port side, and vice versa when the hawser is leading aft.

Fig 3-34. Catching a turn round twin bollards

(6) *To handle a heavy rope which is alternatively slack and under strain.* If space permits, it is best to keep one turn on the bollards and man the rope as shown in (Fig 3-35). As the slack comes in, one person (or two with a very large rope) can fleet it round the bollards, and at the same time be ready to back it up and take more turns when the strain comes on.

Fig 3-35. Handling a hawser which is alternatively slack and under strain

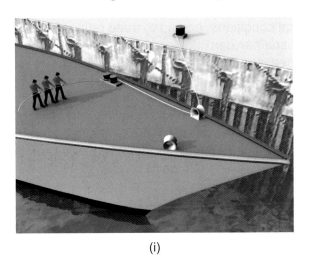

(i)

(ii)

Fig 3-36. Paying out a heavy hawser

(7)   *Surging.* Essential rules for surging are to surge smoothly and not in jerks, and to keep sufficient control to be able to surge with the maximum safe strain on the hawser. A hawser with too many turns round the winch or bollards will not render smoothly and may therefore part, and with too few turns the hawser may take charge and run out. It should be remembered that catching an additional turn round a bollard or winch is easier than taking one off. When too many ratings back up a hawser they are apt to get in each other's way, with the result that efficient control of the hawser is lost.

Success lies in taking a sufficient number of turns to reduce the strain on the hauling part to manageable proportions. Generally speaking, two or three turns should suffice for surging under normal conditions, and up to three ratings should be sufficient for backing up. An expert seaman can handle a 28mm rope by himself and keep it under complete control when surging by catching or removing turns as required. The precise number of turns for surging will always depend on the strain on the rope, the size of the rope and winch or bollards and the resultant friction between them, and the number of ratings backing-up on the hauling part. Under normal conditions when a rating exerts an approximate pull of 30kg when backing-up a wire, each turn round a bollard or winch reduces the strain required on the hauling part to one-quarter of the load, so that one rating will be able to hold:

> One-eighth of a tonne with one turn
> Half a tonne with two turns
> Two tonnes with three turns
> Eight tonnes with four turns

(8)   Thirty kilograms is a very conservative estimate of the effort each person can apply; three persons, by backing-up, could easily part a 16 mm steel wire rope with three turns round a bollard or winch, or 28 mm steel wire rope with four turns. Similarly, a 32 mm steel wire rope with five turns round a bollard or winch could easily be parted when backed-up by one person.

BR 67
RIGGING AND DECK GEAR

It is emphasised that this rough rule applies only with normal conditions of friction between the rope and the bollard or winch. With a greasy or wet rope, or a polished bearing surface on the bollard or winch, more turns or personnel are required. Conversely, a rusty steel wire rope, or a painted or rusty bearing surface on the winch or bollard, may increase the frictional grip of each turn by as much as eight times. For this reason the bearing surfaces of winches, bollards and capstans are to remain painted and kept free of rust.

f. **Stoppers and stoppering**. To belay a rope, which is under strain, the strain must be taken temporarily with a stopper. The type of stopper used depends on whether it is to hold a man-made fibre or a wire rope.

(1) *Tech 12 cordage stopper*. A 14mm Tech 12 stopper, fitted with a stainless steel thimble eye one end is provided for use for fibre hawsers only in ship berthing and towing operations and is used in the following manner:

(a) For use on berthing hawsers the stopper is made fast to an eyeplate or other fixture. The stopper is then laid alongside the hawser with its tails pointing towards the source of strain; the tails are passed by crossing them under and over the hawser in the direction of the source of strain. The ends are kept in hand or stopped to the hawser as shown in Fig 3-37 and Fig 3-39.

Fig 3-37. Tech 12 cordage stopper rigged for use in berthing

Direction of Strain

(b) For use in towing it is used to assist in controlling the speed at which the tow is run out. The check stopper should be rigged with both legs passed over the hawser as shown in Fig 3-38, however where the eyeplate used will not allow both legs to be used then a single leg of the stopper should be passed.

Fig 3-38. Tech 12 cordage check stopper rigged for towing

Fig 3-39. Use of a stopper when berthing ship

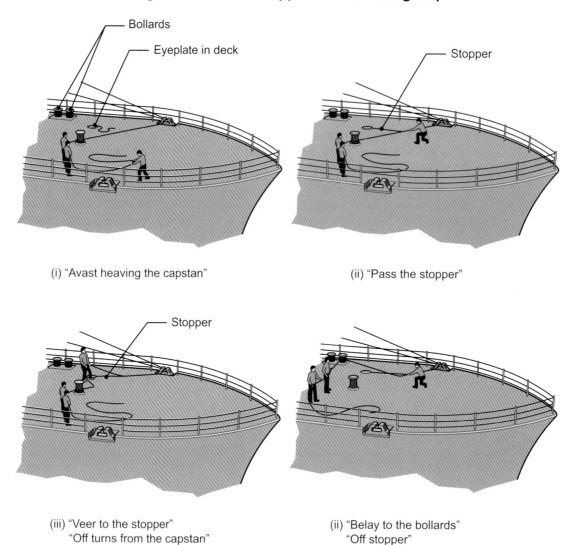

(i) "Avast heaving the capstan"

(ii) "Pass the stopper"

(iii) "Veer to the stopper"
   "Off turns from the capstan"

(ii) "Belay to the bollards"
   "Off stopper"

CAUTION

At no time is the ship to be held only by a stopper. See Para 03014f

---

g.   **Stowage of hawsers**. Hawsers can be stowed on reels (Fig 3-40). A hawser store is usually sited directly below the fo'c'sle deck. The drum and flanges of a hawser reel should be of skeleton construction to allow air to circulate around the hawser and thus keep it dry. Both ends of the hawser should be stopped by their eyes to the drum and flange. The reel should be secured by a lanyard, fitted on the flange, to prevent it rotating when the hawser is stowed. Most ships have been fitted with ventilated bins made either of steel or timber, for the stowage of man-made fibre hawsers. With this type of stowage, man-made fibre hawsers that have been in tension can be stowed away directly, without the need to wait for the hawser to recover its length, a necessary requirement when such hawsers are stowed on reels. Cordage stowed in ventilated bins must be coiled or faked down in the bin on wooden duckboards to ensure adequate air circulation underneath as well as around the hawsers. Yet another type of hawser stowage is the bulkhead saddle, a circular or oval cluster of steel horns around which the hawser is wound.

Fig 3-40. Stowage of hawsers on reels

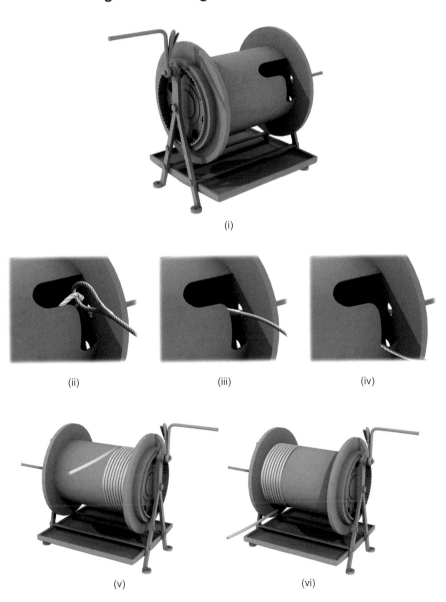

(i)

(ii)   (iii)   (iv)

(v)   (vi)

h.   **Calculating the capacity of a reel or drum**. The following formula, used in conjunction with the information in Fig 3-41, gives an approximate indication as to what length, in metres, of rope of a given size can be placed on any reel or drum.

Fig 3-41. Calculation of drum capacity

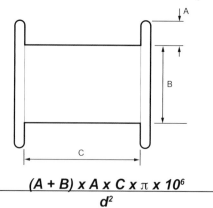

$$\frac{(A + B) \ x \ A \ x \ C \ x \ \pi \ x \ 10^6}{d^2}$$

where A, B and C are quoted in metres and d, the diameter of the rope, is quoted in millimetres

Note.   Ropes are normally manufactured to a maximum oversize tolerance of 4%; therefore the actual diameter 'd' could be nominal diameter + 4%.

03015. High performance mooring and towing equipment – maintenance/inspection criteria

    a.   **Handling and storage**

        (1)   HPMT Ropes, as previously noted, are lighter than legacy ropes. They are handled, worked and rendered differently to obtain the best performance, lifespan and speed/ease of operation.

        (2)   Ropes should be faked-down and not coiled-down – coiling only inverts twist into a torque-balanced rope.

        (3)   When faking-down, always use as small an area as possible – this reduces possible snagging opportunities and reduces wear/abrasion. Fake-down on a shot mat if possible and 'carry' the rope to the mooring position – do not drag ropes over the weatherdecks! HPMT ropes can easily be carried due to their light weight.

        (4)   Store ropes on reels where possible and ensure good ventilation, protect from UV light and possible contaminants.

        (5)   If using 'rope storage bins' fake down in figure of eights – this reduces twist and will facilitate ease of running-out when next required.

        (6)   Do not store any items on top of stored ropes.

        (7)   Ensure all ropes are labelled to identify instantly what type of rope it is.

        (8)   Consider the use of protective covers when ropes deployed – especially if using your ropes when in maintenance periods, docking periods etc.

        (9)   Ice is a unique product that protects the strength member for abrasion, yet allows the rope to be easily inspected for both internal and external fibre wear. Braided from cut and abrasion resistant Dyneema fibre, ice is permanently spliced over the rope, and acts as a sacrificial cover that protects the rope from abrasion and wear in berthing and offshore applications. Always use a Sacrificial Cover for Chafe Prevention on contact areas (see Fig 3-42 and para 03025 sub para f).

Fig 3-42. Sacrificial cover for chafe prevention

b. **Care and maintenance**. All fibre ropes, of any fibre, will benefit and will last longer with regular Care & Maintenance procedures established. Establish the following onboard routines for maintaining your ropes.

(1) *DOs*

(a) Regularly fresh water wash down the ropes – this reduces salt crystallisation and contaminant build up.

(b) Ensure that rope surface contact points (RSCPs) are well maintained, in good order and free of sharp edges.

(c) Ensure that ropes are protected when hot work is carried out in the vicinity.

(d) Ensure that all adjacent ropes are boundary cooled in case of fire.

(e) Remove any external heat sources – heat is the most damaging aspect to HMPE ropes.

(f) Ensure that chafe protection is fitted in the correct places – eyes, fairleads/chocks and on jetties.

(g) Consider the manufacture of PVC protection (covers) for ropes when deployed on bollards especially when in maintenance periods.

(h) Ensure all hawsers have labels stating type, size, designation and MBL. This information should be recorded on the rope history card iaw Annex 3C.

(i) Follow rope retirement guidelines.

(j) Ensure lines are equally sharing loads when rigged, in both length and angle.

(2) *DON'Ts*

(a) Avoid shock loading of HPMT ropes – shock loading permanently weakens the ropes, especially when carrying-out tug assist operations.

c. Using these ropes correctly and carrying out regular inspections before and after use will give a consistent and reliable service. Follow the criteria as shown in Fig 3-43 and complete the Inspection template at Annex 3C when carrying out inspections.

Fig 3-43. Rope inspection criteria

Volume reduction: 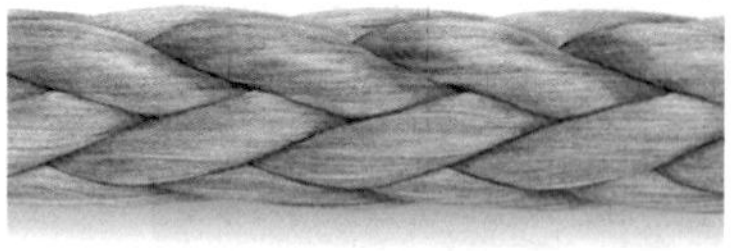 (i)	Rope displaying original bulk.
 (ii)	Rope displaying 25% strand volume reduction from abrasion — rope should be retired from service.
 (iii)	Rope strands reduced by 25% abrasion. Pulled strands should be worked back into the rope so they won't continue to snag and eventually cut.
 (iv)	Rope strands showing full volume.
Cut strands:  (v)	Rope displays two adjacent cut strands. This rope should either be retired or the cut section should be removed and the remaining rope re-spliced.
Compression:  (vi)	Rope exhibits fibre-set from compression. A slight sheen is visible. This is not a permanent characteristic and can be eliminated by flexing the rope. This condition should not be confused with glazed or melted fibre.
Melting or glazing:  (vii)	Damage depicted at left caused by excessive heat, which melted and fused the fibres. This area will be extremely stiff. Unlike fibre compression, melting damage cannot be mitigated by flexing the rope. Melted areas must be cut out and rope respliced or the rope must be retired.

d. **Inspection and retirement**. One question frequently asked is "When should we retire the rope?" The most obvious answer is before it breaks. But, without a thorough understanding of how to inspect it and knowing the load history, you are left making an educated guess. Unfortunately, there are no definitive rules nor are there industry guidelines to establish when a rope should be retired because there are so many variables that affect rope strength. Factors like load history, bending radius, abrasion, chemical exposure or some combination of those factors, make retirement decisions difficult. Inspecting your rope should be a continuous process of observation before, during, and after each use. In synthetic fibre ropes, the amount of strength loss due to abrasion and/or flexing is directly related to the amount of broken fibre in the rope's cross section. In 12-strand single braids such as AmSteel® and AmSteel®-Blue, each of the 12 strands carries approximately 8.33%, or 1/12th, of the load. If upon inspection, there are cut strands or significant abrasion damage to the rope, the rope must be retired or the areas of damage removed and the rope repaired with the appropriate splice. Therefore after each use look and feel along every inch of the rope length inspecting for:

(1) *Abrasion*. When a 12-strand single braid rope such as AmSteel®-Blue is first put into service, the outer filaments of the rope will quickly fuzz up. This is the result of these filaments breaking, which actually forms a protective cushion and shield for the fibres underneath. This condition should stabilise, not progress. If the surface roughness increases, excessive abrasion is taking place and strength is being lost. When inspecting the rope, look closely at both the inner and outer fibres. When either is worn, the rope is obviously weakened. Open the strands and look for powdered fibre, which is one sign of internal wear. Estimate the internal wear to estimate total fibre abrasion. If total fibre loss is 20%, then it is safe to assume that the rope has lost 20% of its strength as a result of abrasion. As a general rule for braided ropes, when there is 25% or more wear from abrasion, or the fibre is broken or worn away, the rope should be retired from service.

(2) *Glossy or glazed areas*. Glossy or glazed areas are signs of heat damage with more strength loss than the amount of melted fibre indicates. Fibres adjacent to the melted areas are probably damaged from excessive heat even though they appear normal. It is reasonable to assume that the melted fibre has damaged an equal amount of adjacent unmelted fibre.

(3) *Discolouration*. With use, all ropes get dirty. Be on the lookout for areas of discoloration that could be caused by chemical contamination. Determine the cause of the discoloration and replace the rope if it is brittle or stiff.

(4) *Inconsistent diameter*. Inspect for flat areas, bumps, or lumps. This can indicate core or internal damage from overloading or shock loads and is usually sufficient reason to replace the rope.

(5) *Inconsistent texture*. Inconsistent texture or stiff areas can indicate excessive dirt or grit embedded in the rope or shock load damage and is usually reason to replace the rope.

e. **Surface contact points.** To enable HPMT to be effective, all Rope Surface Contact Points must be prepared to an acceptable level of operational usage. The maintenance and care of deck fittings will greatly extend the operational lifespan of HPMT ropes. It is imperative that the smoothest possible finish is maintained at all times by removing any sharp edges that may cause abrasion to the rope. Chafe pieces are to be used at all times on RCPs.

03016. Bends and hitches

a.   Strictly speaking, a bend is a method of temporarily joining two ropes, a hitch is a method of temporarily joining a rope to a structure or ring, and a knot is the intertwining of strands or smaller parts of rope(s) to prevent a rope unreeving, or to provide a handhold, a weight or a stopper on any part of a rope. These definitions have become blurred with time and all three terms are now virtually synonymous. Commonly used bends and hitches are described here, and knots and their uses are described in Para 03017.

b.   **Strength of knotted ropes**. All knots, bends and hitches reduce the strength of a rope in that portion of the rope where the knot, bend or hitch is made. This reduction varies from 40-60%, and it should be borne in mind when putting a load on a knotted rope.

c.   **Terms used**. The following terms are used when describing the formation of the various bends and hitches:

Fig 3-44. Terms used in describing bends and hitches

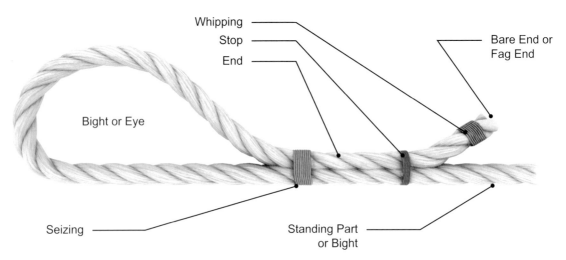

(1)   *Bight*. The middle part of a length of rope. This term also refers to a loop of rope, and **to make a bight** is to form a loop.

(2)   *End*. The short length at the end of a rope, which may be formed into an eye, or used for making a bend or a hitch with which to secure it. The end of a rope is also that length of rope left over after making such an eye, bend or hitch. The **bare end**, or **fag end**, is the extreme end of a length of rope.

(3)   *Standing part*. The part of the bight of a rope, which is nearest the eye, bend or hitch, in contrast to the end.

(4)   *Stopping*. A light fastening for temporarily holding in place a rope or any other object. It is not meant to bear any strain other than that required to keep the rope or other object in place.

(5)   *Seizing*. A seizing is used to fasten two ropes, or two parts of the same rope, securely together, to prevent them moving in relation to each other.

(6)   *Whipping*. The binding round the bare end of a rope to prevent the strands from unlaying.

d.   **Elements of bends and hitches**. Most bends and hitches consist of a combination of two or more of the elements illustrated in Fig 3-45.

Fig 3-45. Elements of bends and hitches

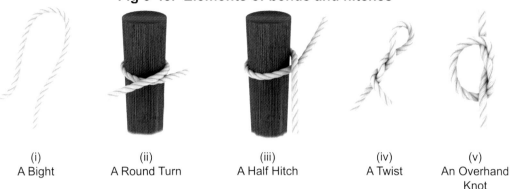

| (i) | (ii) | (iii) | (iv) | (v) |
| A Bight | A Round Turn | A Half Hitch | A Twist | An Overhand Knot |

e.   **Reef knot** (Fig 3-46).   The reef knot consists of two overhand knots made consecutively, and is used as a common tie for bending together two ropes of approximately equal size. It is not likely to come undone when there is no strain on the knot, but it is not reliable if the ropes are of unequal size or very slippery unless the ends are seized back to their standing part. To form a reef knot care must be taken to cross the ends opposite ways each time they are knotted (ie right over left, then left over right, or vice versa), otherwise the result will be a **granny**, which will either slip or jam, depending upon whether it is made with or against the lay of the rope. A granny is also very likely to undo where there is no strain on the knot.

Fig 3-46. Reef knot

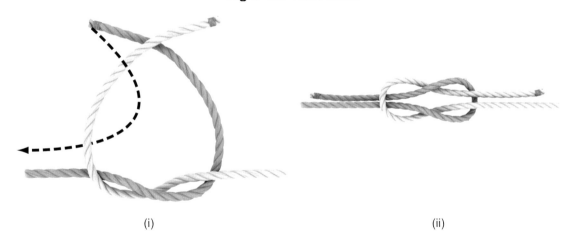

(i)   (ii)

f.   **Figure-of-eight knot** (Fig 3-47). This knot is used to prevent a rope unreeving through a block.

Fig 3-47. Figure-of-eight knot

g.   **Marline spike hitch** (Fig 3-48).   This hitch is for securing a marline spike, or hook, into the bight of a line.   Fig 3-48(ii) and Fig 3-48(iii) show how it is used to haul taut a serving or lashing with a marline spike.   It can also be used to secure a sling or the bight of a rope to a hook when the strain on both parts of the bight is approximately equal see Fig 3-48(iv).

Fig 3-48. Marline spike hitch

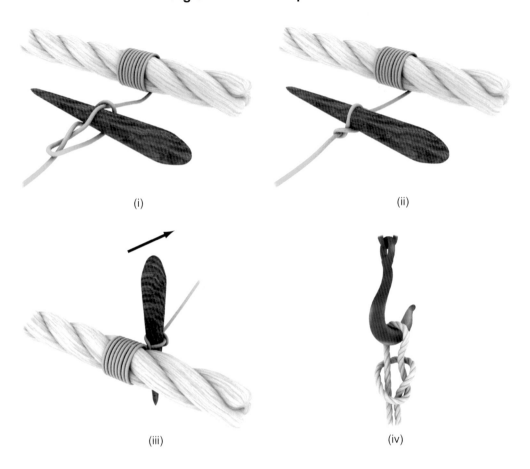

(i)   (ii)

(iii)   (iv)

h.   **Marling hitch** (Fig 3-49).   For lashing long bundles such as awnings.   It can be seen from the illustration that in each hitch the end is passed down through the bight, thus jamming that part against the bundle and enabling the lashing to be hauled taut. The operation of binding together ropes or yarns by a succession of closely spaced marling hitches is known as **marling down**.   Marling is usually begun with a timber hitch if no eye is spliced into the end of the lashing.

Fig 3-49. Marling hitch

i.   **Timber hitch** (Fig 3-50). This hitch is used to secure a rope's end to a spar or bale.

Fig 3-50. Timber hitch

(i)   (ii)

j.   **Timber hitch and half hitch** (Fig 3-51). Used to tow, hoist or lower a spar. If the spar is tapered it should be towed or hoisted thick end first, with the timber hitch at the thin end and the half hitch at the thick end.

Fig 3-51. Timber hitch and half hitch

k.   **Clove hitch** (Fig 3-52). This hitch is used to secure a rope to a spar, rail or similar fitting; also for many other purposes. It will slip along the spar or rail if subjected to a sideways pull. It can be made with the end or with the bight of a rope, as illustrated in Fig 3-52(a) and Fig 3-52(b) respectively.

Fig 3-52. Clove hitch

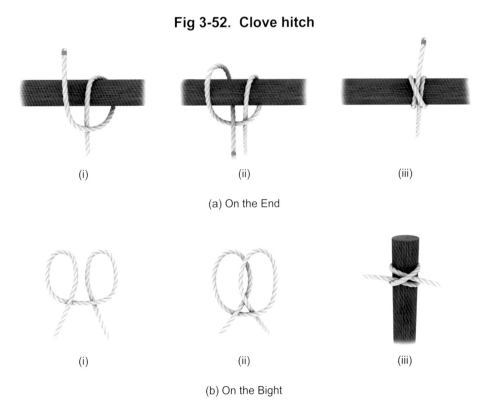

(i)   (ii)   (iii)

(a) On the End

(i)   (ii)   (iii)

(b) On the Bight

l.   **Constrictor knot**. The constrictor knot is a variation of the clove hitch, and is used when a firm grip is required, such as when holding a thimble in place prior to splicing a hawser eye. It is the most secure of all binding knots and the essence of the knot is that it becomes even tighter as tension is applied to the ends without loosening as the strain is taken off. Take a round turn and then follow the method shown in Fig 3-53(i) and haul taut.

Fig 3-53. Constrictor knot

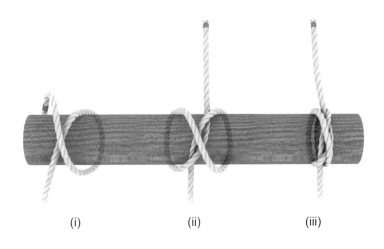

(i)   (ii)   (iii)

m. **Rolling hitch** (Fig 3-54). This hitch is also used for securing a rope to a spar, rail or similar fitting when the pull is expected to be from one side or the other, and to another rope under strain. It is made by passing the end twice round the spar or rope, each turn crossing the standing part. A half hitch on the opposite side completes the hitch. Always pass the two turns on the side from which the pull is expected.

Fig 3-54. Rolling hitch

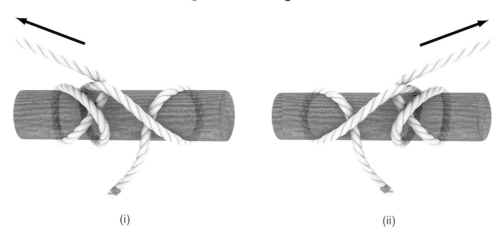

(i)   (ii)

n. **Round turn and two half hitches** (Fig 3-55). This combination is used to secure a heavy load to a spar, ring or shackle such as the buoy shackle of a mooring buoy. It will never jam and can be cast off quickly. The end should be stopped to the standing part.

Fig 3-55. Round turn and two half hitches   **Fig 3-56. Fisherman's bend**

o. **Fisherman's bend** (Fig 3-56). An alternative to a round turn and two half hitches, and normally used for bending a rope or hawser to the ring of an anchor. It is more suitable for a jerking pull, but will tend to jam and is not easily cast off. The end should be stopped to the standing part.

p. **Sheet bend or swab hitch** (Fig 3-57). This is used to secure a rope's end to a small eye, eg, the lazy painter of a boat at a boom to the Jacob's ladder. It is also used to bend a small rope to a large one.

q. **Double sheet bend** (Fig 3-58). A more secure method of achieving the same purpose as a single sheet bend. Used to secure a boat's painter to the eye of the lizard when at a boom.

Fig 3-57. Sheet bend

Fig 3-58. Double sheet bend

r. **Buntline hitch** (Fig 3-59) This hitch is a clove hitch on the standing part, and is used to secure a rope's end to a cringle or a small eye. It is more difficult to cast off than a sheet bend.

Fig 3-59. Buntline hitch

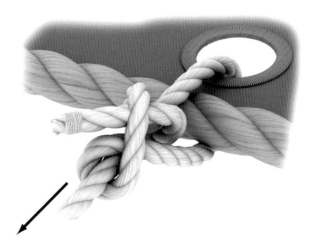

s. **Blackwall hitch** (Fig 3-60). A quick means of attaching a rope to a hook. It is used when the rope and hook are of equal size and it is likely to slip if subjected to more than ordinary strain.

Fig 3-60. Blackwall hitch

t.   **Double blackwall hitch** (Fig 3-61). Used when the rope and hook are of unequal size. It is as secure as the midshipman's hitch (below).

Fig 3-61. Double blackwall hitch

u.   **Midshipman's hitch** (Fig 3-62).   An alternative to the Blackwall hitch; it is preferred if the rope is at all greasy. It is made by first forming a Blackwall hitch and then taking the underneath part and placing it over the bill of the hook.

Fig 3-62. Midshipman's hitch

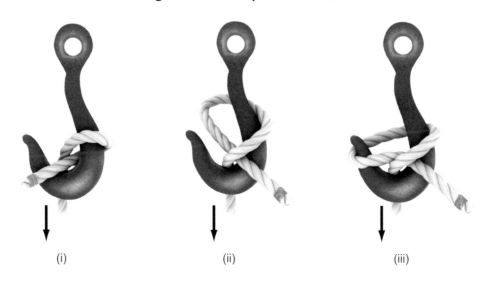

(i)   (ii)   (iii)

v.   **Bowline** (Fig 3-63). This is the most useful knot for making temporary eyes in ropes of all sizes. It is used for bending a heaving-line to a hawser, as a lifeline round a person's waist and for a great variety of similar purposes. Every member of a ship's company should be able to tie a bowline round his waist with his eyes closed. The bowline is usually made in the following manner, which enables it to be formed while there is a strain on the rope. Take the end in the right hand and the standing part in the left. Place the end over the standing part and hold the cross thus formed between the index finger and thumb of the right hand, with the thumb underneath; the loop so formed becomes the bight of the bowline, and if required it can be formed round the body of the person making the knot. Then turn the wrist to the right, away from the body, and bring the end up through the loop so formed. Now hold the cross of the loop in the left hand as shown in Fig 3-63, leaving the right hand free to manipulate the end, and complete the bowline by dipping the end under the standing part, bringing it up again, and passing it down through the loop.

Fig 3-63. Bowline

w.   **Running bowline** (Fig 3-64). Used to make a running eye in the end of a rope; it must never be placed round a person's body.

Fig 3-64. Running bowline

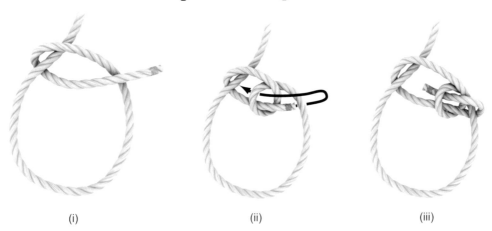

(i)   (ii)   (iii)

x.   **Bowline on the bight**. (Fig 3-65). As its name implies, this bowline is made on the bight, the first two operations in its formation being the same as for a simple bowline. It can be used for lowering a person from aloft or over the ship's side, the short bight being placed under the person's arms and the long one under their buttocks.

Fig 3-65. Bowline on the bight

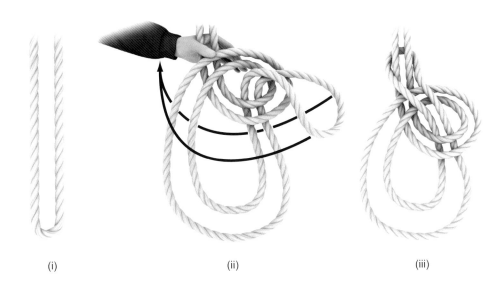

(i)   (ii)   (iii)

y.   **French bowline** (Fig 3-66). An alternative to the bowline on the bight and usually more suitable. It is made in a similar manner to a bowline, except that after the gooseneck has been formed and the end passed up through it the end is brought round and up through it again, so as to form a large bight, which is passed, under the person's armpits. The knot is then completed as a simple bowline. The weight of the person sitting in the main bight keeps the arm bight taut, the knot lying roughly at their breast.

Fig 3-66. French bowline

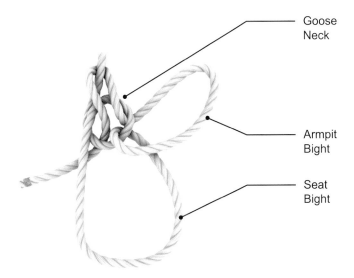

Goose Neck

Armpit Bight

Seat Bight

z.   **Slip knots** (Fig 3-67). The sheet bend, the bowline and the clove hitch are the three main knots, which can be released quickly by using a bight instead of an end in the last phase of making them. Such slipknots will hold steady strain fairly well, but cannot be trusted to stand a jerking pull.

Fig 3-67. Slip knots

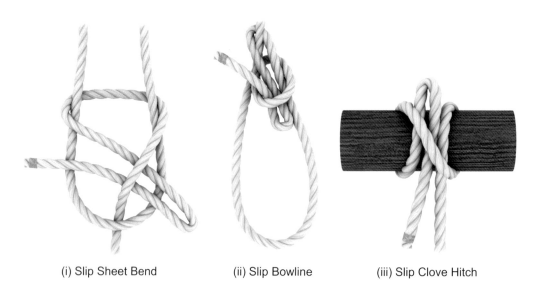

(i) Slip Sheet Bend   (ii) Slip Bowline   (iii) Slip Clove Hitch

aa. **Monkey's fist** (Fig 3-68). This is used to weight the end of a heaving line so that it will carry when thrown against the wind. It is made as follows:

(1)   Wind three turns round the hand.

(2)   Pass a second set of three turns across and round the first three.

(3)   Pass a third set of three turns round and across the second set, but inside the first set and in the direction shown by the arrows; if the knot is correctly made the end will come out alongside the standing part.

(4)   To finish the knot, work all parts taut and splice the end into the standing part; alternatively, tie an overhand knot in the end and finish it by tucking it inside the monkey's fist, then work all parts taut as before.

Fig 3-68. Monkey's fist

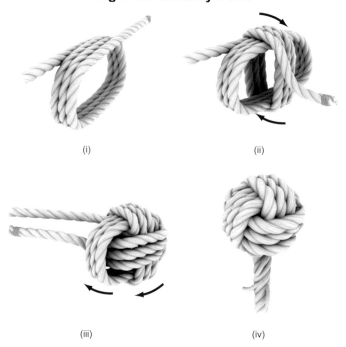

(i)   (ii)

(iii)   (iv)

ab. **Heaving-line knot** (Fig 3-69). This knot is used as an alternative to the monkey's fist and is quickly and easily made. Form a bight about 1.5 metres long at the end of the line. Start frapping the end round both parts of the bight at about 20 cm from the actual bend of the bight, and continue until it is all but expended. Then pass the end through the small loop left and haul on the standing part.

Fig 3-69. Heaving-line Knot

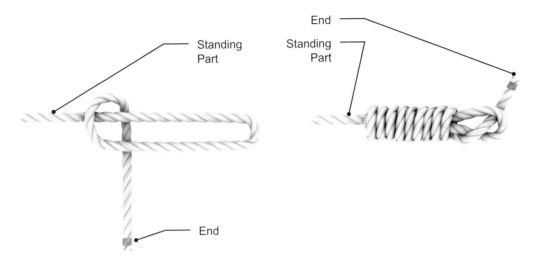

ac. **Fisherman's knots**

(1) *Bending a line to a hook* (Fig 3-70). Reeve the end of the line through the eye, form a bight along the shank of the hook, then take several turns round the bight, starting from the eye and finishing through the end of the bight, Haul taut. This is very similar to the heaving line knot.

Fig 3-70. Bending a polyamide line to a fishing hook

(2) *Joining a polyamide line (Fig 3-71).* Make a heaving-line knot at the end of one length, then pass the other length through the bight before making a similar knot in it. Haul taut. The lines must be moistened before the knot is tied.

Fig 3-71. Joining polyamide lines

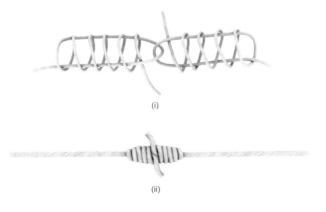

ad. **Sheepshank** (Fig 3-72). This is used to shorten the bight of a rope temporarily without cutting it. The strain on the rope will usually prevent the sheepshank from slipping, but if necessary the loops can be stopped to the standing parts or secured with a toggle.

Fig 3-72. Sheepshank

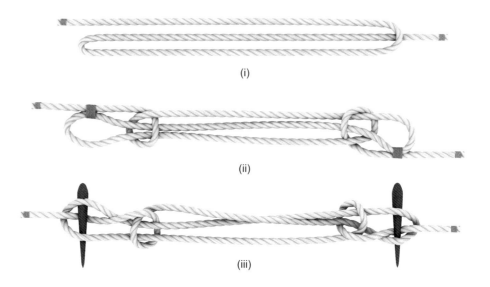

(i)

(ii)

(iii)

ae. **Single carrick bend** (Fig 3-73). Used for joining two hawsers together when the join will have to pass round a capstan or winch. The ends should be stopped to their standing parts. Make a cross in one end of rope with the fag end on top, then bring the other rope's end up through the bight of the first, over the cross, down between the standing part and fag end, and back up through the bight on the **opposite** side to the first fag end.

Fig 3-73. Single carrick bend

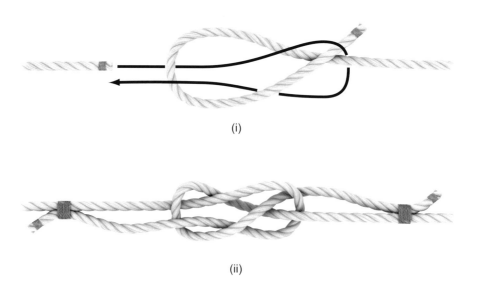

(i)

(ii)

af.   **Double carrick bend** (Fig 3-74). This is used when a more secure bend than the single carrick bend is required.

Fig 3-74. Double carrick bend

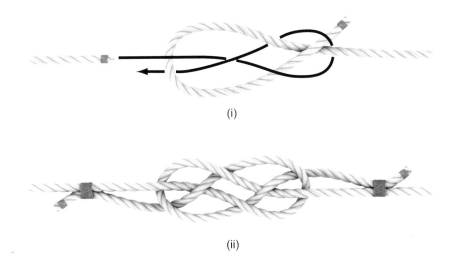

(i)

(ii)

ag. **Lorry-driver's hitch** (Fig 3-75). This hitch is useful as a means of gaining purchase on cover lanyards or frapping lines etc. Form an eye, as for one end of a sheepshank, at a convenient point on the bight of the rope (Fig 3-75(i)). Lead the end of the rope through or round the securing point, then through the formed eye on the bight of the rope (Fig 3-75(ii)). Haul the rope taut and secure with a rolling hitch (Fig 3-75(iii)).

Fig 3-75. Lorry-driver's hitch

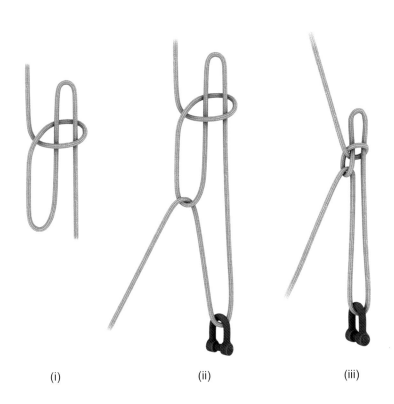

(i)   (ii)   (iii)

03017. Knots

a.   The functions of a knot are described at Para 03016. The following paragraphs described how a few commonly used knots are made. To assist in the description the strands are lettered A, B, C, etc., and their respective bights a, b, c, etc.

b.   **Crown knot** (Fig 3-76). When finished, the crown knot leaves the three strands pointing back along the rope. It is used to begin a back splice and as a basis for more complicated knots, but seldom on its own. To form a crown, whip the rope at a distance from its end equal to 12 times its diameter. Then unlay the strands to the whipping, whip their ends, and spread them out in the form of a star, with the centre strand farthest away from the body. Now (Fig 3-76) bring strand C to the front to form a loop Fig 3-76(i); place strand A over C and behind B Fig 3-76(ii); thread strand B through the loop of C Fig 3-76 (iii); pull all strands taut until knot is tidy and uniform Fig 3-76(iv).

Fig 3-76. Making a crown knot

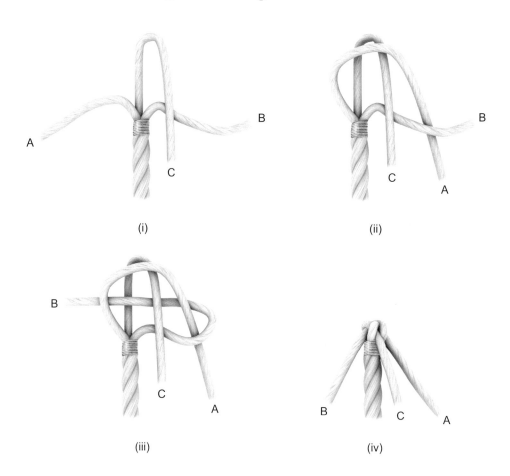

c.   **Wall knot** (Fig 3-77). When finished, the wall knot leaves all three strands pointing in the original direction. It is, in fact, a crown knot turned upside down. Prepare the rope as for a crown; then take strand A and pass it under B; take strand B round A so as to enclose it, and pass it under C; take strand C round B so as to enclose it and bring it **up** through the bight **a**. If the wall is to be used by itself to prevent a rope unreeving, the strands should be whipped together where they emerge from the knot and the ends should then be cut off.

Fig 3-77. Making a wall knot

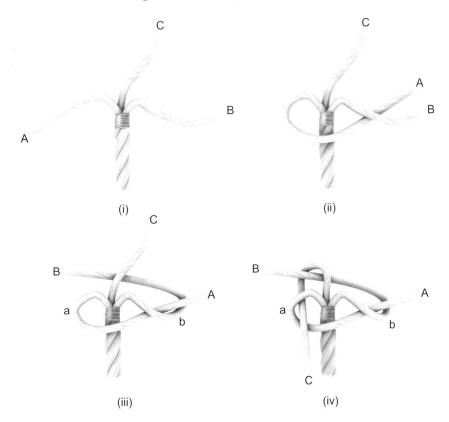

(i)

(ii)

(iii)

(iv)

d.   **Wall and crown knot**. This can be used to prevent a rope such as a rudder lanyard from unreeving, and also to form the foundation for more advanced knots. The whipping is placed at a distance from the end equal to 20 times the diameter of the rope, the wall being formed first and the crown made on top of it.

e.   **Crown and wall knot** (Fig 3-78). This differs from the Wall and Crown Knot in that the crown is made first and the wall formed under it. It is used for finishing off the end of seizings to prevent them from unreeving. The strands are unlaid right down to the turns of the seizings, against which the crown is formed as close as possible. The wall is then made under it and hauled taut, thus jamming the knot in tightly.

Fig 3-78. Making a crown and wall knot

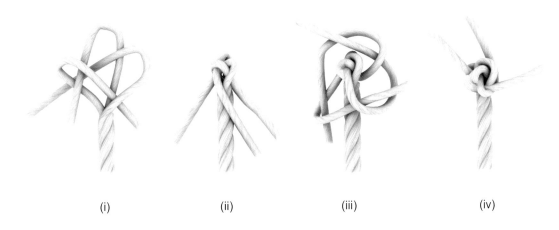

(i)   (ii)   (iii)   (iv)

f.   **Manrope knot** (Fig 3-79). The Manrope knot is a decorative knot made at the ends of gangway manropes to prevent them unreeving, and to afford a handhold for anyone climbing aboard. To make the knot, whip the rope at a distance from its end equal to twenty times its diameter, unlay the strands to the whipping, and whip their ends. Make a wall and crown, keeping the knot fairly loose (Fig 3-79(i)). Then take strand A and follow it round its own part, thereby doubling-up strand A Fig 3-79(ii). Work the other two strands similarly, haul all parts taut, and cut off the ends where they protrude from the base of the knot Fig 3-79(iii).

Fig 3-79. Manrope knot

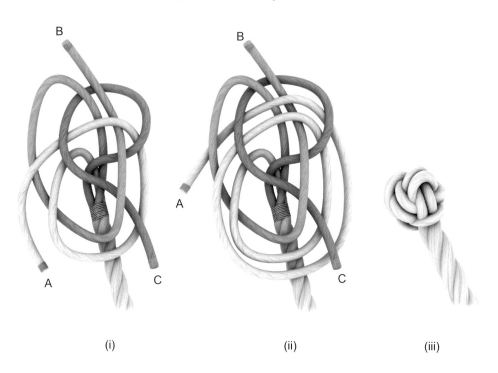

(i)   (ii)   (iii)

g.   **Turks head**. The Turk's Head is an ornamental knot supposed to resemble the turban once worn in Turkey, and should consist of three or more parts followed round two or more times. It may be made either as a standing or a running knot, according to whether it is to be fixed to an end or a bight, or is to be formed round another part of rope or a stanchion for example. Four different forms of this knot are described below.

(1)   *Standing Turk's head*. Made at the end of a rope. This is a manrope knot, but the ends are followed round a third or fourth time. Before starting the knot, however, the strands must be unlaid for a distance of not less than 25 times the diameter of the rope. (See Fig 3-80).

(2)   *Running Turk's head*. Made at the end of a rope and round its own bight (as in a running lanyard), this is similar to a standing Turk's head made at the end of a rope, except that the wall and crown with which it is begun are made round the bight of the rope. The strands are then followed round two or more times, thereby forming a knot, which will slide up and down the bight. (See Fig 3-81).

Fig 3-80. Standing Turk's head   **Fig 3-81. Running Turk's head**

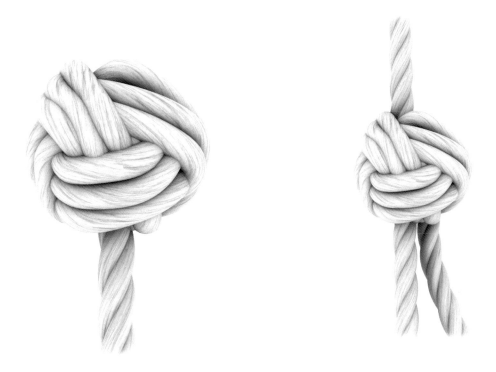

(3)   *Standing Turk's head*. Made on the bight of a rope. This is formed from a three parted length of line, called a **spider**, which is tucked into the centre of the rope so that its parts emerge from the strands equidistantly. The Spider is made up by tucking a length of line into the bight of another line (Fig 3-82(i)). The length of each leg should not be less than 20 times the combined diameters of the rope and line. Having inserted the Spider (Fig 3-82(ii)), crown the ends round the rope left-handed (Fig 3-82(iii), and then turn round and crown them back right-handed (Fig 3-82(iv)). Now follow each part round with its own end two or more times (Fig 3-82(v)), work all parts taut, and cut off the ends.

Fig 3-82. Standing Turk's head on a bight

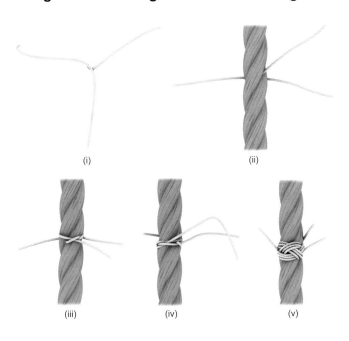

(4)   *Running Turk's head.*   Made round a bight of rope, a stanchion or other fitting is formed out of a single length of rope. A half hitch is made round the rope or fitting, and then followed by a round turn; the end is then dipped under the bight of the half-hitch (Fig 3-83(i)). The bights round the rope are crossed, the bight which is on the same side as the end of the line being placed underneath. The end is then passed down between the bights (Fig 3-83(ii)) and brought over the other side. The second and third operations are repeated until the rope is encircled (Fig 3-83(iii)). The ends are then followed round as often as may be required, all parts are hauled taut (Fig 3-83(iv)) and the two ends finished off with a crown and wall.

Fig 3-83. Running Turk's head on a bight

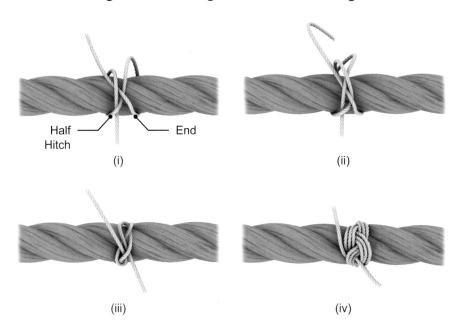

Half — Hitch   — End

(i)   (ii)

(iii)   (iv)

03018. Whippings

a.   **Introduction.** A whipping is the binding round the bare end of a rope to prevent the strands unlaying. Four types of whipping are described below.

b.   **Common whipping** (Fig 3-84). Seaming or roping twine is used when the rope is not large, and small stuff is used on a large rope. Place the end of the twine along the rope as in Fig 3-84(i); pass turns of the twine over the rope against its lay, working towards the end of the rope, and haul each taut. Then lay the other end of the twine along the rope, as in Fig 3-84(ii), and pass the remaining turns over it, taking the bight of twine over the end of the rope with each turn. When the bight becomes too small to pass over the end of the rope, haul this second end of the twine through the turns which you have passed over it until taut, thus completing the last turn round the rope, and cut off the end (Fig 3-84(iii) and Fig 3-84(iv)). An alternative finish, which can be used when the whipping is on the bight of the rope, is to take the last three or four turns loosely over one finger and pass the end back through them. Work the turns taut, and haul the end taut as above.

Fig 3-84. Common whipping

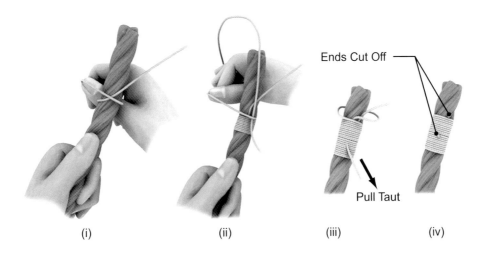

Ends Cut Off

Pull Taut

(i)   (ii)   (iii)   (iv)

c.   **West country whipping** (Fig 3-85). Middle the twine on the rope in the position required, pass the two ends round the rope in opposite directions and half-knot them on the other side (an alternative and more secure start is with a constrictor knot). Now bring the ends up and half-knot them again, and continue in this manner, making a half-knot every half turn so that the half-knots lie alternately on opposite sides of the rope. Finish off with a reef knot.

Fig 3-85. West country whipping

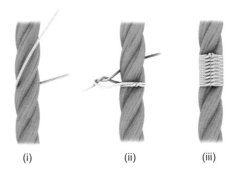

(i)   (ii)   (iii)

d.   **American whipping** (Fig 3-86). This is similar to the common whipping except that the first end of twine is left out clear between the first and second half of the turns. The two ends are secured together with a Reef knot and cut off.

Fig 3-86. American whipping   **Fig 3-87. Sailmakers whipping**

   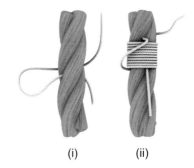

(i)   (ii)

e. **Sailmaker's whipping** (Fig 3-87). This whipping is the most secure, but of course it can only be used on hawser-laid rope. Unlay the end of the rope by about three times the diameter and hold it in the left hand pointing upwards, with the middle strand farthest away. Make a bight in the twine about 200 mm long and pass this bight over the middle strand only, with the two ends towards you. With the bight of twine hanging down the back of the rope and the ends pointing down in front, lay up the rope with the right hand. Leave the short end of twine where it is and, with the long end, pass the turns of the whipping, working towards the end of the rope against the lay. When sufficient turns are on, take the bight of twine, pass it up outside the whipping, following the lay of the strand around where it was originally put, and pass it over that strand, where the latter comes out at the end of the rope (Fig 3-87(i)). Now haul on the short end so as to tighten the bight, then bring this end up outside the whipping, again following the lay of the rope, and then reef knot the two ends in the middle of the rope and out of sight (Fig 3-87(ii)).

03019. Mousing

a. **Introduction**. A mousing is used for keeping the pin of a screw shackle or slip in position, or to prevent inadvertent unhooking from an open hook. Shackles and slip pins must always be moused with seizing wire (Fig 3-88 and Fig 3-89). All hooks now in use in the Royal Navy incorporate a spring-loaded safety catch; however, should an open hook be encountered the method of mousing it with seizing wire is shown in Fig 3-90.

b. To allow quicker transfer and greater use of working running rigging, whilst retaining basic safety, INSULOK ties may be used for non-standing parts. Ships may use INSULOK ties instead of wire mousing for screw shackle bolts on temporary working rigging. On completion of the evolution, temporary working rigging is to be de-rigged. Where rigging which is required to remain rigged for more than 24 hours, a wire mousing should replace INSULOKs. Where any doubt exists as to whether rigging is temporary or permanent, wire mousing should be used. Likewise INSULOKs are not to be used where there is a risk of personnel sustaining injuries or cuts, eg. on guardrails, gangway screens, hatch shackles and distance lines (cyalume attachment) etc. INSULOKs come in three sizes and are easy to apply:

(1) For screw shackles up to 3 tonnes proof load:

0262/746-8554 186 mm x 4.7 mm
0262/746-8555 360 mm x 4.7 mm

(2) For screw shackles of 3 tonnes proof load and above:

0262/746-8556 339 mm x 7.6 mm

Note. *To permit ease of access for damage control and fire-fighting teams, shackles attaching safety chains/wires to stanchions around internal hatches are not to be moused. However, these shackles must be regularly checked to ensure the pins are fully screwed home.*

c. **Passing a mousing**

(1)   To mouse a shackle pin with stainless steel seizing wire (Fig 3-88) middle a 250 mm length of the wire through the eye of the pin and twist the two parts together two or three times to attach the wire to the pin; then pass the two ends of the wire in opposite directions three or four times round the shank of the shackle and back through the eye of the pin, making sure that each turn is tight. Finish off by twisting the two parts tightly together two or three times, then cut off any surplus wire 20mm from the final twist and bend down the ends.

(2)   When mousing a slip pin (Fig 3-89) attach one end of a 250 mm length of seizing wire to the eye of the pin, then wind the wire tightly in figure-of-eights across the tongue of the slip and round the pin, locking the pin in position. Three or four turns of wire are normally required, but because of the possibility of an emergency breakaway, a mousing on a slip used in replenishment rigs and towing consist of one full figure-of-eight turn.

(3)   A mousing on an open hook is applied as shown in Fig 3-90. 'R' clips have replaced straight pins in slips and these do not require mousing.

Fig 3-88. Mousing a shackle

Fig 3-89. Mousing a slip

Fig 3-90. Mousing an open hook

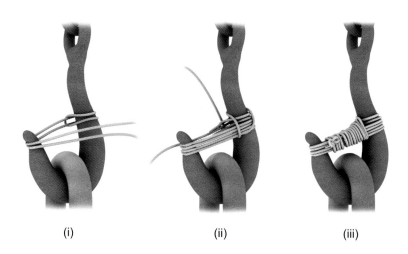

(i)   (ii)   (iii)

03020. Seizings

a.   **Types of seizings**. A seizing is a method of fastening together two parts of rope sufficiently strongly to stand a required strain. Three standard seizings designed to meet certain specific standards are employed in the Royal Navy. Although, on occasion, departure from them in detail may be made, they should be regarded as the basis of all round work of this description.

(1)   *Flat seizing*. A light seizing for use when the strain on the two parts of rope is equal. It consists of one layer of approximately eleven round turns.

(2)   *Round seizing.* Also used when the strains on the parts of a rope are equal, but it is stronger than a flat seizing. It consists of approximately eleven round turns and ten riding turns; the number of riding turns is always one less than the number of round turns.

(3)   *Racking seizing.* When the strains on the parts of the rope are unequal or exerted in opposite directions a racking seizing is used. It is formed by passing one layer of racking turns, and then passing one of round turns so that they lie between the racking turns. The number of round turns is necessarily one less than the number of racking turns. Sufficient turns are taken for the length of the seizing to be equal to three times the diameter of the rope, eg, for racking two 24 mm ropes, an overall length of seizing of 72 mm is required.

b.   **Strength of seizings**.   For seizing cordage it is usual to use small stuff (polypropylene line, size appropriate to the rope being seized), although Spunyarn is sometimes used for temporary seizings. When seizing wire ropes, flexible mild steel wire is used. The number of turns to be used for a seizing depends upon the strength of the seizing stuff and the strain to which the seizing will be subjected. For cordage, eleven and 21 turns are recommended for flat and round seizings respectively, and a width of seizing equal to three times the diameter of the rope is recommended for the racking seizing. These seizings are based on a size of seizing stuff of about one-seventh of the size of the rope, eg 6 mm polypropylene line would be required for seizing a 40 mm diameter polyamide rope.

c. **Making up seizing stuff** (Fig 3-91). Wind the seizing stuff round one hand, clockwise for left-hand lay, anti-clockwise for right-hand lay, with as many riding turns as are required, and finish with a clove hitch on the bight around the middle. Work with the first end which is drawn out through the opposite side of the coil, thus thorough-footing the seizing stuff and making it easier to work by taking the turns out of it. The turns in the coil are held in place by the clove hitch.

Fig 3-91. Making up seizing stuff

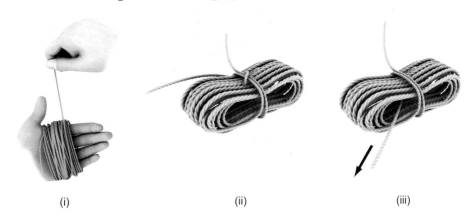

(i)   (ii)   (iii)

d. **Use of a heaving mallet and a Spanish windlass**. When seizing heavy rope the turns must be hauled more than hand-taut, and for this purpose the following mechanical aids may be used:

(1) *Heaving mallet* (Fig 3-92). The lower turns of a seizing can be tautened with a Heaving Mallet as follows:

(a) Lay the mallet in the bight of the line, as shown in Fig 3-92(i), and as close up to the work as possible.

(b) Take a turn diagonally round the head of the mallet, bringing the end up the opposite side of the handle Fig 92(ii).

(c) Take half a turn round the handle, and take the end again behind the head Fig 92(iii)

(d) Jam the end between the head and the standing part, and bring it up over the handle, as indicated by the arrowed line in Fig 92(iii).

(e) Place the head against the rope and heave, using the handle as a lever Fig 92(iv).

(2) *Spanish windlass* (Figs 3-93 and Fig 3-94). This can also be used for tautening the lower turns of a seizing. The windlass is formed by taking a turn round a suitable bar with the line to be tautened, and then turning the bar with a lever inserted through a bight of this line, as shown in Fig 3-93. A Spanish windlass can also be used to rack the two parts of rope together before putting on the seizing. For this purpose it is formed with a strand, well greased along its middle part, with a spike inserted at each end of the bar for use as levers, as shown in Fig 3-94.

Note. *A metal heaving mallet is used for wire seizings, and after each heaving the mallet should be run up and down the part of the wire that has been round it, in order to straighten out the turns.*

Fig 3-92. How to use a heaving mallet

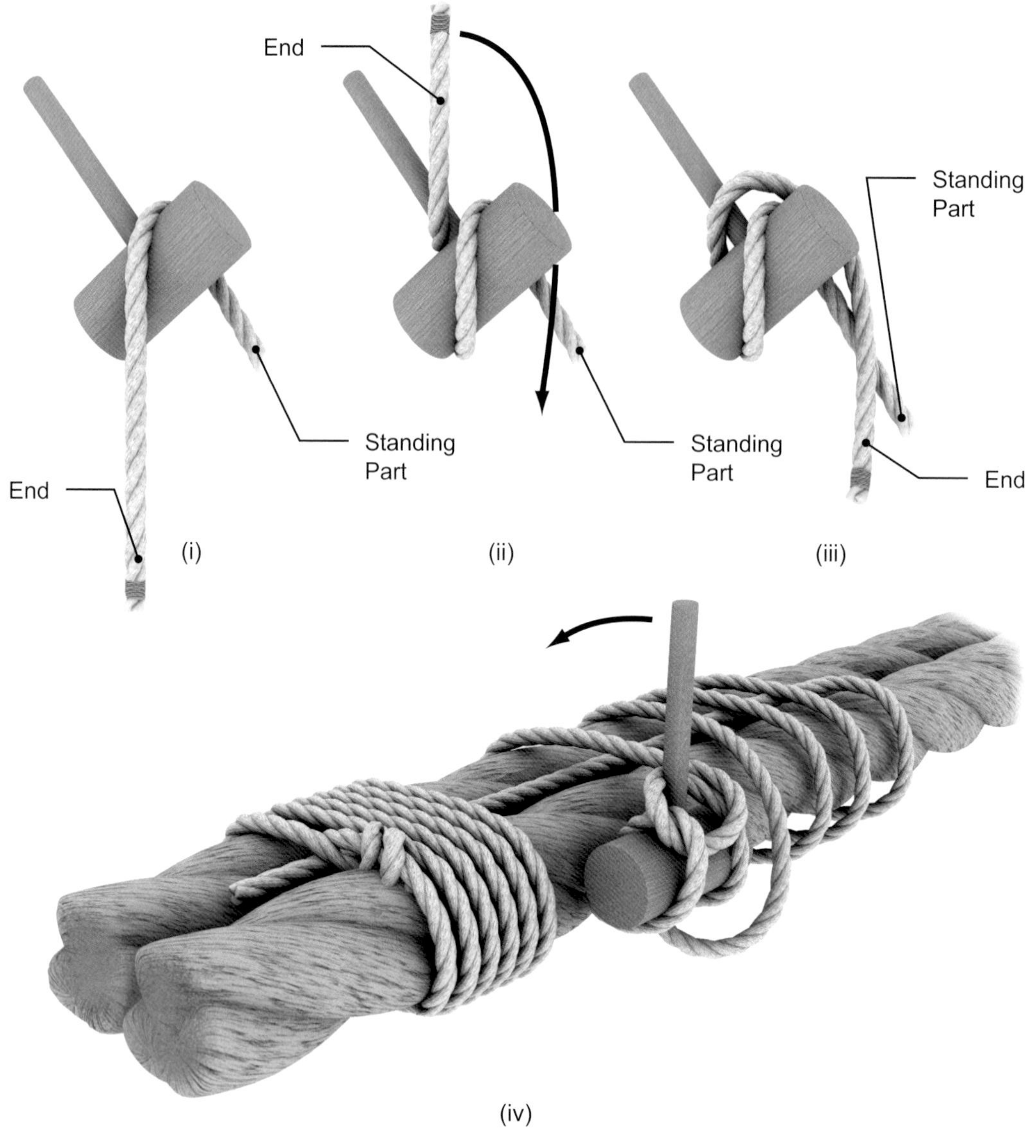

End

Standing
Part

End

(i)

Standing
Part

(ii)

Standing
Part

End

(iii)

(iv)

Fig 3-93. Spanish windlass

Fig 3-94. Racking two ropes with a Spanish windlass

e.   **Starting a seizing**. Cordage seizings are begun by making a small eye in the end of the seizing stuff, wire seizings are started by taking the end round one of the ropes to be fastened and then half-hitching it round its own part. Take care to keep the eye or half-hitch in the centre and clear of both parts of the rope (Fig 3-95(i)).

f.   **Passing a flat seizing**. Having begun the seizing as described, take the round turns very loosely round both parts of the rope, then pass the end back, along and between the two parts of the rope, under the turns and through the eye or half hitch of the seizing as in Fig 3-95(ii). Then heave each turn taut and take a cross turn round the seizing between the two parts of the rope as in Fig 3-95(iii). Now haul the seizing taut and secure its end with a clove hitch, one part of the clove hitch being on each side of the round turn as in Fig 3-95(iv). Finally, unlay the seizing stuff and finish off with a crown and wall close up against the hitch, or, if a wire seizing, break off the wire close to the hitch, and tuck away the ends so no harm will result when the rope is handled.

Fig 3-95. Passing a flat seizing

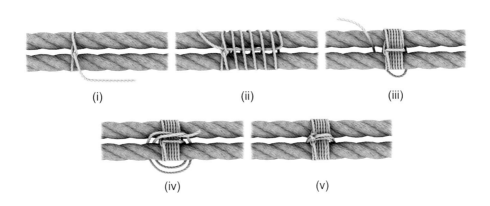

g. **Passing a round seizing**. Having begun the seizing as previously described, take the same round turns as in the flat seizing, pass the end down between the parts, up through the eye, and heave each turn taut with a heaving mallet or Spanish windlass as before (Fig 3-96(i)). The end is now in position to begin passing the upper or riding turns, which will become exactly between the parts of the lower turns. The number of riding turns is one less than the number of lower turns, and they are hove taut by hand. After passing the last riding turn, lead the end under the last turn of the lower turns and heave it hard taut (Fig 3-96(ii)). Then take a cross turn round all parts of the seizing (Fig 3-96(iii)), heave it well taut, and secure with a clove hitch each side of the round turn, as in the flat seizing (Fig 3-96(iv)). Finish off as for a flat seizing.

Fig 3-96. Passing a round seizing

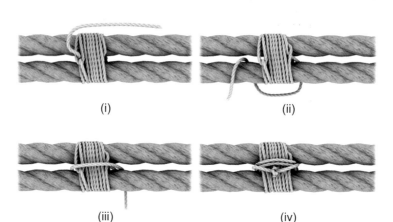

(i)   (ii)

(iii)   (iv)

h. **Passing a racking seizing**. Start the seizing as already described in sub para e. If the seizing slips when taken round both parts of the rope, take the end round one part only and reeve it through the eye. Then dip the end between the two parts of rope and take a number of figure-of-eight turns round each part alternately, taking care to have the same number round each part and to leave room between each racking turn for the round turn which will come later (Fig 3-97(i)). When the racking turns have been hove taut, dip the end under the last turn and pass the round turns back towards the eye, filling the spaces between the racking turns Fig 3-97(ii). When the last round turn has been passed, (see that there is one less than the racking turns), complete the seizing by taking one round turn around the whole seizing and forming a clove hitch between the two parts of the rope. Finish off as for a flat seizing.

Fig 3-97. Passing a racking seizing

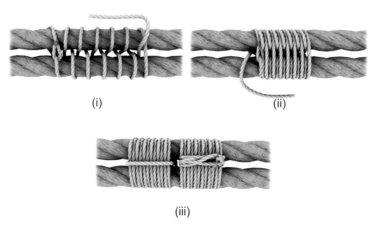

(i)   (ii)

(iii)

i.   **Rose seizing** (Fig 3-98). Used to secure an eye in a rope to a spar.

Fig 3-98. Rose seizing

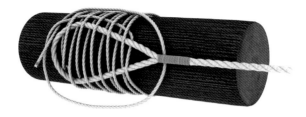

03021. Worming, parcelling and serving

a.   A rope or part of a rope is wormed, parcelled and served (Fig 3-99) to protect its outer surface against wear from chafing; make its outer surface smoother, so as to prevent other ropes from chafing when led over it; and, in the case of a steel wire rope, to protect the hands of those using it from the sharp ends of wire projecting from any splice in it. Worming, parcelling and serving is not necessarily damp-proof, and there is a danger that a rope may rot underneath its covering. Ropes so treated should therefore be inspected frequently for deterioration.

b.   **Worming.** This consists of filling in the spaces between the strands with lengths of spunyarn or small stuff laid along the lay of the rope, and its object is to make the rope smooth and round.

c.   **Parcelling.** This consists of binding the rope with strips of rot-proofed canvas, hessian or similar material. The strips should be between 50-75 mm wide and it is customary to bind them on in the direction of lay of the rope, working towards the eye. Each turn should overlap that preceding it by half the width of the strip, and the rope, if not man-made fibre, should first be well tallowed. When parcelling and serving a stay throughout its whole length the parcelling should be worked upwards from the eye of the lower splice to the eye of the upper splice, as this affords the maximum obstruction to the entry of water.

Fig 3-99. Worming, parcelling and serving

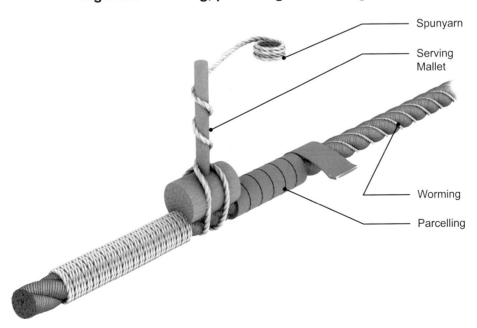

Spunyarn

Serving
Mallet

Worming

Parcelling

d.   **Serving**. This consists of binding a splice or a length of rope with close turns of polypropylene line or spunyarn. (Flexible mild-steel wire rope can be used for serving steel wire rope). Each turn is hove taut with a special serving mallet, which has a score in its head, to fit the rope, and a wooden handle about 40 cms long. A service is always bound on in the direction opposite to that of the parcelling, so as to avoid bunching up the latter. It is therefore put on against the lay of the rope, a rule which can be memorised thus: **Worm and parcel with the lay, turn and serve the other way**. A serving is begun as for a common whipping, although when serving with the larger sizes of flexible mild-steel wire it may be necessary to stop the first end down to the rope until sufficient turns have been applied to hold it firmly. The first few turns are put on by hand and hauled taut with a spike or heaving mallet. The serving mallet is then placed on the rope and the turns of the service are passed as follows:

(1)   Take a half-turn round the handle; then one turn round the fore end of the head of the mallet and the rope; then dog the serving around the handle of the mallet.

(2)   To put on a serving, stand with the rope on your left side while facing in the direction in which the turns are advancing. Then pass the ball of spunyarn round and round in step with the serving. Having completed the required length, finish off the service by passing the end back under the last four turns, hauling all parts taut, and making a crown and wall, or, if finishing a wire seizing, break off the wire close to the hitch, and tuck away the ends so no harm will result when the rope is handled. Also, it is customary to finish the serving of a wire serving on an eye splice in a similar manner to that of a seizing; a cross turn is therefore taken round the last few turns of the serving, inside the neck of the eye, and is followed by a clove hitch, the ends of the wires being then broken off and tucked away.

Note.   *If serving over a restricted length of rope – up to an eye splice for example – which does not allow the mallet to advance ahead of the last turns; the serving stuff should be brought to the mallet as follows:*

(a)   Up over the cut in the fore in the fore end of the head; one-quarter turn round the handle; one turn round the rope and rear end of the head (taken in the direction of the service, ie against the lay of the rope); and then dogged round the handle.

03022. Lashing

Two crossed spars can be secured together either with a **square lashing** or a **diagonal lashing**. Specific types of lashing are employed in rigging sheers or gyns and they are described later in this chapter. A Square Lashing is used when the spars are to be secured at right angles to each other and the Diagonal Lashing when they are to be secured at an acute angle to each other.

a.   **Square lashing** (Fig 3-100). Make fast one end of the rope to one of the spars with a timber hitch and haul it taut. Then cross the spars with the smaller spar lying underneath. Bring the other end of the lashing up over the larger spar, down and under the smaller, up and over the larger, and so on until sufficient turns have been taken. To avoid riding turns, the turns on the larger spar should lie in succession outside those first applied, and those on the smaller spar should lie in succession inside those first applied. Finish by taking two or three frapping turns round the parts between the spars, and make fast with a clove hitch round all parts or round one of the spars.

b.   **Diagonal lashing** (Fig 3-101). Make fast one end of the rope as for a square lashing, and pass as many turns as are required diagonally round both spars. Then bring the end up over one spar and take a few more turns across the opposite diagonal, finishing off as for a square lashing.

Fig 3-100. Square lashing   **Fig 3-101. Diagonal lashing**

03023. Splicing hawser-laid and multi-plait cordage

a.   Splicing is a method of joining the ends of two ropes together, or of making an eye in the end of a rope, by interlocking the strands. Unless otherwise stated it should be accepted that all splices reduce the strength of a rope by 10%. The tools and equipment required for splicing hawser-laid or multiplait cordage are: a fid, which is a pointed wooden spike made of hardwood, a heaving mallet for heaving tucks into place, a sharp knife, and seaming twine, sailmaker's twine and PVC insulating tape for marling or taping up where necessary. A hot knife or candle should be available to heat-fuse the ends of man-made fibre cordage.

b.   **Special considerations when splicing man-made fibre cordage**. Special care is needed when splicing man-made fibre cordage because an unsatisfactory splice may be dangerous. When unlaying strands ensure that the yarns are disturbed as little as possible. Each strand should be marled, or taped every 50mm, along its length to maintain its form. Firm whippings of twine or tape must be used and the ends of the strands must be heat fused.

When making an eye splice, a throat seizing is recommended. Serving a man-made fibre cordage splice is not recommended because it tends to loosen when the rope's diameter decreases under load; if such a rope has to be served it must be very tight. When splicing man-made fibre hawser-laid rope five full tucks should be made if the ends of strands are to be dogged; to complete the splice the ends of strands should be fused. Four full tucks reduced to two-thirds and one-third should be made if the splice is tapered. If the splice is then served the first three tucks should be left uncovered. When splicing man-made fibre cordage take care that:

(1)   Strands lifted for tucking are not kinked. To avoid strand distortion, use a small fid of oval cross-section; then follow this with larger fids until it is just possible to pass the strand without distorting it.

(2)   Strands are pulled back as far as possible.

(3)   The rope is kept level the whole time and strands are lifted only high enough for the tuck to take place.

(4)   The rope itself is not allowed to kink.

c.   **Types of splice**

(1)   *Back splice*. For finishing the end of a rope, which is not required to be rove through a block; it is to prevent it from unlaying.

(2)   *Eye splice*

(a) For making a permanent eye in the end of a rope. A soft eye is a small eye spliced in the end of a rope. A thimble eye is formed by fitting and splicing the end of the rope round a thimble, the splice holding the thimble in place. Thimble eyes are fitted in the ends of cordage and wire ropes, which are intended to be used in conjunction with a joining shackle or other rigging fittings. The hawser eye is an alternative to the thimble eye and just as efficient.

(b) The eye is first spliced larger than the thimble, then the thimble is fitted into the eye and secured in place by a strong seizing just below it. This enables the thimble to be easily removed and replaced, merely by cutting the seizing and then renewing it. A **bollard eye** is a long soft eye, 1.5 metres long from crown to splice, fitted in the ends of berthing hawsers so they can be placed over bollards.

(3)   *Short splice.* For joining two ropes not required to pass through a block.

(4)   *Long splice.* For joining two ropes which are required to pass through a block. A well-made long splice does not increase the diameter of the rope and should not reduce its strength.

(5)   *Cut splice.* For making a permanent eye in the bight of a rope.

(6)   *Chain splice.* For splicing a rope tail into a chain which has to be led through a block or fairlead. The chain splice is not more than two-thirds of the strength of the rope.

d.   **Back splice in hawser-laid rope** (Fig 3-102). If splicing man-made fibre cordage, read Para 03023 sub para a. This method of finishing the end of a rope must not be used if the rope is to pass through a block, eyeplate or similar fitting. Whip the rope at a distance from its end equal to twenty times the diameter of the rope, then unlay the strands to the whipping and whip the end of each strand. Make a crown knot Fig 3-102(i), cut the whipping and then tuck each strand over one strand and under the next, to the left and against the lay of the rope, as shown in Fig 3-102(ii). After each strand is tucked, pull the strands taut and tidy up this first tuck until each strand is uniform. Repeat this tucking twice more in natural fibre cordage Fig 3-102(iii), four times more if splicing MMF cordage. Always tuck to the left, using the next strand to the left. If the splice is to be served, as shown in Fig 3-103, taper it down after the third tuck (or fourth if splicing man-made fibre) as follows:

(1)   Take one-third of the yarns out of each strand and tuck the remaining two-thirds once, as already described; though discarded, the thirds should not be cut off until the splice is completed.

(2)   Halve the reduced strands, then tuck one-half of each and leave the other.

(3)   Haul all parts taut, including the discarded ends, which should now be cut off.

Fig 3-102. Making a back splice

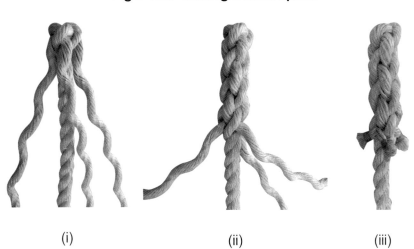

(i)   (ii)   (iii)

Fig 3-103. Tapering and serving a back splice

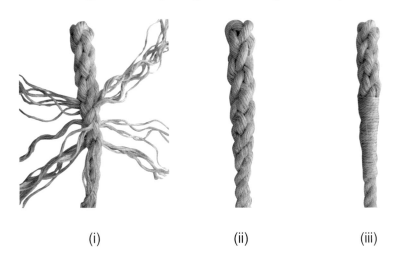

(i)   (ii)   (iii)

e.   **Soft eye splice in hawser laid cordage**. If splicing man-made fibre cordage read Para 03023 sub para b.

(1)   Whip the rope at a distance from its end equal to twenty times the diameter of the rope, then unlay it to the whipping and whip the end of each strand.

(2)   Mark the place intended for the crown of the eye, and bend the rope back from there so as to bring the unlaid strands alongside the standing part where the splice is to be made, with the left and middle strands lying on the top of the rope (Fig 3-104); the set of the splice will depend on selecting this middle strand correctly.

Fig 3-104. The start of an eye splice in hawser-laid cordage

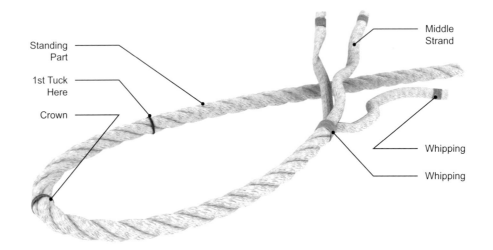

Fig 3-105. Making an eye splice

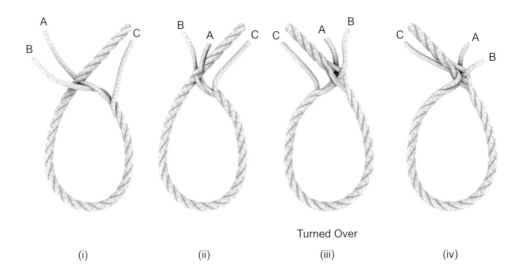

(3)   Now refer to Fig 3-105, in which the middle strand is marked A, the left-hand strand B, and the right-hand strand C, and make the splice as follows:

(a) Tuck A, from right to left, under the nearest strand of the standing part Fig 3-105(i).

(b) Tuck B, from right to left, under the next strand of the standing part Fig 3-105(ii).

(c) Now turn the rope right over so as to bring the remaining strand C on the top Fig 3-105(iii), and then tuck C from right to left under the unoccupied strand of the standing part Fig 3-105(iv). Care must be taken to retain the lay of the rope in the last strand tucked, as this enables it to lie closer.

(d) Now, beginning with C, heave each strand taut with a heaving mallet. Then tuck all three strands a second and third time, (fourth and fifth time if splicing man-made fibre cordage).

(e) Finish off by tapering the splice as described for the back splice or, if the appearance of the splice is of secondary importance and maximum strength is required, dogging the ends by halving each of the three strands and whipping each half to its neighbour over the adjacent strand as shown in Fig 3-106(i) and (ii).

f. **Thimble eye splice in hawser-laid cordage**. A thimble eye (Fig 3-106(iii)) is formed by fitting and splicing the end of the rope round a thimble, the splice holding the thimble in place. It is fitted in the ends of cordage and wire ropes, which are intended to be used in conjunction with a joining shackle or other rigging fittings. The procedure for seizing the thimble in place temporarily while the rope is spliced is by using two constrictor knots to hold the rope firmly round the thimble then splicing the rope as described for a soft eye.

Fig 3-106. Finished eye splices

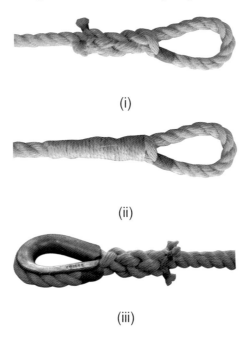

(i)

(ii)

(iii)

(i) Dogged soft eye, (ii) served soft eye and (iii) dogged thimble eye

g. **Short splice in hawser-laid rope**. (Fig 3-107 and Fig 3-108). If splicing man-made fibre cordage read Paragraph 03023b. The strands of each rope are tucked between the strands of the other rope against the lay, each strand being taken over the strand on its left, then under the next strand and emerging between this and the subsequent strand. In Fig 3-107 the ends of the rope are lettered A and B, and their unlayed strands C, D and E, and F, G and H respectively. Certain whippings and stops have been omitted to show the tucking of the strands more clearly.

(1) Whip each rope at a distance from its end equal to twenty times the diameter of the rope (this whipping has been omitted from rope A in the illustration).

(2)   Unlay the strands to the whipping and whip their ends (these whippings have also been omitted).

(3)   Marry the two ropes so that one strand of each lies between two strands of the other (Fig 3-107(i)).

(4)   Having ensured a close marry, whip the strands strongly around the join to prevent them slipping, and stop ends C, D and E to rope B with a strong stop (whipping and stops have been omitted).

(5)   Cut the whipping on A.

(6)   Take F over C, under E, and bring it out between D and E Fig 3-107(ii).

(7)   Take G over E, under D, and bring it out between D and C Fig 3-107(ii) and Fig 3-107(iii).

(8)   Take H over D, under C, and bring it out between C and E Fig 3-107(iii).

(9)   Stop G, F and H to A, cut the stop and whipping on B, and tuck C, D and E in similar manner.

(10) Heave all six strands equally taut with a heaving mallet.

(11) Again tuck each strand over the strand on its left and under the next one, and then repeat this operation a third time (fourth and fifth time if splicing MMF cordage).

(12) Finish off as described for an eye splice.

Fig 3-107. Making a short splice

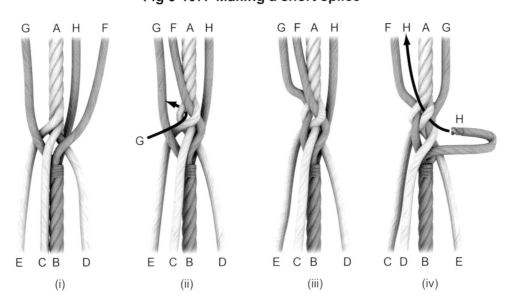

Fig 3-108. Finishing a short splice by dogging

h. **Cut splice in hawser-laid cordage**. If splicing man-made fibre cordage read Para 03023 sub para b. This splice is used when it is required to make a permanent eye in the bight of a rope. Whip each rope at a distance from its end equal to twenty times the diameter of the rope, then unlay it to the whipping and whip the end of each strand, (Fig 3-109(i)). Place the ends of the two ropes alongside and overlapping each other, and stop them together. Tuck the unlaid strands of both ropes as for an eye splice and finish off as for an eye splice.

Fig 3-109. Making a cut splice

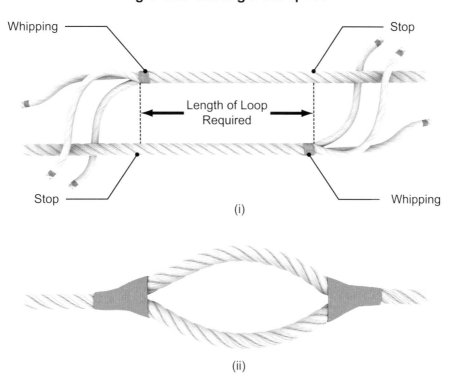

(i)

(ii)

i. **Long splice in hawser-laid cordage** (Natural fibre cordage only). This splice is used to join two ropes, which are required to pass through a block. Provided the splice is well made, it will not increase the diameter or weaken the rope. It is possible to make a long splice in man-made fibre cordage, but results are usually unsatisfactory. The principle of the long splice (Fig 3-110) differs radically from that of the short splice. One strand from each rope is unlaid, and the corresponding strand of the other rope is given a twist and laid up in its place; the remaining strand from each rope remains at the marry, resulting in three pairs of strands spaced equidistantly along the married ropes. One third of the yarns is now taken out of all strands (not shown in Fig 3-110(iv)) and, though discarded, these yarns should not be cut off until the splice is completed. Each pair of strands is then tied in an overhand knot (left over right for a right-hand laid rope), and each strand is tucked over one strand and under the next, as for a short splice. Half of the yarns in each strand are now taken out and the remaining yarns tucked once more, to give a gradual taper Fig 3-110(v). The splice is finished off by stretching it, hauling all ends taut (including the discarded yarns) and then cutting them off. To make a long splice, whip each rope at a distance from its end equal to forty times the circumference of the rope, then unlay the strands to the whipping and whip their ends. Marry the two ropes together, as in a short splice. Each strand unlaid as described above is followed up by the strand from the other rope which lies on its right in the marriage, so that H is unlaid and followed up by E, D is unlaid and followed up by F, and C and G remain at the marry. Each strand is unlaid until the length of the end of the strand following it up is reduced to twelve times the diameter of the rope. The splice is now finished off as described above.

Fig 3-110. Making a long splice

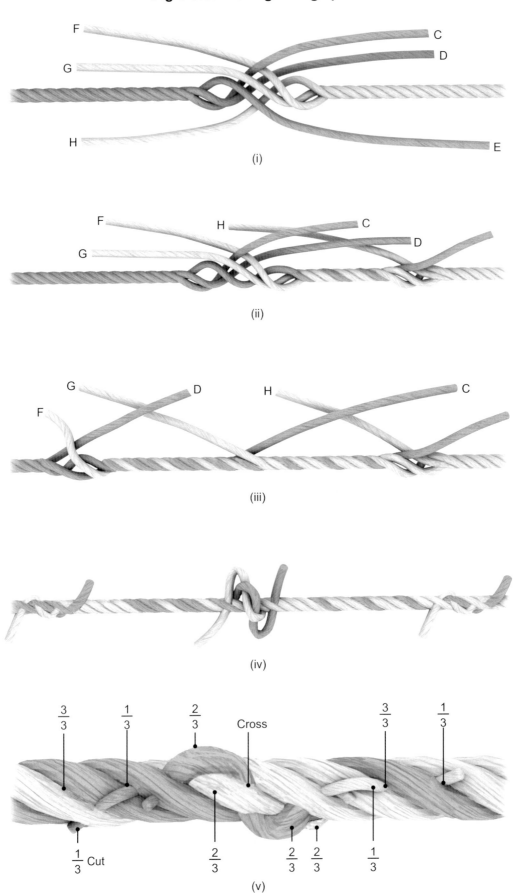

j.   **Chain splice in hawser-laid rope** (Natural fibre cordage only). This splice is used for splicing a cordage tail into a chain which is required to be led through a block or fairlead. Its strength is not more than two-thirds the strength of the rope. Prepare the rope as for an eye splice, but do not place a whipping round the rope, and unlay the strands to a length 30 times the diameter of the rope. Then unlay one strand, A, for another 150 mm, or twice the intended length of the eye Fig 3-111(i). Now pass strands B and C through the link on the end of the chain and marry up with A, thus forming the eye Fig 3-111(ii). Then further unlay strand A and lay up B in its place for about 300 mm, and finish off these two strands as for a long splice Fig 3-111(iii) and Fig 3-111(iv). Now tuck strand C into the standing part below the eye as for a short splice, with about three tucks, so as to meet strand A Fig 3-111(v). All ends are then hauled taut and cut off; the one-third strands of A and B are not shown in Fig 3-111(v).

Fig 3-111. Making a chain splice

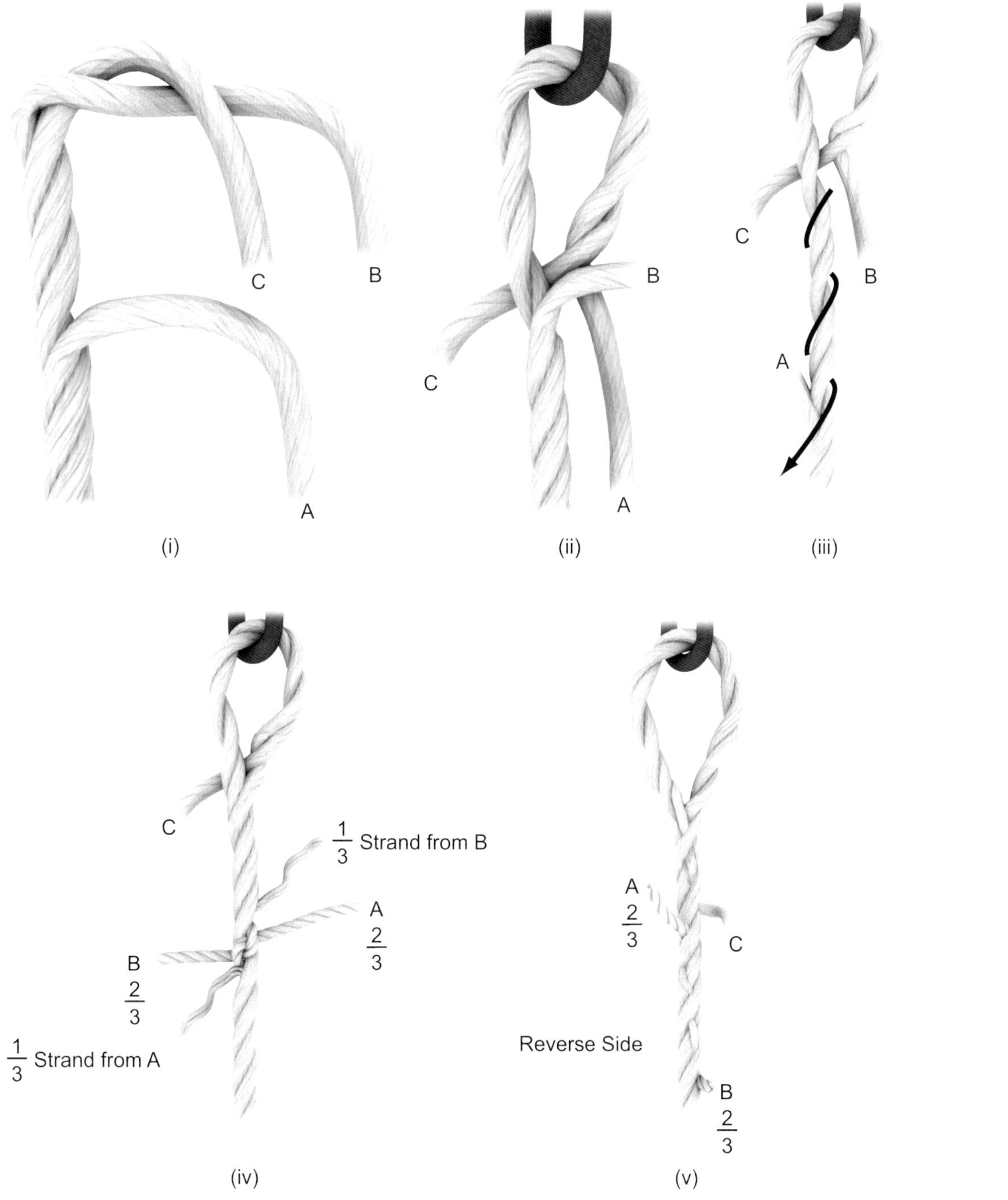

k.   **Eye splice in eight-strand plaited rope (multi-plait)**. The eye splice in multi-plait rope is governed by the construction, which has both Z (right-handed) lay strands and S (left-handed) lay strands. Fig 3-112 shows the stages of making the splice, as follows:

(1)   Read Para 03023 sub para b.

(2)   Make a seizing at a distance of eight 'knuckles' from the end of the rope (point of splice), then unlay the strands. (see Note).

(3)   Marry pairs of Z strands and pairs of S strands making four pairs in all.

(4)   Commence the tucking sequence by passing a pair of Z strands under the nearest convenient pair of Z-lay strands in the standing part of the rope, followed by the adjacent pair of S strands, tucked under the pair of S-lay strands of the rope unoccupied adjacent to the Z lay. (Fig 3-112(i)).

(5)   Turn the rope right over and repeat sub para (3) with the remaining two pairs of Z and S strands Fig 3-112(ii). This completes the first full tuck required using paired strands.

(6)   Divide all four pairs of Z and S strands and tuck these strands singly, one S strand under one S strand in the standing part and one Z strand under one Z strand in the standing part Fig 3-112(iii). Continue this tucking sequence for four tucks thus giving a total of five tucks to the splice Fig 3-112(iv). (see Note).

(7)   The ends of the strands should now be dogged as shown in Fig 3-108.

Fig 3-112. Eye splice in multi-plait rope

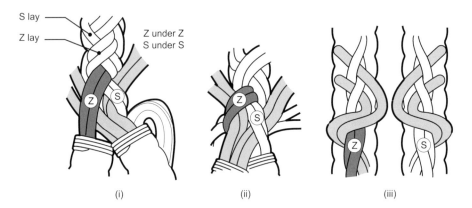

(i)   (ii)   (iii)

(iv)   (v)

l.   **Thimble eye splice in eight-strand plaited rope (multi-plait).** A thimble eye is fitted in the ends of cordage which is intended to be use in conjunction with a joining shackle or other rigging fittings. It is formed by fitting and splicing the end of the rope round a thimble, the splice holding the thimble in place. The procedure for seizing the thimble in place temporarily while the rope is spliced is by using two constrictor knots to hold the rope firmly round the thimble then splicing the rope as described for a soft eye.

m.   **Short splice in eight-strand plaited rope (multi-plait)**. Fig 3-113 shows the stages in the short splicing of multi-plait rope. For clarity the strands are numbered and referred to as black or white strands.

(1)   Read Para 03023 sub para b.

(2)   Unlay each rope for a distance equal to eight 'knuckles' along its length, this ensures sufficient length of strand to complete the four tucks required (see Note). Separate the pairs of strands, and temporarily whip the ends of the pairs together. In Fig 3-113(i) the right-hand strands are black; left-hand strands are white. The pairs are designated 1R to 4R meaning right-hand lay (black) and 1L to 4L meaning left-hand lay (white).

(3)   Marry the strands of the **same lay** in each rope together and tie off the ends. Tie together 2R and 3R, 2L and 4L, 1L and 3L, 1R and 4R Fig 3-113(ii). Tying together these strands ensures easy identification during the tucking sequence.

(4)   Untie strands 1L and 3L and commence tucking 1L under the nearest convenient pair of (black) strands as shown in Fig 3-113(iii) and Fig 3-113(iv). Tuck 1L for 4 tucks, following the same direction as the white strands in the whole portion of the rope.

(5)   Follow number 1L with 3L in the opposite direction and complete four tucks (v).

(6)   Repeat the tucking sequence for 2L and 4L, thus completing the tucking of all white right-handed strands as shown in Fig 3-113(vi).

(7)   Repeat sequence 3 to 5 with 1R and 4R, followed by 2R and 3R, for four tucks. (see Note).

(8)   To finish off the splice remove the temporary whippings and dog the ends of the strands as shown in Fig 3-108.

Note.   *When splicing HMPE an additional four full tucks must be taken, making a total of eight tucks. Therefore a length equal to twelve 'knuckles' must be unlaid before commencing the splice.*

Fig 3-113. Making a short splice in multi-plait rope

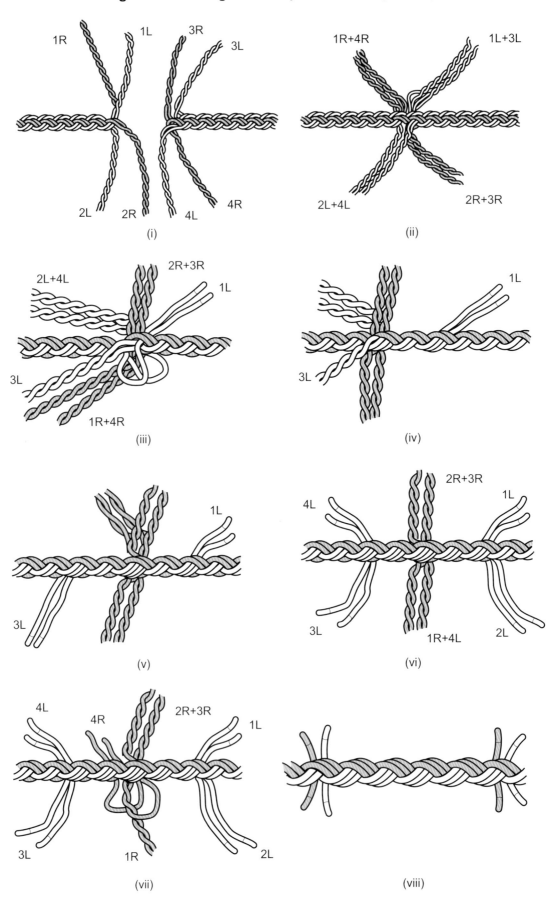

03024. Splicing braided cordage

The splicing of braided cordage differs from orthodox splicing in the techniques and tools, which are employed. As explained in Para 03003 sub para b(7) braided cordage falls into four main categories and by examining the end of any length of braidline cordage, the general construction of the rope can be identified. However, because all man-made fibre cordage must be spliced in accordance with the manufacturer's recommendations, and there are numerous variations to the construction of braided cordage within the four main categories, it is not practical in this publication to provide detailed guidance for splicing all versions that the seaman may encounter. Therefore the splicing of such cordage can only safely be carried out by the manufacturers of the rope, or by suitably trained personnel within a recognised rigging organisation. Damaged braidline ropes that cannot be readily replaced should be substituted temporarily with a suitable size and strength hawser-laid rope until a proper replacement can be obtained.

03025. Splicing HMPE (HPMT) ropes

a. **Introduction.** All ropes, no matter what material, size or construction require a termination of some kind, be it a knot, eye splice or mechanical termination. As professional seamen, we all know that a bend or hitch can reduce the strength of any given rope by up to 60%. HPMT splicing techniques retain 90-100% of rope strength. Splicing HPMT ropes differs from standard rope splicing techniques but, if these instructions are followed, this will ensure trouble-free rope service. HPMT introduces three bespoke splicing techniques and two Lock-Stitching Procedures

(1)   12-Strand Class II (see Note 1, Note 2 and Note 3) rope – eye splice

(2)   12-Strand Class II rope – joining splice

(3)   12-Strand Class II chafe cover – ICE splice

(4)   Lock-Stitching Class II ropes – eye splice

(5)   Lock-Stitching Class II ropes – joining splice

Notes:

1.   It is absolutely critical that the proper splicing technique be used when splicing Class II Rope.

2.   ALL HPMT ropes are to be lock-stitched and inspected prior to operational use.

3.   Class II Ropes – High Performance Fibre content utilising High Modulus fibres such as Dyneema (HMPE), Technora or Vectran. These ropes impart the strength and stretch characteristics of the ropes produced which have tenacities greater than 15 grams/denier (GPD) and a total stretch, at break of less than 6%.

b. **HPMT – splicing fid lengths.** Fid lengths for splicing all HPMT ropes are 21 times the diameter of the rope in inches or millimetres. The proper sized fid for the rope size must be used in performing a splice. There are two styles of fids: Aluminium Tubular Fids and Wire Fids. The Aluminium Tubular Fids are used by inserting the end rope section into the fid while the Wire Fids are attached to the end of the rope section. Tubular Fids are pushed through the rope with an appropriate sized pusher where Wire Fids are either fed through the rope or pulled through by attaching a feed line.

Fig 3-114. Aluminium tubular fid

Short Section

Full FID Length

Table 3-14. Rope diameter to fid size required

Rope diameter	Fid size	Full fid length	Fid lengths for splicing	Actual measurements
20mm to 22mm	Size 1	340mm (12¼")	1 Full Fid plus 1 short section	410mm (16")
24mm	**Size 2**	**530mm (21")**	**1 Full Fid Only**	**530mm (21")**
28mm to 32mm	Size 2	530mm (21")	1 Full Fid Plus 1 short section	660mm (26")
36mm to 40mm	Size 2	530mm (21")	1½ Full Fid sections	790mm (31")
44mm to 48mm	Size 2	530mm (21")	2 Full Fid Lengths	1060mm (42")

c. **HPMT – splicing tools**

1. Wire fid
2. Pusher
3. Tubular fid
4. Lock stitchn
5. Lock-stitch twine (1.75mm dia. HPMT)
6. Electrical tape
7. Tape measure
8. Sharp rigging knife

Fig 3-115. HPMT splicing tools

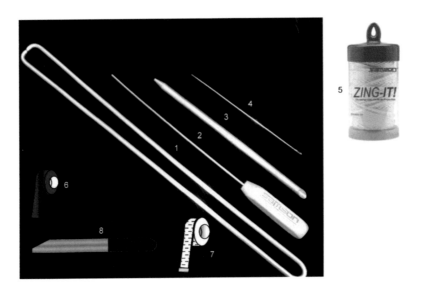

d.　**HPMT – eye splice procedure**

(1)　*Step 1.* **Measuring and marking the rope**. Tape the end of the rope to be spliced, measure one wire fid length from the taped end and **MARK 1.** Then from Mark 1 measure two wire fid lengths and **MARK 2** now, form the size of the eye required and **MARK 3** as shown in Fig 3-116(i).

Fig 3-116.　HPMT tapering details

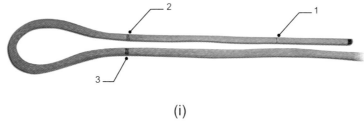

(i)

(2)　*Step 2.* **Performing the taper**. From **MARK 1** in the direction of the taped end, mark every second left and right strand for three strands as shown in Fig 3-116(iii). Then pull out each strand and cut off as shown in Fig 3-116(iv) to Fig 3-116(vii). The tapered end will then have only six strands remaining. Re-tape the bitter end to prevent the rope from unbraiding.

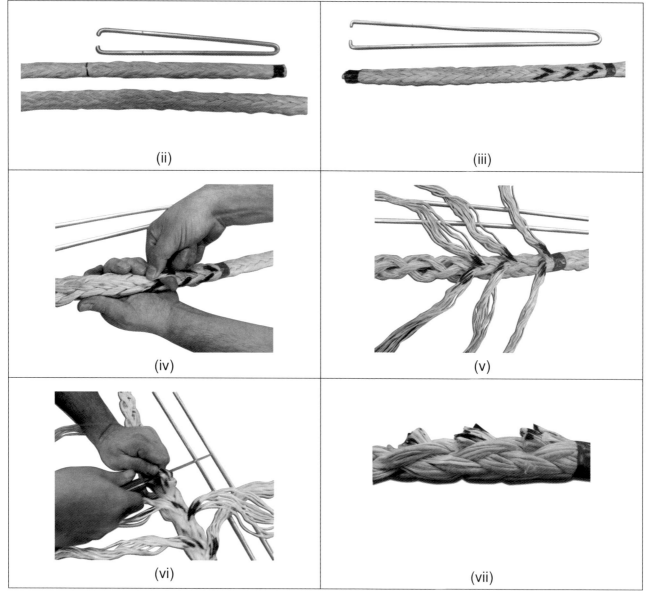

(ii)

(iii)

(iv)

(v)

(vi)

(vii)

(3) *Step 3.* **Burying the tapered tail into the standing part of the rope.** Lay out the rope as shown in Fig 3-117(i).

Fig 3-117. Rope laid out in preparation for splicing

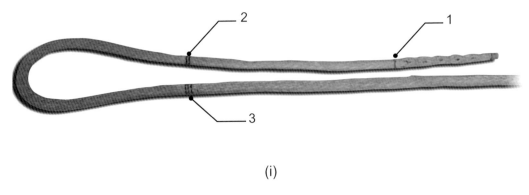

(i)

Measure 1.5 wire fid lengths beyond where the tapered tail (bitter end) meets the standing part of the rope. This will be the fid insertion point.

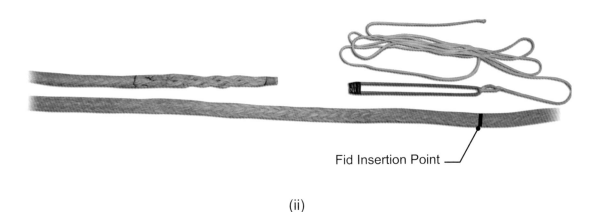

Fid Insertion Point

(ii)

At the fid insertion point, open the standing part of the rope and insert the wire-fid into the centre of the rope. Then using both hands, slide the fid carefully all the way up to mark 3 and exit the rope on the same side as mark 2.

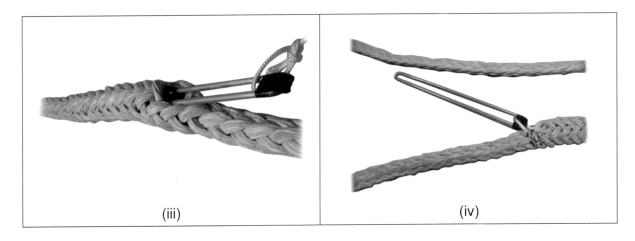

(iii)   (iv)

Turn the fid 180° so that the taped end of the fid is outermost. Re-insert the smooth end of the fid back into the rope from where it has exited (where the pull-through cord exits) as shown in Fig 3-117(vi). Then remove the tape from the end of the fid. Attach the wire-fid prongs over the tapered tail end and secure with electrical tape as shown.

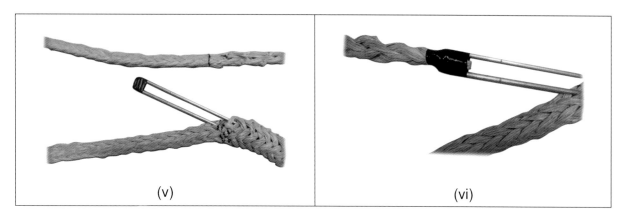

(v) (vi)

Tie-off the pull-through cord and using both hands, gently 'milk' the rope towards the eye. The tail will start to disappear into the rope. 'Milk' gently to begin with and increase the firmness as you progress towards the eye. Continue this until mark 2 meets with mark 3 as shown.

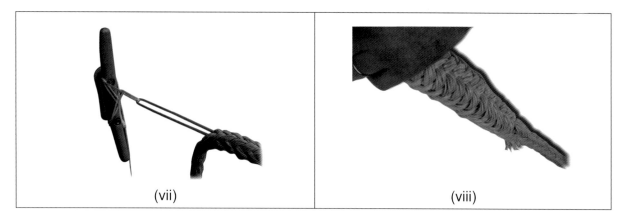

(vii) (viii)

Work the fid out of the rope and some 200mm of tapered tail. Remove the fid and all tape from the tapered end. Randomly select two strands approximately 200mm in length and cut off as shown in Fig 3-117(xii).

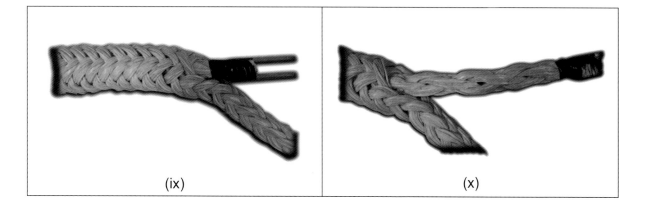

(ix) (x)

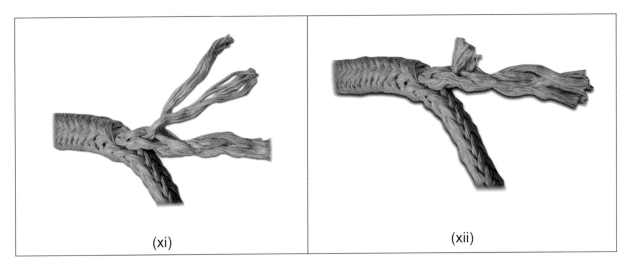

| (xi) | (xii) |

Secure the eye end. Then using both hands, 'milk' the rope firmly away from the eye end. You will notice that the tapered tail will disappear inside the rope. Continue 'milking' the rope beyond this point. Do this twice to ensure the splice is fully embedded. The splice is now complete and ready for lock-stitching.

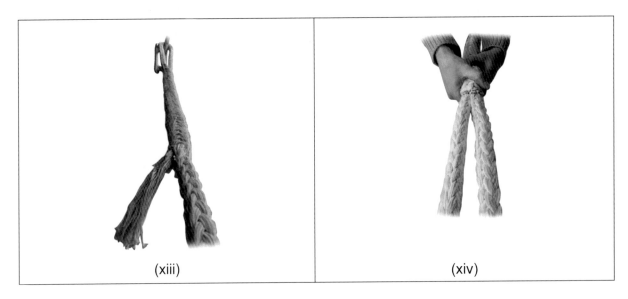

| (xiii) | (xiv) |

e. **HPMT – Eye splice lock stitch procedure.** This procedure is critical to the HPMT splicing technique and should be applied immediately following splicing. All stitches should be pulled snug, not tight using the 10" Straight Round, Pointed Needle and 2.25m (6 – 8ft) of Lock-Stitch Cord. Figure 3-115 shows the Lock-Stitch Cord and Needle. The following Lock-Stitch procedure is to be carried out:

Fig 3-118. Locking stitch tools

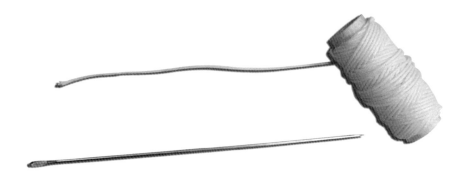

(1)   *Step 1.* **Measure and initial stitch.** Measure three 'Picks' down from the throat of the eye splice and open up the outer strands of the rope. This is the initial insertion point (Fig 3-119(i)) Once this is complete pass the threaded lock-stitch needle through the inner strands of the splice only at 45° directly through the centre of the spliced rope leaving a small 3" tail as shown in Fig 3-119(ii).

Fig 3-119. Lock stitch procedure

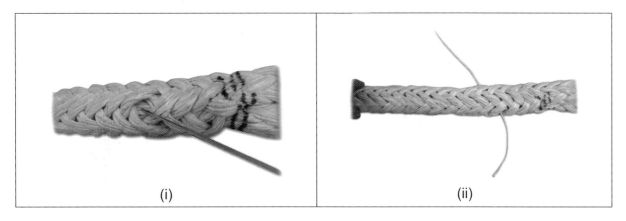

(i)   (ii)

Re-insert the needle at 45° to form the first full stitch. Each stitch should be the equivalent to the 'Pick Length' (see Note) of each strand in the rope (Fig 3-119(iii)) then continue until four full stitches are on each side of the rope (Fig 3-119(iv)).

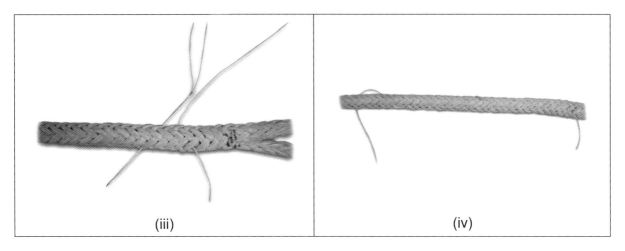

(iii)   (iv)

After the fourth stitch, turn the rope 90° and re-insert the needle (Fig 3-119(v)) to stitch back towards the eye in the same manner as above. The spliced area will now be lock-stitched on two planes perpendicular to each other. Then extract the last stitch at the same point as the initial insertion (Fig 3-119(vi)).

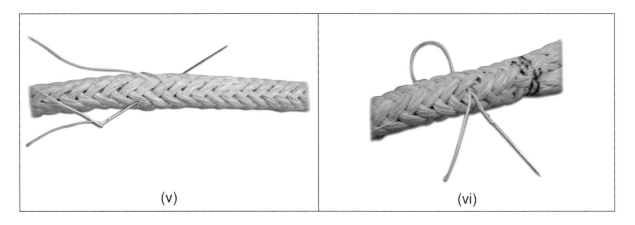

(v)   (vi)

Tie a reef knot in the two ends and re-insert the needle back into the rope (Fig 3-119(vii)), pulling the reef knot firmly into the rope (Fig 3-119(viii)) then cut off both ends close to where they exit the rope.

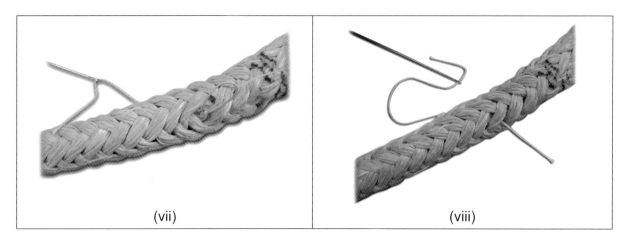

(vii)   (viii)

Note.   *'Pick', 'Pick Length' is the length of each visible strand within the rope structure.*

f.   **HPMT – Splicing ice procedure for 12 strand eye chafe protection**. This procedure must be carried out prior to splicing the eye but, after the eye splice has been measured and marked. Tools required are a Tubular Fid, a Pusher and a short length of Tie-off Cord as shown in Fig 3-120.

Fig 3-120. ICE splicing tools

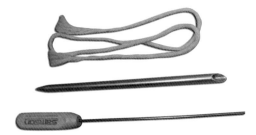

The Ice formula required is 2.3 times the length of the eye to be covered ie. a 2m long eye (4m in straight length) requires 2m (length of eye) x 2.3 = 4.6m of ICE. However, for ropes of 22mm and below 3.8m of ICE is required.

(1)   *Step 1.* **Measurement and marking the ICE protection**

  •   Using the ice formula above, measure and cut the 'ICE' to the required length to cover the eye. You will notice that a white nylon cord is present within the ice, this should be removed (pulled out) and is ideal for use as a pull-through cord for splicing as shown in Fig 3-121.

Fig 3-121. Nylon cord within ICE protection

(2)   *Step 2.*   **Splicing ICE protection**

(a) Pass the ice protection over the bitter end of the rope, less than one fid length from the bitter end of the ice. Then carefully slide the rope through the centre of the ice protection taking care not to snag any strands as shown in Fig 3-122.

Fig 3-122. Passing the ICE protection

(b) Position the ice in the eye area and milk the ice from the apex of the eye. You should ensure that both 'legs' of the ice are equal in length from the apex of the eye. When in position and snug fitting, tie a constrictor knot 1.5 fid lengths from the bitter end of each ice leg. (Fig 3-123) The rope should now be eye spliced. When the eye is spliced and lock-stitched the ice can be spliced into the eye area.

Fig 3-123. Ice in position with constrictor knot secured

(c) Forming the ice into pairs - de-strand the ice from the bitter end to the constrictor knot. You now have 12 single strands – six travel clockwise around the rope and six travel anti-clockwise around the rope. Pair three clockwise strands and three anti-clockwise strands; ensure the pairs are not inter-crossed by other strands on the working side of the constrictor knot. Tape each pair together as seen in Fig 3-124(i) and Fig 3-124(ii), making one strand slightly longer than the other to form a 'point'.

Fig 3-124. Taped strands

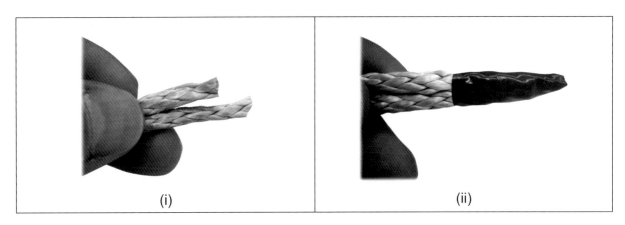

(i)   (ii)

(d) Tucking the ice into the rope - take one pair and, in the direction of travel (either clockwise or anti-clockwise) tuck under two strands of the rope against the lay. Do this for all 6 pairs always going against the lay. When each pair is tucked once, check that each pair is not inter-crossed at any point. Take one pair and tuck a further four times straight down the rope – over one and under two strands of the rope. Move to the next pair and do the same. Continue until all six pairs have been tucked for five full tucks. After all tucks have been completed, remove the constrictor knot and pull each strand snug. Follow the sequence of tucks as shown in Fig 3-125(i) to Fig 3-125(iv).

Fig 3-125 Tucking sequence

(i)   (ii)

(iii)   (iv)

(e) Burying the ice tails inside the rope Fig 3-126(i) to Fig 3-126(vi). Where each pair exits after the last tuck, open up the rope and using the tubular fid pass the fid directly up the centre of the rope – insert the taped end of the ice into the recess of the fid and using the pusher, push the pair all the way through to exit the rope. Do three long pairs and three shorter pairs for all six pairs of ice. Cut each pair close to where it exits and milk the area to conceal the cut pairs inside the rope. Do the same procedure for the other leg of the ice.

Fig 3-126.   Sequence for burying the ICE tails inside the rope

(i)

(ii)

(iii)

(iv)

(v)

(vi)

Fig 3-127. Completed ICE splice

g. **HPMT – joining splice procedure**. This splice is designed to join together two ropes of equal diameter or to manufacture a grommet (endless loop). This splice technique, however, will reduce the strength of the rope by a maximum 5% and should only be performed as a "get me home" splice when a replacement rope could be delayed. All "get me home" spliced ropes should be replaced at the earliest opportunity. For ease of identification of Rope A and Rope B, we have used two contrasting coloured ropes.

(1) *STEP 1.* **Measurement and marking of the ropes.** (Mark both ropes at the same time). Lay both ropes parallel to each other and tape the ends of the ropes. Measure 1 wire-fid length from the taped end and mark 1. Then from mark 1 measure two wire-fid lengths and mark 2 as shown in Fig 3-128.

Fig 3-128. Marked up ropes

Note. On darker coloured ropes the use of white chalk (in addition to permanent marker pen) for marking is advisable

(2) *STEP 2.* **Perform the taper**. (On both ropes). From mark 1 in the direction of the taped ends, mark every second left and right strand for three strands as shown in Fig 3-129.

Fig 3-129. Second left and right strands marked

Pull out each marked strand and cut off. The tapered ends will each have only six strands remaining. Re-tape the bitter ends to prevent unbraiding as shown in Fig 3-130.

Fig 3-130. Tapered ends

(3) *STEP 3.* **Position the ropes.** Re-position the ropes so that the mark 2's on each rope are directly opposite each other with the bitter ends facing in opposite directions as shown in Fig 3-131(i) and Fig 3-131(ii).

Fig 3-131. Mark 2s opposite each other

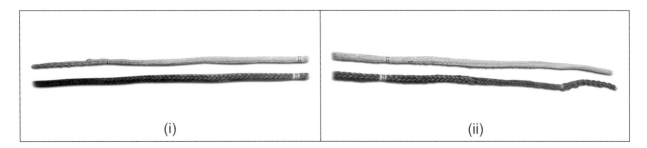

(i)	(ii)

(4) *STEP 4.* **Burying rope A inside rope B and rope B inside rope A.** Measure 1.5 wire-fid lengths beyond where the tapered tail (bitter end) meets the standing part of rope B. This will be the fid insertion point as shown in Fig 3-132(i). Open the standing part of the rope and insert the wire-fid into the centre of the rope B. Using both hands, slide the fid carefully all the way up to mark 2 and exit the rope as shown in Fig 3-132(ii).

Fig 3-132. Burying the rope

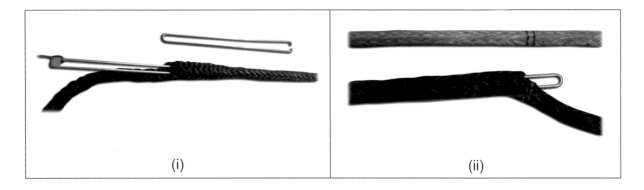

(i)	(ii)

Turn the fid 180° so that the taped end of the fid is outermost. Re-insert the smooth end of the fid back into the rope from where it has exited. Remove the tape from the end of the fid and attach the wire-fid prongs over the tapered tail end of rope A and secure with electrical tape as shown in Fig 3-133.

Fig 3-133. Fid re-inserted

Tie-off/secure the pull-through cord and using both hands, gently 'milk' the rope towards the mark 2 of rope A. Continue this until mark 2 of rope a meets with mark 2 of rope B. as shown in Fig 3-134(i) and Fig 3-134(ii).

Fig 3-134. Pull through secured

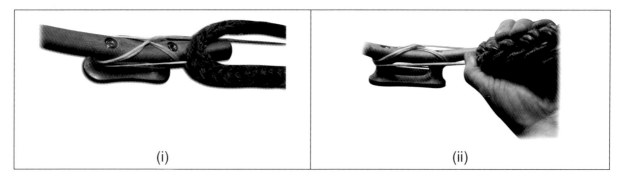

(i)   (ii)

Work the fid out of the rope and some 200mm of tapered tail. Remove the fid and all tape from the tapered end. Randomly select two strands approximately 200mm in length and cut off.

Fig 3-135. Fid worked out of rope

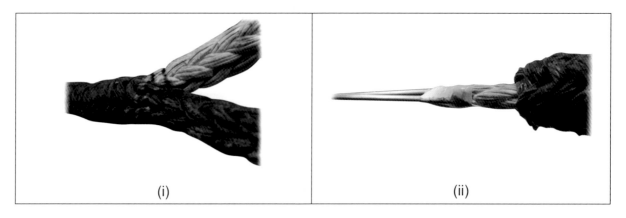

(i)   (ii)

Transfer to rope B and follow the steps above so that both ropes are tucked into one another. This forms the cross-over point between the ropes. The cross-over point should measure approximately, the diameter of the original rope if done correctly as shown in Fig 3-136(i) to Fig 3-136(iv).

Fig 3-136. Cross over point

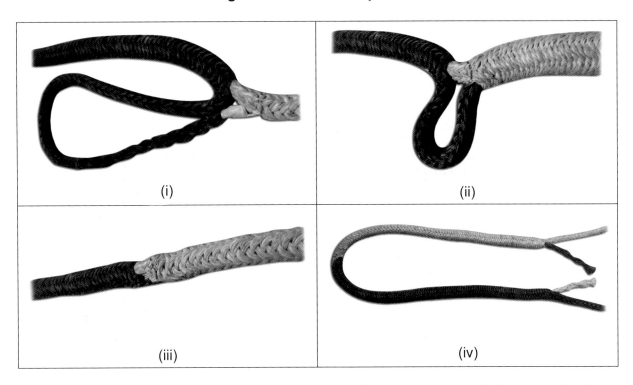

(i)

(ii)

(iii)

(iv)

Securely hold the cross-over point and milk each rope towards the tapered tails. As the tails disappear inside the ropes, continue beyond this point. Do this twice for each rope. We now have rope A inside rope B and rope B inside rope A as shown in Fig 3-137(i) and Fig 137(ii).

Fig 3-137. Rope A inside rope B and rope B inside rope A

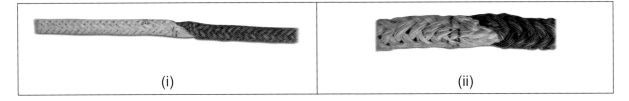

(i)

(ii)

h.   **HPMT – lock stitch procedure for the joining splice**. This procedure is critical to the HPMT splicing technique and should be applied immediately following splicing. All lock-stitches should be pulled snug, not tight. Tools required are the same as those required for the eye splice.

(5)   *STEP 5.*   **Measure and initial stitch.**   Measure twelve 'picks' (see Note) down from the cross-over point and open-up the outer strands of the rope. This is the initial insertion point. Pass the threaded lock-stitch needle through the inner strands of the splice only, at 45° directly through the centre of the spliced rope leaving a small (3") tail as shown in Fig 3-138.

Fig 3-138. Initial insertion point

Re-insert the needle at 45° to form the first full 'stitch', each stitch should be the equivalent to the 'pick length' of each strand in the rope. Continue as above until five full stitches are on each side of the rope through the cross-over point: as shown in Fig 3-139.

Fig 3-139. Stitches through the cross over point

After the fifth stitch, turn the rope 90° and re-insert the needle to stitch back towards the eye as in above steps. The cross-over point spliced area will now be lock-stitched on two planes perpendicular to each other as shown in Fig 3-140.

Fig 3-140. Needle re-inserted

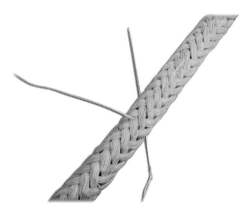

Extract the last stitch at the same point as the initial insertion as shown in Fig 3-141.

Fig 3-141. Last stitch at initial insertion point

Tie a reef knot in the two ends and re-insert the needle back into the rope, pulling the reef knot firmly into the rope. Cut-off both ends close to where they exit the rope as shown in Fig 3-142(i) to Fig 3-142(ii).

Fig 3-142. Reef knot tied and needle re-inserted

(i)	(ii)

Fig 3-143. Completed joining splice

Note. *'Pick' 'Picks' or 'Pick Length': the length of each visible strand within the rope structure as shown above.*

03026. Bullivant locking splice (RFA and MN only)

a.   Put a strong whipping/Serving either side of the point where it is to be cut off the coil.

b.   Now put a strong whipping/Serving on your piece of wire about 40 times the diameter from the end to be spliced. Form the eye by stopping the whipping already on the wire at 40 times the diameter to the standing part of the wire giving an eye of the size required. Remove the whipping from the end to be spliced then unlay the strands to the whipping at 40 times the diameter, put three adjacent strands to one side of the standing part and three on the other. (Fig 3-144(i)).

c.   When using the marlin spike to open up the wire be careful not to damage the wire or heart. When the spike has been inserted under the strand to be lifted push it well in to leave sufficient room to pass the strand that is to be tucked. Be careful not to kink this strand or it will not lie flat.

d.   The strands are numbered from right to left with the eye formed and working strands at the side nearest to you. The strands are tucked as follows:

(1)   No 1 - Under two strands with the lay. (Fig 3-144(ii)).

(2)   No 2 - Enters the wire at the same place as Strand No 1 but only goes under one strand with the lay. (Fig 3-144(iii)).

(3)   No 4 - Enters the wire one strand to the left of where Strands No 1&2 enter the wire and goes under one with the lay. (Fig 3-144(iv)).

(4)   No 3 - Enters the wire where Strand No 4 comes out but this time going against the lay under the same strand as Strand No 4 thus causing a lock. (Fig 3-144(v)).

(5)   No 6 - Enters the wire one strand to the left of where Strand No 4 enters the wire & is tucked under two strands against the lay. (Fig 3-144(vi)).

(6)   No 5 - Enters the wire at the same place as Strand No 6 but only goes under one strand against the lay. (Fig 3-144(vii)).

(7)   All slack is now removed from all 6 strands, then bed in the tuck using two hammers of equal size. The first tuck is now complete, to prevent slip back a constrictor knot may be applied around this tuck and subsequent tucks.

(8)   Every strand is now tucked over one and under one against the lay of the wire thus completing the second tuck which is then bedded in and constrictor applied to prevent slip back. If required remove the cores from each strand.

(9)   Complete the third tuck in the same manner then extract one third of the wires from each strand do not cut off but bend down out of the way.

(10) Complete fourth tuck then extract half of the remaining wires from each strand again do not cut off but bend down out of the way.

(11) Complete the fifth and final tuck this time by going over one strand and under two strands against the lay.

(12) Finally bed in the whole splice from crown to tail and bend off or cut off all of the small wires sticking out from the finished splice.

Fig 3-144. Making a bullivant locking splice

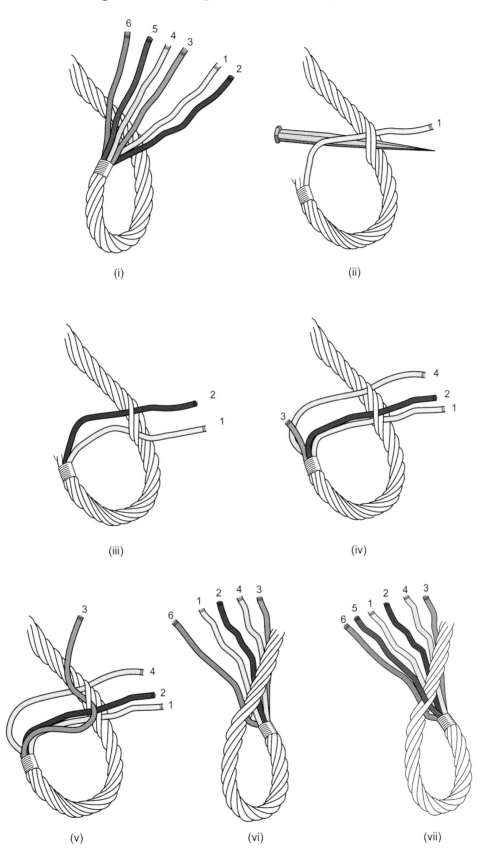

03027. Mechanical splicing

a.   Mechanical splicing, known under various trade names including Marisplice, Superloop and Talurit is carried out by Naval Base authorities, commercially under contract, or in capital and repair ships. The splice gives comparable strength to a hand splice, and has the following advantages: it uses less wire, requires no worming, parcelling and serving, and is completed in much less time; in a great many cases it has superseded the hand splice. A mechanically spliced wire should be tested by a competent testing authority before use; however, if this is not possible, a local test is acceptable in the short term, but the splice must be properly tested at the first opportunity. The use of mechanical splicing machines in Royal Navy ships is to be controlled, and a list of all gear produced must be kept by the Boatswain or Chief Boatswain's Mate.

b.   **Making a mechanical splice**. Ensure that any excessive oil or grease is cleaned off the wire in the position where the ferrule is to be fitted. Thread the end of the rope through an alloy ferrule of suitable size (Table 3-15) and back on itself through the ferrule to form a loop (Fig 3-145(i)). The bitter end of the rope must not terminate within the ferrule; it should extend past the end of the ferrule for a distance of at least one half of the rope diameter. If a thimble or other type of fitting is required, it is placed in the loop in the necessary position. The ferrule is then put in the hydraulic press between two swages, which are of a size to deal with that particular ferrule, and the swages are closed until they slightly grip the ferrule. The rope is then pulled through until a loop of the required size is fashioned or the tightest possible fit to the thimble or other fitting is obtained. Further pressure is then applied until the swages meet; the splice is then complete. The pressure exerted does not harm the rope in any way, neither is the lay disturbed - the metal of the ferrule flows round the rope strands, holding each strand firmly in position. (Fig 3-145(ii)). Mechanical splicing is occasionally used to splice man-made fibre and natural fibre ropes; however, such splices are not to be used where life and limb will be endangered if the rope parts.

Table 3-15. Size of ferrules for use with SWR

Size of Rope	Naval stores No of ferrule	Size of Rope	Naval stores No of ferrule	Size of rope	Naval stores No of ferrule
1 mm	0263/411-9765	6.5mm	0263/411-9772	24 mm	0263/411-9743
1.5 mm	0263/411-9766	7 mm	0263/411-9773	28 mm	0263/411-9744
2 mm	0263/411-9767	8 mm	0263/411-9735	30 mm	0263/411-9745
2.5 mm	0263/411-9768	10 mm	0263/411-9736	32 mm	0263/411-9746
3 mm	0263/411-9732	12 mm	0263/411-9737	36 mm	0263/411-9747
3.5 mm	0263/411-9769	14 mm	0263/411-9738	38 mm	0263/411-9748
4 mm	0263/411-9733	16 mm	0263/411-9739	40 mm	0263/411-9749
4.5 mm	0263/125-0131	18 mm	0263/411-9740	44 mm	0263/411-9750
5 mm	0263/125-0132	20 mm	0263/411-9741		
6 mm	0263/411-9734	22 mm	0263/411-9742		

Fig 3-145. Making a mechanical splice

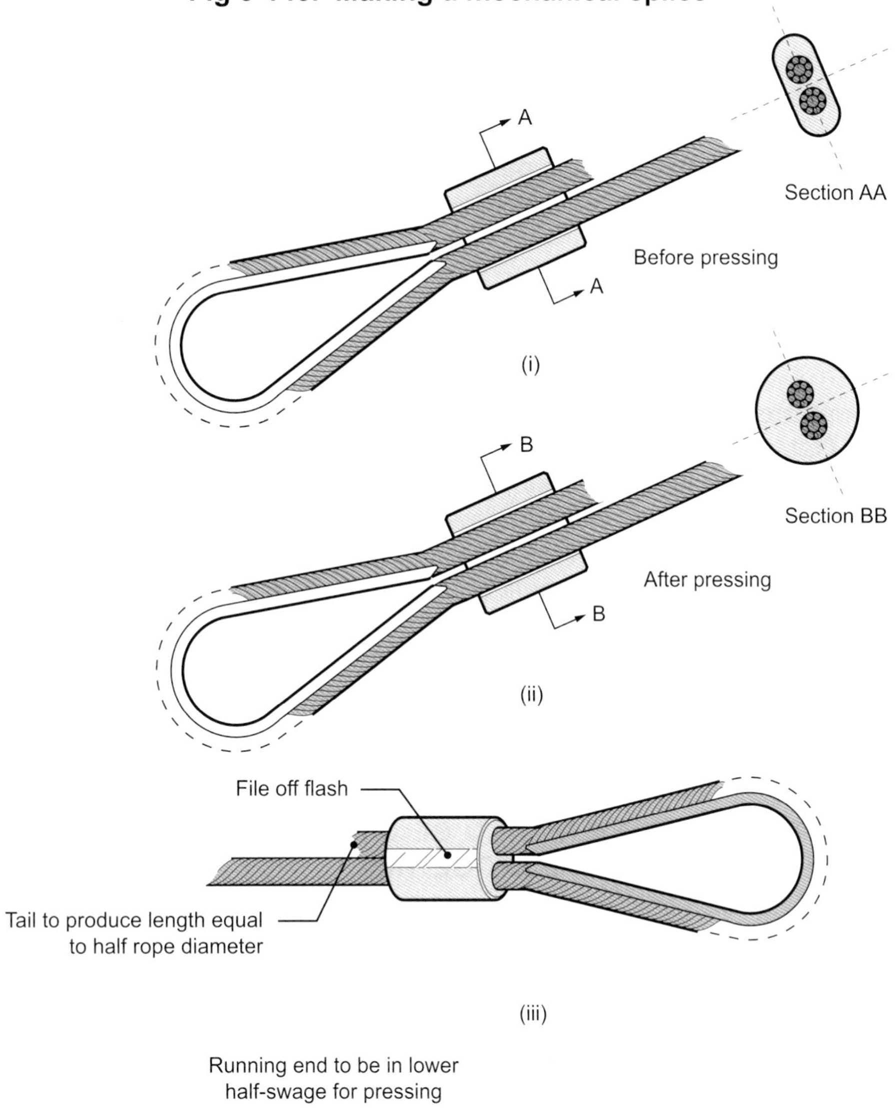

Section AA

Before pressing

(i)

Section BB

After pressing

(ii)

File off flash

Tail to produce length equal
to half rope diameter

(iii)

Running end to be in lower
half-swage for pressing

03028. Making a temporary eye using bulldog grips

a.   A temporary eye, either soft or thimble, can be made in wire rope by using bulldog grips (Fig 3-146), which are screwed clamps holding the two parts of the rope together. It is important that the grips should be fitted with the U-bolt over the tail end of the rope and the bridge on the standing part, as shown in Fig 3-146. Grips should be spaced at a minimum distance of six times the diameter of the rope as follows:

SWR up to 19 mm   -   3 grips

20 mm to 32 mm   -   4 grips

b.   Grips are supplied in various sizes to fit each size of wire rope up to and including 32 mm (Table 3-16). Bulldog grips for larger ropes are not available in the Royal Navy. It is essential that the correct sized grip is used and that grips are fully tightened to the effect that the wire is locally squeezed down to two-thirds of its normal diameter. Failure to comply with these requirements will greatly reduce the efficiency of the termination. Grips are apt to mark or crush the rope, and both grips and rope should be inspected for security and wear before and after use and grips retightened as necessary. Bulldog grips must not be used to join two wire ropes together.

WARNING

BULLDOG GRIPS ARE NOT TO BE USED FOR LIFTING PURPOSES OR JOINING TWO WIRE ROPES TOGETHER.

Fig 3-146. Making a temporary eye with bulldog grips

Fig 3-147. Dimensions of bulldog grips

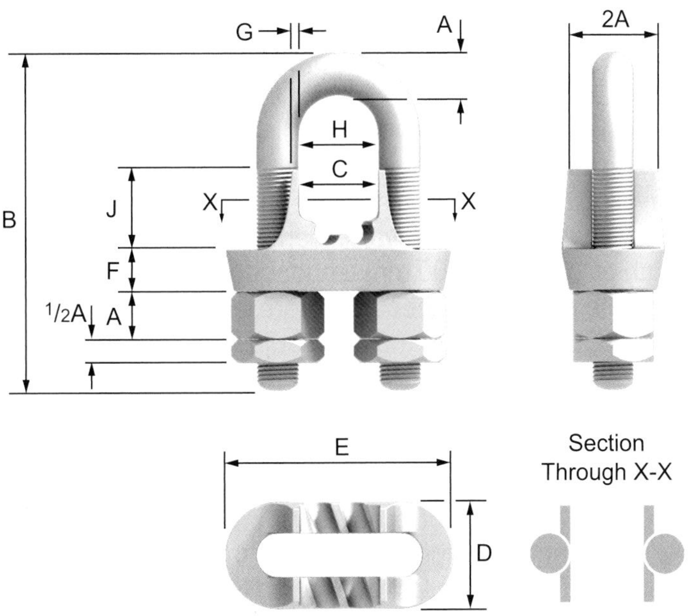

Table 3-16. Details of bulldog grips available through naval stores

Naval stores No.	For use with SWR diameter	Dimensions								
		A	B	C	D	E	F	G	H	I
0263/571-	mm	millimetres								
5319	4	5	27	5	14	28	5	2	9	7
5320	6	6	30	7	14	25	6	-	7	5
5312	8	8	40	9	18	33	8	-	9	6
5313	11	12	58	12	28	48	12	-	12	10
5314	13	14	68	14.5	32	56	14	-	14.5	11
5315	14	14	70	16	32	58	14	-	16	11
5316	22	18	98	25	41	79	18	-	25	14
5317	29	20	118	32	46	92	20	-	32	16
5318	32	22	130	35	51	101	22	-	35	28

03029. Nets - provision and cargo

The nets most commonly used in the Royal Navy for handling provisions and stores in bulk are manufactured from polyester webbing, man-made fibre cordage or steel wire rope. The flat polyester webbing nets, usually associated with Vertrep, are discussed fully in Chapter 7. Man-made fibre cordage and steel wire rope provision nets are available for general use and are obtainable through naval stores, sizes and NSN Numbers as follows:

Type of net	Dimensions	SWL	Naval stores No
SWR provision net	2.45 m square	3 tonnes	0246/923-9438
MMFC provision net	2.5 m square	1.5 tonnes	0246/923-3572

03030. Nets - brow safety

a.   Whenever a brow is rigged into a ship, a brow safety net must be rigged beneath it. Each net must be secured by means of its fitted lanyards and positioned so that it is directly beneath the brow with the centre of the net lower than its edges. The net must extend from ship to ship or ship to dock wall and have sufficient spread on both sides to catch a person or object falling from the brow safely. Where no suitable securing positions are available on the jetty, a spreader bar of sufficient length is to be secured to or through the brow so that the net lanyards can be secured to it, thus achieving the correct spread. A length of 100 mm x 100 mm timber or other suitable material is to be used as a spreader. The nets must be inspected before and after use, and at frequent intervals whilst they are rigged; and they must be adjusted as necessary to allow for the rise and fall of tide. When longer than usual brows are put into a ship, for example if a frigate docks down in a large dry dock, nets suitable for the task should be requested from the shore-side authorities. In such circumstances, a ship's own brow safety nets can be securely lashed together for fitting beneath one of the brows.

b.   The brow safety net is designed to capture the load by the breaking of the insulocks on each corner allowing the net to travel down the side jackstays. The brow safety net comes in three sizes, individually bagged and labelled with a Certificate of Conformance and are procured through the Naval Stores system. The following sizes are available:

(1)   3.0 m x 3.0 m (Small) MM/PP: NSN F219-3940-99-968-4717

(2)   7.62 m x 4.5 m (Medium) FF/DD   NSN F219-3940-99-888-3783

(3)   12.2 m x 7.62 m (Large) Capital Ships   NSN F219-3940-99-742-7291

c.   Further detailed instruction on rigging Brow safety nets are at Para 03070

03031. Rigging shackles

a.   Rigging Shackles are coupling links used for joining ropes, webbing and chain together or to some fitting, and are usually forged from carbon magnesium steel. This section deals only with shackles used with rigging; shackles, which form part of anchor and cable, or towing arrangements, are dealt with in the relevant Chapter. Details of rigging shackles available through naval stores are given in Table 3-17 to Table 3-22. U-shaped shackles are called **straight** or **D shackles**, and those which have curved sides, are called **Bow shackles**. A bow shackle is weaker than a straight shackle, but is the more convenient to use with hooks or sling chains because a large hook may be used with such a shackle having a relatively short pin; bow rather than straight shackles are also used in conjunction with boats' webbing slings because the relatively greater width in the clear at the crown of the shackle prevents pinching of the webbing at the bearing point. The size quoted for a straight or bow shackle used with rigging is the diameter of the metal at the crown. The safe working load for each size and type of shackle is therefore included in the details given in Table 3-17 to Table 3-22.

b.   **Parts of a shackle** (Fig 3-148). The ends of a shackle are called the **lugs**, the space between them is called the **jaw,** and the part opposite the jaw is called the **crown**. The inside width or length of a shackle is called the clear; thus a shackle may be described as being 'long in the clear' or 'wide in the clear'; the jaw is closed by a removable **bolt** which passes through a hole in each lug. Rigging shackles are usually named by reference to the manner in which its bolt is secured in place.

Fig 3-148. Parts of a shackle

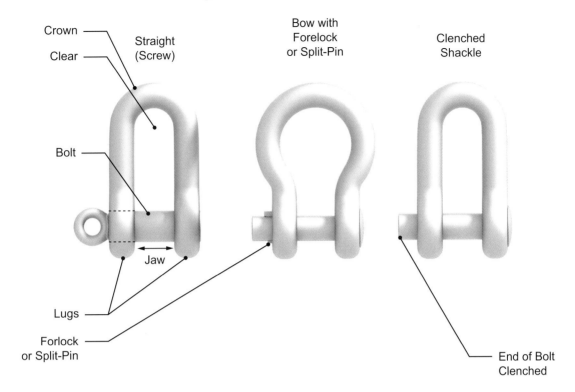

c. **Types of shackle**

(1) *Screw shackle.* May be a bow or straight shackle. The end of the bolt is screwed into one of the lugs, and the bolt is fitted with a flange at its head. This type of bolt should be moused.

(2) *Forelock shackle.* May be a bow or straight shackle. The end of the bolt projects beyond one of the lugs, and a flat tapered split-pin (forelock) is passed through a slot in the end of the bolt. For most applications the forelock shackle has been superseded by a split-pinned shackle (see below), but the forelock method of securing the bolt is still used on moorings. The forelock may be attached to the shackle by a keep chain.

(3) *Split-pinned shackle.* May be a bow or straight shackle. This type of shackle is of similar design to the forelock shackle, but is supplied with a galvanised split pin to serve the same purpose as a forelock. The split-pin is attached to the shackle by a keep chain.

(4) *Pin and pellet shackle.* A tapered hole is drilled through one of the lugs and the end of the bolt. The bolt is secured in place by a similarly tapered pin being driven into this hole and held in place by a lead pellet hammered into the mouth of the hole over the head of the pin. This very secure method of locking the shackle bolt is a common arrangement on shackles that are part of anchor and cable outfits, but is also used on the shackle that attaches the hook to a picking-up rope. Details of these shackles are given with the details of the hooks used for picking-up ropes Para 02008.

Table 3-17. Rigging shackles - straight shackle with screw bolt

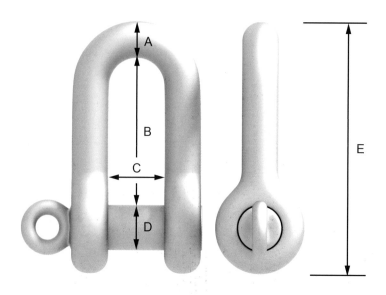

Naval stores No.	Nominal size	Dimensions					SWL
	A	B	C	D	E		
	mm	mm	mm	mm	mm		tonnes
0263/721-6087	6	24	10	10	45		0.3
0263/721-6088	10	35	16	13	64		0.6
0263/721-6089	13	46	21	16	83		1.05
0263/721-6090	16	57	25	19	102		1.8
0263/721-6091	19	68	31	25	125		2.55
0263/721-6092	22	81	36	29	146		3.55
0263/721-6093	25	92	41	32	165		4.6
0263/733-1299	29	103	46	35	184		5.6
0263/721-6094	32	114	51	38	203		7.1
0263/721-6095	35	125	56	44	226		8.15
0263/721-6096	38	138	61	48	248		10.9
0263/721-6097	41	149	67	51	266		13.2
0263/721-6098	44	160	71	54	285		15.0
0263/721-6099	48	171	76	57	305		17.0
0263/721-6100	51	183	82	64	330		19.5

Table 3-18. Rigging shackles - straight shackle with forelock

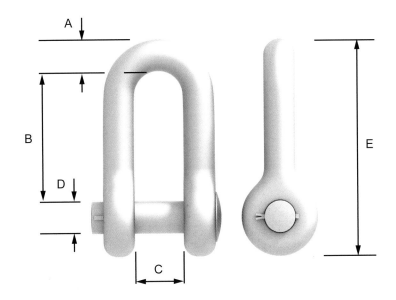

Naval stores No.	Nominal size	Dimensions					SWL
	A	B	C	D	E	
	mm	mm	mm	mm	mm	tonnes
0263-543-4298	13	46	21	16	83	1.05
0263-543-4299	19	68	31	25	125	2.55
0263-543-4300	25	92	41	32	165	4.6
0263-543-4301	32	114	51	38	203	7.1
0263-543-4302	38	138	61	48	248	10.9
0263-543-4303	44	160	71	54	285	15.0
0263-543-4304	50	183	82	64	329	19.5

Table 3-19. Rigging shackles - straight shackle with split pin

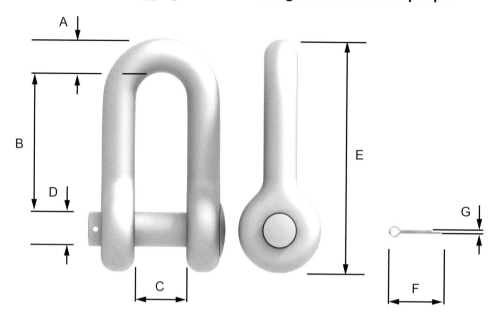

Naval stores No	Nominal size	Dimensions							SWL
	A	B	C	D	E	F	G	
	mm	mm	mm	mm	mm	mm	mm	tonnes
0263-543-4528	6	24	10	10	45	15	2.5	0.3
0263-543-4529	10	35	16	13	64	20	4.0	0.6
0263-543-4530	13	46	21	16	83	25	4.0	1.05
0263-543-4531	16	57	25	19	102	30	4.0	1.8
0263-543-4532	19	68	31	25	125	40	5.0	2.55
0263-543-4533	22	81	36	29	146	45	5.0	3.55
0263-543-4534	25	92	41	32	165	50	5.0	4.6
0263-543-4535	29	103	46	35	184	55	6.3	5.6
0263-543-4536	32	114	51	38	203	60	6.3	7.1
0263-543-4537	35	125	56	44	226	70	6.3	8.15
0263-543-4538	38	138	61	48	248	75	8.0	10.9
0263-543-4539	41	149	67	51	266	80	8.0	13.2
0263-543-4540	44	160	71	54	285	85	13.0	15.0
0263-543-4541	48	171	76	57	305	90	13.0	17.0
0263-543-4542	51	183	82	64	330	100	13.0	19.5
0263-543-4543	54	216	87	67	349	105	13.0	20.5
0263-543-4544	57	228	92	70	372	110	13.0	23.0
0263-543-4545	60	241	97	73	395	115	13.0	25.5

Table 3-20. Rigging shackles - Bow shackle with screw bolt

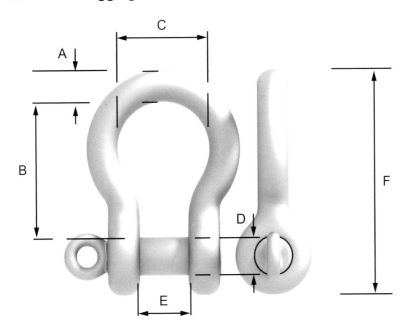

Naval stores No.	Nominal size	Dimensions						SWL
	A	B	C	D	E	F		
	mm	mm	mm	mm	mm	mm		tonnes
0263/721-6101	6	25	19	10	13	46		0.15
0263/721-6102	10	38	29	13	17	67		0.45
0263/721-6103	13	51	38	16	24	88		0.75
0263/721-6104	16	64	48	19	29	109		1.25
0263/721-6105	19	76	57	25	35	133		2.05
0263/721-6106	22	89	67	29	41	154		2.80
0263/721-6107	25	102	76	32	46	175		3.80
0263/721-6108	29	114	86	35	52	195		4.85
0263/721-6109	32	127	95	38	57	216		5.85
0263/721-6110	35	140	105	44	64	241		7.35
0263/721-6111	38	152	114	48	70	262		8.65
0263/721-6112	41	165	124	51	75	282		9.65
0263/721-6113	44	178	133	54	81	303		11.7
0263/721-6114	48	191	143	57	86	326		13.2
0263/721-6115	51	203	152	64	92	350		15.25

Table 3-21. Rigging shackles - Bow shackle with forelock

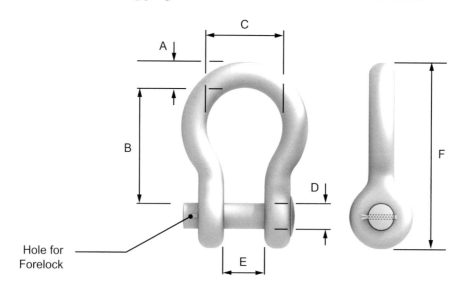

Hole for
Forelock

Naval stores No.	Nominal size	Dimensions						SWL
	A	B	C	D	E	F		
	mm	mm	mm	mm	mm	mm		tonnes
0263-543-4291	13	51	38	16	24	88		0.75
0263-543-4292	19	75	57	25	35	132		2.05
0263-543-4293	25	102	76	32	46	175		3.80
0263-543-4294	32	127	95	38	57	216		5.85
0263-543-4295	38	152	114	48	70	262		8.65
0263-543-4296	44	178	133	54	81	303		11.70
0263-543-4297	51	203	152	64	92	349		15.25

Table 3-22. Rigging shackles - Bow shackle with split pin

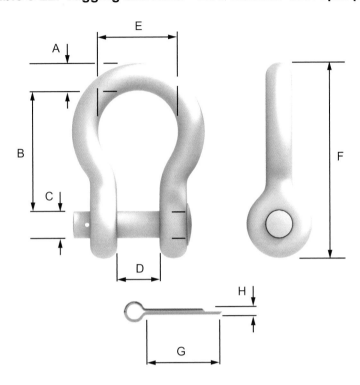

Naval stores No.	Nominal size	Dimensions								SWL
	A	B	C	D	E	F	G	H		
	mm	mm	mm	mm	mm	mm	mm	mm		tonnes
0263-543-4546	6	25	10	13	19	46	15	2.5		0.15
0263-543-4547	10	38	13	17	29	67	20	4.0		0.45
0263-543-4548	13	51	16	24	38	88	25	4.0		0.75
0263-543-4549	16	64	19	29	48	109	30	4.0		1.25
0263-543-4550	19	76	25	35	57	133	40	5.0		2.05
0263-543-4551	22	89	29	41	67	154	45	5.0		2.8
0263-543-4552	25	102	32	46	76	175	50	5.0		3.8
0263-543-4553	29	114	35	52	86	195	55	6.3		4.85
0263-543-4554	32	127	38	57	95	216	60	6.3		5.85
0263-543-4555	35	140	44	64	105	241	70	6.3		7.35
0263-543-4556	38	152	48	70	114	262	75	8.0		8.65
0263-543-4557	41	165	51	75	124	282	80	8.0		9.65
0263-543-4558	44	178	54	81	133	303	85	13.0		11.7
0263-543-4559	48	191	57	86	143	325	90	13.0		13.2
0263-543-4560	51	203	64	92	152	350	100	13.0		15.25
0263-543-4561	64	254	76	114	191	432	115	13.0		22.85

03032. High performance mooring and towing – fairlead shackles

a. **Introduction.** HPMT introduces Mandal Type Stainless Steel Fairlead Shackles (Fig 149) for joining and insertion of the Shock Mitigation Strops and the P7 Pendants. These Shackles are made from Grade 2387 Martensitic Stainless Steel and therefore have a higher Carbon/Nickel content to facilitate the strength requirements. They are magnetic and as such will have to be maintained regularly. Each Shackle comes in four parts:

    A   Shackle body
    B   Shackle pin
    C   Ring guard
    D   Grub screw

Each Shackle is provided with a 'Buffers Toothbrush' Tool (E) for assembling and disassembling.

Fig 3-149. Fairlead shackle and parts

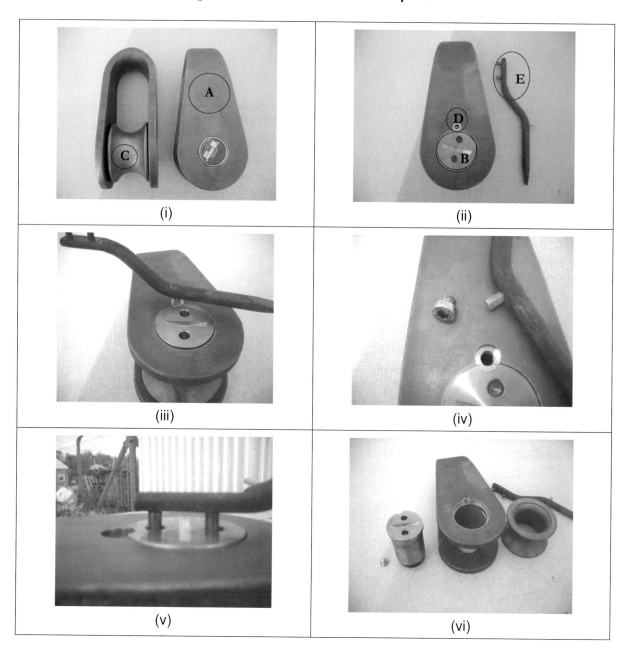

b.   **Maintenance.** Each Fairlead Shackle should be disassembled by inserting the Allen Key part of the Buffers Toothbrush into the Grub-Screw Fig 3-149(iii) and Turn Anti-Clockwise to remove, then insert the "Teeth" of the Buffers Toothbrush Tool Fig 3-149(v) in the corresponding holes on the Fairlead Shackle's Pin, turn anti-clockwise to remove the pin after each use and the following Maintenance Routine is to be carried out:

(1)   All parts of the Shackle should be thoroughly scrubbed using a stiff bristled brush (not a wire brush) using fresh water then, thoroughly dried.

(2)   A Stainless Steel Passivation Paste (Wichinox for example (see Note)) should be applied and left for 20 minutes (or as per manufacturer's instructions)

(3)   After 20 minutes, wash with fresh water removing all Passivation paste.

(4)   Thoroughly dry all parts.

(5)   When totally dry, lightly oil the Shackle Body and Ring-Guard

(6)   The thread of the Shackle Pin and Grub-Screw should be Silicon Greased

(7)   Re-Assemble the Fairlead Shackle and Store in a dry environment

c.   Should the Fairlead Shackles be stored for long periods without use then the above Maintenance Routine should be carried before storage and followed every three months whilst in storage.

d.   Fairlead Shackles are 'Lifed on Condition' and should <u>not</u> be subjected to Re-Testing/Proof Load Testing.

e.   Fairlead Shackles and Buffers Toothbrush Tools should be stored separately from Carbon Steel items (Not loose in the Cable Bag).

Note.   *Passivation paste – This is used to protect, remove corrosion and polish Stainless Steel. It also promotes a self-forming barrier within the molecular structure of the steel to reduce corrosion over time.*

03033. Roller blocks

a.   Roller blocks are very wide in the clear, and used for diverting the lead of a rope or line in situations where a conventional leading block is inappropriate. For example where two wires have been shackled together and the shackle is required to pass through the block. The three types of roller block commonly used in the Royal Navy are described below:

b.   **Astern fuelling roller block** (Fig 3-150). This roller block, NSN 0263/770-9716, is used during astern refuelling to provide the hose-line with a fair lead to the capstan. It has a Safe Working Load of 6.1 tonnes.

Fig 3-150. Astern fuelling roller block

c. **Roller block with pivotal cheek plates** (Fig 3-151). This roller block, NSN W200/525-6391, is used with the easing-out recovery rope during ship-to-ship towing evolutions. The cheeks of the block can pivot around the centre sheave pin, enabling the block to be attached to the bight of a rope before the two cheeks are shackled together. It has a Safe Working Load of 1.5 tonnes.

Fig 3-151. Roller shackle with pivotal cheek plates

d. **Awning roller blocks** (Fig 3-152 and Fig 3-153). As their name implies, these roller blocks are used in the rigging of awnings. There are two types, the **short link roller block**, NSN 0263/766-7781, and the **long link roller block**, NSN 0263/767-2435. Ship's drawings specify the type to be used for particular applications.

Fig 3-152. Short link roller block (awnings)

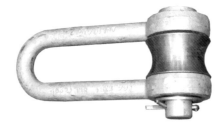

Fig 3-153. Long link roller block (awnings)

03034. Swivel ring shackles (Fig 3-154)

These shackles, also known as a swivel eye and jaw, are used predominantly on boat anti-shock strops. There are four sizes available, detail as shown in Table 3-23.

Table 3-23. Details of swivel ring shackles

Naval stores No.	Dimensions			SWL
	A	B	C	
	mm	mm	mm	tonnes
0263/414-9939	22.5	48	41.5	1.52
0263/414-9938	25	57.5	45	2.54
0263/414-9940	29	67.5	51	3.55
0263/414-9941	35	83.5	57.5	5.08

Fig 3-154. Swivel ring shackle

03035. Thimbles

a. Thimbles (Fig 3-155) are classified according to the diameter of the rope for which they are intended and also their shapes; most thimbles are manufactured from galvanised mild steel, although for certain applications stainless steel, phosphor bronze or polyamide thimbles are used. The latter three types are not available through Naval Stores and can only be obtained through local purchase. When an eye splice is formed at one end of a fibre or wire rope a thimble is inserted to take the chafe of a shackle or shackle bolt and also to support the eye formed in the rope. The support given by the thimble prevents a bad nip in the rope when under tension. Large thimbles are made from material of special section and bent to shape; small thimbles are cast in one piece. Thimbles are either round or heart-shaped and open or welded. The gap formed at the throat can be sprung open to allow the eye of a tackle hook or lug of a shackle to enter. Heart-shaped thimbles are preferable for thimble or hawser eyes, in both wire and fibre ropes, because the rope can be spliced close to the throat of the thimble. Details of thimbles available though naval store are given in Table 3-24 to Table 3-26.

Fig 3-155. Thimbles

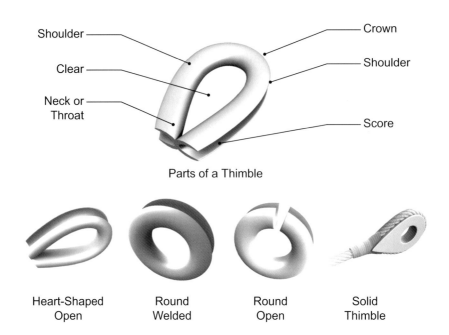

Parts of a Thimble

| Heart-Shaped Open | Round Welded | Round Open | Solid Thimble |

b. **Types of thimble**

(1) *Round welded thimbles.* These are used for the corners of awnings.

(2) *Round open thimbles.* These are used when it is necessary to insert something in them; for example, the wire grommet at the end of a light jackstay, or the eye at the tail of a block.

(3) *Heart-shaped open thimbles.* These are the most commonly used thimble for forming a hard eye or hawser eye in the end of a rope or wire.

(4) *Solid thimbles.* These are fitted to the end of certain crane and davit whips. The thimbles are designed to accept a bolt or pin and are sufficiently robust not to collapse under stress. They are normally supplied commercially. They are not available through naval stores.

c. **Selecting the correct size thimble**. The size of rope which a thimble will take depends on both the width and depth of the score, but for practical purposes the sizes are as follows:

Wire rope $\qquad\qquad\qquad d = w$

Served wire rope $\qquad\qquad d = 0.83w$

Fibre rope $\qquad\qquad\qquad d = 0.91w$

Where d is the diameter of the rope in millimetres, and w is the width of the score in millimetres.

d. **Strength of a thimble**. Thimbles have no specific strength, but a mild steel thimble should not be distorted by a pull of $d^2/128$ tonnes, where d is the diameter of the wire in millimetres for which the thimble is designed, and it will usually crush at about $d^2/85$ tonnes.

Table 3-24. Details of round welded thimbles

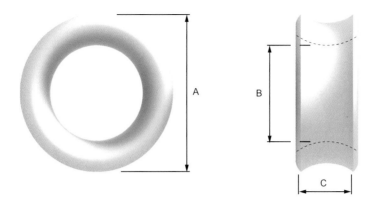

Naval stores No.	A	B	C
	mm	mm	mm
0263/421-8799	35	20	13
0263/421-8800	45	25	16
0263/421-8801	50	30	19
0263/421-8802	65	45	22
0263/421-8803	75	50	25
0263/421-8804	75	50	29
0263/421-8805	90	64	32

Table 3-25. Details of round open thimbles

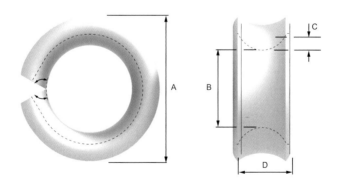

Naval stores No.	A	B	C	D
	mm	mm	mm	mm
0263/421-8807	30	15	3	12
0263/421-8808	45	25	5	16
0263/421-8809	50	30	5	19
0263/421-8810	60	35	6.5	26
0263/421-8974	100	57	10	39

Table 3-26. Details of heart-shaped open thimbles

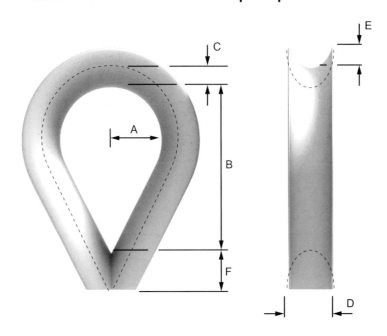

Naval stores No.	A	B	C	D	E	F
	mm	mm	mm	mm	mm	mm
0263/414-9630	8	25	4	8	3	6
0263/923-6988	11	40	4	10	4	8
0263/923-6987	13	50	5	11	5	10
0263/414-9633	17	60	5	14	6	12
0263/414-2980	20	70	6	16	7	14
0263/414-9635	22	80	8	18	8	16
0263/332-5187	27	95	8	23	10	20
0263/414-9637	32	110	10	27	12	24
0263/414-9638	37	130	11	31	14	28
0263/414-9639	40	140	13	35	16	32
0263/414-9640	45	155	20	42	18	36
0263/414-9641	50	180	20	42	20	40
0263/414-9642	55	195	25	55	22	44
0263/414-9643	60	205	25	55	24	48
0263/414-9644	65	225	27	57	36.5	52
0263/414-9645	80	280	29	60	38	54

03036. Common rings

Common rings are forged from carbon magnesium steel, and the size quoted for a ring is the diameter of the metal. It is intended that in the future all common rings will be marked with their safe working load; however it is likely that a number of rings not marked in such a manner will remain in service for many years to come, therefore the Safe Working Load for each size of common ring is included in the details given in Table 3-27.

Table 3-27. Details of common rings

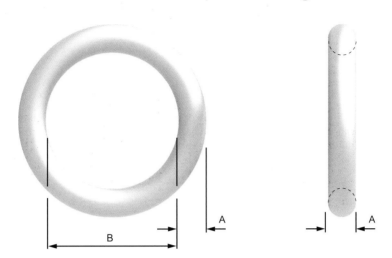

Naval stores No.	A	B	SWL
	mm	mm	tonnes
0263/549-1952	76	260	23
0263/549-1953	70	241	19
0263/549-1954	64	222	15.75
0263/549-1955	57	228	12.7
0263/549-1956	50	178	10.15
0263/549-1957	44	165	7.6
0263/549-1958	41	165	6.6
0263/549-1959	38	152	5.6
0263/549-1960	35	140	4.85
0263/549-1961	32	127	3.9
0263/549-1962	29	114	3.05
0263/549-1963	25	102	2.55
0263/549-1964	22	89	2.05
0263/549-1965	19	76	1.55
0263/549-1966	10	57	0.25

03037. Hooks

a.   There are various types of hooks used in the Royal Navy. They are usually made of carbon manganese steel, and are generally much weaker than shackles of similar size. All hooks used for lifting purpose in the Royal Navy must be fitted with a safety catch (spring-mousing). Open (tackle) hooks may still be encountered in certain roles, for example on awning tackles, but it is likely that all such hooks will eventually be replaced with a spring-moused equivalent. Open hooks must always be moused. It is intended that eventually all hooks in service will bear evidence of their safe working load. Details of hooks in regular use are given on the following page and in Table 3-28 and Table 3-29.

Fig 3-156. Hooks used in the service

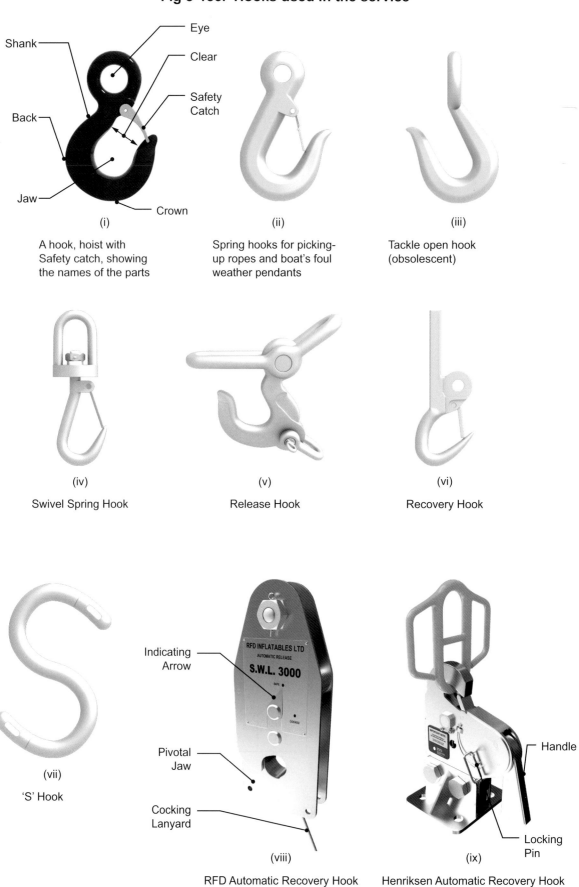

(i)

A hook, hoist with
Safety catch, showing
the names of the parts

(ii)

Spring hooks for picking-
up ropes and boat's foul
weather pendants

(iii)

Tackle open hook
(obsolescent)

(iv)

Swivel Spring Hook

(v)

Release Hook

(vi)

Recovery Hook

(vii)

'S' Hook

(viii)

RFD Automatic Recovery Hook

(ix)

Henriksen Automatic Recovery Hook

(1)   *Hook, hoist, with safety catch* (Fig 3-156(i) and Table 3-28). This type of hook is the most commonly used in the Royal Navy; it has a safety catch in the form of a spring-operated tongue, which dispenses with the requirement for a mousing. The hook is designed for use in conjunction with an appropriate size shackle, although in certain applications it is acceptable to spring a thimble though the eye and splice the cordage or wire round the thimble. Cordage must not be spliced direct to the eye.

(2)   *Spring hook for picking-up ropes and boat's foul weather pendants*. (Fig 3-156(ii)). This hook also has a safety catch to prevent accidental unhooking. It is used in conjunction with a pin and pellet shackle and has machined surfaces either side of the shackle bolthole to facilitate a snug fit between shackle and hook. Details of the hook and corresponding shackle are shown in Table 3-29.

(3)   *Tackle hook*. (Fig 3-156(iii)). As explained earlier, this hook, which is incorporated into the eye of metal and wooden tackle blocks, is gradually being replaced by the hook, hoist, with safety catch, which can be shackled to a synthetic resin bonded fibre block. The tackle hook is no longer available from naval stores.

(4)   *Swivel spring hook*. (Fig 3-156(iv)). These hooks, NSN 0263/414--9753, are fitted with a swivel, which prevents any twists in the whip being transmitted to the hook. They are specified for certain minesweeping and storing tasks. The hook has a Safe Working Load of 0.625 tonnes.

(5)   *Release hook*. (Fig 3-156(v)) This hook, NSN 0263/414-9746, is designed for slipping a load in mid-air. An eye is forged at the back of the hook to which a tripping line is secured; this line is turned up when the load is to be released; by continuing to lower the load the hook is up-ended and the load released.

(6)   *Recovery hook*. (Fig 3-156(vi)). This hook, NSN 0232/414-9748, is used in conjunction with an aluminium stave, Patt No 0573/529-6304, to attach the whip of a crane or derrick to an object in the water. The end of the crane whip is shackled to the eye of the hook, then the squared shank of the hook is inserted into the recess in the end of the stave, and held in place by maintaining light tension in the whip. The stave is then used to place the hook onto the object to be recovered. Once the hook is attached the tension is relaxed on the whip and the stave is pulled clear. The hook has a safe working load of 0.65 tonnes.

(7)   *'S' hook or awning hook*. (Fig 3-156(vii)). This hook is used in certain awning configurations. The hook is available in two sizes, NSN 0263/414-9627 for frigates and destroyers, and 0263/414-9628 for larger ships. The hook has no specific safe working load.

(8)   *RFD automatic release hook Mk 5*. (Fig 3-156(viii)). This hook NSN F218/513-8208 is designed for the Royal Navy and RFA Service for deploying RIBs and inflatable seaboats. The RFD hook is attached to the end of the boats fall and is not to be used for lifting operations other than the launch and recovery of boats. If the boat davit is to be used for other lifting operations, the RFD hook must be removed and an appropriate end attachment fitted to the hard eye of the davit whip. Fitting and operating procedures for the hook are described in Chapter 5 Para 05099.

(9)   *Henriksen release hook.* (Fig 3-156(ix). Like the RFD Automatic Release Hook the Henriksen Release Hook NSN F218-25-160-2946 is designed for the Royal Navy and RFA Service for deploying RIBS and inflatable seaboats. However unlike the RFD hook which is attached to the boat davits fall the Henriksen Release Hook is fitted in the boat. Fitting and operating procedures for the hook are described in Chapter 5 Para 05098.

(10) *Screw-gate karabiner.* This hook is used during astern fuelling to attach the float assembly to the hose-line. It is illustrated in Fig 7-46.

Table 3-28. Details of, hook, hoist, with safety catch

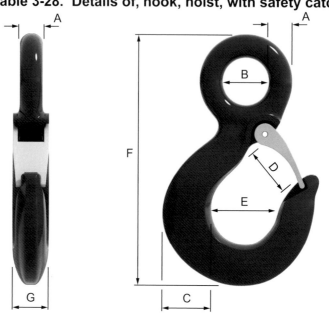

Naval stores No.	A	B	C	D	E	F	G	SWL
	mm	mm	mm	mm	mm	mm	mm	*tonnes*
0263/539-3519	9.0	19	21	26	30	110.0	14.0	0.75
0263/539-3520	11.0	23	24	29	35	126.0	16.0	1.0
0263/539-3521	11.5	29	30	29	37	140.5	19.0	1.5
0263/539-3522	14.5	32	33	33	40	163.0	21.5	2.0
0263/539-3523	17.5	40	41	40	49	200.0	29.0	3.0
0263/539-3524	23.0	51	52	49	64	256.0	35.0	5.0
0263/539-3525	28.5	62	67	60	70	316.0	41.0	7.5

Table 3-29. Details of spring hooks and shackles for picking-up ropes and boat's foul weather pendants

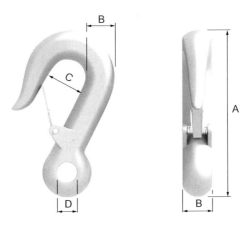

Naval stores No of hook	For use with SWR:		SWR	Dimensions			
	Diameter	Naval stores No.		A	B	C	D
	mm		tonnes	mm			
0263/414-9774	20	0235/523-8649	3.03	303	38	44	27
0263/414-9773	28	0235/523-8640	6.09	241	44	60	33
0263/414-9775	32	0235/523-8641	7.62	286	51	64	46

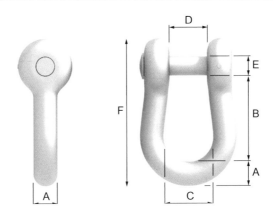

Naval stores No of pin and pellet shackle	For use with SWR:		SWR	Dimensions					
	Diameter	Naval stores No.		A	B	C	D	E	F
	mm		tonnes	mm					
0263/2024	20	0235/523-8649	3.03	25	89	54	35	25	155
0263/414-9606	28	0235/523-8640	6.09	32	108	64	46	32	193
0263/414-9608	32	0235/523-8641	7.62	38	127	76	64	44	233

03038. Rigging screws (also known as turn-buckles or bottlescrews)

a.   Rigging screws (Fig 3-157) are used to **set-up**, ie adjust rigging equipment for length or tension. There are two types;

(1)   A screw fitting into an internally threaded sleeve, with a swivel eye at the head of the screw and a standing eye on the sleeve.

(2)   A similar assembly, but with the standing eye incorporating a slip.

b.   Details of both types are given in Table 3-30 and Table 3-31.

Fig 3-157. Rigging screws

Screw Without Slip   Screw With Slip

Table 3-30. Details of rigging screws without slips

Naval stores No.	Suitable for SWR	SWL
0263/413-5784	40 mm	14.62 tonnes
0263/413-5785	36-32 mm	9.93 tonnes
0263/413-5786	28 mm	6.12 tonnes
0263/414-9745	20 mm	3.25 tonnes
0263/413-5787	16 mm	1.81 tonnes
0263/413-5788	14-12-10-8-6 mm	1.25 tonnes

Table 3-31. Details of rigging screws with slips

Naval stores No.	Suitable for SWR	SWL
0263/413-5781	36-32 mm	9.93 tonnes
0263/413-5782	28 mm	6.12 tonnes
0263/414-9743	20 mm	3.25 tonnes
0263/413-5783	16 mm	1.81 tonnes
0263/414-9744	14-12-10-8-6 mm	1.25 tonnes

03039. Guardrail turnbuckle assemblies

Turnbuckle assemblies are designed for tightening and slipping guardrails. The turnbuckle is available with a slip (Fig 158(ii)), and without a slip (Fig 158(iii)). The Naval Stores Numbers for the stainless steel turnbuckles are given in Table 3-32.

Fig 3-158. Guardrail turnbuckle assemblies

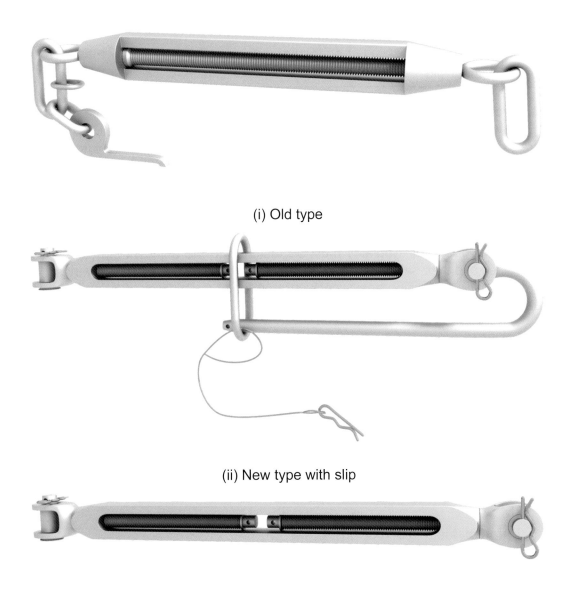

(i) Old type

(ii) New type with slip

(iii) New type without slip

Table 3-32. Details of stainless steel guardrail turnbuckle assemblies

Description	Naval stores No.	SWL
Turnbuckle assembly with slip	0263/539-6386	0.75 tonnes
Turnbuckle assembly without slip	0263/539-6387	0.75 tonnes

03040. Eyeplates and eyebolts

Steel eyeplates (Fig 3-159) are used for securing an eye to a structure. In steel ships they are usually welded permanently in position, but in certain instances they may be bolted in place when required for a specific task, then removed on completion. Eyeplates in GRP ships may be bolted to a backing plate, or screwed to a plate set in the gel, or glued in position with a special adhesive. It must never be assumed that the strength of an eyeplate is necessarily determined by its size, because the strength of the structure to which it is attached is equally important. For this reason there is a requirement that a tally plate giving details of the testing and safe working load of eyeplates must be fastened to the adjacent structure. Details of eyeplate sizes and their safe working loads are given in ship's 'As Fitted' drawings. Eyebolts are often employed for lifting heavy concentrated loads such as machinery. They are fully described in BR 3027.

Fig 3-159. Eyeplate

03041. Union plates (Fig 3-160)

These are triangular or square metal plates with a hole drilled at each corner. They are used as links for shackling the ends of three or four ropes or lengths of chain together; the triangular plates are usually known as **monkey faces** or **shamrock plates**.

Fig 3-160. Union plate or monkey face

03042. Swivels

A swivel is a connection allowing revolution between component parts, usually wires or ropes, either when slack or under strain. There are two types of swivel; the general-purpose swivel, (Table 3-33), used for target towing operations, and the swivel assembly incorporating thimbles in the end links (Table 3-34) used with dressing lines.

Table 3-33. Details of general purpose swivels

Size of swivel	Naval stores No.	SWL	Dimensions			
			A	B	C	D
mm		*tonnes*	*mm*			
10	0573/422-9985	0.89	11	19	54	190
13	0573/422-9974	1.52	14	25	76	258
19	0263/422-9924	3.05	19	29	89	364

Table 3-34. Details of Swivels for Dressing Lines

Size of Swivel	Naval Stores No.	SWL
		tonnes
For use with 8 mm SWR	0263/414-9624	1.01
For use with 12 mm SWR	0263/414-9625	1.01

03043. Rigging slips

a.   A Rigging Slip is a quick-release link used for joining the end of a rope or chain to a fitting when the end may have to be cast off frequently or rapidly; all such slips are properly called senhouse slips, with the tongue of the slip passing though an end link in the rope or chain. There are three types of rigging slip used in the Royal Navy and they are described below. They differ little in design, and although certain slips are specified for certain evolutions, the main criterion for their use is that the safe working load of the slip must not be exceeded.

b. **Types of rigging slip.**

(1) *Slip and shackle for general use.* (Fig 3-161). This slip, NSN 0263/414-9835, is always used with a straight screw shackle Pattern No 0263/721-6096. The slip has a Safe Working Load of nine tonnes and is predominantly used for replenishment at sea (RAS) heavy jackstay and RAS jackstay refuelling.

Fig 3-161. Slip and shackle for general use

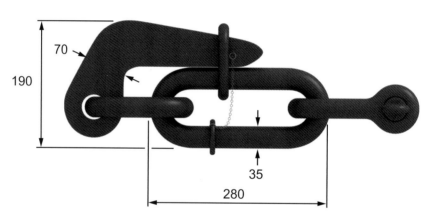

All measurements are in millimetres

Note.   To ensure the slip operates correctly, the clearance between the pin hole and the buckler link (end link) when the slip is rigged must not exceed 15mm. If this distance can be exceeded the slip must be removed from service.

(2) *Slip for replenishment rigs.* (Fig 3-162). This slip, NSN 0263/414-9747 with shackle 0263/721-6093 (for MM's F905/867-8379 with shackle F219/132-6804), is primarily used in replenishment operations, where it is used to secure the light jackstay, and during certain refuelling operations, the sliprope and hose-hanging pendant.

Note. *To ensure the slip operates correctly the clearance between the pin hole and the buckler link (end link) when the slip is rigged must not exceed 15mm. If this distance can be exceeded the slip must be removed from service.*

Fig 3-162. Slip for replenishment rigs

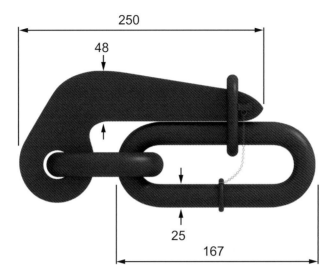

(3) *Slip for rigging.* (Table 3-35). This type of slip, available in four sizes, is now not used often but still has certain specific applications, for example in minesweeping operations.

Table 3-35. Details of slip for rigging

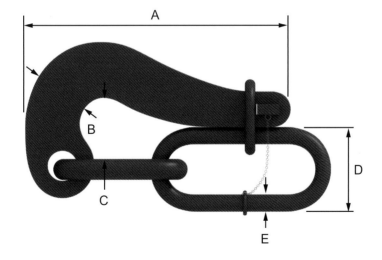

Naval stores No.	A mm	B mm	C mm	D mm	E mm	SWL tonnes
0263/414-9831	145	30	32	45	10	0.825
	190	40	43	60	15	1.525
	230	45	50	70	20	2.350
	295	50	52	75	20	3.430

03044. Blocks

a.   A block is a pulley, made of metal, metal and synthetic-resin bonded fibre (SRBF) or, in some cases, wood and metal. Only SRBF and metal blocks are used in the Royal Navy, and Naval Stores Numbers for those in common use are given in Table 3-36 and Table 3-37.

b.   **Parts of a block.** (Fig 3-163(i)). The main parts of a block are called the **shell** or body; the **sheave** or wheel over which the rope runs; the **pin** on which the sheave turns; the **bush** or bearing between the sheave and the pin; and the **head fitting**, usually an eye, by which the block is secured in the required position. The top of the block is called the **crown**; the bottom of the block is the **tail**; the sides of the shell are called the **cheeks**, the opening between the sheave and shell through which the rope passes is the **swallow**; and the eye sometimes fitted at the tail is called the **becket**. Blocks may have more than one sheave: a single block has one sheave, a double has two, a triple block has three, and so on. A **snatch block** is a single block, metal or SRBF, in which part of the shell is hinged to form a 'gate' which allows a bight of rope to be inserted into the swallow from one side. Snatch blocks should not be used when a solid block is suitable for the job. They should never be used when the safety of life depends on them, because the gate may open if a sideways pull is exerted. Fig 3-163(ii) and Fig 3-163(iii) show an SRBF snatch block with the gate open and closed.

c.   **Classification and description of blocks**. Blocks are classified and described by their type (SRBF or metal); the number of sheaves; the head fitting (the means of attachment, usually a swivel eye); the size and type of rope for which they are designed and the safe working load (SWL) of the block. The SWL, stock number, maker's name and year of manufacture is usually marked on the block by stamping on the metal **binding**, but see also sub para e.

d.   **Types of block**

(1)   *Synthetic Resin-bonded Fibre (SRBF) Block*. This block is built up of steel bindings, and its means of attachment and sheave pins are of steel; the cheek plates and sheave(s) are made of synthetic-resin bonded fibre. SRBF blocks are for use with man-made fibre and natural fibre ropes, and can be single, double or triple blocks or snatch blocks with safe working loads of one, two or four tonnes. They are designed to accept a maximum size of cordage and must not be used for wire rope. Details of those SRBF blocks in common use are given in Table 3-36.

Fig 3-163. Parts of a block

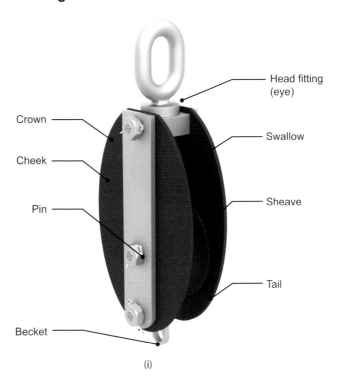

Head fitting (eye)

Crown

Swallow

Cheek

Sheave

Pin

Tail

Becket

(i)

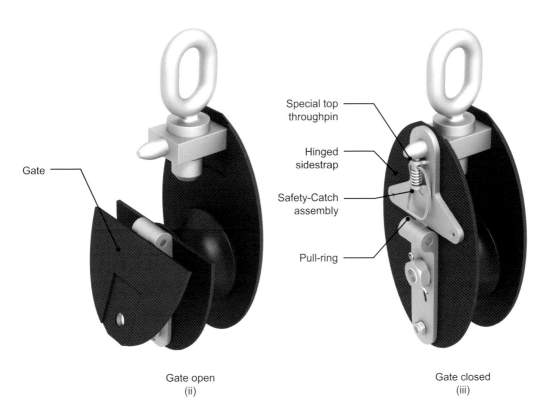

Gate

Special top throughpin

Hinged sidestrap

Safety-Catch assembly

Pull-ring

Gate open
(ii)

Gate closed
(iii)

Table 3-36. Details of synthetic resin bonded fibre blocks in common use

Description of block	Naval stores No.		Maximum size of rope	SWL
	0246/521-		mm	
Treble with swivel oval eye and becket		2725	20	See Annex 3A
		2726	20	See Annex 3A
		2727	36	See Annex 3A
Double with swivel oval eye and becket		2791	20	See Annex 3A
		2792	20	See Annex 3A
		2793	36	See Annex 3A
Single with swivel oval eye and becket		2797	20	See Annex 3A
		2798	20	See Annex 3A
		2799	36	See Annex 3A
Snatch with swivel oval eye		2794	20	See Annex 3A
		2795	20	See Annex 3A
	0246/190-	6915	36	See Annex 3A

(2) *Metal blocks*. These blocks are usually made up from steel plates and fittings, their shells have a binding, which supplies the strength, but the cheeks, etc., are of light plating. However, some types of metal block have their shells cast in one piece. Certain special-purpose blocks are made entirely of gunmetal or phosphor bronze, which do not corrode as easily as steel when exposed to the weather and are unlikely to cause sparks when working. Details of metal blocks in common use are given in Table 3-37.

Table 3-37. Details of metal blocks in common use

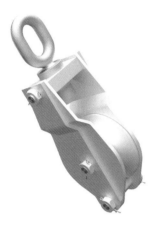

Description of block	Naval stores No.	Size of SWR rope	SWL
	0246/521-	*mm*	
Single with swivel oval eye and becket	0660	12	See Annex 3A
	0661	16	See Annex 3A
	0662	20	See Annex 3A
Snatch with swivel oval eye	0663	12	See Annex 3A
	0664	16	See Annex 3A
	0665	20	See Annex 3A

e.   **Safe working load of blocks**. The safe working load (SWL) of a block is the maximum load that can be safely applied to the head fitting of the block, but the seaman must be aware that this loading depends on the way the block is used; for example, the loading on the head fitting of a block used as the standing or upper block of a purchase is not the same when it is used as the lower or moving block of the same purchase. This principle is illustrated in Fig 3-164. In Fig 3-164(i), ignoring friction, angle and weight of block, the head fitting of the single block is subjected to a load equal to twice the weight of the load being lifted. Therefore in such circumstances a single block with a SWL at the head fitting of at least two tonnes must be used to lift a one tonne load if rigged as shown in Fig 3-164(i). Similarly, a single sheave block with a SWL at the head fitting of 1.5 tonnes is adequate to lift a one tonne weight if rigged as the standing block in the configuration shown in Fig 3-164(ii). The Table at Annex 3A gives the SWL of the head fitting for all blocks in use in the Royal Navy and shows the maximum load that can be lifted with each block in its various tackle configurations (See also Para 03047).

Note.   At present blocks are marked with a variety of data. Some bear only the proof load, others show the SWL at the head fitting. To avoid errors and confusion when using blocks the seaman should refer to the information given at Annexe 3A. This information is accurate. (See also Para 03045).

Fig 3-164. Examples of different loading on a block

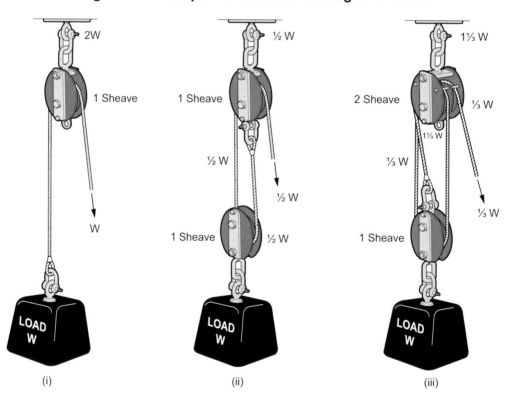

03045. Marking and identifying portable rigging fittings

It is MOD (N) policy that all portable items of rigging equipment (often referred to as loose gear), will be marked with the following information:

a.   The safe working load of the equipment.

b.   The date of test.

c.   Test authority's unique mark (if different from manufacturer).

d.   Markings and symbols which indicate the manufacturer of the equipment and means of identifying the equipment with the manufacturer's certificate of test and examination.

e.   The NATO stock number.

03046. Purchases and tackles – introduction

a.   A purchase is a mechanical device by means of which an applied pull or force is increased; it may be a system of levers, a system of revolving drums or wheels geared to one another, or a combination of blocks or pulleys rove with rope or chain. A tackle is a purchase consisting of a rope rove through two or more blocks in such a way that the force of any pull applied to its hauling part is increased by an amount depending upon the number of sheaves in the blocks and the manner in which the rope is rove through them.

b.   **Parts of a tackle** (Fig 3-165). The blocks of a tackle are termed the standing block and the moving block; the rope rove through them is called the fall, which has its standing, running and hauling parts. The size of a tackle is described by the size of its fall; a 24 mm luff, for example, would be rove with a 24 mm fall.

c.   **Mechanical advantage**. The amount by which the pull on the hauling part is multiplied by the tackle is called its Mechanical Advantage (MA) and, if friction is disregarded, this is equal to the number of parts of the fall at the moving block. In Fig 3-166 for example, there are two parts at the moving block, therefore the MA is two; in other words, a pull on the hauling part of 50kg, would, if friction were disregarded, hold a weight of 100kg. Friction has been taken into account when determining the SWL of a block. However, when calculating the effort (pull) required to lift a weight using a block or tackle the general approximate rule for estimating the amount of friction set up in a tackle is to allow one-tenth for every sheave in the tackle. Therefore if one tonne is to be lifted and there are six sheaves in the tackle, the total allowance for friction will amount to six-tenths of a tonne. The formula for this calculation is given on the following page in sub para f.

Fig 3-165. Parts of a tackle

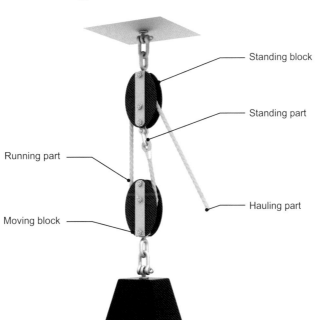

Standing block

Standing part

Running part

Hauling part

Moving block

d. **Velocity ratio**. MA is gained only at the expense of the speed of working. In Fig 3-166, for example, the weight will be raised only half a metre for every metre of movement of the hauling part. The ratio between the distance moved by the hauling part and that moved by the moving block is known as the Velocity Ratio (VR) and is always equal to the number of parts of the fall at the **moving** block.

e. **Reeving a tackle to advantage and disadvantage**. The number of parts at the moving block, and therefore the MA, is always greater when the hauling part comes away from the moving block, and such a tackle is said to be **rove to advantage**. Conversely, a tackle in which the hauling part comes away from the standing block is said to be **rove to disadvantage** (see Fig 3-167). Where practicable, it is beneficial to rig a tackle so that the hauling part leads from the moving block, and the block with the greater number of sheaves is the moving block.

f. **Calculating the effort (pull) required to lift a weight with a tackle**

(1) To calculate the effort (pull) to lift a given load using a tackle the following formula should be used

$$P = \frac{W}{V} \left(1 + \frac{N}{10} \right)$$

P = Pull required (in Kgs)
W = Weight to be lifted (in Kgs)
V = Velocity Ratio
N = Number of sheaves in tackle

(2) The average man can comfortably exert a pull of 25kgs. Therefore to determine the number of personnel required to man the hauling part of the tackle divide the answer to the equation above by 25.

Fig 3-166. Mechanical advantage and velocity ratio of a tackle

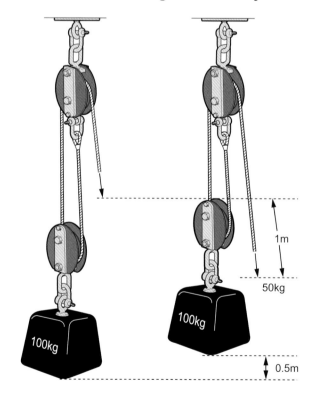

Fig 3-167. Reeving a tackle to advantage and disadvantage

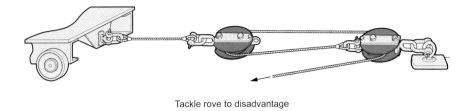

Tackle rove to disadvantage

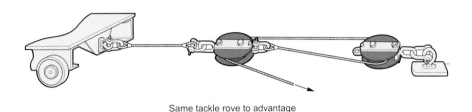

Same tackle rove to advantage

Fig 3-168. Load on the standing block

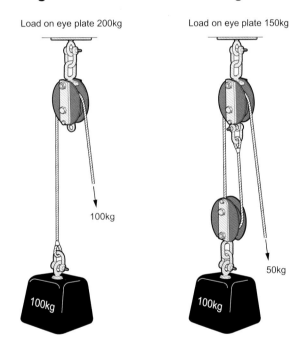

03047. **Examples of tackles and purchases**

a. Examples of whips, tackles and purchases, together with their velocity ratio (VR) and mechanical advantage (MA) are given below; in each the approximate loss of MA due to friction has been taken into account. Tackles should be rove as illustrated; this is particularly important for the three fold purchase to prevent turns forming in the tackle and avoid any tendency for the block to cant sideways as the load comes on it.

b. **Single whip** (Fig 3-169). This consists of a fall rove through a single standing block; no MA is gained. It is used for hoisting light loads, and where speed of hoisting is an important factor.

c. **Runner** (Fig 3-170). This consists of a rope through a single moving block. As there are two parts of the fall in the moving block, the VR is 2 and the MA is 1.82.

d. **Double whip** (Fig 3-171). This is a purchase used for hoisting and consists of two single blocks with the standing part of the fall made fast near, or to, the upper block, and it cannot be rove to advantage. The VR is 2 and the MA is 1.67.

e. **Gun tackle** (Fig 3-172). This is the term usually applied to a purchase consisting of two single blocks, but which is not used for hoisting; it cannot then be called a double whip, a term applied only when it is used for hoisting. In the gun tackle the standing part of the fall is always made fast to one of the blocks. The name originates from the small tackle, which was used to run out the old muzzle-loading guns after they had recoiled. The VR is 3 if rove to advantage, or 2 if rove to disadvantage, and the MA is respectively 2.5 or 1.67.

Fig 3-169. Single whip   **Fig 3-170. Runner**

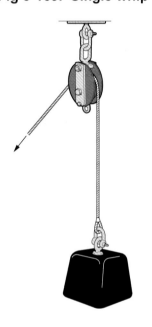

Fig 3-171. Double whip

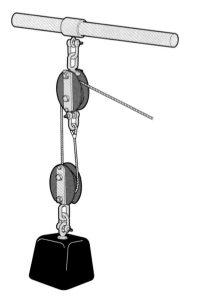

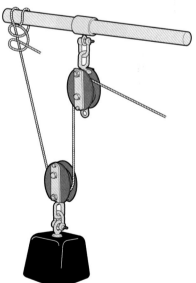

Fig 3-172. Gun tackle

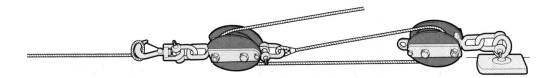

f.   **Luff** (Fig 3-173). This is a purchase of size 24 mm or greater. It consists of a double and a single block, with the standing part of the fall made fast to the single block. The VR is 4 if rove to advantage, or 3 if rove to disadvantage, and the MA is respectively 3.08 or 2.3.

g.   **Jigger**. This is similar to a luff, but is from 16 mm to 20 mm in size.

h.   **Handy billy**. This is a small tackle of less than 16 mm in size; it is usually rove as a jigger but can be rove as a small gun tackle.

i.   **Two-fold purchase** (Fig 3-174). This consists of two double blocks and is a useful general-purpose tackle. The VR is 5 if rove to advantage, or 4 if rove to disadvantage, and the MA is respectively 3.57 or 2.86.

Fig 3-173. Luff   **Fig 3-174. Two-fold purchase**

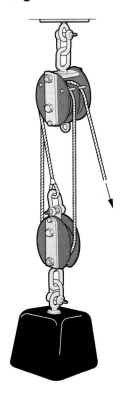   

j.   **Three-fold purchase** (Fig 3-175). This consists of two treble blocks; the VR is 7 if rove to advantage, or 6 if rove to disadvantage, and the MA is respectively 4.37 or 3.75. The method of reeving a three-fold purchase with the hauling part coming from the centre sheave helps to prevent turns forming in the tackle and avoids a tendency for the block to tilt as the load comes on. Tackles having more than three sheaves are not provided because they are too cumbersome to handle efficiently and because the friction in their sheaves reduces their gain in mechanical advantage. If additional mechanical advantage is required it is better to combine two simple tackles.

Fig 3-175. Three-fold purchase

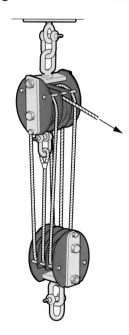

k. **Luff upon luff.** This is a general term used to describe the combined use of two tackles in which the moving block on one is **clapped on** (secured) to the hauling part of the other; its mechanical advantage is the product of the mechanical advantage of each tackle. Fig 3-176 shows two luffs rove to advantage and as a luff upon luff whose VR = 4 x 4 = 16; its MA is 9.49.

Fig 3-176. Luff upon luff

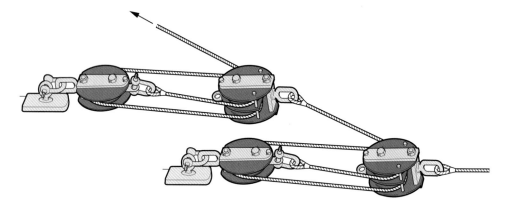

l. **Dutchman's purchase**. This is a tackle used in reverse to take advantage of the velocity ratio of the tackle; an example of its use is to drive a light whip at fast speed from a slow but powerful capstan. In the example illustrated in Fig 3-177 the whip would move a distance of five metres for every metre travelled by the moving block. When using a tackle in this manner the pull exerted by the capstan must be equal to the product of the weight to be hoisted and the velocity ratio of the tackle, plus the friction in the tackle and its leading blocks; in this case a pull of at least 5.6 times the weight to be hoisted.

CAUTION

Ensure the tackle and pendant is strong enough for the job.

---

tFig 3-177. Dutchman's purchase

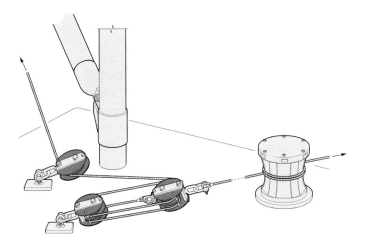

03048. Hand operated chain blocks (Fig 3-178)

Hand operated chain blocks are mechanical purchases designed for lifting weights and have a number of advantages over the simple tackle. They usually consist of a sprocket, worked by an endless hand chain, which operates the load sprocket through gearing; the load sprocket carries the load chain, to which the hoisting hook is attached. The blocks may be of a suspended or a built-in pattern. Suspended types Fig 3-178(i) have a top hook, shackle, or eye from which the block is hung and which allows a degree of articulation between the block and the supporting structure. Built-in types Fig 3-178(ii) are usually combined with a purpose made travelling trolley. Chain blocks supplied for use in confined spaces have a lever and ratchet Fig 3-178(iii) instead of the endless chain. Geared blocks have a very large mechanical advantage and little friction, so that the full safe working load of the gear equipment can be raised by one man. Blocks supplied to the Royal Navy have safe working loads from 0.25 tonnes to as much as ten tonnes, but those of over four tonnes are not widely used.

Fig 3-178. Types of chain block

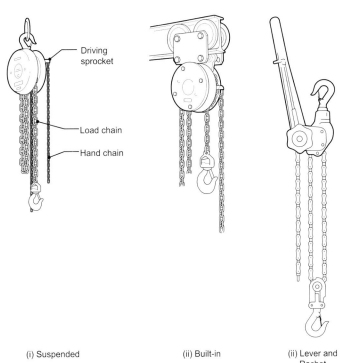

Driving sprocket

Load chain

Hand chain

(i) Suspended   (ii) Built-in   (ii) Lever and Rachet

03049. Tirfor pulling and lifting machines (Fig 3-179)

The Tirfor is a patented hand-operated pulling and lifting machine similar in operation to the lever and ratchet chain block, although wire rope rather than chain is used as the fall. It works by pulling directly on the rope, the pull being applied by means of two pairs of self-energising smooth jaws which exert a grip on the rope in proportion to the load being lifted or pulled. The initial pressure, which causes the jaws to grip the rope and give the self-energising action, is provided by powerful springs. Each machine has a stub operating handle over which an operating handle fits and by pumping the handle back and forth the hook is drawn towards the block (hoisting the load); shear pins that activate when the safe working load of the machine is exceeded by 60% are fitted to the handle stub of the two smallest type of machine. To reverse the process, ie, to move the hook away from the block (lower the load), the operating handle is placed over the reversing lever and pumped as described above. To release the jaws from the rope, the rope release lever is operated. This must never be attempted when the machine is under load. Maxiflex wire rope falls are supplied with each machine; other types of wire must not be used. There are three sizes of machine available through Naval Stores. Details of NSNs for the machines and the wire whips are given in Table 3-38. An operator's handbook is supplied with each machine.

Table 3-38. Details of pulling and lifting machines

Pattern No of machine	SWL	Pattern No of wire whip
0246/202-9035 0246/137-2655 0246/137-1594	0.762 tonne 1.625 tonne 3.04 tonne	0246/202-9037 (10 m length) 0246/202-9038 (18 m length) 0246/202-0013 (10 m length) 0246/137-1595 (37 m length)

Fig 3-179. Pulling and lifting machine (tirfor block)

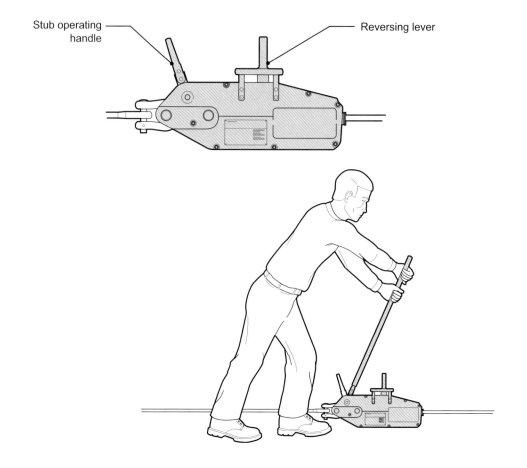

Stub operating handle

Reversing lever

03050. Air-powered Hoist (Fig 3-180(i))

The air-powered hoist relies on compressed air for power. The unit is connected to a low pressure (LP) air supply, and operated by a **pendant control handle** (Fig 3-180(ii)). The pendant handle control is fitted with separate levers for raising or lowering the load, and a safety lever which must be depressed by gripping the handle, before the hoist becomes operative. Depression of the 'up' or 'down' levers on the control handle causes air pressure to be released on the appropriate side of the throttle valve so that it moves to one side of the chamber and air passes to the motor. The brake is held in the 'off' position by air pressure, so that if the operator releases the pendant control, the brake is automatically applied and will safely hold the maximum load until the 'down' lever is operated. The hoist, which has a maximum lifting distance of six metres, has a safe working load of 400 kgs and is available from Naval Stores on NSN F205/772-9185.

WARNING

AIR-POWERED HOISTS ARE NOT TO BE USED FOR THE LOWERING OR HOISTING OF PERSONNEL.

Fig 3-180. Air-powered hoist

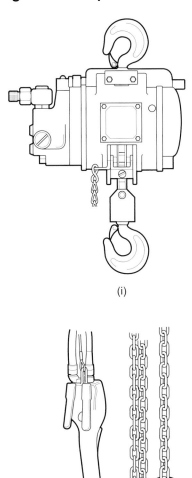

(i)

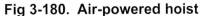

(ii)

03051. Lifting and slinging

a. **Safe system of work**. Before any lifting operation is carried out you are to ensure a risk assessment has been made to identify the nature and level of any risk associated with that operation and a safe system of work put in place to reduce or eliminate any risks identified.

b. All lifting operations should be planned to ensure that they are carried out safely. Planning should be carried out by personnel who have the appropriate expertise and have been appointed for the purpose.

c. In cases of repetitive or routine operations, this planning may only be necessary in the first instance, with periodic reviews to ensure that no factors have changed.

d. Planning should include consideration of the following:

(1) The load, its characteristics and the method of lifting.

Note. It may also be necessary to make allowance for any adhesion between the load and its support.

(2) The selection of a suitable crane(s) appropriate to the operation ensuring that adequate clearances are maintained between the load(s) and the crane structure.

(3) The selection of lifting equipment, the weight of which should be taken into account when assessing the load on the crane(s).

(4) The position of the crane(s) and the load before, during and after the operation.

(5) The site of the operation taking into account proximity hazards, space availability and suitability of the ground or foundations.

(6) Any necessary erection and dismantling of the crane(s).

(7) The environmental conditions that exist or may occur at the site of the operation, which may necessitate stopping the operation when conditions are unsuitable.

e. By applying these procedures to every lift, all persons concerned should be able to work in an efficient and safe environment so far as is reasonably practicable without risk to themselves or others.

f. A safe system of work lift plan at annex 3B is to be completed before any lifting operation is carried out.

g. The information given here provides an introduction to slinging. More information on slinging is given in **BR 6004 Slingers Handbook**, and **BR 3027 Manual of Inspection and Test of Lifting Plant.** Slings are used for hoisting, lowering or supporting loads; they may be directly attached to (or passed round) the load, and, depending on the nature of their duty, can be of chain or steel wire rope, or proprietary man-made fibre lifting slings made of polyester or polyamide. Hawser-laid cordage slings are no longer used in the Royal Navy.

The choice of sling and the manner in which it is used depends upon whether one or a number of objects are to be slung in one hoist, the weight of those objects and whether they are robust or fragile. If a number of loads are to be slung in one hoist the load is called a **set**. The main requirement when slinging is that the sling should be sufficiently strong to hold the load securely without crushing it, and the simpler the sling the easier it will be to handle.

h.   The duties and responsibilities of a slinger are:

(1)   To prepare the set or load.

(2)   To select and prepare the appropriate slings, pan them round or connect them to the set or load.

(3)   To hook or shackle the sling or slings to the crane, derrick or lifting appliance correctly.

(4)   To tend and steady the load before lifting and to control by line while the load is slung; and to tend, steady and position the load on lowering.

(5)   To be fully responsible for the safe transfer of the load from one position to the other.

(6)   To be solely responsible for giving the orders to the crane driver, derrick winchman, or man tending the lifting appliance. (Second slinger).

(7)   To be conversant with the Standard Crane Signals and to use them at all times. (See Fig 3-203).

(8)   To inspect the lifting equipment before use to ensure it is in a satisfactory condition and suitable for the job. Also to inspect the equipment after use and report any defects.

(9)   To check that each item of lifting equipment employed is marked with its safe working load and identification number.

(10) To make sure that the outriggers of mobile cranes are extended **before** lifting operations commence.

i.   **Slinging constraints.** The constraints that apply to safe slinging are:

(1)   All slings must be recorded in the lifting plant register. The use of unregistered slings is unlawful.

(2)   A load label is attached to all multi-leg slings showing the total weight (safe working load) the complete sling is designed to lift with the legs at an angle to the vertical of not more than 45° (90° angle between sling legs), and with all legs in use and if required a reduced capacity for angles between 45°-60°. If only one leg of a double-leg sling is used then only half the weight indicated by the load label can be lifted.

(3)   A sling must not be used to lift a weight greater than that indicated on the label. Therefore the weight of the load must be determined prior to slinging.

(4)   Use long slings whenever possible to reduce the angle of the sling. It is important to remember that the lifting capacity of the sling is affected by the angle of the sling legs.

(5)   Always use two or more legs of a wire rope sling with hook and spliced eye. A single wire can untwist allowing the splice to open and slip.

(6)   When an object with sharp corners or rough edges is to be lifted, slings must be protected by pads of suitable thickness and material.

(7)   Do not rest a load on a sling. If necessary use suitable supports to avoid trapping the sling.

(8)   Slings must not be knotted.

(9)   Slings must not be dragged either loaded or unloaded across the deck. This is particularly important with fibre slings.

(10)   Ensure the crane hook is placed centrally over the load to prevent swinging when the load is being raised.

(11)   Stow slings in their designated stowage; don't leave them lying about.

j.   **Sling configuration.** Each of the different types of material may be encountered in any one of five basic configurations for general purpose slings, eg. single leg, two leg, three leg, four leg and endless sling.

(1)   *Single leg sling*. This sling may be used to connect a lifting appliance to a load with a single lifting point such as the eyebolt on an electric motor (Fig 3-181(i)). It may also be used as a choke hitch, either by back hooking Fig 3-181(ii) or reeving one end of the sling through the other Fig 3-181 (iii), Fig 3-181 (iv) and Fig 3-181(v). Or, where possible, it may be passed as a basket hitch through the load to be lifted Fig 3-181(vi). Two single leg slings may be used to form, in effect, a two leg sling (Fig 3-182).

(2)   Where this is done, the included angle between the sling legs should not exceed 90° and care must be taken to ensure that the hook is not overcrowded. The method of attaching the sling to the crane hook should ensure that the sling's eyes, links or rings are not damaged. Two single legs slings used as a two leg sling must be treated as a two leg sling for rating purposes and the combined safe working load when used at all angles between 0 and 45° to the vertical must be considered at 1.4 times the safe working load of the single sling.

Fig 3-181. Single leg sling in various configurations

Note 1. The total load that may be lifted is that marked on the sling
Note 2. A vertical or straight lift is only suitable for lifting a load which is stable when suspended from a single lifting point

(i) Vertical or straight lift

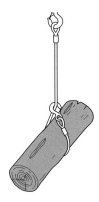

Note. The total load that may be lifted is 0.8 of that marked on the sling

(ii) Backing hooking

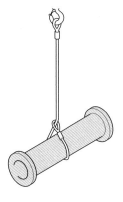

Note. The total load that may be lifted is 0.8 of that marked on the sling

(iii) Simple choke hitch

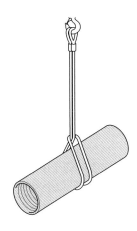

Note. The total load that may be lifted is 1.5 of that marked on the sling

(iv) Double and choked

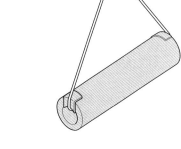

Note. The total load that may be lifted is 0.8 of that marked on the sling

(v) Choke hitch double wrapped

Note. The total load that may be lifted when the angle to the vertical does not exceed 45 degrees is 1.4 of that marked on the sling

(vi) Basket hitch

Fig 3-182. Two single leg slings in various configurations

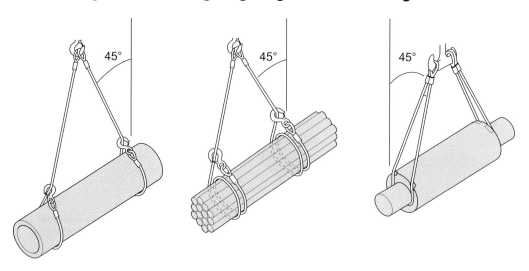

Note: the total load that may be lifted when the angle to the vertical does not exceed 45° is 0.8 X 1.4 times that marked on the single sling

Note: the total load that may be lifted when the angle to the vertical does not exceed 45° is 0.8 X 1.4 times that marked on the single sling

Note: the total load that may be lifted provided no angle to the vertical exceeds 45° is 2.1 times that marked on the sling

(3)   *Two leg sling* (Fig 3-1830). A two-leg sling comprises two legs connected at their upper ends by a master link. Two leg slings may be used to handle a wide range of loads.

(4)   *Three leg sling* (Fig 3-183). A three-leg sling comprises three legs connected at their upper ends by a master link. Three legs are commonly used to handle circular or irregularly shaped loads where the legs can be equally spaced.

(5)   *Four leg sling* (Fig 3-183). A four-leg sling comprises four legs connected to a main lifting ring via two intermediate rings. Four legged slings are mainly used to handle square or rectangular (four-cornered) loads.

Fig 3-183. Two- three- and four legged slings

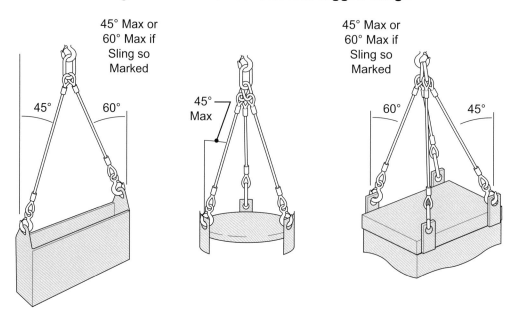

The total load that may be lifted is that marked on the sling assembly

k. **Method of rating lifting slings.** When a multi-leg sling is used with the slings at an angle, the tension in the individual sling legs will increase as the angle to the vertical becomes greater (Fig 3-184). If a sling is to be used safely, allowance must be made for this angle; there are various ways of calculating this allowance but the simplest way is by the uniform load method. This method permits only one working load limit (WLL) for angles up to 45° to the vertical and a reduced WLL for angles between 45° and 60° to the vertical. This is the only method to be used for all multi-purpose slings. The calculation is made by utilising mode factors as follows:

Single leg sling	=	1.0 x WLL of a single leg
Two leg sling (included angle 0-45°)	=	1.4 x WLL of a single leg
Two leg sling (included angle 45°-60°)	=	1.0 x WLL of a single leg
Three and four leg sling (included angle 0-45°) =		2.1 x WLL of a single leg
Four leg sling (included angle 45°-60°)	=	1.5 x WLL of a single leg

Notes:

1. These calculations assume that: the slings are symmetrically disposed in plan, and equally stressed under load; that all legs of multi-leg slings are made of identical material, and the method of attachment to the load allows for a 'straight pull', ie the legs are not bent around the load, choked, back-hooked or otherwise prevented from taking up a straight line under load.

2. Three and four leg slings are rated the same for 0-45°. This takes into account that at any one time one leg may have no load.

3. Three leg slings MUST NEVER be rated for angles greater than 45° due to the excessive stresses created at the larger angles.

4. The mode factors used are based on the percentage of loading in the single leg of the sling regardless of the material used.

l. **Markings on the sling.** Uniform method rated slings (range of angles).

WLL/SWL xt 0 - 45°

WLL/SWL yt 45° - 60°

Note.   *Older slings may be marked for the included angle: 0-90° and 90°-120°.*

m. **Multi-leg slings with less than the full number of legs in use.** If a multi-leg sling is used with less than the actual number of legs attached to the load, then the safe working load of the sling must be reduced. An easy way of ensuring that the sling is never overloaded is to reduce the safe working load from that marked on the sling according to the number of legs in use in the following manner;

(1)	Two leg sling with one leg in use	=	half of marked SWL
(2)	Three leg sling with two legs in use	=	third of marked SWL
(3)	Four leg sling with three legs in use	=	three quarters of marked SWL

n. **Rating assumptions and deviations from the sssumed conditions.** Both rating methods assume certain conditions of use, which ensure that no part of the sling is overloaded. It is important to understand that although the weight to be lifted may be within the maximum lifting capacity of the sling, using it in the wrong way can overload part of the sling. Some deviations from the assumed conditions are prohibited such as loading a hook on the tip. Others are permitted provided an appropriate allowance is made. With multi-purpose slings, the designer has little if any information about the intended use so the onus to make such allowances falls on the user.

Fig 3-184. Illustration of how tension increases in legs of slings as angle increases

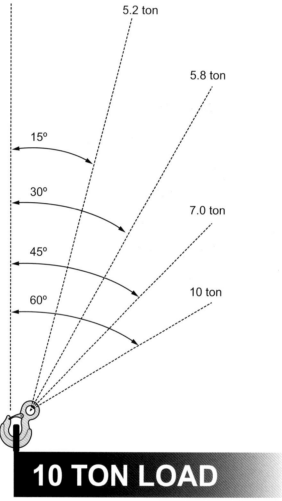

o. **Other factors affecting the strength of slings.** If a wire or chain sling is hooked back on itself, or secured by a choke hitch, ie by reeving one end of the sling through the other, it is said to be **snickled**. This method of securing the slings to the load will reduce the working strength of a chain sling by 50%, and a wire sling by up to 66%. The reduction in working strength with regard to proprietary polyester slings is given in Table 3-39.

p. **Estimating sling angles**. In practice it is not possible to measure sling angles accurately, and the slinger must therefore use his judgement. Fig 3-185 shows how to estimate angles of 30°, 60°, 90° and 120° by relating the span to the length of one leg of the sling. All references to sling angles refer to the angle to the vertical that the sling creates when in use.

Fig 3-185. Estimating sling angles

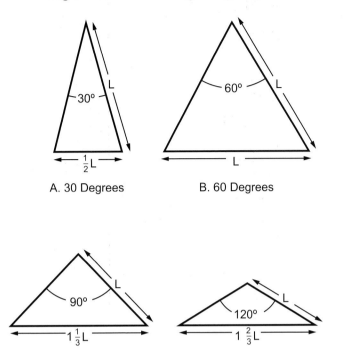

A. 30 Degrees

B. 60 Degrees

C. 90 Degrees

D. 120 Degrees

q.   **Using spreaders** (Fig 3-186). Spreaders are used in conjunction with slings primarily to prevent the sling crushing and damaging the load in instances where softwood or other packing in way of the sling gives insufficient protection. Spreaders are usually made of 180 mm x 180 mm Canadian elm or English oak up to about 3.6 metres in length. It is important that the correct length of spreader for the job is used; as a rule of thumb the spreader should be no longer than is necessary to prevent crushing of the load.

Fig 3-186. Using spreaders

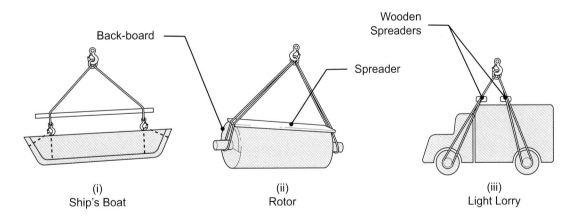

(i)
Ship's Boat

(ii)
Rotor

(iii)
Light Lorry

r.   **Slinging boats**. When a boat, normally hoisted by davits, is hoisted by dockside or mobile crane, either a two leg sling with a spreader is used (Fig 3-186(i)), or two specially made flat webbing slings are passed around the keel and positioned at pre-determined points to ensure a balanced lift. Whenever possible it is advisable to seek advice from an experienced slinger before undertaking this evolution.

s.   **Slinging a vehicle**. Special wheel net slings are normally used for loading and discharging vehicles from ships (Fig 3-187). These slings can also be used for loading and unloading stores. The gear consists of two wire nets 2.6 x 1.0 metres fitted with shackles, two wooden spreaders 3.0 x 0.1 x 0.1 metres fitted with slotted ends and retaining bolts, four 24mm SWR single slings 7 metres in length fitted to intermediate links and a master link at the top and a thimble eye at the bottom, and eight bulldog grips. The bulldog grips are secured to the single slings on each side of the spreaders to prevent them slipping. The SWL of this type of vehicle sling is six tonnes. The correct procedure for lifting is as follows:

(1)   Move the vehicle as near to the crane plumb as possible, and spread out the nets in front of each pair of wheels.

(2)   Move the vehicle onto the nets, making certain that the wheels rest centrally upon them.

(3)   Lower the four-leg sling about the vehicle and shackle each pair of legs to a net; leave the vehicle's brakes off.

(4)   Take up the slack of the sling and the nets and, with padded material, pack between the nets and the body where the nets may bear.

(5)   Lift the vehicle, taking care that the wheels are riding snugly in the nets.

(6)   Points to remember when using vehicle lifting gear:

(a) Spreaders must be used, otherwise much damage will be done.

(b) Ensure the bulldog grips are firmly in position and place the bolt through the end of the spreader.

(c) When lowering a vehicle, lower the purchase slowly once the vehicle has touched, otherwise the spreader may damage the vehicle or the stores.

(d) It is often possible to leave the nets shackled to the slings, and to run the next vehicle onto them without dismantling the gear.

Fig 3-187. Slinging a vehicle

t.   **Cargo nets** (Fig 3-188(i)). Cargo nets are a practical way of handling loads which will not suffer damage when subjected to the bowsing-in movement inherent when lifting equipment in nets; objects such as drums are most safely transferred in this manner.

u.   **Pallet and pallet sling (palnets)** (Fig 3-188(ii)). The pallet is of wooden or aluminium construction which, when loaded with stores can be lifted by fork-lifted truck or can be hoisted by the pallet sling without the necessity of reeving the sling under the pallet before it is loaded. This arrangement is ideal for the transfer of bulk stores of the same size.

Fig 3-188. Cargo nets and palnets

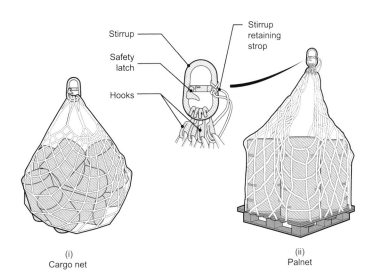

(i)
Cargo net

(ii)
Palnet

03052. Proprietary lifting slings

a.   An increased use is being made of proprietary lifting slings for a wide variety of tasks in the Royal Navy. These slings are usually standard stock items which either meet a specific lifting requirement, or provide a general lifting facility on a ship. They are available in a number of lengths, with a variety of end termination. The types of proprietary lifting sling used in the Royal Navy are described below:

b.   **Basic polyester roundsling** (Fig 3-189). This type of sling is the most commonly used in the service. It has an outer protective casing made from reinforced monofilament polyester yarn with the inner core made up from an endless hank of polyester. The slings are colour coded in accordance with the relevant British Standard, which helps to ensure easy recognition of the safe working load of the sling; in addition the safe working load is marked at regular intervals on the sling's outer case. This safe working load applies only when the sling is used in a straight lift, in any other configuration the safe working load is changed. Details are given in Table 3-39. Every roundsling bears a unique identification number and is issued with a certificate of conformance. In use the roundsling flattens to provide a safe grip on its load; it is extremely light in weight, is very resistant to wear and damage, and the elongation at the safe working load is only 3%. The sling requires little or no maintenance other than an occasional cleaning in fresh water with a mild detergent. It is fully resistant to corrosion and has a high resistance to hydrocarbons, most chemicals and solvents. However, ammonia, alkalis and certain acids can cause damage. These slings are never load tested, but are subject to inspection before and after use, and are periodically inspected in accordance with BR 3027.

c.   If the outer casing is intact the slings may be considered usable, because the inner core determines the strength of the sling. If the outer case is damaged to the point where the inner yarns are visible the sling should be cut up and discarded.

Fig 3-189. A basic polyester roundsling

Table 3-39. Details of basic polyester roundslings

SAFE LIFTING CHART (ROUNDSLING)

Safety Factor 7:1 Complies with Supply of Machinery (Safety) Regulations Amended 1994 Source BS EN 1492 -2: 2000

	Straight Lift	Choked Lift	Basket Hitch			Two Leg Sling		Three/Four Leg Sling	
			Kg	Kg	Kg	Kg		Kg	
M = Mode factor for symmetrical loading			Parallel	β 0 - 45°	β 45° - 60°	β 0 - 45°	β 45° - 60°	β 0 - 45°	β 45° - 60°
Colour	Kg M = 1	Kg M = 0.8	M = 2	M = 1.4	M = 1	M = 1.4	M = 1	M = 2.1	M = 1.5
Violet	1000	800	2000	1400	1000	1400	1000	2100	1500
Green	2000	1600	4000	2800	2000	2800	2000	4200	3000
Yellow	3000	2400	6000	4200	3000	4200	3000	6300	4500
Red	5000	4000	10000	7000	5000	7000	5000	10500	7500
Brown	6000	4800	12000	8400	6000	8400	6000	12600	9000
Blue	8000	6400	16000	11200	8000	11200	8000	16800	12000

Larger Capacity Slings Available. Mode factor!! Important – The Max W.L.L. Depends on the Angle!!

d.   **'Supra' polyester roundslings and associated fittings**.   'Supra' polyester round slings are manufactured, marked and colour-coded in the same way as basic polyester roundslings; however, the outer protective sheath of the 'Supra' version is of superior quality to the basic roundsling and for ease of identification the word 'Supra' is woven at intervals into the outer casing. Metal end fittings are available for 'Supra' roundslings, enabling them to be assembled into one, two, three or four leg sling configurations; in addition; three types of anti-chafing sleeves are available for use with the slings. Although at present the supply of this type of sling and the associated fittings is limited to certain ships for the removal of equipment from machinery rooms and other specified tasks, it is likely that in the future the equipment will be made available for use in all vessels, for most slinging tasks.

e.   There are four metal component end fittings for use with the 'Supra' roundslings. They are as follows:

(1)   *Master link* (Fig 3-190(i)). This consists of a main link with two intermediate links attached. It is available in two sizes, NSN 0263/930-5752 for use with slings that have a SWL of 1 and 2 tonnes, and NSN 0263/404-2154 for use with slings that have a SWL load of 3 and 5 tonnes. The former bears the manufacturer's mark OTF-6-8 and the latter is marked OTF-10-8.

(2)   *Roundsling coupling* (Fig 3-190(ii)). This fitting has a faired bearing surface that permits direct contact with the roundsling without causing chafe; it has a double and a single lug which interlock into corresponding lugs on the half link. The coupling is available in two sizes, NSN 0263/660-2625 for use with slings that have a SWL of 1 and 2 tonnes, and NSN 0263/594-5352 for use with slings that have a SWL of 3 and 5 tonnes. The former bears the manufacturer's mark SKR 7-8 and the latter is marked SKR 13-8.

(3)   *Half link* (Fig 3-190(iii)). The half link is of round section and has a double and single lug which interlocks into corresponding lugs on the roundsling coupling. Each half link is supplied complete with a locking set consisting of a collar and locking pin. The collar fits between the lugs of the half link and roundsling coupling as shown in Fig 3-220(iii), and the complete assembly is locked together by the locking pin. There are two types of locking set in service and the pins and collars are not interchangeable. Locking sets must only be used with the half link with which they have been supplied. The half link is available in two sizes, NSN 0263/255-4156 for use with slings that have a SWL of 1 and 2 tonnes, and NSN 0263/133-4642 for use with slings that have a SWL of 3 and 5 tonnes. The former bears the manufacturer's mark G 7-8 and the latter is marked G 13-8.

(4)   *Swivel safety hook* (Fig 3-190iv)). This hook is fitted with a spring-operated tongue, and incorporates a swivel link eye for attachment to a half link. The hook is available in two sizes, NSN 0263/513-5616 for use with slings that have a SWL of 1 and 2 tonnes, and 0263/877-7632 for use with slings that have a SWL of 3 and 5 tonnes. The former bears the manufacturer's mark BKL 7-8 and the latter is marked BKL 13-8.

Notes:

1.   Metal component end fittings are not available for use with the 20 tonne SWL roundslings.

2.   By design, metal component end fittings of a given size are not interchangeable with any other size.

3.   Metal component end fittings are periodically surveyed in accordance with BR 3027.

Fig 3-190. End fittings for use with 'supra' roundslings

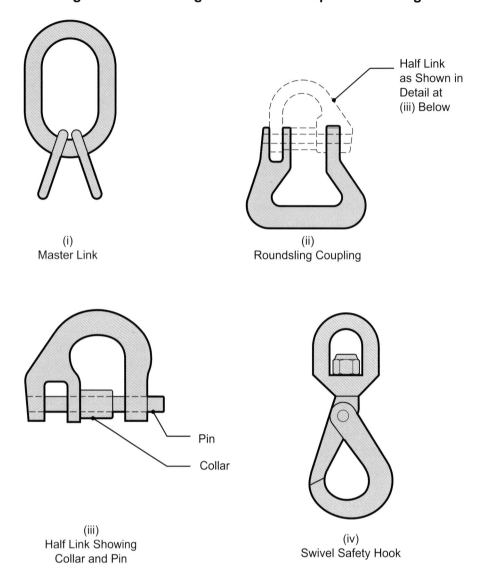

(i)
Master Link

Half Link
as Shown in
Detail at
(iii) Below

(ii)
Roundsling Coupling

Pin

Collar

(iii)
Half Link Showing
Collar and Pin

(iv)
Swivel Safety Hook

f.   There are three types of chafing piece available for use with either basic or 'Supra' round slings. They are as follows:

(1)   *Sleeve, anti-abrasion* (Fig 3-191(i)). This tubular sleeve consists of two pieces of webbing stitched together; it is slid over the sling and positioned as required where chafe is expected. Anti-wear sleeves are available in different lengths and sizes as follows:

(a) Length 0.5 metres for use with slings that have a SWL of 1 and 2.0 tonnes. NSN 0263/110-0736.

(b) Length 1.5 metres for use with slings that have a SWL of 1 and 2.0 tonnes. NSN 0263/720-9679.

(c) Length 0.5 metres for use with slings that have a SWL of 3 and 5.0 tonnes. NSN 0263/906-7617.

(d) Length 1.5 metres for use with slings that have a SWL of 3 and 5.0 tonnes. NSN 0263/215-2741.

(2) *Sleeve, anti-cutting, double sided* (Fig 3-191(ii)). This sleeve, manufactured from a polyurethane polymer, is highly resistant to cuts and abrasions. It is slid over the sling and positioned as required where very heavy chafe or abrasions are expected. Two sizes are available, details as follows:

(a) Length 0.5 metres for use with slings that have a SWL of 1 and 2.0 tonnes. NSN 0263/227-5956.

(b) Length 0.5 metres for use with slings that have a SWL of 3 and 5.0 tonnes. NSN 0263/807-1268.

(3) *Sleeve, anti-cutting, clip-on* (Fig 3-191(iii)). This sleeve is a short, clip-on version of the anti-cutting sleeve described above. It can be clipped to a sling where cutting or chafing points occur, without the need to unhook or dismantle sling assemblies.

Fig 3-191. Chafing piece attachments for use with roundslings

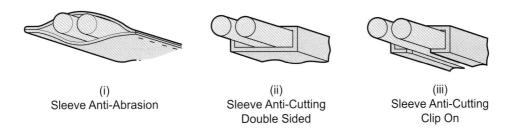

(i)	(ii)	(iii)
Sleeve Anti-Abrasion	Sleeve Anti-Cutting Double Sided	Sleeve Anti-Cutting Clip On

g. **Assembling single and multi-leg 'supra' polyester roundslings.** With the use of the associated metal component end fittings, 'Supra' polyester roundslings can be assembled into two, three and four leg sling assemblies, or a single leg sling fitted with a lifting hook at one end. Tools and equipment required for the job are: a hammer, a block of timber and a roll of masking tape. Always select the correct size end fittings appropriate to the roundslings being used, and ensure all legs of a multi-leg sling have the same SWL. After assembly of multi-leg slings, consult Para 03055 sub para (e) to ascertain the SWL of the complete assembly, have the complete sling examined by ME 427 trained staff, enter it in the register and then attach a tally, marked with the SWL, to the assembly.

(1) Assembling a single leg with swivel hook end attachment

(a) Study Fig 3-192. Lay out the sling to its maximum effective length, and tape a soft eye into one end; this eye should be large enough to accommodate the appropriate roundsling coupling comfortably (Fig 3-193(i)). Introduce the coupling into the soft eye (see Note 1).

(b) Insert the half link into the swivel eye of the hook. Then, with the collar positioned as shown in Fig 3-193(i), offer up the half link to the coupling.

(c) When the coupling, collar and half link are accurately aligned (Fig 3-193(ii)) and with the timber block positioned under the assembly, tap the locking pin home. When the pin is fully home (Fig 3-193(iii)), check that the collar rotates freely.

Notes:

1.   Ensure a coupling, not a half link, is inserted into the soft eye. If a half link is used the SWL of the sling is considerably reduced.

2.   A single leg sling fitted with a swivel hook at one end does not require a master link in the 'free end'; the free end of the sling can be directly hooked over the hook of the crane or lifting appliance.

Fig 3-192. Components of a single leg sling

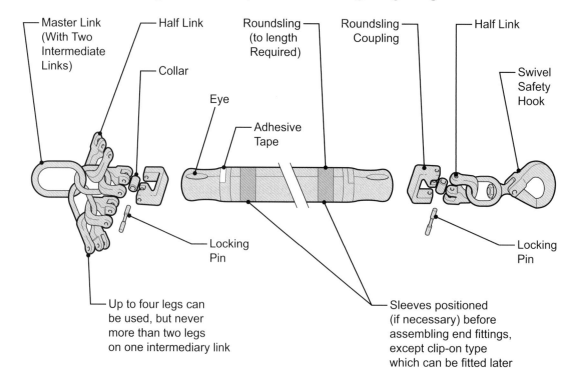

Fig 3-193. Securing a half-link to a coupling with a locking set

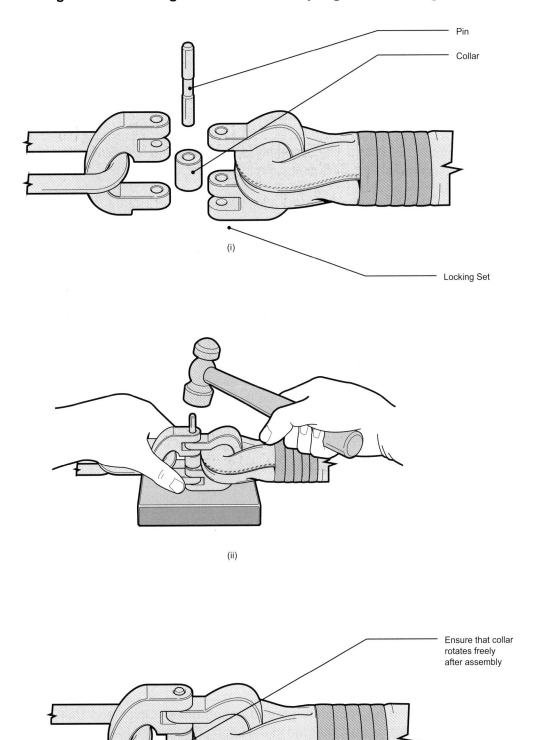

Note. *The pin is held in position by a helical spring sited inside the collar.*

(2)   *Constructing a two-leg sling assembly* (Fig 195(i))

(a) Fit one end of each of the two legs with a swivel hook, as described for the single leg sling.

(b) Select the appropriate size master link, and, using the correct size couplings and half links, connect a leg to each of the two intermediate links attached to the master link.

(c) Attach to the assembly a tally showing the SWL. (Details of how to establish the SWL are given in paragraph 03052e).

(3)   *Constructing a three-leg sling assembly* (Fig 194(ii))

(a) Fit one end of each of the three legs with a swivel hook, as described above for the single leg sling.

(b) Select the appropriate size master link, and using the correct size couplings and half links, connect two of the legs to one of the intermediate links on the master link, and the remaining leg to the remaining intermediate link.

(c) Attach to the assembly a tally showing the SWL. (Details of how to establish the SWL are given in paragraph 03052e).

(4)   *Constructing a four-leg sling assembly* (Fig 194(iii))

(a) Fit one end of each of the four legs with a swivel hook, as described above for the single leg sling.

(b) Select the appropriate size master link, and using the correct size couplings and half links, connect two legs to each of the intermediate links attached to the master link.

(c) Attach to the assembly a tally showing the SWL. (Details of how to establish the SWL are given in paragraph 03052e).

Note.   *To dismantle the end fittings, position the assembly on a wooden block but with the base of the pin clear of the block. Then use an appropriate sized drift to drive out the pin.*

h.   **Accounting for roundslings and assemblies**. Ships and Units are to ensure that all Roundslings are recorded in the Lifting Equipment Register.

Fig 3-194. Two, three and four – leg slings

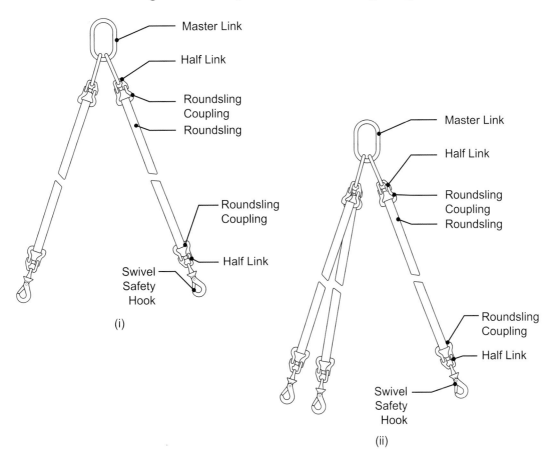

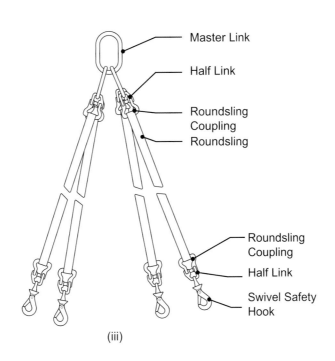

i.   **Flat webbing slings** (Fig 3-195). These types of slings are fabricated from a single length of polyester webbing, with various terminals as appropriate; Simplex slings have the webbing stitched close to the terminals, whereas Duplex slings are effectively stitched through two thicknesses throughout most of their length. Slings are terminated either in a reinforced soft eye or in any combination of metal end fittings. The marking, colour coding, maintenance and sling configuration safe working loads for flat webbing slings is the same as that for polyester roundslings. Flat webbing slings are used where a flat bearing surface can be critical in protecting the surface of the load, examples being GRP boats, machine bearings and pipework; they are also used in the Royal Navy for hoisting and lowering rigid inflatable boats.

Fig 3-195. Examples of flat webbing slings

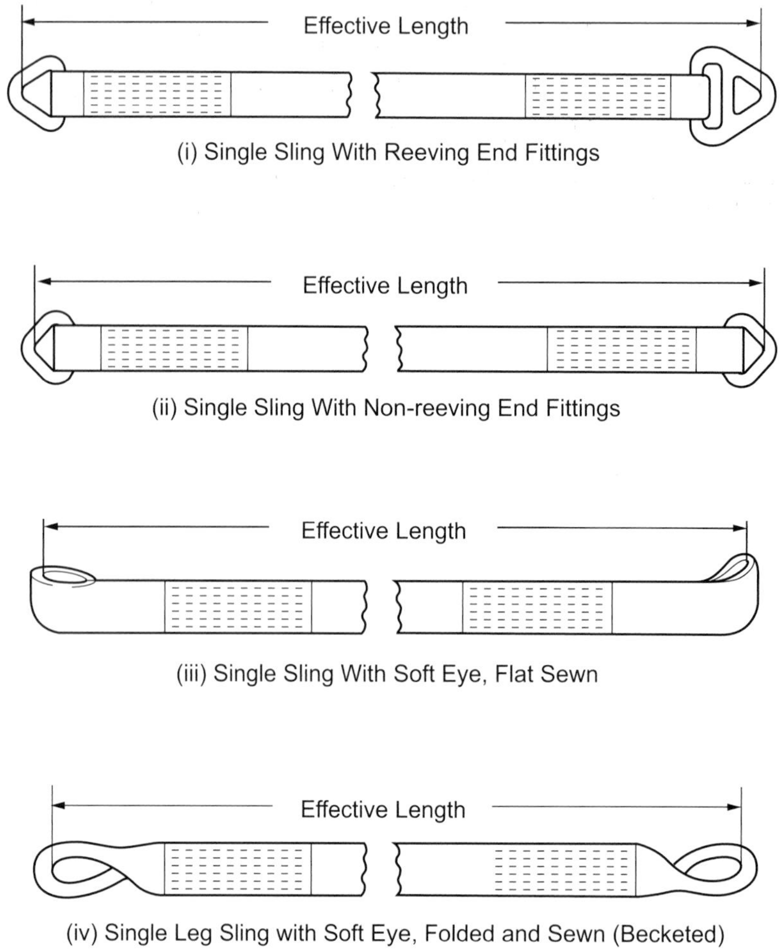

(i) Single Sling With Reeving End Fittings

(ii) Single Sling With Non-reeving End Fittings

(iii) Single Sling With Soft Eye, Flat Sewn

(iv) Single Leg Sling with Soft Eye, Folded and Sewn (Becketed)

03053. Special slinging precautions

a.   **Slinging from shoreside crane to a vessel afloat.** Great care should be taken when the load is being transferred to or from the hook of the crane. Keep a close watch on the water level of basins and docks, which may alter considerably while lifts are in progress. A drop in the water level may cause the rings to tighten, and impose dangerous stresses on slings, the load and the crane. An increase in the water level will cause the slings to slacken with consequential surging of the load. Therefore check frequently the tension of the slings when such lifts are being made, and adjust as necessary. Never leave a job unattended; a competent slinger must always be in attendance when a lift is in progress.

b.   **Slinging from a floating crane to a vessel afloat**. Great care should be taken when the load is being transferred to or from the hook of the crane. Make full allowance for the heel of the crane and of the ship; it may be necessary to adjust the jib while these lifts are being made.

03054. Slinging and responsibilities in HM ships

a.   The supervision and responsibility for all slinging tasks undertaken in HM Ships must be planned and overseen by a fully qualified departmental Slinging Supervisor. To obtain this Adqual it is necessary to complete the ME 418 ADSLING course at HMS SULTAN. Seaman Specialists and other departmental senior rates drafted to nominated billets within a ship's scheme of complement are required to undertake this course as a targeted employment module (TEM) before joining a ship. The qualification will remain extant unless the Licence holder or his/her line manager feels that he/she is incapable of carrying out a slinging operation. In this case guidance laid down in BR 3027 Vol 1 should be followed. Specialist departmental lifting equipment must be registered and controlled. Within individual departments, however for general slinging requirements the Chief Bosun's Mate is responsible for the control of the general lifting plant.

b.   **General ship to shore straight lift slinging controllers**. The Chief Bosun's Mate is responsible for the auditing, control, supervision and training of personnel required to direct cranes during general ship to shore storing operations. The controllers/slingers must have completed all aspects of the computer-based ME418A AD Stevedore training course available at all Waterfront Learning Centres (WLCs) and be the holder of the correct photo card licence. Designated slingers tasked to conduct slinging duties must assess the task to hand and inspect and draw correct portable lifting equipment from the Chief Bosun's Mate. The slinger in charge is to consult with, and notify the crane driver of the nature of lifts to be undertaken and clarify who will be giving the signals.

c.   **General considerations.** Controllers/Slingers must wear an Orange Safety Helmet and a Day-glow Orange armband and should be positioned so that the crane driver has clear visual observations of the signals at all times during the lifting operations. Under no circumstances is a load to be directly attached to the crane hook until it has been ascertained that the load is free from any restraining connections.

d.   **Photo card licence**. All qualified personnel having completed the ME418A Adhook and/or the ME418 Adsling course will carry a photo card licence showing the qualification. Examples shown overleaf are, Top ME418A, coloured white and Bottom ME418 coloured Grey.

Fig 3-196. Specimen photo card licences

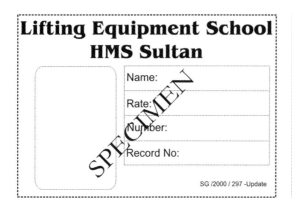
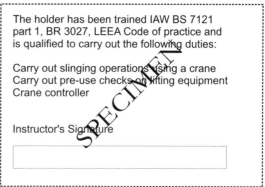
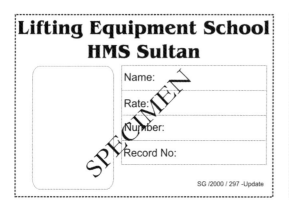
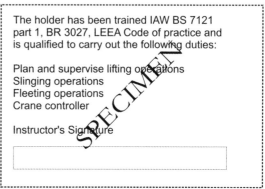

03055. Ammunition secondary re-supply equipment

a.   The safe re-supply of ammunition by Secondary Route relies on adequate training, comprehensive briefing and firm control. **JSP 862, MOD Maritime Explosives Regulations** is the authoritative publication on the subject and all personnel involved in the evolution should be conversant with the relevant chapter. The Weapon Electrical department has custody of the lifting equipment and a nominated Senior Rate with the Additional Lifting Equipment Examiner qualification as the Competent Person to inspect and test this equipment, but it is the responsibility of the **Relevant Officer of the Quarter (OOQ)** to ensure that ammunition re-supply equipment is rigged in accordance with the ship's drawings, and operated correctly. It is not possible to produce a detailed procedure for each of the diverse arrangements used in the Fleet, but the following general guidance, along with regular practice, should ensure safe operation:

(1)   Clear, concise orders are to be used by the rating in charge, normally a Senior Rating who is responsible for the supervision and safe operation including rigging/unrigging of each Secondary Supply route.

(2)   Only the approved rig in accordance with ship's drawings is to be used. All shackles must be moused.

(3)   When heavy objects are being rigged, unrigged, hoisted or lowered, personnel beneath are to keep well clear.

(4)   Two ratings must always be used to rig and unrig Miller's Flaps. One rating holds the flap in place whilst the other inserts the securing pins.

(5)   Sufficient hands must be detailed to operate tackles and other lifting equipment safely.

03056. Estimation of stresses in derricks and cranes

a.   Before cranes and derricks etc. are described, it is first necessary to emphasise that the seaman must be able to calculate the stresses in the parts of the gear that he is using. Without this knowledge it is possible that a derrick, while hoisting an apparently safe load, will collapse; or that one of its fittings or a part of the rigging will fail, with dangerous consequences.

b.   **Triangle of forces**. The stresses to which a derrick or fittings may be subjected when supporting a load can be estimated approximately and very simply by the diagrammatic method known as the **triangle of forces**. The principles upon which this method is based can be stated as follows:

(1)   If the magnitude and direction of a force are known, they can be represented by a straight line, called a **vector,** the length of which indicates the magnitude, and the direction of which, denoted by an arrow, gives the direction in which the force acts.

(2)   If three forces acting at a point are in equilibrium, and the vectors representing them are drawn end to end so that the directions in which they act are maintained, ie, so that the arrows follow one another, they will form the three sides of a triangle.

(3)   If three forces acting at a point are in equilibrium and the magnitude and direction of only two of them are known, the magnitude and direction of the unknown force can be found as follows. Draw the vectors of the known forces end to end so that the arrows follow one another. Complete the triangle. The third side will then represent the unknown force in magnitude and direction, the arrow pointing from the head of the second vector to the foot of the first.

(4)   When three forces acting at a point are in equilibrium, if the magnitude and direction of one force and the direction only of the other two are known, the magnitude of these two unknown forces can also be found by drawing a triangle of forces.

c.   For three forces in equilibrium, the arrows denoting the directions of the vectors always follow one another round a triangle of forces. If more than three forces in equilibrium and acting at a point are involved, the same principles apply. The resulting figure, whose sides represent these forces, is then known as a **polygon of forces.** The following two examples show the application of this method for finding the approximate stresses in masts, derricks and their rigging and fittings. In the examples it is assumed that the systems and their loads are at rest, and the effects of any friction are disregarded.

EXAMPLE 1

A derrick is topped at an angle of 45° with the horizontal and is supporting a weight of five tonnes hung on the end of its whip (Fig 3-197). Find the magnitude and direction of the tension in the strop of the head block.

Fig 3-197. Estimation of stresses by triangle of forces (1)

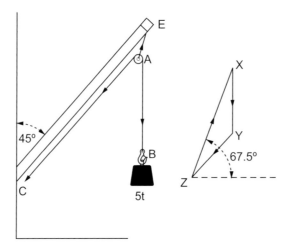

d.   The tensions in the running and hauling parts of the whip are the same, namely five tonnes, so by drawing a triangle of forces based on the block **A**, the tension in the strop **AE** and the direction in which it acts can be found in the following manner. To a scale of four tonnes to 10 mm draw the vector **XY**, 12.5 mm in length, to represent the vertical downward pull of the weight on the running part of the whip, and on it mark its arrow pointing downwards. From the point **Y** draw another vector **YZ**, parallel with **AC** and 12.5 mm in length, to represent the downward tension in the hauling part of the whip, and on it mark its arrow, also pointing in a downward direction. Complete the triangle by joining **Z** to **X**. Then: **ZX** is the vector representing the tension, both in magnitude and direction, in the strop **AE** of the head block, and when measuring it will be found to be approximately 24 mm, representing a tension of 9.5 tonnes acting upwards at an angle of 67.5° with the horizontal.

EXAMPLE 2

A span is rigged between two masts, and a weight of ten tonnes is hung on it so that the left leg of the span makes an angle of 65° with its mast (Fig 3-198). Find the pull on each of the shackles, which join the span to the masts.

Fig 3-198. Estimation of stresses by triangle forces (2)

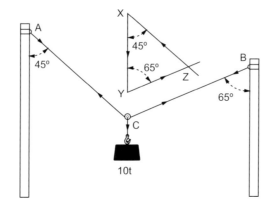

e.   The pull on the shackles will be equal and opposite to the tensions in the respective legs of the span, and these tensions are found by considering the forces acting at the point **C**, where the magnitude and direction of the pull of the weight on the span are known, ie ten tonnes vertically downwards, and the directions of the tensions in the legs of the span are known, ie upwards at an angle of 45° and 65° respectively with the perpendicular. To a scale of four tonnes to 10 mm draw the vector **XY** 25 mm in length, to represent the vertical downward pull of the weight, and on it mark its arrow, pointing downwards. From the point **Y** draw a line parallel with **CB** and on it mark an arrow to represent the direction of the upward tension in the right leg of the span. From the point **X** draw a line parallel with **AC** so that it cuts the preceding line at **Z**, and on it mark an arrow to represent the direction of the upward tension in the left leg of the span. Then: **YZ** is the vector representing the tension in the right leg of the span, which will be found to be 19 mm long (approximately), representing a force of 7.5 tonnes; and **ZX** is the vector representing the tension in the left leg of the span, which will be found to be 25 mm long (approximately), representing a force of ten tonnes.

f.   The approximate pull on the shackles at **A** and **B** will therefore be ten tonnes and 7.5 tonnes respectively.

g.   In a similar manner the stresses on other parts or fittings of a mast and a derrick, such as the tension in the topping lift and the thrust in the derrick, can be found if the magnitude and direction of two of the three forces involved are known, or if the magnitude and direction of one force and the direction of the two other forces are known. Care should be taken when determining the direction in which a force acts; for example, when considering the stresses at the derrick head the tension in the topping lift of a derrick will be acting in a direction from the head of the derrick towards the mast, but when considering the stresses at the masthead fitting it will be acting in the reverse direction.

03057. Derricks

a.   A derrick is a spar, made of wood or steel, rigged as a swinging boom and used for hoisting boats, stores, cargo, ammunition or gear in and out of a ship. It can be fitted to a mast or a king post, when it is called a **mast derrick**, or to the side of a ship's superstructure, when it is called a **screen derrick**. Only screen derricks are fitted in HM warships. The lower end or heel is pivoted in a **gooseneck**, allowing the derrick to pivot both vertically and horizontally. The upper end or **head** is supported by a topping lift and stayed by guys. The load is hoisted or lowered by a whip or a purchase, which is rove through a block at the derrick head and a leading block at the heel and then taken to a winch. The rig of a derrick varies considerably in detail according to the purpose for which it is provided, the weight it is designed to hoist, and the position in which it is fitted. A simple mast derrick as fitted in merchant ships is illustrated in Fig 3-199. The topping lift and guys are shackled to a spider band at the derrick head. The topping lift of a mast derrick is usually led to the masthead, and that of a screen derrick to a point on the superstructure directly above the heel of the derrick; the guys are led to positions on deck near the ship's side and well before and abaft the heel. Topping lifts are of two main kinds, **standing** and **working.**

b.   Guys usually take the form of short pendants tailed with tackles; two are usually fitted, but heavy derricks may be fitted with as many as four; some derricks are provided with standing guys called **preventer guys**, which are fitted to prevent the derrick from swinging too far in a certain direction. A screen derrick as fitted in warships is illustrated at Fig 3-200. This is shown rigged with a standing topping lift but sometimes it may be rigged with a working topping lift. As well as the simple mast derrick illustrated at Fig 3-199, merchant ships may be fitted with derricks of different types and rigs, capable of very heavy lifts, and employing various methods of operation; further information on these rigs is contained in British Standard MA: 1976, **Design and Operation of Ships' Derrick Rigs**.

Fig 3-199. A simple mast derrick (Merchant Navy)

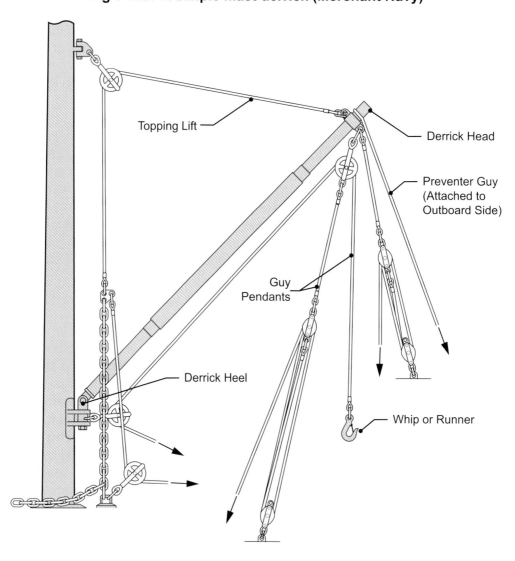

Topping Lift

Derrick Head

Preventer Guy
(Attached to
Outboard Side)

Guy
Pendants

Derrick Heel

Whip or Runner

Fig 3-200. Screen derrick (Royal Navy)

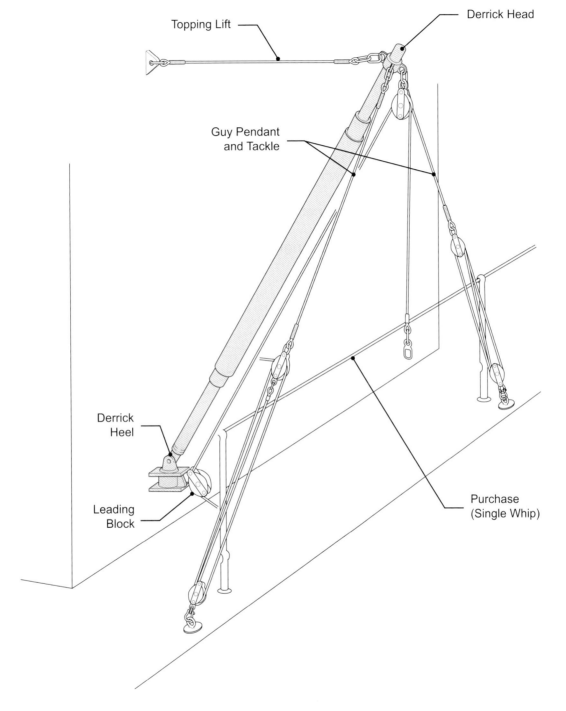

03058. **Cranes**

a.   Cranes supplied for shipborne use are quicker and more convenient in operation than derricks. They are used for hoisting boats, stores, cargo, ammunition or gear in and out of a ship. The characteristic feature of a crane is a jib, or projecting hinged arm, which may be rigid, or telescopic, or articulated and telescopic. Fixed cranes in use in the Royal Navy fall into two categories; the rigid jib type of crane, fitted only in major warships, RFAs and certain hydrographic survey ships, and the articulated and/or telescopic jib type fitted in many warships, primarily as a method of deploying the seaboat. Both types are described overleaf. Certain major warships carry mobile cranes, of the telescopic jib type.

b.   **Rigid jib crane (RFAs only)** (Fig 3-201). The wire rope purchase is rigged as a single or double whip and leads from the purchase winding drum to a sheave at the head of the jib. Between the purchase wire and the lifting hook is a **ponders ball**, the function of which is to assist the purchase to overhaul when there is no load on the hook; in some cranes the ponders ball is made in two halves for ease of removal, and some incorporate a shock-absorbing device. Besides hoisting and topping, the crane can be trained to plumb a hoist, the arc of training being restricted by an electrical limit switch to prevent damage to the crane and superstructure. The topping and purchase motions are similarly protected by limit switches at the extremities of their travel and the topping motion is usually protected by buffers at its fully topped-up position (see Note). The safe working load and maximum radius permitted are marked on a tally, and must in any case be known by the crane driver.

Note.   *Fixed jib cranes must not be operated below 45° of elevation.*

Fig 3-201. Example of a rigid jib crane as fitted in RFAs

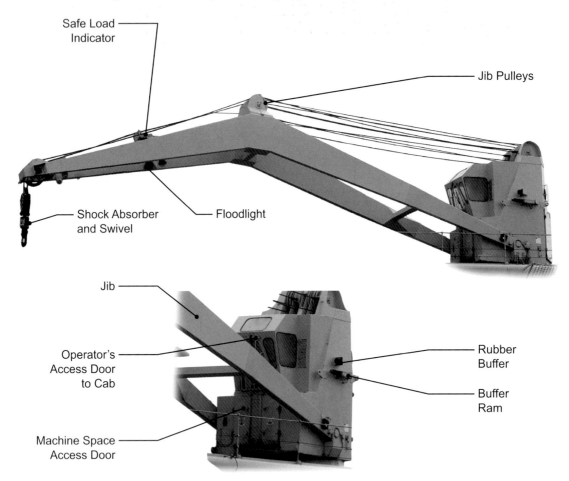

c. **Articulated and/or telescopic-jib crane** (Fig 3-202)

(1) There are a variety of cranes in use in the Fleet that fall into this category. The jib is articulated and the outer section of jib may be telescopic; to protect the surfaces of the chromium plated hydraulic cylinders the jib can be folded into the 'stowed' position when the crane is not required for use. In use, the telescopic outer section of jib can be 'jibbed out' to increase its length (see Note). It is important that operators are aware of the safe working load of the crane for any given radius of operation. The radius of operation is the horizontal distance between the cranes centre of rotation and a vertical line drawn through the centre of the hook.

> **WARNING**
>
> **THE SAFE WORKING LOADS FOR ANY GIVEN RADII OF OPERATIONS MUST BE MARKED ON A TALLY PLATE CLEARLY VISIBLE TO THE OPERATOR.**

(2) These types of cranes are not normally fitted with limit switches, and because guardrails, aerials, launchers, lockers etc may all be within the operating radius of the crane careful operation is essential. The rig of the wire purchase rope from the winch to the hook varies with the type of crane and on-board documentation must be checked to ascertain the precise fit.

Note. *Articulated and/or telescopic-jib cranes must not be operated with the jib lower than 0° elevation.*

Fig 3-202. Example of an articulated, telescopic-jib folding crane

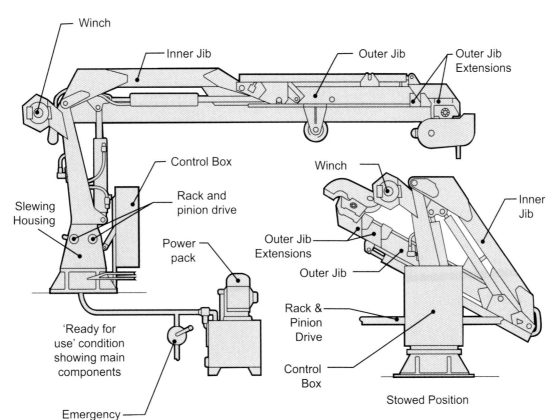

d. **Operation of cranes**. Personnel acting as crane drivers or crane controllers must be trained to a level that enables them to perform competently day or night; details are as follows:

(1) *Crane/davit controllers.* The Chief Bosun's Mate is responsible for the supervision and training of personnel required to direct cranes. The controllers must be fully conversant with standard crane signals, have a sound knowledge of slinging procedures, and the operating limitations of the crane/davit they are controlling. Before being allowed to carry out the duty of crane/davit controller they must be examined and confirmed competent. A certificate to this effect (example below) is to be completed and retained in the Seamanship Data Book. The certificate expires when the holder is re-assigned. Crane controllers must wear an orange safety helmet and a day-glow orange armband and should be positioned so that the crane driver has clear visual observations of the signals at all times during the lifting operation. Under no circumstances is a load to be directly attached to the crane hook until it has been ascertained that the load is free from any restraining connections. If for any reason the load cannot be freely suspended, for example if adjusting or 'inching' a load that is being bolted or welded into position on the ship, then a chain block, pull lift or similar **manual** apparatus must be inserted between the load and stationary crane hook. Standard crane signals are illustrated in Fig 3-203. Signals must be made clearly and distinctly.

CERTIFICATE OF COMPETENCE

This is to certify that ...NAME AND RATING...has proved themselves to be competent to carry out the duty of Crane/Davit Controller in accordance with BR 6004.

Signed...Chief Bosun's Mate

Name...Rate..

Date..HMS.......................................

---

e. **Standard crane signals**

(1) Fig 3-203 shows the recognised crane signals (as directed by BS 7121) to be used to provide instructions to a crane driver. The signaller should stand in a secure position where he can see the load and can be seen clearly by the crane driver and be facing the driver if possible. Each signal must be clear and distinct.

Fig 3-203. Standard crane signals (animated Graphic – see CD for demonstration)

Signal		Description	Hand Signal for Crane Operation.
Operations start		Follow my instructions	
Operations cease		Cease to follow my instructions	
Stop		Raise one hand above the head	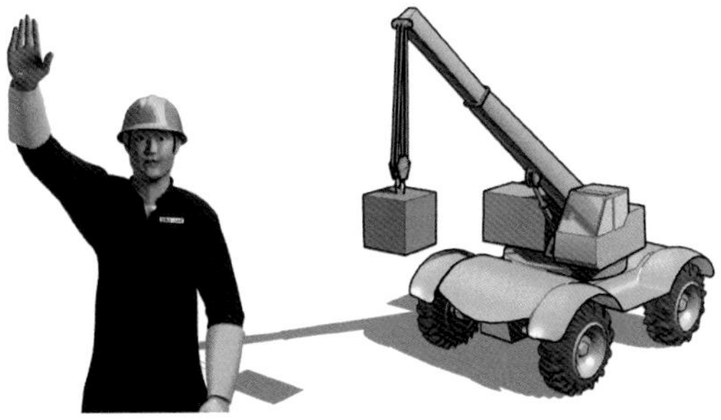
Emergency STOP		Both hands and arms raised above the head	

Controlling the movement of the load.	a	Inch and hoist	
	b	Inch = opening and closing of the hand. Is used for raising and lowering. Hoist = rotation of forearm	
	b	Lower	
	c	Lower slowly	

| Slew | a | Slew in the direction indicated | |
| | b | Slew in the direction indicated | |

Jib telescoping (horizontal)	a	Jib up	
	b	Jib down	
	c	Extend (trolley out)	
	d	Retract (trolley in)	

Moving the crane (for mobile cranes)	a	Travel to me	
	b	Travel from me	
	c	Travel in the direction indicated	
	d	Travel in the direction indicated	

(2) *Crane/davit drivers*. Ships' cranes/davits must be driven by competent persons. Where no evidence exists that the potential crane/davit driver has completed a recognised course, instruction must be carried out on board by the crane/davit maintainer, using information given in the relevant operator's guidance instructions, and **BR 3027, Manual of Inspection and Tests of Lifting Plant**. The driver must be fully conversant with standard signals. The Chief Bosun's Mate and the maintainer must be satisfied that the person is capable of carrying out the task safely and in accordance with the operating instructions. A certificate to this effect (example below) is to be completed and retained in the Seamanship Data Book. The certificate expires when the holder is drafted.

CERTIFICATE OF COMPETENCE

This is to certify that ...NAME AND RATING...has proved himself competent to carry out the duty of Crane/Davit Driver on ...TYPE OF CRANE/DAVIT.....................................

Signature CBM..Signature Maintainer...................................

Name...............................Rate....................Name ....Rate....................

Date..HMS.......................................

---

    f.   **Maintenance and testing of cranes**. Maintenance and testing of cranes is to be carried out in accordance with the Maintenance Management System (MMS).

03059. Winches

Winches are used for heaving and veering ropes and wires. Those fitted in Royal Navy ships may be powered either electrically or hydraulically, and various forms of drive, clutch and brake are fitted, depending on the use for which the winch is intended. Winches are normally stool-mounted, and fitted with a single **warping drum** as shown in Fig 3-204. To bring a rope to a warping drum take three turns of the rope round the drum in the required direction and back up the hauling part as it comes off the drum. Three turns are usually sufficient when hawsers are being hove in, but for heavy loading it may be necessary to take an extra one or two turns, giving due regard to the size and strength of the rope and equipment involved. As the rope passes round the drum the turns have a tendency to ride from the middle towards one end; this tendency is counteracted by the load on the rope forcing the turns down the curve to the narrowest part of the drum. To hold the rope stationary while the drum is heaving in, ease the pull on the hauling part sufficiently to allow the turns to slip, or **surge** round the drum. Never surge the rope when the drum is veering, and do not allow riding turns to develop on a warping drum, because if this happens control of the rope is lost unless the drum is stopped. To ensure reasonably even distribution of the rope on the drum it may be necessary to use wooden handspikes to force the lead of the rope back and forth across the drum. If a sliprope is required, it should be fed onto the drum immediately the hoseline has been removed, then the outboard end rigged as a sliprope. When a remating line is employed it must be taken to the warping drum.

Fig 3-204. A typical winch

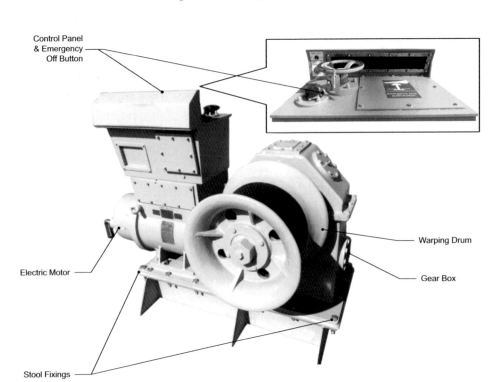

Control Panel & Emergency Off Button

Electric Motor

Stool Fixings

Warping Drum

Gear Box

03060. Introduction to Improvised Rigs of Derricks, Sheers, Gyns and Ropeways

a.   With modern developments of hydraulics, and the increasing availability of portable and mounted cranes, the requirement to improvise lifting rigs has greatly reduced; however, in certain circumstances the seaman may still be called upon to use his ingenuity, either on board or ashore, to rig some form of derrick, sheers or gyn to lift or handle heavy stores or equipment. He will have to do this using his own ship's gear, supplemented sometimes by anything he can find ashore. Ships no longer carry timber spars specifically for improvised lifting rigs and the only available on-board source of timber is the Douglas Fir shores supplied for Damage Control purposes. Table 3-40 gives the approximate safe working thrust applicable to most timber other than softwoods and allows a factor of safety of ten. However, timber obtained from outside sources or cut down ashore should be treated with caution and the seaman must exercise his judgement in deciding the realistic loading such timber is likely to withstand safely. The derrick is a single upright spar; the swinging derrick consists of an upright spar with a swinging boom pivoted at its foot. Sheers consist of two upright spars with their heads lashed together and their feet splayed out. A gyn is a tripod formed by three spars with their heads lashed together. A ropeway consists of an overhead jackstay of rope set up between two sheers, or gyns, along which a travelling block is hauled back and forth.

Table 3-40. Approximate safe working thrust of timber spars

Mean Diameter	Length								Size of Equivalent Square Baulk
	mm								
	3000	4000	5000	6000	7000	8000	9000	10000	
mm	*Approximate Safe Working Thrust in tonnes*								*mm*
150	0.78	0.46	0.30	0.21	0.16	0.12	0.10	0.08	133
175	1.40	0.84	0.55	0.39	0.29	0.22	0.18	0.14	155
200	2.29	1.40	0.93	0.66	0.49	0.38	0.30	0.24	177
225	3.50	2.17	1.46	1.04	0.78	0.60	0.48	0.39	199
250	5.19	3.21	2.18	1.56	1.17	0.91	0.72	0.59	222
275	7.09	4.57	3.12	2.25	1.69	1.32	1.05	0.86	244
300	9.55	6.24	4.31	3.14	2.37	1.85	1.48	1.21	266

b.   **Standing derrick.** A standing derrick is a single spar (Fig 3-205) stayed by rigging and having a tackle at its head for hoisting a load. Its head is supported by a **topping lift**, or, if there is a no suitable overhead attachment point for a topping lift, it is supported by a **Back Guy. Side guys** are fitted to give lateral support and, if there is a suitable attachment point, a martingale or **Fore Guy** may be lead downwards from the head to prevent the head from springing upwards or backwards when hoisting or lowering a load. If it has an efficient topping lift led from a point vertically above the heel, the derrick can be slewed to a limited extent as well as being topped and lowered. If the load is heavy, or if a Back Guy is fitted, or if the topping-lift attachment point is not vertically above the heel, slewing must not be attempted. The safe working load of the derrick is governed by the size and material of the spar and the strength of the rigging gear available.

Fig 3-205. Standing derrick

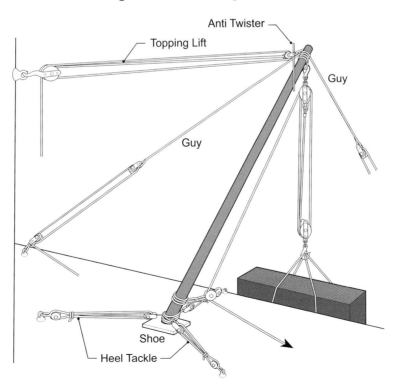

c.   **Swinging derrick**. A swinging derrick is made up of two spars (Fig 3-206), one upright and well stayed by guys, and the other secured to the first by a strop called a **snotter** and a topping lift, so that it forms a swinging boom. Working guys are led from the head of the boom as in a permanent derrick, and the boom can be topped, lowered and slewed through an angle up to 120° when the load is slung. A derrick of this type is not suitable for heavy loads, because of the stress imposed on the snotter. In addition, it is often difficult to rig a martingale (fore guy) for the upright spar, though another spar lashed to it so as to form a strut (called a **prypole**), as illustrated in Fig 3-206, affords an effective alternative. Although this derrick is more complicated in rig than either a standing derrick or sheers, it is particularly useful for disembarking stores from a boat to a jetty.

Fig 3-206. Swinging derrick

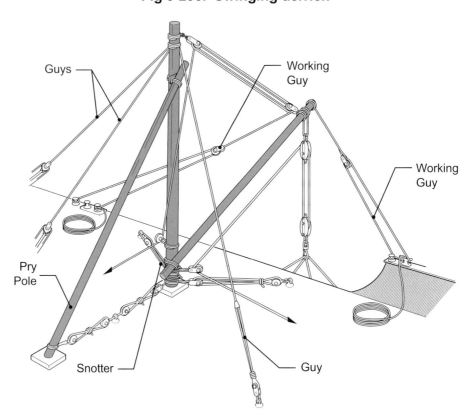

d.   **Sheers**. Sheers consist of a pair of spars called **legs**, which are lashed together and crossed near their heads (Fig 3-207); the cross is called the **crutch.** They are supported in a vertical or an inclined position by rigging, and a tackle for hoisting the load is secured to the crutch. The overhead rigging consists of either a topping lift and martingale or a back guy and fore guy; as sheers need no lateral support, side guys are not fitted. If a topping lift is fitted it should be led to a point aloft so that it makes, as nearly as possible, a right angle with the sheers **when they are loaded.** If a back guy is fitted it should be led to a point equidistant from the heels of the legs and making as broad an angle as possible with the sheers. Sheers can be topped-up or lowered through a limited angle, the extent depending on the lead of the topping lift; if a back guy is rigged, however, neither sheers nor derricks may normally be canted to an angle of more than 20° with the vertical. As sheers are made from two spars they are, of course, stronger than a derrick of equal size and of the same materials. Sheers are particularly suited for use when the load is not required to be slewed, such as on the edge of a wharf or the banks of a river, or in lifting a weight from a boat to the deck of a ship.

Fig 3-207. Sheers

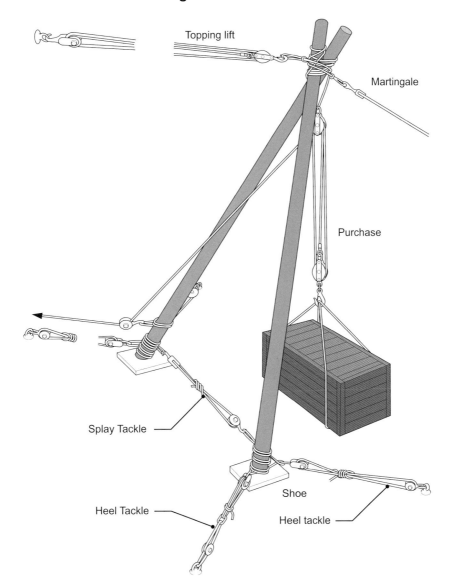

e. **Gyn**. A gyn (Fig 3-208) consists of three spars with their heads crossed and lashed together and their heels splayed out to form a tripod. A gyn is stronger than sheers and derricks, and it requires no rigging to support it, but it can only be used for a straight lift and cannot normally be traversed with its load slung.

f. **Ropeway**. A ropeway (Fig 3-209) is used to transfer loads across a river or a ravine. Gyns are preferable to sheers as supports for the jackstay, because they are more stable and need less guying. An improvised ropeway is usually confined to transferring light stores and equipment, because of the heavy stresses set up in the jackstay when transferring a load; a 60 m x 24 mm SWR jackstay, for example, is limited to a maximum load of only 1118 kgs, using a safety factor of four. The formula to calculate the theoretical tension in a jackstay between supports at the same level is:

$$Tension = \frac{W1}{4s}$$

Where:

> *W* is the total weight of the load, including traveller and slings,
> *l* is the distance between supports,
> *s* is the dip of the centre of the jackstay (in same units as *l*).

Fig 3-208. A gyn

Splay Tackle

Note.   *A winnet or thumb piece can be secured above the snotter to stop it rising up the pole.*

Fig 3-209. Simple ropeway

03061. Gear required and principles involved when rigging improvised lifting gear

a.   The rigging for derricks, sheers and ropeways must be led so that it does its work efficiently. As already stated the best lead for a topping lift is at right-angles to the derrick and towards a point vertical above the heel, but this will often not be possible in practice; an angle of 60° or more between the topping lift or back guy and the derrick will be reasonably effective, and it should never be less than 45°. Similarly, the angle between the side guys and the derrick should, if possible, be 60° or more, and these should not be inclined at a greater angle than 30° – ie at a slope of not more than 1 in 2 – with the horizontal.

b.   **Guys**. The guys of derricks and sheers, particularly those used for heavy loads, stretch considerably when under load, and all guys must therefore be working guys so that the tensions can be adjusted. When picking up a load, a derrick or sheers should be heeled over to a few degrees less than the required angle to allow for the stretch in the topping lift or back guy; with heavy sheers this allowance may be as much as 8°. For light derricks or sheers the guys are usually wire pendants tailed with luff tackles, but for heavy derricks and sheers the guys should be at least runners rove through blocks at the head of the derrick or sheers and tailed at their hauling part with luff tackles or two-fold purchases. If sheers are required only to traverse a load as far as their heels, the martingale (or fore guy) only acts as a preventer and therefore may be about half the strength of the topping lift or back guy; but if a load is to be traversed to a position behind their heels the martingale and topping lift must be of equal strength. If a derrick is required to slew a load through an angle of less than 90°, the side guy on the training side and the martingale (or fore guy) act only as preventers and need not be as strong as the other guys or topping lift; but if the slewing angle is 90° or more, all guys and the topping lift should be of equal strength. To give a guy a slope of one in two when ashore and on firm and level ground, the distance of a **holdfast**, described in sub para f, from the foot of a derrick or sheers should be twice the effective length of the derrick or sheers, and to give it a slope of one in three, it should be three times the effective length. To obtain the correct lead for the guys on sloping ground the uphill and downhill holdfasts must be placed closer to and farther from the foot than is normally done (Fig 3-210). If a guy holdfast is inaccessible - for example, an anchor laid offshore - the hauling part of the guy tackle must be led to the head of the derrick or sheers and thence to the foot.

c.   **Shoes.** A shoe for a light derrick, sheers or a gyn is usually a square slab of hardwood with a recess in its upper surface to take the heel of its spar. The length of each of its sides should be not less than four times the diameter of the spar. For heavy spars the shoe is of metal or made up from baulks of timber. A shoe is used to distribute the weight of the load and the thrust of the spar over an area of deck, or, when used ashore, to distribute the weight so as to prevent the spar from sinking into the ground. When used ashore the shoe should be sunk level and held in place by **pickets** (described later) driven in at intervals along its sides and with their heads flush with the shoe. Shoes should always be used for spars of improvised lifting rigs, except when handling light loads, and must be placed at the same level; otherwise an undue stress will be placed on one of the legs and the sheers or gyn will tend to capsize. When using spars aboard ship, the deck on which they stand must be well shored-up below.

d.   **Heel tackles**. Heel tackles are used to prevent unwanted movements at the heels of spars used for derricks and sheers. However, the heel tackles can be used to move sheers about the deck if required. The angle between the tackles should be 120° wherever possible (Fig 3-207).

Fig 3-210. Correct lead for guys on sloping ground

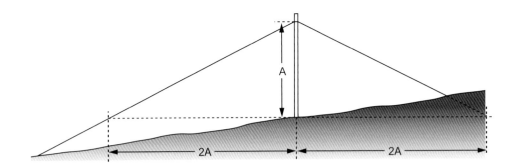

e. **Splay tackles and belly tackles**. A splay tackle is used to prevent the heels of spars from moving farther apart (Fig 3-208). Belly tackles are secured to the middle of a spar when there is doubt concerning its strength for a particular job. The spar is then stayed to the deck or ground.

f. **Holdfasts for use on shore**. In a warship it is a relatively simple task to find eyeplates or other permanent fittings to hold fast improvised rigging; but when ashore, and probably under adverse conditions, the seaman must find or construct an anchorage to hold his improvised gear firmly and safely in place. Holdfasts (Fig 3-238) may consist of existing natural or structural features; or pickets driven singly or in combination into the ground; or baulks of timber placed behind a line of driven pickets; or ships' anchors embedded in the ground and held by driven pickets; or baulks of timber buried in trenches dug in the ground. Whatever the type of holdfast it must be more than strong enough for the stress it is intended to bear, because once a holdfast starts to give it is difficult to strengthen it. A holdfast must be so arranged that the maximum resistance it can offer is in line with the stress it can bear; a buried baulk of timber, for example, should lie at right angles to the pull, whereas a combination of pickets should be driven exactly in line with the direction of the pull.

(1) *Existing holdfasts.* Used whenever it is practicable, provided that they are conveniently situated and strong enough for the job. The holding power of a tree is uncertain, because so much depends on the depths of its roots and the nature of the soil; a tree can be considerably strengthened, however, by fitting it with a back guy, and if two trees are growing close together their combined holding power can be used by placing a baulk of timber across them. A baulk of timber placed across a gap in masonry makes a good holdfast, provided that the stress is distributed over a sufficiently large area of the masonry by placing planks vertically and horizontally between the baulk and the masonry. The pier of a bridge or the base of a tower can be used by encircling it with a strop, but the strop should be protected from chafe or bad nips.

(2)   *Picket holdfasts.* Used in ordinary soils for pulls not exceeding two tonnes. The normal picket is an ash stake 1.5 metres long and 75 mm in diameter, with one end pointed (and, when possible, shod with iron) and the other end bound with an iron hoop; it should be driven to a depth of one metre at an inclination of about 20º to the vertical. Pickets may be used singly, or lashed together in combinations of one-and-one, two-and-one, or three-two-and-one, as shown in Fig 3-211.

(3)   *A bulk and picket holdfast,* consists of a baulk of timber placed behind a line of driven pickets, which are backed, by another line of pickets; it may be used for pulls of between two and ten tonnes. Only two lines of pickets should be used, driven in combinations of one-and-one or two-and-one, with each combination at least half a metre from the next. A three-two-one combination of pickets should not be used, because of the difficulty of driving the pickets so that each will bear its fair proportion of the stress. The front row of pickets should be exactly in line so that the stress on the baulk is divided equally among them, and the ground under the baulk should be cut away to allow the face of the baulk to bear evenly against the inclined pickets (Fig 3-211). The baulk should be well parcelled where the strop passes round it.

(4)   *An anchor holdfast,* consists of an Admiralty Plan anchor embedded and supported by pickets, as shown in Fig 3-211. If the pull is horizontal it will take a stress up to the strength of its ring, but it is not very suitable as the holdfast for a guy, because the upward pull of the guy tends to dislodge the anchor. When an offshore underwater holdfast is required for the fore guy of a derrick or sheers the anchor should be laid in a position which gives the guy plenty of scope and its angle of scope should not be steeper than one in three; that part of the guy which will be underwater should be of chain. Backing one anchor with another gives greater holding power, provided that the anchors are well separated.

(5)   *A buried holdfast.* Used for pulls of over ten tonnes consists of a baulk or baulks of timber laid in a trench and then covered with well rammed earth. The trench should be 600cms longer than the baulk and have a vertical face; its depth will depend on the nature of the soil and the pull, which the holdfast is required to withstand. A subsidiary trench to take the strop must be cut, as shown in Fig 3-211; its slope should not be steeper than one in three and chocks should be placed to support the baulk clear of the bottom of the trench to enable the strop to be passed. Planks can be laid vertically and horizontally between the baulk and the face of the trench to distribute the stress over a greater area.

Fig 3-211. Holdfasts

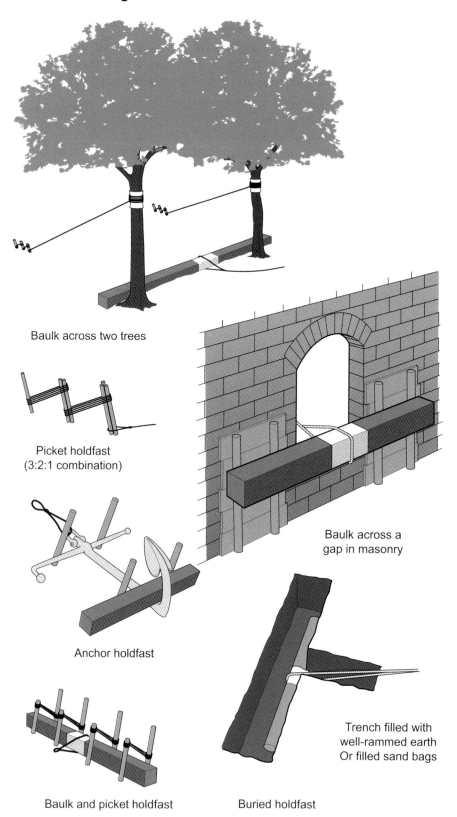

Baulk across two trees

Picket holdfast
(3:2:1 combination)

Anchor holdfast

Baulk and picket holdfast

Baulk across a
gap in masonry

Trench filled with
well-rammed earth
Or filled sand bags

Buried holdfast

03062. Rigging derricks, sheers, gyns and ropeways

a.   Obstructions in the vicinity, lack of a clear lead for purchase, topping lift or guy, and other special circumstances make it impossible to give detailed instructions for rigging these appliances, so the seaman must do his best with the available equipment.

b.   **To rig a standing derrick** (Fig 3-205 and Fig 3-212). Strops for attaching the purchase and topping lift (or back guy) are placed over the derrick head, and are prevented from slipping down either by wooden projections called **thumb-pieces** (Fig 3-212(i)) screwed or nailed in place, or by a rope **collar** (Fig 3-212(ii)) put on the spar like a whipping. These strops should lie close together so as to avoid a bending stress on the spar. The guys, which consist of single parts of cordage or rope, are then middled and clove-hitched over the head of the spar, above the strops, tackles being attached if required. The distance from the foot of the derrick to the point of attachment of the purchase and topping lift is known as the **effective length** of the derrick. The heel of the derrick is kept in place by tackles, which must be led so that they will support it in every direction, and particularly from that in which the derrick will be raised and lowered. The strops for the heel tackles must be kept as low as possible; otherwise the tackles will be heavily stressed as the derrick is raised.

**Fig 3-212. Methods of rigging the head of a derrick
using rope collars or thumb pieces**

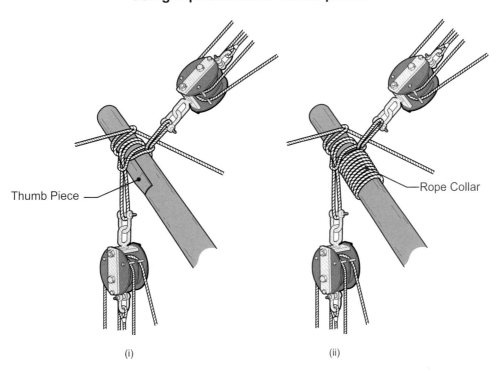

Thumb Piece

Rope Collar

(i)   (ii)

c.   **To rig a swinging derrick** (Fig 3-206 and Fig 3-212)

(1)   The upright spar is first erected, and is inclined somewhat away from the load so that it will become vertical as the boom takes the weight. It must be well supported by guys, each strong enough to take the entire pull of the topping lift as the boom swings round. The arc through which the boom is required to swing must, of course, be left clear. A strop to take the upper block of the topping lift is placed over the head of this spar above the guys. The spar, which is to form the boom, is now laid midway between the intended limits of its horizontal travel, and with its heel close against the upright spar and projecting on the side away from the load. The head of the boom is rigged as for a standing derrick, but the heel is attached to the upright by a snotter, as shown in Fig 3-206. If no suitable strop is available, a bight of rope can be passed round the boom, then through its own bight and then half-hitched and dogged round the upright spar in the same way as a stopper is put on a wire rope. The falls of the topping lift and purchase are led through blocks shackled to strops at the foot of the upright spar, the strops being kept in place by thumb-pieces or rope collars.

(2)   As the leading block for the hauling part of the purchase fall is to one side of the boom, the latter is subjected to a sideways pull when the purchase takes the weight, and the boom must therefore be adequately guyed. In order to keep the stresses on the boom, topping lift and guys to a minimum the boom should cross the upright as low down as possible without fouling the ground or deck, and the effective length of the boom (from where the spars cross to the topping lift and purchase are attached) should be as short as the reach required will allow.

d.   **To rig sheers**. (Fig 3-207, Fig 3-213 and Fig 3-214)

(1)   The spars for the legs are laid side by side, with their heels together and their heads supported conveniently clear of the ground or deck. Those parts which will be covered by the lashing are then parcelled to prevent chafe, and the heads are then lashed together as described below and illustrated in Fig 3-213. The legs are crossed and the lashing is made fast to one of the legs by a timber hitch, either above or below the cross, and then a sufficient number of round turns (usually 14 or more) to cover the cross are taken round both legs. The end is then brought up between the legs, passed down between them on the opposite side of the cross, and brought up again as before, so as to form a frapping turn binding the whole lashing together. Four or five frapping turns are applied and the lashing is completed by a clove hitch taken round the leg opposite to the one to which it was originally attached. It is important that the frapping turns are correctly put on, close to each other, and hauled taut. Choice of the rope to be used for the head lashing depends on the size of the spars and the weight to be lifted; this is best judged at the time, but the following is given as a general guide:

Weight to be lifted	Lashing
Below 2 tonnes	20 mm Polypropylene
2 tonnes to 5 tonnes inclusive	22 mm HMPE multiplait
Over 5 tonnes up to 20 tonnes	22 mm HMPE multiplait

Fig 3-213. Passing the head lashing of sheers

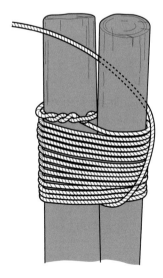
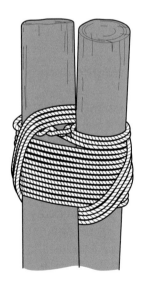

(2)   When the head lashing is completed the heels of the legs are opened out to the required distance; the action of opening them out sets up the head lashing so taut that it binds the legs securely together where they cross. The strop for the purchase is now put on by slipping it up to the top leg and passing it down over the head of the lower leg, so that it will bind the two together when under load (Fig 3-214). It must be long enough to enable the block to swing clear between the legs. Chafing pieces must be placed under the strop to prevent it chafing the lashing. The topping lift and martingale, or fore and back guys, are then secured to the head of the sheers. There are several equally effective ways of doing this, two of which are illustrated in Fig 3-214. In both cases, the pull of the guys should assist in binding the sheers together and the purchase strop should be free to take up its natural position as the weight comes on it.

Fig 3-214. Head of sheers – methods of rigging

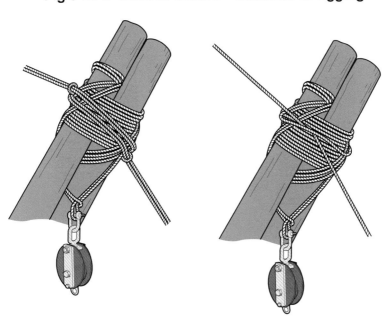

(3)   The necessary tackles for the guys and other rigging are then shackled to the strops or clapped on to the end of the ropes, as required, and finally if required, a small block is attached to each leg above the cross and a single whip then rove through each to serve as gantlines for sending a person aloft to make any adjustments after the sheers have been raised. The sheers are then placed roughly in position for raising, the heels being pointed to the shoes prepared for them and supported laterally by **splay** and **heel tackles**. The distance between the shoes should be one-third of that from the foot of the sheers to the crutch, which is the effective length of the sheers. As its name implies, the splay tackle leads from the heel of one spar to the heel of the other, being secured to each by a strop. The heel tackles guy down the heels laterally and, as with a derrick, their strops should be kept as low down as possible. The leading block for the fall of the purchase is then attached to one leg, and, after fitting thumb-pieces or rope collars to prevent all the strops at the feet of the legs from slipping upwards, the sheers are then ready for raising.

e. **To rig a gyn** (Fig 3-208 and Fig 3-215)

(1)   The position for the head lashing is first marked on all three spars to be used for the legs. The legs are then laid parallel with each other, about 50 mm apart and with the heel of the centre leg pointing in the opposite direction to those of the other two. The centre spar is called the **Prypole** and the other spars the **Cheeks**. The marks must be in line and the heads of the legs should be supported clear of the deck. The lashing is then put on at the marks. It is begun with a timber hitch round one cheek, then from six to eight figure-of-eight turns are taken, as shown in Fig 3-215, and the lashing is completed with a clove hitch round the other cheek.

Fig 3-215. Passing the head Lashing of a gyn

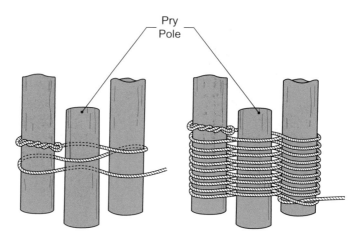

(2)   The lashing must be applied loosely; it cannot slip down once the Gyn is erected, and if it is too taut great difficulty will be experienced in raising the gyn; it is usual, however, to place a rope collar round the Prypole below the lashing to prevent it slipping down during the process of raising. The heels of the cheeks are now opened out, and the splay tackles are rigged between the feet of each pair. The Gyn is then raised by lifting its head and hauling the heel of the prypole towards the heels of the cheeks by means of the splay tackles. When the head reaches a convenient height the strop for the upper block of the purchase is put on and the block itself secured to it. Then tackles are rigged as required to haul the feet into place on their shoes. When correctly placed the heels are secured by lashing or heel tackles led so as to give the necessary lateral support and the hauling part of the purchase is led through a block secured to the heel of one cheek. As with derricks or sheers, thumb-pieces or rope collars are required to prevent the strops at the heels from slipping up the spars. With very small gyns splay tackles are not necessary, and their feet can be manhandled into place and then secured, either by lashings or by short spars lashed across them.

f. **To rig a ropeway** (Fig 3-209, Fig 3-216 and Fig 3-217)

(1)   Where no suitable trees are available for supporting the jackstay of a ropeway, gyns or sheers must be used. Gyns are preferable to sheers because they are more stable, but sheers may have to be used for long jackstays with a high ground clearance if suitable spars are available. The stresses set up in a jackstay are considerable and in practice can be taken as being up to five or six times the weight of the load.

Strong holdfasts must therefore be provided for the jackstay or any back guys, and they should be placed so that the slope of the jackstay or guy from the ground to the head of the support is not steeper than one in four. The tauter the jackstay the greater will be the stresses imposed on its anchorages and supports, but the easier it will be to haul the load across. On the other hand, if the jackstay is too slack, though the stresses in it will be reduced it will be difficult or impossible to haul the load across, and also the load will tend to become laterally unstable. The practical compromise between these extremes is to adjust the tension in the jackstay to give it a dip of between one fiftieth and one-twentieth of its effective length when loaded, so that when loaded at its centre it will assume a dip of between one-twentieth and one-tenth of its effective length. For practical purposes the dip in the jackstay when loaded at its centre should not exceed one-tenth of its effective length.

(2) The jackstay can be rigged with each end secured to a holdfast and rove through a block slung from the head of each of its supports; or its standing end can be secured to the head of one support, which will then require a back guy. It is usual to set up a tackle on its running end, but for heavy loads its final adjustment must be made by a rigging screw. The traveller can be an inverted block hooked to a light tackle for hoisting the load to the required height before it is traversed, but for heavy loads the traveller should consist of two blocks lashed to a spar fitted with lifting tackles as shown in Fig 3-216.

Fig 3-216. Traveller for slinging heavy weights on a jackstay

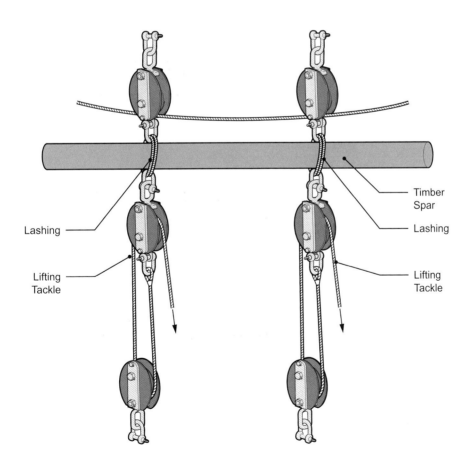

(3)   The gyn or sheers must be stepped sufficiently far back from the edge of the gap to allow room to sling the gear on one side and land it on the other. For light loads no leading blocks are required for the traveller inhauls or outhauls, but for heavy loads the inhaul should be led through a leading block at the head of the gyn or sheers but below the jackstay block. If gyns are used each should be stepped with the heel of its prypole towards the gap but slightly to one side of the jackstay, and the inhauls should be led on the opposite side of the prypole to the jackstay. A simple ropeway using a gyn and a tree as supports is shown in Fig 3-209.

(4)   A method of rigging a ropeway between two sheers in which the jackstay is used to erect both sheers is shown in Fig 3-217. The sheers are laid with their heels facing each other and with the standing end of the jackstay secured to the head of the sheers marked B, which are temporarily secured to the ground. The sheers marked A are first raised as high as possible by hand, and then to their full height by hauling on the tackle at the hauling end of the jackstay. The back guy of sheer A is then set up and sheer B are raised in a similar manner.

Fig 3-217. A light ropeway

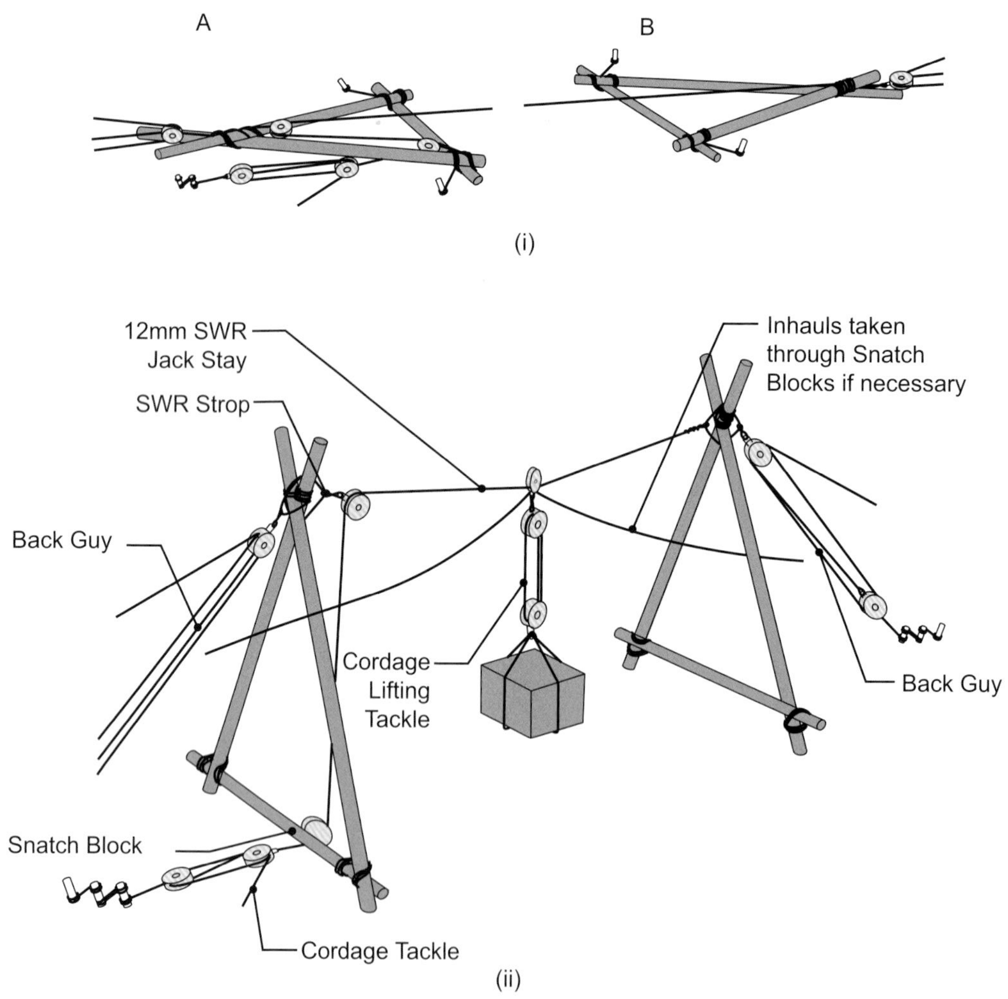

03063. Raising derricks and sheers

a.   The methods of raising a derrick described here can be applied equally well to sheers. It is assumed that the derrick is fully rigged with its head lashing, main tackle, guys and heel tackle, and that its heel is pointed towards its shoe. As the derrick is swayed up, the side guys must be tended to guide the foot into its shoe and then to prevent it from slipping. Before the derrick becomes vertical the martingale or fore guy must be tended to prevent the derrick from falling backwards. A derrick is hauled upright mainly by its topping lift or back guy, but its head must first be raised high enough to allow the pull of the guy to exert an effective leverage without putting undue stresses on the guy, the derrick and its heel tackles. The head of the derrick must therefore be raised by some means until the angle between the back guy and the derrick is between 15–20º; the greater this angle the less will be the stresses involved. Lowering derricks or sheers is carried out in the reverse manner to that in which they are raised.

b.   **By manhandling**. The head of a light derrick can be manhandled to the required height by means of a long handspike placed under and athwart the derrick head, which is then lifted by two or more men on each end of the handspike. A low trestle should be placed under the derrick and worked towards its heel with each lift until the head of the derrick has been raised high enough.

c.   **By moving lever**. The moving-lever method (Fig 3-218) is suitable for a derrick, which is rather too heavy to be raised initially by manhandling, and which is fitted with a back guy consisting of a pendant tailed with a tackle. The lever should be a light spar about half as long as the derrick and fitted with side guys, and it is placed alongside the derrick, with its heel at about a quarter of the way from the heel of the derrick to its head. The head of the lever is then lashed to the back guy at a position which will allow it to be raised through an angle of at least 45º before it begins to raise the head of the derrick (Fig 3-218). The lashing is made with figure-of-eight turns and finished with a slipknot, and its end should be long enough to enable the lashing to be slipped from the ground as soon as the lever ceases to act. The head of the lever is raised initially by manhandling and then by the back guy, while its head is kept over the derrick by means of its side guys. When the lever has been raised by an angle of 45º, it will begin to raise the derrick and will continue to do so until it is a little beyond the vertical, when it will cease to act. At this stage the lashing is slipped and the lever is withdrawn, otherwise it will be lifted off the ground as the derrick is raised by its back guy. The derrick side guys are not shown in Fig 3-218.

d.   **By standing lever**. The standing-lever method (Fig 3-219) is suitable for a rather heavier derrick, which is fitted with a back guy rigged as a runner and tailed with a purchase. The lever can be a spar or light sheers, and its length and position in relation to the derrick are the same as those for a moving lever. The lever is fully guyed with strong fore and back guys and is fitted with an extra guy on the side where the hauling part of the guy is rove. If the lever is a spar, a slot is cut in its head into which is placed the standing part of the back guy; if sheers are used as a lever the standing part is placed over the crutch. The lever is then raised and its guys are set up, except the additional side guy, which is rove **underneath** the hauling part of the back guy and left slack. The derrick is then raised by hauling on its back guy, and as the head rises so the hauling part of the back guy will rise until it fouls the side guy of the lever. Raising the derrick is then halted while the additional side guy of the lever is set up and the other side guy is cast off. The raising of the derrick is then completed by means of its back guy. The derrick side guys are not shown in Fig 3-219.

Fig 3-218. Raising a derrick by a moving lever

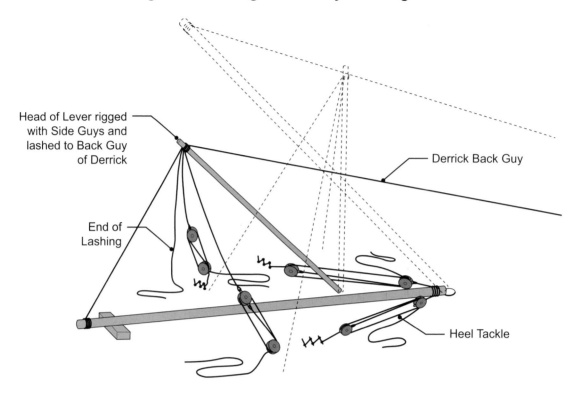

Head of Lever rigged
with Side Guys and
lashed to Back Guy
of Derrick

Derrick Back Guy

End of
Lashing

Heel Tackle

Fig 3-219. Raising a derrick by a standing lever

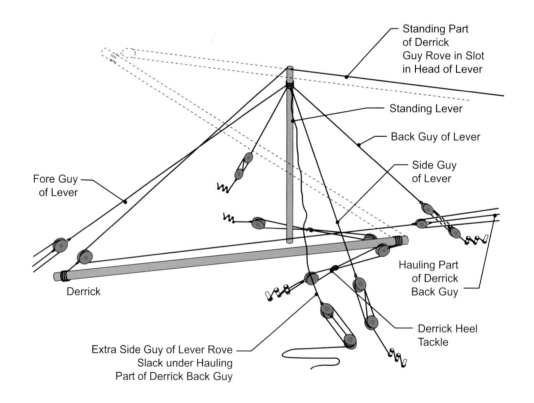

Standing Part
of Derrick
Guy Rove in Slot
in Head of Lever

Standing Lever

Back Guy of Lever

Side Guy
of Lever

Fore Guy
of Lever

Hauling Part
of Derrick
Back Guy

Derrick

Derrick Heel
Tackle

Extra Side Guy of Lever Rove
Slack under Hauling
Part of Derrick Back Guy

e.   **Walking a derrick or sheers.** If it is not convenient to erect a derrick at the place where it is required, it must first be rigged and raised and **walked** there. It is not usual on shore to walk a derrick on its shoe; the shoe is first embedded in its proper position and the derrick is then walked over the ground to its shoe. If the ground is too soft it is walked along a gangway of planks, reinforced if necessary by baulks of timber. To walk a derrick, cross-lash a spar to its foot about three-quarters of a metre above the heel (above the ground for sheers); then, by lifting on the spar, levering the heel(s) with handspikes, and hauling on the forward heel-tackles, the derrick or sheer is walked towards its shoe(s). A derrick must be kept upright by adjusting the side guys. If fitted with a strong fore-guy, walking is facilitated by inclining the derrick or sheers backwards about 10º; a rear heel-tackle must be fitted – otherwise the inclination should be slightly forward.

03064. Plank stage

a.   Plank stages are used to support **a maximum of two people only** when working over the ship's side, or on superstructures and funnels. The lanyards are constructed from 20 mm polypropylene rope and are secured to a small crosspiece of wood, called a **horn**, at each end of the stage. The horns **project** from the stage and so keep it a convenient distance from the fleet to be worked.

Fig 3-220. Securing a lanyard to the end of a plank stage

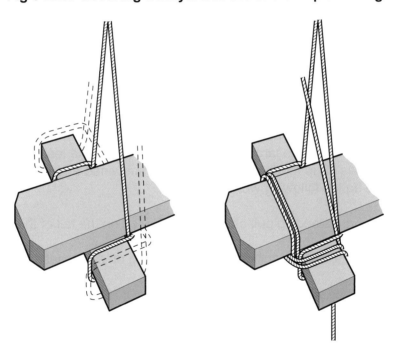

b.   A long soft eye is either spliced or made with a bowline in one end of each lanyard and then placed under the end of the stage, with a half-hitch taken round each horn (Fig 3-220). The lanyard is then passed round a cleat or similar tested fitting near the gunwale above, and the end brought down and belayed round the horns of the stage, thus enabling those working on the stage to lower themselves to the position required. **The lanyard should never be rove round or secured to a guardrail.** Maintenance schedules are given in the ship's Maintenance Management System and Service Drawing Number 020032722/02 gives details of the plank stage and the associated test requirements.

03065. Bosun's chair

A Bosun's chair, 300mm extension strop and a karabiner (Fig 3-221) has the same life restrictions as WaH PPE as stated in the Water Safety Equipment Log (WSEL) PMS 1-5986-0000. The chair is to be used with a 20mm polypropylene gantline secured to the rigging plate. The Full Body Harness should be connected to the chair using the front 'D' ring of the harness and the 300mm extension strop and karabiners onto the rigging plate of the chair. The Full Body Harness and Bosun's Chair are to be tended by their own lifeline and belayed to their own individual tested anchor point. The maximum operation load is not to exceed 130kg including tools.

Fig 3-221. A Bosun's chair

03066. Manpower calculations

a. The force a person can be expected to exert depends chiefly on whether the effort is momentary or sustained, whether it is made quickly or slowly, and on the manner in which the force is to be applied. It also depends to a certain extent on the number of personnel employed; the larger the body of personnel; the less will be the individual effort. In parties of up to 30 personnel, and for sustained efforts, each person can be expected to do the following work:

    (1)   Exert a standing pull of from 25-40kg (eg on the fall of the tackle).

    (2)   Exert a walking pull of from 18-22kg (eg on a purchase fall).

    (3)   Push or pull with a force of from 7-9kg.

    (4)   Carry from 25-40kg.

b. In parties of up to four persons, and for short periods only, each person can be expected to work as follows:

    (1)   Exert a standing haul of from 55-60kg (provided they have a good foothold).

    (2)   Exert a stationary push of 45kg (provided they have a good foothold)

    (3)   Bear down on a lever with a force from 30kg to their own weight.

    (4)   Lift up a lever at knee-level with a force of 70kg.

    (5)   Carry on their shoulders a weight of 60kg.

03067. Accommodation ladder. (Fig 3-222).

a.   The standard accommodation ladder is made of aluminium; it has an upper and lower platform for ease of embarkation and disembarkation. The ladder hinges from the after end of the upper platform, which in turn hinges on the main deck edge. The lower platform is bolted to the ladder and is supported by two stays fastened to the ladder. Both the lower platform and the ladder are braced from the ship's side by either, **telescopic arms on FF/DD,** which fit into sockets recessed into the ship's side. The lower platform has two positions to keep the platform at a convenient height above the water at deep and light conditions of the ship. The gangway **furniture** consists of wooden handrails, complete with electric-light fittings for illumination, which are supported by lightweight stanchions mounted on the ladder and platforms. On some ladders a wire or braidline guardrail is rove through the stanchions halfway between the wooden handrail and the ladder. For raising and lowering the ladder refer to ships drawings.

WARNING

AN ACCOMMODATION LADDER SHOULD NOT BE USED WHEN THERE IS A SEA OR SWELL HIGH ENOUGH TO RENDER BOATS LIABLE TO BE CAUGHT UNDERNEATH THE LOWER PLATFORM; A PILOT/BOARDING LADDER SHOULD BE USED INSTEAD.

---

b.   **Gangway and ladder gear**

(1)   The **gangway boatrope**, similar to that described for the boom boatrope except both ends are finished with a whipping, can be of great assistance to a boat coming alongside in a rough sea or tideway, but it is useless unless led well forward so that it lies nearly in the fore-and-aft line of the boat when she is alongside.

(2)   A length of smaller rope, known as a **strayline**, is spliced into the boatrope near the after end and belayed to a cleat abreast the upper platform; it is used for tricing up the boatrope when not in use. It is the duty of the gangway staff to lower the boatrope to each boat as she comes alongside, so that the bowman can belay it in the boat; the weight of the boat must be taken by the boatrope and not by the strayline. The coxswain of the boat can be assisted in positioning his boat alongside correctly, if the boatrope is marked at a point where the bowman belays it in the boat. When a ship is secured head and stern to buoys in a tideway, a second boatrope should be rigged abaft the ladder for the use of boats coming alongside bow to stern.

(3)   **Check line** is a short length of cordage, spliced round one of the outboard stanchions of the lower platform of the accommodation ladder, and it is used by boats for checking their way and for keeping the stern in the proper position relative to the ladder. When a boat approaches, a member of the gangway staff should be at the bottom of the ladder to pass the check line to the boat; the line requires careful watching, because, if washed off the platform, it may foul the propeller of the boat. When not in use the line is cheesed down.

Fig 3-222. Typical styled accommodation ladder

c. **Safety measures**. When lying in a strong current or tidal stream it is necessary to prevent a boat that overshoots the gangway from being jammed by the current under the ladder, and if ships' boats only are concerned this can be done by rigging a simple **tide spar**. This spar is laid out from the outer stringer of the ladder to the ship's side and lashed in position, but it must not project outboard of the stringer. If the ship is moored head and stern so that she cannot swing with the tide, a similar spar must be rigged abaft the ladder to protect boats coming alongside bow to stern when the ship is stern-on to the tidal stream. When heavy harbour craft are employed as tenders, a ship lying in the stream should secure **catamarans**, some 3.5 or 4.5 metres long, on either side of her accommodation ladder.

Note.   *Personnel rigging or de-rigging the accommodation ladder while working over the side should carry out the safety precautions as stated in Para 06042.*

03068. Mediterranean ladder (Fig 3-223)

The Mediterranean ladder is a portable, rigid, vertical ladder usually provided in smaller ships for use on occasions when the accommodation ladder is not rigged or not available; in many ships it is chiefly used for diving operations. The treads and side stringers are of aluminium channel bars with the latter reinforced at the lower end with Canadian elm and the ladder is braced off the ship's side by an aluminium holding-off bracket padded with Canadian elm. Tubular aluminium handrails are fitted to the top of the ladder and drop-nose pins passed through lugs on the ladder and deck secure the ladder inboard.

Fig 3-223. Mediterranean ladder

03069.   Pilot/boarding ladder (Fig 3-224 and Fig 3-225)

a.   This is a portable 'roll-up' ladder that can be hung over the ship's side for embarking and disembarking boat passengers.   The ladder when rigged is to terminate 300 mm above the surface of the water in calm conditions, when the ship is in its normal seagoing state; ie, fully stored, manned and upright.   The pilot/boarding ladder is constructed of serrated; non-slip treads with side ropes threaded through their ends.   The bottom four treads are made of moulded rubber and the remainder from hardwood; winnets are seized between the two parts of each side rope to keep the treads in position. 3 m x 20 mm polypropylene securing lanyards are spliced to thimble eyes at the inboard end of the ladder.   It should be secured by shackling the thimble eyes direct to suitable strong points in the ship, but where this is not possible (RFAs), the lanyards must be used to lengthen the scope of the ladder.   To prevent the ladder twisting, 1.8 m anti-twist spreaders with an integral serrated tread are fitted to the ladder at regular intervals, depending on the length of the ladder; details are given in Table 3-41.

Table 3-41.   Position of anti-twist spreaders fitted to pilot/boarding ladders

Total number of treads in ladder	Position of spreader
6-13	As the 5th tread
14	As the 5th and 12th tread
15	As the 5th and 13th tread
16-22	As the 5th and 14th tread
23	As the 5th, 14th and 21st tread
24	As the 5th, 14th and 22nd tread
25-30	As the 5th, 14th and 23rd tread

b.   An additional IMO compliant Pilot ladder is to be held by all DD/FF for the embarkation of pilots from specialist pilot craft.   This ladder is approximately 1 metre shorter than the standard embarkation and terminates approximately 1.3 m above the waterline; this allows the ladder not to interfere with the majority of pilot vessel decks, allowing them to rest directly on the ship's side with no danger of entrapment or dragging of the ladder.

c.   **Additional shortening requirements**:

(1)   Whilst the new length ladder is proving to be at the correct height for the majority of pilot transfers, there may be a requirement to increase the height from the waterline on some occasions.

(2)   A safe and approved method has been developed to shorten the pilot/ boarding ladder further if required and can be seen in Fig 3-225.   Additional rigging equipment required is two green 0.5 m round slings (2T SWL) and four 1m lengths of 6mm polyester line whipped and heat-sealed.

(3)   To shorten the ladder, the round slings are thoroughfooted below the rung required and secured to the existing shackles, the ladder is then lashed to the shackles and the end thimbles are secured to prevent the top of the ladder from lifting up if grabbed.

(4)   Details of boat transfer positions are contained in Table 3-42.

Table 3-42. Authorised boat transfer positions whilst underway

Class/Ship	Approved Method
CVS	Pilot door transfer
LPH	Pilot door
LPD	Pilot door
Type 45	Transfer vessel brow to flight deck (using enhanced bollards) iaw nchq 141125z jan 11 Pilot door transfer up to sea state 3
Type 23	Pilot/boarding ladder midships cross passage (port and starboard) Transfer vessel brow to flight deck or cross passage
MCMV Sandown	Pilot/boarding ladder transfer position port or starboard aft
MCMV Hunt	Pilot/boarding ladder transfer position port or starboard waist
River Class	Pilot/boarding ladder transfer position port or starboard quarterdeck
OPVH	Pilot/boarding ladder transfer position port or starboard quarterdeck and port or starboard midships
Echo/Enterprise	Pilot/boarding ladder transfer position ax
Scott	Pilot/boarding ladder transfer position port and starboard side fwd of the bridge. (Port is the preferred position).
Protector	Pilot/boarding ladder transfer position port or starboard aft of accommodation tower
P2000	Step up to 1 deck
SSN Submarine	Pilot/boarding ladder transfer position starboard side
SSBN Submarine	Pilot/boarding ladder transfer position port side
Astute Class	Pilot/boarding ladder transfer position starboard side
RFA Argus	Gun port doors port and starboard
RFA Diligence	Gun port doors port and starboard
Rover Class RFA	In line with samson posts port and starboard
Leaf Class RFA	Fwd of samson posts port and starboard
Fort Class RFA	Aft end amidships accommodation block port and starboard
Fort Victoria	Aft of accommodation ladder position on tank deck port and starboard
LSDA Class	Gun port doors port and starboard
Wave Class	Aft end port and starboard shade decks

d. Two 24mm staple spun polypropylene manropes must be provided. These are to be rigged at all times when the ladder is in use. They must be securely hitched, above the middle knuckle of the handhold stanchions where possible, or to other suitably positioned fixtures. The manrope ends should be whipped and heat sealed and extend for the length of the ladder.

e.   A Marine rescue strop and line, properly tended, must be available at the transfer position.   When this is used it is only supplied as assurance to the wearer and not provided as fall restraint.

f.   When underway and embarking or disembarking stores or personnel via the pilot/ boarding ladder, a boatrope must be rigged and taken by the boat to hold the boat in position under the ladder and the transfer is to be conducted in accordance with Annex 5A. **THIS IS A MANDATORY REQUIREMENT WHEN USING THE PILOT/ BOARDING LADDER.**

Note.   FF/DD are not to use the Quarterdeck position for boat transfers other than in totally benign conditions and with the Commanding Officer's approval due to the pitch of the ship and the positioning of the propeller guards.

Fig 3-224. Pilot/boarding ladder

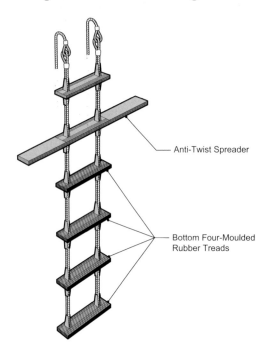

Anti-Twist Spreader

Bottom Four-Moulded Rubber Treads

Fig 3-225. Shortened pilot/boarding ladder

03070. Brows

a. **Introduction**. The purpose of a brow is to provide a gangway between ship and shore or ship and ship. As a general rule, ship-to-shore brows are provided by the dockyard authorities and ship-to-ship brows are provided by the outer ship. To fulfil the latter requirement, destroyers and below are supplied with a portable ship-to-ship lightweight brow of aluminium construction, NSN 0232/736-7283 (Fig 3-226). It is supplied as two identical 3 m units that may be used singly or joined together to make one 6-metre brow. At some small commercial ports where no dockyard brow is available, it may be necessary to rig the lightweight brow for ship-to-shore use. Gaps between the inserted brow and the guardrail stanchions are to be fitted with temporary guardrails as explained in Chap 6 para 06045 sub para b(2).

Note. *Brow and guardwires must bear evidence of test.*

Fig 3-226. Ship-to-ship lightweight brow

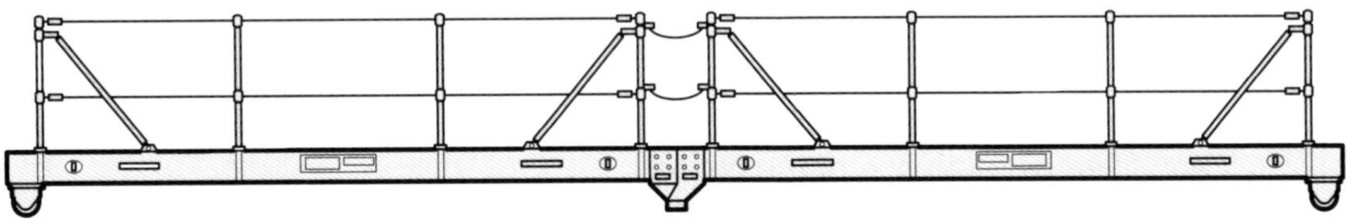

b. **Rigging a brow and general safety measures**

(1) *General principles.* When a Naval Base-supplied brow is put into a ship in a non-tidal basin it is the responsibility of the Naval Base staff to secure the inboard end, whereas at tidal berths the Naval Base staff are responsible for seeing that the inboard end is properly secured by ship's staff. Any gap between the break in the ship's guardrails and the brow must be securely roped off using 12 mm polyester cordage. This roping must form an effective and safe barrier for personnel and is to extend from the stanchion at which the guardrails have been broken to an appropriate stanchion on the brow that is in line with, or inboard of, the fore-and-aft line of the ship's guardwires. On no account is the line of the roping to lead outboard of the fore-and-aft line of the ship's guardwires. The minimum height of the roping must not be less than 1.15 metres, and to achieve this it may sometimes be necessary to rig a temporary stanchion or extend an existing one by lashing to it a suitable length of 50mm x 50mm timber. The lanyards, which secure the brow, must be secured to eyeplates, bollards, or other permanent fittings, and never to stanchions. The approaches to the jetty end of the brow must be kept clear of obstacles and at night, brows must be well illuminated. The brow handling party must wear safety helmets, restraint belt, lanyard and hazardous duty life jackets (HDLJ).

(2) *Ships berthed alongside each other.* When ships are berthed alongside each other it is the responsibility of the outer ship or the ship with the higher freeboard to supply a properly rigged brow, but it is the responsibility of the outboard ship to ensure that her end of the brow is properly tended and secured, and that any gap between the ship's guardrails and the guardwires of the brow is securely roped off as described in sub para (1).

(3)   *Fendering.* A mat, fender or other suitable material should be used as a Scotsman, and placed under the end of a brow which is in contact with the deck; if a brow is fitted with a roller, a sheet of metal should be placed over the area of movement, and a guard fitted or notice displayed warning people of the danger as the brow rolls with the movement of the ship.

(4)   *Rigging a brow safety net.* Two nets per ship are to be carried. Whenever a brow is rigged a brow safety net must be rigged beneath it. Each net must be secured by means of its fitted lanyards and positioned so that it is directly beneath the brow with the centre of the net lower than its edges. The net must extend from ship to ship or ship to dock wall and have sufficient spread on both sides to catch a person or object falling from the brow safely (see Note 3). Where no suitable securing positions are available on the jetty, a spreader bar of sufficient length is to be secured to or through the brow so that the net lanyards can be secured to it thus achieving the correct spread. A length of 100 mm x 100 mm timber or other suitable material is to be used as a spreader. The nets must be inspected before and after use, and at frequent intervals whilst they are rigged. They may need to be adjusted to allow for the rise and fall of tide. When longer-than-usual brows are put into a ship – for example if a ship docks down in a large dry dock – nets suitable for the task should be requested from the shoreside authorities. In such circumstances a ship's own brow safety nets may be securely lashed together and fitted beneath one of the brows.

Safety notes:

1.   When a ship is berthed close to a quay or jetty that has no fendering, the safety net must be rigged so that it affords protection from the area immediately below the brow position.

2.   When a ship is berthed close to a quay or jetty that has no fendering, and with a brow that is at a steep angle, the net must be positioned so that it affords protection for a person or object falling from the upper portion of the brow or the gangway area. This may involve reducing the size of the safety net by folding it over, or increasing the area of net by lashing two nets together and adding extra securing lines (12mm polyester).

3.   The height of the net must always be sufficient to ensure the safety of a person falling into it. If any doubt exists a functional test is to be carried out by pushing the Man Overboard dummy over the edge of the brow into the net and checking that the fall of the dummy is arrested before it comes into contact with the fendering/jetty. This should not be considered as proof that the net is safe for all eventualities but will provide a means of establishing the likely distortions of the net downwards should a person fall into it. It may be necessary to repeat the tests for various states of the tide.

4.   Once the safety net is securely rigged it, and any roped off sections, must be monitored and adjusted to take account of the range of tide.

5.   In some specific circumstances (for example a ship alongside a jetty without catamarans and the brow almost horizontal) it may not be possible to rig a safety net that achieves any useful function. In such circumstances appropriate warning notices are to be placed at each end of the brow and firm control of personnel should be exercised in the gangway area.

6.   *No one is allowed to cross a brow until it is secured, the guardrails are set up and a safety net is rigged.*

7.   *A ship in dry dock presents a particular risk to personnel crossing a brow and for this reason added safety measures are necessary. The stanchions and guard chains that surround a dock must always be in position. If for any reason their removal is necessary, the gap must be patrolled by a sentry until they are replaced.* **At night these stanchions and chains must never be unshipped.**

8.   *When preparing to leave harbour ships are not to single up their own berthing lines until brow slings have been shackled to the brow, hooked to the fixed dockside crane, all slack taken up and brow securing lanyards have been singled up and are in hand. If a mobile is used the brow should be removed before singling up any berthing lines.*

9.   *Dockyard supplied berthing lines can be singled up/removed at any time at the discretion of the Commanding Officer in consultation with the relevant port authorities.*

03071. Scrambling nets
Scrambling nets made of 16 mm polypropylene cordage are provided for situations such as abandon ship when it is necessary to get large numbers of personnel safely into liferafts or the water without them having to jump. The nets may also be used by boarding parties when embarking or disembarking from a boat and are also available as an option for enabling survivors to board a ship, although it should be borne in mind that the effort of climbing a scrambling net is likely to be beyond the capabilities of personnel who have been in the water for any length of time, or who are suffering from shock or exposure. The nets are stowed along the ship's side at places where freeboard is lowest, but well clear of propellers. When unstopped they hang about 300 mm clear of the ship's side with the lower end at least one metre under the water when the ship is at light draught. The nets are spread on wooden battens fitted at one-metre intervals and when the net is suspended over the ship's side the battens must be on the inboard side of the net, ie, between the net and the ship's side. The lower end of the net is weighted with metal tubes or bars. In the stowed position the nets are protected from the elements and funnel gases etc by PVC covers which have eyelets to allow drainage of water.

03072. Sounding
A measurement of the depth of water is called a **sounding**. On modern charts it is measured in metres or metres and decimetres; on older charts it may be measured in feet or fathoms, or a combination of both. A fathom measures 6 feet (1.8288 metres). Soundings are usually taken by echo sounder, or a **lead and line**, described below. However, the simplest method of taking a sounding in shallow water is with a pole, and for this reason boat hook staves of ship's boats should be marked off in metres.

03073. Boat's lead and line (Fig 3-227)

In shallow water, harbour craft and boats use a boat's lead and line for sounding. It consists of a weighted line marked at intervals along its length. The weight or **lead**, NSN 0262/463-7107 is of leg-of-mutton shape and weighs 3 kg and the **line** consists of 26 metres of 9 mm pre-stretched polyester NSN 0350/120-8692. When soundings are taken, due allowance must be made for the speed of the boat through the water. This is done by heaving the lead ahead of the boat and reading off the sounding when the line is vertically up and down with the lead on the bottom. The lead must also be heaved ahead when the boat is stationary but stemming a tidal stream and the sounding is taken when the line is vertical.

Fig 3-227. Boat's lead and line

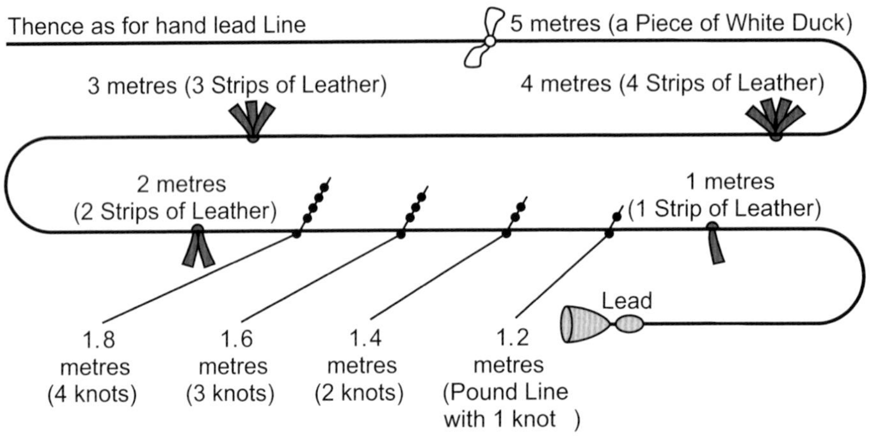

Thence as for hand lead Line

5 metres (a Piece of White Duck)

3 metres (3 Strips of Leather)

4 metres (4 Strips of Leather)

2 metres (2 Strips of Leather)

1 metres (1 Strip of Leather)

Lead

1.8 metres (4 knots)

1.6 metres (3 knots)

1.4 metres (2 knots)

1.2 metres (Pound Line with 1 knot)

Between each metre mark up to 5 metres, the line should be marked
Every 0.2 metres with knots as between the 1st and 2nd metric marks

03074. Hand lead and line (Fig 3-228)

a.   **Introduction**. For emergency use in ships should the echo sounder fail, a hand lead and line can be used for sounding to a depth of 40 metres and at speed not exceeding 10 knots. An echo sounder can be checked by means of a hand lead line in harbour, if the bottom is firm and flat. The lead consists of a tapered bar of lead, NSN 0232/545-7948, weighing 6.3kg, to which is bent a 50 m length of 9 mm pre-stretched polyester cordage, NSN 0350/120-8692. The base of the lead is hollowed out to receive tallow, and the head is shaped into an 'eye' through which is rove a hide becket. The placing of tallow in the base of the lead is called **arming** it, and its purpose is to pick up a sample of the seabed for examination if required. The lead line has a long eye splice at one end and a back splice at the other. It is bent to the lead by reeving the eye splice through the hide becket and passing the lead through the eye.

b.   **Markings**. The hand lead line is marked as follows:

2 m	–	two strips of leather	13 m – a piece of **blue serge**
3 m	–	**three** strips of leather	15 m – a piece of **white duck**
5 m	–	a piece of **white duck**	17 m – a piece of **red bunting**
7 m	–	a piece of **red bunting**	20 m – **two** knots
10 m	–	a piece of **leather** with a **hole** in it	then repeat up to 40 m.

Fig 3-228. Hand lead and line

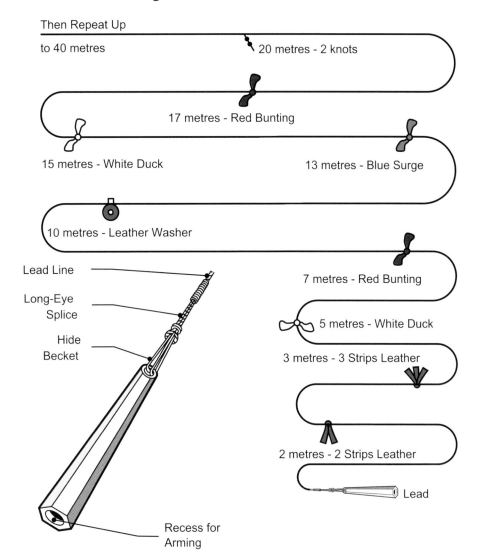

Then Repeat Up
to 40 metres

20 metres - 2 knots

17 metres - Red Bunting

15 metres - White Duck

13 metres - Blue Surge

10 metres - Leather Washer

Lead Line

Long-Eye Splice

Hide Becket

7 metres - Red Bunting

5 metres - White Duck

3 metres - 3 Strips Leather

2 metres - 2 Strips Leather

Lead

Recess for Arming

03075. Awnings

a. **Introduction**. Awnings are fitted over certain exposed decks to give protection from the sun. Side curtains and gable ends are provided to screen and shelter the areas below large awnings such as those fitted over fo'c'sles or flight decks. Awnings are supplied to HM ships in accordance with an as fitted drawing for the class or individual ship that shows the general arrangement of the awnings, rigging fittings and the stores required to complete the outfit; they are manufactured from flax canvas that has been chemically treated to increase its resistance to rot. Most modern ships are provided with one major awning under which a large number of people may be sheltered or entertained, and smaller awnings for suitable areas to protect the gangway staff. Certain older ships may, in addition, carry minor awnings for waists, bridge wings and other areas. Major awnings are supported by a central wire called the 'ridge rope' or backbone and are hauled out at the edges to awning stanchions by awning tackles and earrings; minor awnings are laced to a wire rope passing through the tops of the surrounding stanchions, called the edge rope. Technically a backbone is a ridge rope sewn into the awning, but this is now seldom found and the separated ridge rope will hereafter be referred to as the backbone.

b.   **Major awnings**. Fo'c'sle and flight deck awnings, classified as major awnings, are made of RN No. 2 canvas for large ships and RN No. 4 canvas for Destroyers and Frigates. These awnings are supported by a backbone of canvassed SWR shackled to an eyeplate or special stanchion at the midships end and secured by bottle-screw and slip at the jackstaff or ensign staff. The edges are hauled out to awning stanchions (see Fig 3-229) and the edge rope. The description that follows is of a destroyer or frigate flight deck awning. (A fo'c'sle awning is in every way similar except the awning is shaped to fit, and is secured at, the after end and hauled out forward). The awning is made of cloth running athwartships. It has a wire boltrope, served with spunyarn and marled with polypropylene to its outboard edges; and a cordage boltrope at its forward end. A thimble is fitted to an eye worked into the boltrope at the after end, and a large cringle is worked into the cordage boltrope at the centre of the fore edge. Cringles are worked into the outboard edges abreast the stanchions, and holes with thimbles between the stanchions. The latter are used for sloping awnings, and at both positions the canvas is strengthened by patches. The centre-line is strengthened by a 600mm wide 'saddle-cloth' or 'middle-band' sewn under the awning to take the chafe of the backbone, and hide patches are sewn on where there is additional chafe from the screw slip, centre stanchions or structural corners. A curtain line of polypropylene line is attached at intervals on the topside of the awning, close to the outboard edges, to which the top of the side curtain is secured. Furling stops for securing the awning, when it has been rolled before stowage, are sewn on top of the awning at alternate seams. Where an outboard edge is attached to the ship's structure running fore and aft, it is fitted with S-hooks moused into brass grommets with roping twine. Athwartship edges are always rope laced.

Fig 3-229. Awning stanchion

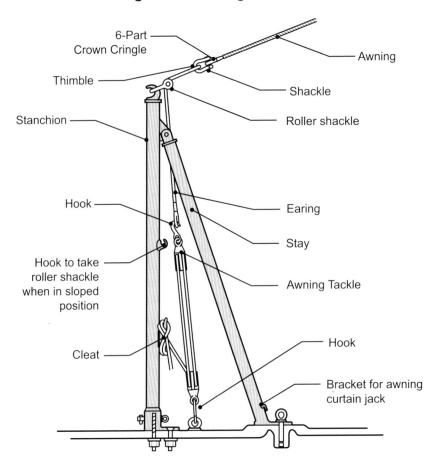

(1)   *Securing the awning.* The flight deck awning is cut to fit at selected points of its fore-end, and any stretch is allowed for by cutting the remainder slightly smaller than the area it is designed to cover. Therefore, whenever the awning is spread it must be secured first at its fitted end. The centre cringle of the fore end is secured by shackle to an eyeplate or special stanchion just above the securing point of the backbone. The other selected points are then secured. A pendant (earring) is shackled to the thimble eye in the wire boltrope at the after end; and a tackle, secured to the ensign staff above the backbone, hauls the awning aft. The sides are then hauled out by the awning tackles (Fig 3-256). Inboard edges are clipped by S-hooks or rope lacings to jack rods welded to the superstructure.

c.   **Minor awnings**. Waist and bridge wing awnings are classified as minor awnings. They have boltropes sewn round all edges on the underside to strengthen them and help to retain their shape. Brass grommets, through which the awning is laced to the edge rope, are inserted at regular intervals. Where an inboard edge abuts the ship's structure running fore and aft, S-hooks clip the awning to a jack rod or wire. Athwartship edges should always be rope laced. When an awning has to pass round obstructions, such as rigging, davits or fan trunking, a laced opening called a **shark's mouth** or a slotted approach to a hole called a **banjo** is made; if the obstruction is a ladder, portions of the awning are cut away and the edges roped. When one awning butts against another a canvas flap, called an **apron**, is sewn to one and laced across the gap to fill a narrow flap, called a **frog**, sewn on the other.

d.   **Awning curtains and gable ends**. Awning curtains of RN No. 6 flax canvas are provided to screen and shelter major awnings. They are fitted with grommets for stopping the top to the curtain line, the bottom to screwed eyes in the deck or a fine wire tricing line secured to the foot of each stanchion and the sides for lacing to each other. The quarterdeck can also be screened by a gable end, of the same material as the curtains, running athwartships. It is stopped to a line sewn across the topside of the awning; the bottom is weighted, and one or two flap entrances are cut in it.

e.   **Ceremonial awnings**. Frigates (hanger only) and larger ships are supplied with a ceremonial awning and side curtains made from bunting of alternate coloured and white cloths: the colour may be red, blue or green. The awning is spread beneath the main awning on ceremonial and state occasions, cocktail parties, etc. The side curtains are hooked at the curtain line and laced at the bottom.

f.   **Spreading awnings**. Since the canvas of an awning is subject to stretching, care must be taken to preserve its shape when spread. A baggy, wrinkled or torn awning is usually the result of mistreatment. A minor awning such as a bridge wing or waist awning, should first be lashed by the earrings on its windward clews, and then unfurled to leeward and its leeward clews secured. The clew earrings can then be hauled taut and the sides hooked or laced to the edge ropes or awning rails. A major awning needs more care, and the method of spreading a flight deck awning is given here as a guide; but it is necessary to know how an awning is folded for stowage. Before stowing an awning it is spread on the deck with its upper side down, and the two sides are then folded to the centre-line and squared off. The two doubled sides are then rolled towards one another to meet at the centre-line and the whole is then secured by the stops fitted along the top of the centre-line. The earrings and tackles are always detached and stowed separately, but the lacings of a small awning can be made up with it.

g.   When spreading an awning in a cross wind it should always be passed over the backbone from the leeward to the windward side; if passed over from the windward side the pressure of the wind on its sloping surface up to the backbone will make it difficult to haul over. Before spreading a flight deck awning it is laid out along the deck with its stops uppermost. The stops are then cast off and each side is unrolled, and the boltrope on each side is then hauled clear to the leeward side of the deck. The leeward earrings are then secured to their cringles, which are rove slack through their roller shackles and belayed to their cleats. Then hauling-over lines are bent to the windward cringles and passed over the backbone to the other side, where they are manned. In a high wind the awning tackles on the windward side can be clapped on to the hauling-over lines and used to assist in hauling the awning over the backbone; these tackles are also useful for anchoring the weather edge to the far side and for holding it down while the earrings are being secured and rove. Similarly, the leeward awning tackles can be hooked direct to the lee cringles and set up to ensure that the wind does not blow under the lee side of the awning. It is usual to rig **tent lines** over the backbone, from the feet of the leeward awning stanchions, to support and guide the awning as it is hauled over. At the order 'Haul over' the awning is hauled over the backbone to the other side and the fore end of the awning is secured to its fixed points. The earrings are then shackled on and rove, and the awning tackles are hooked on and manned. The after clew is hauled aft by its earring tackle, thus tautening the centre-line of the awning; then the side earrings are hauled out together, care being taken to keep the centre of the awning in line with the backbone. The tackles are then belayed to the cleats and the ends cheesed down at the feet of the stanchions.

h.   **Care of spread awnings**. A new awning will stretch considerably athwartships but very little in a fore-and-aft direction, and this is allowed for when the awning is first cut to shape. If a good final spread is to be obtained the stretching must be done gently and gradually. A new awning must therefore never be hauled out or kept too taut until it has been fully stretched, and this stretching must be done by hauling it out a little more each day. Canvas shrinks when wet, but it should regain its shape when dry if meanwhile it has not been overstretched. A fully stretched awning has little elasticity and may easily be ruined by overstretching when damp or wet. Earrings should be eased off in damp weather, and always at night on account of dew. Awnings should not be fully spread until they are dry.

(1)   *Sloping awnings*. When it is raining awnings should be sloped. This is done by shifting the roller shackle of alternate earrings to the lower hook (if fitted) and by unshackling the remaining cringles and hooking them directly to their awning tackles by which the awning is bowsed down. This should prevent pools of water from collecting on top of the awning and forcing it out of shape.

(2)   *Frapping an awning*. If caught unawares or short-handed by a sudden squall a major awning should be fully sloped and **frapping lines** rove. These lines, of strong cordage, are rove athwartships over the awning and belayed at each side on deck so that they help to keep the awning from billowing and slatting. To rig frapping lines overnight as a matter of routine is not advised because even in light winds their chafe will soon wear holes in the awning. They should be rigged only when a sudden blow is possible but it is better still to furl the awning overnight. If frapping lines are rigged, hauling-over lines should also be rigged, and tent lines, if used, should be rove and stopped to the heads of the awning stanchions and all gear should be prepared for furling.

i.   **Furling awnings**. Major Awnings, if well fitted, fairly flat and tautly spread, will stand up to winds of about Force 5 Beaufort scale, but in stronger winds they are liable to slat badly and may then carry away. Minor flat awnings should stand up to winds of Force 6 quite comfortably. All awnings should be furled well before the danger point is reached, and it is always best to furl them if in doubt rather than have them suddenly blown away. An awning is usually furled to windward and the procedure is the reverse of that by which it is spread. With a flight deck awning, tent lines and hauling-over lines are rigged, earrings are eased away squarely and evenly, and the earring tackle at the after end of the centre-line is eased off. The lee earrings are unrove and manned; the weather earrings are unrove and, if the wind is strong, the weather awning tackles are hooked into the weather cringles and belayed. The after clew is eased forward on its earring; the fore end of the awning is cast off and then, at the order 'Haul over', the lee side is hauled over the backbone. As the lee side is hauled over, the weather side is hauled across the deck to the lee side, so that the awning is eventually laid out underside uppermost and ready for making up. When furling an awning in a strong wind care must be taken that the wind does not get under the awning and blows it overboard. In a short-handed ship, when it comes on to blow hard the flight deck awning may be safely furled to leeward under frapping lines in the following manner. The awning is fully sloped, with the awning tackles secured to the cringles, and a large tackle is then shackled to the fore weather clew and belayed. The after clew is let go from its earring and gathered, and the awning is passed over progressively from aft forward, each part being gathered as it comes to hand. Eventually all hands are available to hold and gather the windward clew as it is eased over by its tackle.

j.   **Maintenance of awnings**. An awning – or for that matter, any canvas gear -should never be stowed below wet, because it will not only rot but may easily catch fire from spontaneous combustion. A wet awning should be temporarily stowed in a sheltered place on deck until an opportunity occurs for drying it; the quickest way of drying it is to spread it in good weather. An awning should always be lifted and carried, never dragged along the decks and if it is necessary for it to be laid down on deck, it should be laid on battens or gratings in order to keep it clear of the deck and any dirt. As awnings are spoilt by frequent scrubbing, every care should be taken to keep them clean. Decks should be swept before spreading or furling awnings, and when made up they should be protected from dirt and damage. Bags or covers are provided for gable ends and ceremonial awnings, and they should be stowed in them when not in use. When stowing away equipment, awning tackles should be hung up, and earrings and backbones coiled up and tallied to assist in identification on the next occasion of their use. Cleaning, repair or the manufacture of new awnings, upperdeck covers and ceremonial canvas work is to be assessed by the Chief Bosun's Mate or Bosun and discussed with the area Surveyor of Stores who will produce a contract for any necessary work required.

03076. Fendering

a.   A ship going alongside another ship or a jetty requires a resilient fender to absorb any impact, but the fender must be sufficiently unyielding to provide protection and sufficient separation to allow for any overhanging structure, proud propellers, etc. For boats and other small craft whose sides are strong in comparison with the weight of the vessel, fendering presents no difficulties and any soft fender is adequate. For larger vessels fendering must be sufficiently robust to withstand the crushing of the weight of the ship, and it must be large enough and sufficiently resilient to spread and absorb the shock over a large area of comparatively weak hull plating. Fenders must be placed where the hull can best withstand the impact; to some extent this applies to all ships, but in modern warships they must be placed at specified positions where the hull is strengthened by additional stiffeners near the waterline; tally plates on the weatherdeck show the limit of the stiffening. The fenders described below are divided into three categories, those that are fixed to the structure or jetty of a pier, those that are mobile and provided in port (too heavy for ships) and those that are portable (carried in ships).

b.   **Fixed fendering**. The solid walls of berths and the piles of jetties have vertical baulks of timber attached to protect the masonry or concrete and to provide fendering to ships alongside. In some commercial ports no other form of fendering is provided, but the use of suspended rubber units is increasing. In a tideway, to lessen the impact when a ship is brought alongside, some springing device is included between the timber and the masonry.

c.   **Port fenders**

(1)   *Catamaran*. This is a stoutly constructed rectangular wooden or steel raft used in dockyards between ship and jetty. The bearing surfaces are usually fitted with rubber rubbing pieces.

(2)   *Compression catamaran*. Designed for use with light-hulled vessels, this catamaran consists of two rectangular tanks, of a length not less than three ship-frame spaces, separated by resilient units fitted vertically on chains. The bearing faces and corners are fitted with rubber rubbing pieces.

(3)   *Pontoon*. (Fig 3-230). This may be any floating structure used as a buoyant support. It may be used in salvage work to buoy up a damaged vessel, or it may be used to support a bridge across water. In tidal waters a pontoon is used as a landing place for boats and ferries on a muddy foreshore, or alongside piers and jetties where the range of tide is considerable; such pontoons are usually connected to the shore or jetty by a hinged bridge.

(4)   *Large pneumatic fenders* (Fig 3-231). These are increasingly being used instead of catamarans for ships lying alongside a dock wall or other ships, although they are not suitable for use on piled jetties unless the area on which they will bear has first been sheeted over with steel plate or similar material to ensure the load is spread. The fenders are manufactured from textile reinforced rubber, and there are two types in use, the low pressure type with a diameter of 2.3 metres and a length of 12 metres, NSN 0232/605-6437, and the high pressure type, produced in various sizes.

Fig 3-230. Pontoon

Fig 3-231. Port fendering – large pneumatic fender

d. **Portable fenders**. (Fig 3-232) Portable fendering currently in use in the Royal Navy are the *High Pressure Pneumatic Fenders.* They are high-energy absorbing, lightweight, non-marking and durable, with an expected life of at least ten years. They are grey in colour and are fitted with a towing eye at each end. Each ship's outfit of fenders comes complete with an operating manual and an inflation/repair kit. Supply details are given in Table 3-43; allowances are listed in Table 3-44.

Table 3-43. Supply details of high pressure fenders

Stores No.	Description	D of Q	Status
0232/535-3390	Fender pneumatic. Rubber HP. 0.5 m dia x 1.0 m long. Towing eye each end. Grey in colour.	Each	P
0232/885-0321	Fender pneumatic. Rubber HP. 1m dia x 1.5 m long. Towing eye each end. Grey in colour.	Each	P
0232/623-9360	Yokohama Fender Repair Kit	Each	P

Table 3-44. Allowances of high pressure pneumatic fenders

Class of vessel	Patt No of fender 0232/885-0321	Patt No of fender 0232/535-3390
Capital Ships	6	8
Frigates and Destroyers	3	8
Minor War Vessels	2	6

Note. *Portable fenders are to be fitted with 16mm polypropylene lanyards of sufficient length to permit the fender to reach the waterline.*

Fig 3-232. High pressure pneumatic portable fender

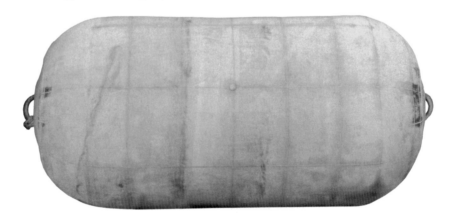

e.   **Submarine fenders – deployment.**   For submarines, the ship will deploy two fenders to port. The submarine fenders are stowed in the designated stowages in the aft well deck. These fenders are approximately five metres in length, made up of eight solid rubber strips mounted on an octagonal metal frame and the fender is shackled in position alongside. RFA DILIGENCE carries up to four different types of fender for use with ships or submarines alongside. This standard operating procedure highlights their use and methods of deployment.

(1)   The submarine fender is designed to hang vertically against the ship's side and remain mostly submerged. Each fender has two wires shackled to the top, which allows the fender to be lifted by crane, and lowered into position and then the securing wire shackled to the designated ringbolt on the ship's side (these are painted yellow). Each fender weighs about 5.5 tonnes in air, but in water weigh about 3.5 tonnes. Thus when moving the forward fender using the forward crane (Snoopy), the fender MUST remain in the water to avoid using Snoopy beyond its Safe Working Load.

(2)   The seven-tonne crane (port aft) will pick-up and deploy the aft fender directly. The forward fender is initially hoisted and swung over the port side using the aft crane and then transferred to the five-tonne Snoopy crane whilst alongside outboard.   The Snoopy crane is hooked on and the weight transferred slowly between cranes; the seven-tonne crane is disconnected to allow the fender to be moved forward to the ringbolt next to the taught wire winch.   These fenders are difficult to control when suspended from the crane, owing to their weight, and caution should be exercised, avoid any uncontrolled swings as railings, liferafts and other fittings are susceptible. Allow an hour to deploy both.

(3)   RFA DILIGENCE has an outfit of four 6.25 tonne tyred Yokohama fenders, which are stowed in the aft Well Deck. These are used to allow ships to berth alongside, particularly to port.

(4)   There is a greater difficulty deploying these fenders to starboard owing to their weight, the safe working load of 'Snoopy' and the reach of the 15 tonne crane, (it is only advised if the conditions are benign – see later). Deploying to port is straight forward using the 7 tonne aft crane. The fenders can be lifted using the doubled up red strops, which are long enough to allow unhooking from the Main Deck. The aft fender can be placed directly in position, but the forward fender has to be towed forward by hand from the main deck – if necessary the ship can drop astern to help the positioning. Ensure the fender is raised high enough before swinging outboard to avoid damage to the railings.

(5)   Do not secure the picking-up line, connected to the strops, to the railings as any swell will cause snatching and distort the railings. Use an adjacent cleat. The forces involved in a swell can cause failure of either the fender securing lines or cleats. Do not underestimate the movement of 6.25 tonnes of fender.

(6)   Deploying to starboard should only be attempted if the launch and recovery conditions are benign. The 15 tonne crane has to be used, but it can only clear the rail if a shortened double-up red strop is used. The main disadvantage is that the only way to unhook is to place a man over the ship's side by jumping-ladder to reach the lifting strop, and similarly to hook back on for recovery.

Note. In the Persian Gulf in March 2003, owing to the rough weather and swell, two large Yokohama fenders deployed to starboard could not be recovered for four days until the weather abated and then only with the use of the ships rigid inflatable boat (RIB) to hook the fenders on. It is preferred to use the smaller man managed (MM) fenders to starboard.

(7) Ensure the securing lines are regularly checked as chafing can occur from adjacent scupper lips and quickly part the lines. A long lead on the forward fender helped reduce the snatching effect that led to failures highlighted above. If necessary, run a mooring line from the fo'c'sle to connect the forward securing line.

(8) DILIGENCE has four small Yokohama fenders in rope cages, (not the tyre cage), which are used for smaller vessels such as MMs, weighing 2.5 tonnes These are easily deployed on either side using either the five-tonne or seven-tonne cranes and pulled into position by hand. MMs berth to starboard when fuelling with the fenders positioned either side of the fuelling manifold.

f. **Safety.** When deploying the fenders the following safety precautions should be taken:

(1) Personal Protection Equipment is to be worn, this includes but not necessarily limited to:

> **PPE**
> DMS Boots
> Foul Weather Clothing
> In date Industrial Safety Helmets
> Hazardous Duty Life Jacket (fitted with light or Cyalume if rigging at night
>
> Rigging Set
> Torches available
> Upper Deck lighting switched on; consider use of the directional Bridge floodlights.
> Ensure the crane hook is fitted with a steadying rope at all times.
> Utilise the securing lines as steadying ropes.

(2) The person in charge of the evolution, (usually the Chief Petty Officer CPO (Deck)), conducts a brief prior to deployment to ensure that all personnel are aware of the dangers and understand their responsibilities. Ensure VHF Radio communications are available between the Bridge and the Deck.

03077. Berthing

At least 48 hours before a ship enters a harbour to berth a signal is sent to the relevant port authorities, detailing logistic requirements (LOGREQ). The LOGREQ is the responsibility of the Logistics Department and includes any requirement for tugs and cranes, and the position that the brow(s) are required (See Table 3-45). If berthing in a foreign or commercial port, details of the ship's length and draught are also included. In naval bases a common system of berth marking has been adopted for the guidance of ships' officers. The marks are tabulated below but it must be noted that the bow and stern marks are optional and that night marking is provided only if the lighting at the berth is insufficient for the day marking to be identified.

Table 3-45. Berthing marks at naval bases

Berthing marks at Naval bases			
	Bow	**Compass**	**Stern**
Day	Red Flag*	Green Flag	Blue Flag*
Night	Fixed Red Light*	Fixed Green Light	Fixed Blue Light*

* These marks are optional

a. **Briefing for berthing alongside.** Before a warship enters harbour to berth, the Navigating Officer briefs Senior Officers, Bosun, Chief Bosun's Mate, I/Cs Parts of Ship and Part of Ship Safety Officers on the berthing plan. At this briefing, in addition to ship-handling aspects of the evolution, it is established if a pilot is to be embarked, whether it is intended to use tugs to assist the berthing, which side to the ship will berth, and, if known, relevant details of the jetty, pier or wharf to which the ship is going, including the siting of bollards. It is advisable that a priority rope is declared by the Command to enable first line securing. Part of Ship hands in turn will be briefed and the seaman department then prepares accordingly.

b. **Preparing sheet anchors for letting go when berthing.** Sheet Anchors, when in the a-cock bill position present an increased snagging hazard and can impede berthing or tug operations. In ships fitted with vertical hawse pipes a sheet anchor is unlikely to jam on release, therefore in this instance it is of little benefit to veer the sheet anchor to the a-cock bill position as it can be fully prepared for letting go from the close home position whilst avoiding impeding safe tug and berthing operations. At the Commanding Officers discretion, Type 23 and Type 45 sheet anchors may be kept close home, held on the capstan brake with the blake slip on as a preventer, rather than being veered clear of the hawse pipe.

c. **HPMT – idealised mooring pattens** (Fig 3-233). A Mooring Pattern is the distribution of lines about the ship to hold the ship effectively and safely alongside with due regards to environmental criteria and forces acting upon the ship.

(1) *Breasts:* Restraint **off** the berth – situated as perpendicular to the longitudinal centre line of the ship as possible and as far fwd and aft as possible.

(2) *Springs:* Restraint **along** the berth – situated as parallel to the longitudinal centre line of the ship as possible.

(3)   *Head/stern ropes:* Manoeuvring only, generally ineffective in restraining the ship in any direction.

(4)   *All lines:* The greater the length and the less vertical angle between ship and shore the better.

(5)   *All lines:* The same material, elasticity, size and strength.

(6)   *All lines:* Balanced and sharing loads evenly.

(7)   *All lines*: A shorter line will assume greater load bearing than a longer line used in the same service.

Fig 3-233. Example for small ships under 4500 tonnes

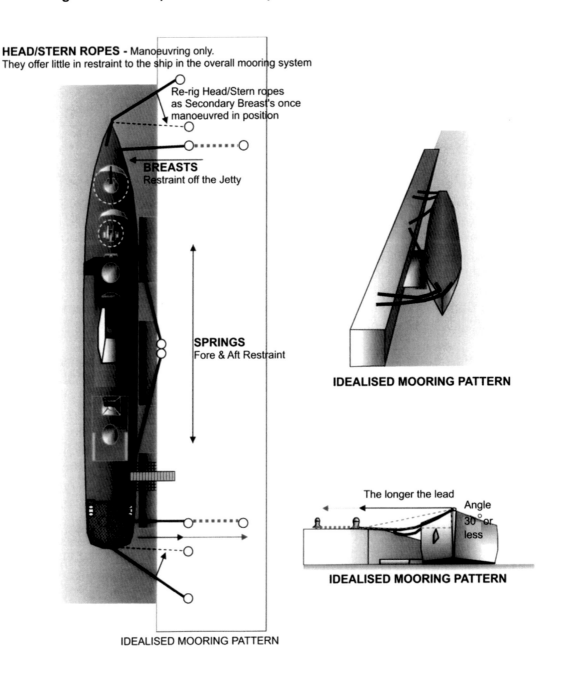

HEAD/STERN ROPES - Manoeuvring only.
They offer little in restraint to the ship in the overall mooring system

Re-rig Head/Stern ropes as Secondary Breast's once manoeuvred in position

BREASTS
Restraint off the Jetty

SPRINGS
Fore & Aft Restraint

IDEALISED MOORING PATTERN

IDEALISED MOORING PATTERN

The longer the lead
Angle 30° or less

IDEALISED MOORING PATTERN

d.   **HPMT – general mooring patterns** (Fig 3-234)

(1)   *Four line system* – most simplistic of mooring patterns

(a)   Two breast reast ropes as perpendicular to the longitudinal centre line of the ship and as far forward and aft as possible.

(b)   Two springs as parallel to the longitudinal centre line of the ship as possible.

(c)   Below with additional head and stern lines deployed as breast ropes.

Fig 3-234. Simplistic of mooring patterns

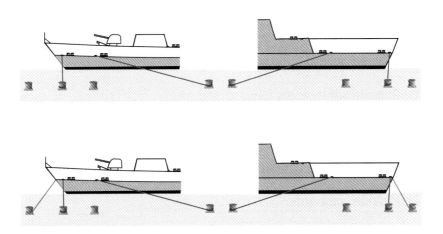

e.   **HPMT – More complex mooring patterns** (Fig 3-235)

(1)   With additional springs/foul weather pendant added – NOT ideal.

(2)   Below with additional springs/foul weather pendant added as more effective due to better matching of angles and rope lengths.

Fig 3-235. More complex mooring patterns

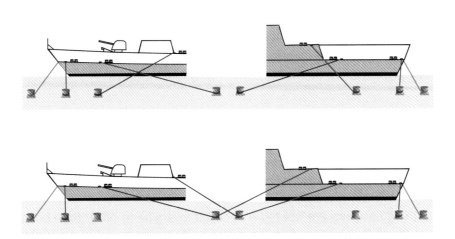

f.   **Material preparations for berthing**. The following preparations must be made before a ship goes alongside:

(1)   Fake out springs, breasts and head and stern ropes.

(2)   Check locking stitching on all berthing hawsers.

(3)   Position fenders ready for use.

(4)   Prepare the brow and its gangway position.

(5)   Rig ensign staff and jackstaff. (Safety Helmets are to be worn, if guardrails are struck then HDLJ, restraint belt/full body harness is to be worn).

(6)   Provide stoppers.

(7)   Make up heaving lines for throwing.

(8)   Provide bollard strop and slip.

(9)   Provide safety tools forward and aft.

(10) Prepare both anchors ready for letting go.

(11) Provide line recovery grapnels.

(12) Provide ratguards.

g.   **Securing alongside**. When a ship goes alongside, the berthing hawsers required for working the ship to her berth will normally be a head rope, a stern rope, one head spring and one back spring, and perhaps two breast ropes. The order in which they will go out depends upon the circumstances, but each berthing hawser required for working the ship should be ready faked for running. Its bollard eye is led out through the correct fairlead, then back inboard where it will be ready for a heaving line to be bent to it by the time the ship is within heaving distance of the jetty. If the capstans are going to be used, it will probably be for breasting the ship in with the breast ropes, or for adjusting her distance along the jetty with the head and stern ropes. When a ship is secured alongside in a tideway, particular attention must be paid to her berthing hawsers as she rises and falls with the tide, and, whenever possible, the hawsers should be so belayed that they can be tended without disturbing another. A berthing hawser may be **doubled up** by a second hawser between ship and shore; such hawsers are usually **singled up** as soon as the brow is removed when the ship is due to unberth. A berthing hawser may also be **rove doubled** when there is nobody on shore to cast it off when the ship unberths. Both ends of the hawser are made fast inboard.

Notes:

1.   The procedure for doubling-up the berthing lines is as follows: heave in the first line on the capstan, pass and turn up the second line, then transfer the first line from the capstan to the bollards. At no point should the ship be held only by a stopper.

2.   Berthing hawsers are not to be secured to anything other than bollards/capstans. cleats or staghorns are not to be used when berthing the ship alongside.

3. Chafing pieces must be correctly positioned at fairleads, bollards and bad nips.

4. Rat/vermin guards must be positioned on all lines when deemed necessary by the Commanding Officer.

h. Fig 3-236 and Fig 3-237 respectively show a fo'c'sle and quarterdeck prepared ready for berthing starboard side to.

Fig 3-236. Foc'sle prepared for berthing starboard side to

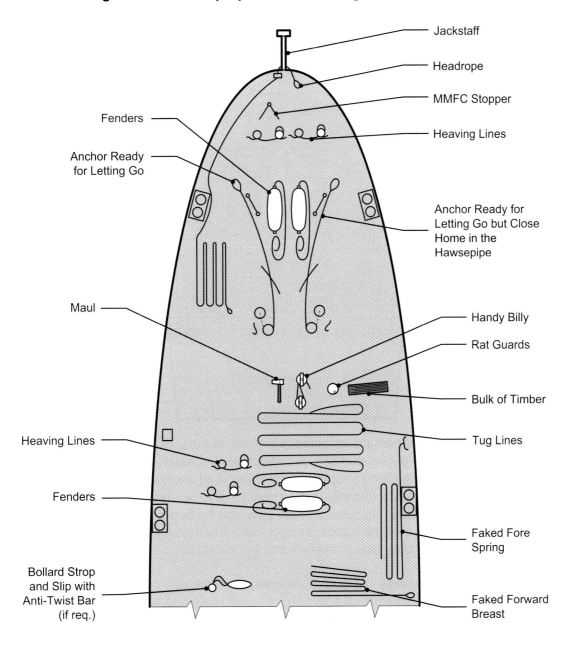

Fig 3-237. Quarterdeck/top prepared for berthing starboard side to

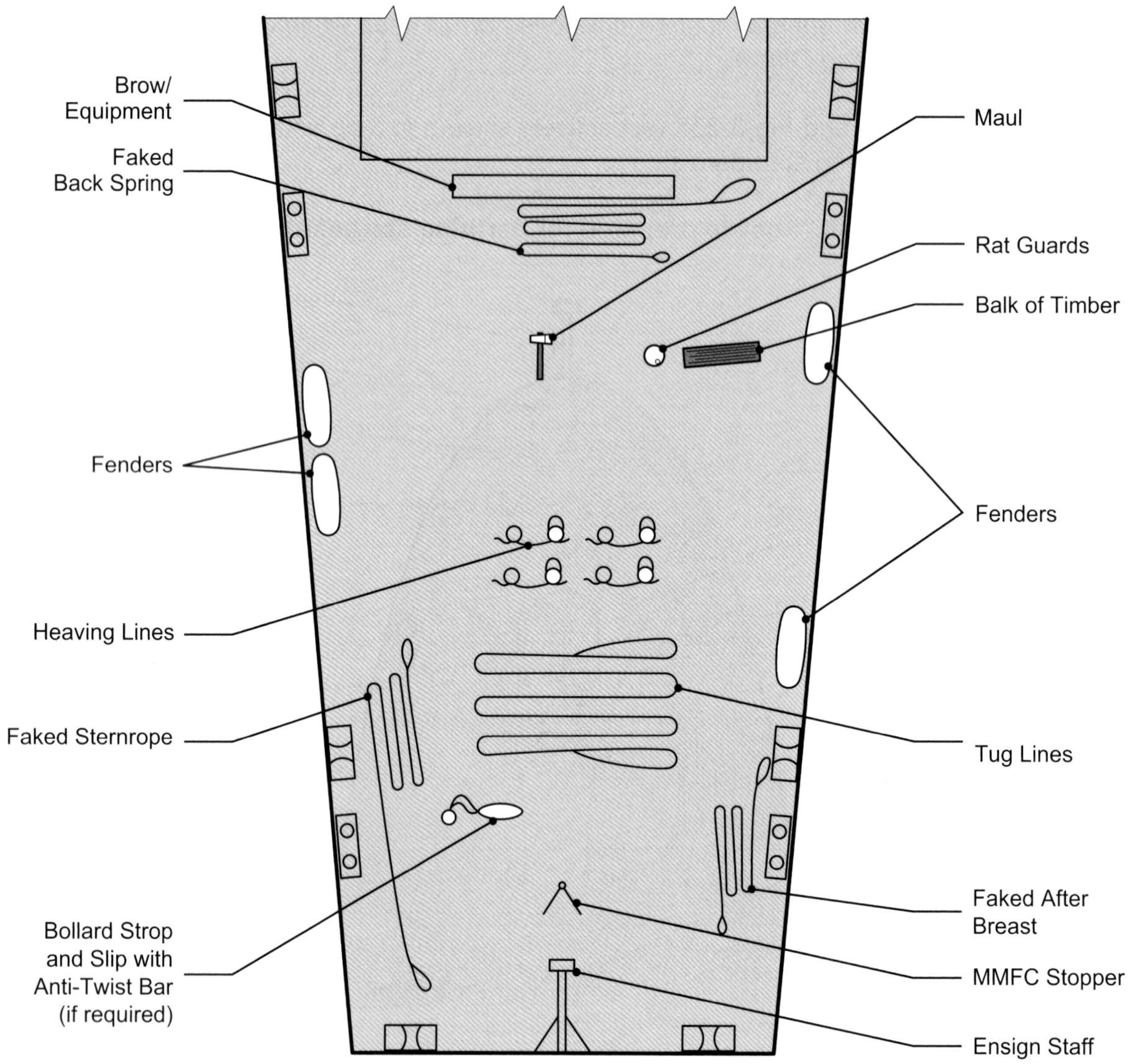

i.   **Casting off**. When a ship leaves a jetty the number of berthing hawsers required will depend upon circumstances, but normally the head and stern ropes and one head and one back spring should suffice. The head and stern ropes may have to be brought to the capstans and the springs may have to be surged. When a ship is being **warped** (moved along the jetty without engines) by berthing hawsers, each hawser should be tended, and the hands tending them should back-up, surge, take down the slack, bring to the capstan, or belay them, as required.

j.   **Off-fast moorings**. At certain exposed berths a ship can be hauled just clear of the berth by using special off-fast or hauling-off moorings laid for this purpose. Each mooring consists of an anchor, a length of chain and a wire, which is normally secured to one of the jetty bollards. On taking up the berth, a ship takes the ends of the wires, brings them through the outboard fairlead, and adjusts the tension in them according to the weather. When properly adjusted, the risk of damage to a ship alongside is much reduced.

k. **On-fast moorings**. At certain exposed berths, usually where the shore bollards or dolphins may not be strong enough to hold a ship in high winds, on-fast or holding-on moorings are provided. Each mooring consists of an anchor, a length of chain and a wire, which is normally secured to one of the bollards. On taking up her berth, a ship takes the ends of the wires, brings them (sometimes the chain as well) through her inboard fairleads and secures them.

l. **Rat and vermin guards for HPMT mooring lines.** When a ship is berthed alongside and the Captain deems there is a risk of rat or vermin infestation, rat and vermin guards are to be placed on all berthing hawsers whether singled or doubled up as soon as the ship is secured. These guards are explained in Annex 3E.

m. **Foul weather pendant and hurricane hawsers.** Heavy duty berthing hawsers provide extra security when a ship is alongside a berth in heavy weather, or alongside a berth where factors such as passing traffic are likely to cause excessive movement of the ship.

(1) *HPMT foul weather hawser.* Is made up using the Foul Weather Pendant and Shock Mitigation Strop (SMS). The SMS is a super strong 2 in 1 Parallay Nylon Rope used extensively within HPMT. The Foul Weather Hawser and Foul Weather Pendant are Quantum 12 and are used for when exposed berths/severe weather berthing is encountered. Foul Weather Pendants are assembled as shown in Fig 3-238. They are to be rigged slightly tauter than the springs that they supplement. The longest tail of the HPMT Spring Hawser goes to the ship and the shortest goes to the jetty.

(2) *Dockyard lines.* (Fig 3-239). These are held and supplied by the dockyard only. Like the Foul Weather Hawser they are to be rigged slightly tauter than the Berthing Hawsers that they supplement so that they are first to come under strain if the ship moves. The shortest tail of the hawser goes to the ship and the long tail is turned up on bollards on the jetty.

n. **Additional shore supplied lines**. The acceptance or use of Shore Supplied Lines has to be carefully weighted and judged as to the benefits that they can offer to the ship. Dockyard supplied lines are a requirement in certain environmental conditions but, will only benefit the ship if they are of correct strength, are rigged correctly and are supporting the ships original Mooring Pattern. Note that Shore Supplied Lines may disrupt the original ship mooring pattern and should be balanced throughout the ship when used. Be aware of the following:

(1) Do not take shore lines if no requirement exists or if the lines offered to the ship are either of inadequate strength, material or condition and/or, they are too strong for the ships fittings.

(2) The ship has her own foul weather pendants that are designed to add additional holding and flexibility to the mooring pattern.

(3) Mooring lines are at their most effective when under reasonable tension – be wary of 'tending' (adjusting) the lines unless absolutely necessary.

(4) Of over-tension within the mooring lines and look for the tell-tale signs of over-tension – fender compression – ship listing – line failure.

(5)   Slack lines within the mooring pattern – this can lead to shock-loading of the ropes and movement within the berth – monitor the movement of the gangway, safety net etc, to judge slack line movement.

(6)   A good, well-balanced mooring pattern will generally counteract any expected environmental force acting upon the ship.

Fig 3-238. HPMT foul weather pendant with shock mitigation strop attached

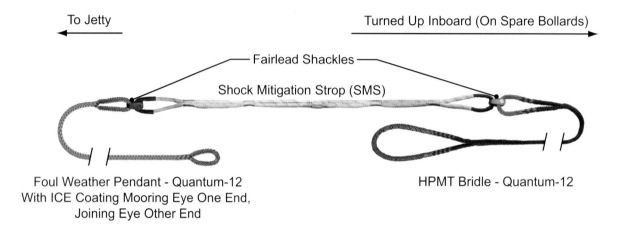

Fig 3-239. Dockyard foul weather line

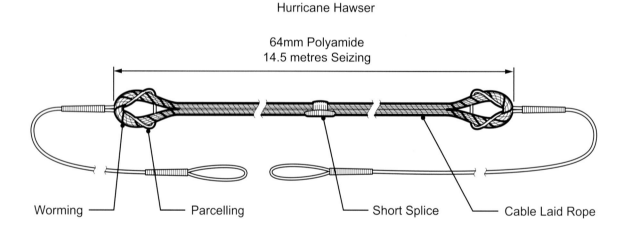

03078. Submarine berthing and slipping

a.   **Personnel.** Berthing and slipping are the most regularly practised seamanship evolutions. These evolutions require the maximum number of participants and form the basis for most other seamanship evolutions. The actual number of personnel in the casing party depends on the class of submarine, the minimum requirements are:

(1)   **VANGUARD CLASS**

Casing Officer - I/C of the casing.
2nd Coxswain - 2 I/C of the casing.
1 x Leading Hand and 2 x Able Rates on the forward casing party.
4 x Able Rates on the missile compartment casing party.
1 x Leading Hand and 2 x Able Rates on the after casing.
1 x Swimmer of the Watch (2nd swimmer dressed and to remain below unless required).

(2)   **TRAFALGAR CLASS**

Casing Officer - I/C of the casing party.
2nd Coxswain - 2 I/C of the casing (I/C After Casing).
2nd Coxswains' Assistant (I/C Forward Casing).
4 x Able Rates on the forward casing party.
4 x Able Rates on the aft casing party.
1 x Swimmer of the Watch (second swimmer on standby).

(3)   **ASTUTE CLASS**

2 x Casing Officers I/c of the casing party (cannot transit around the fin, so one fwd and one aft).
2nd Coxswain 2 I/c of the casing (I/c aft casing).
2nd Coxswains Assistant (I/c fwd casing.
4 x AB on fwd casing party.
4 x AB on aft casing party.
1 x Swimmer of the Watch (second swimmer on standby).

b.   **Equipment.** The following details the minimum equipment that is required by the casing party for entering/leaving harbour.

(1)   **Man overboard equipment**

Casing Keys	Capstan Keys
Casing Screwdrivers	Bollard Keys
Heaving Lines (at least 8)	Casing Bag

(2)   **Contents of the casing bag**

Screwdrivers	Hammer
Adjustable Wrench	Assorted Spanners
Spare Casing Bolts	Spare Drop Nosed Pins for fairleads
Grease Gun	Grease
Torch	Soft Wooden Wedges
Cordage	Rags
Assorted Cable Ties	Gunline
Sharp Knives	Various size spanners
Hacksaw and blades	Cyalume light sticks
Spare Blanks for Fin fixtures	Fox wedges
Spare screws for casing plates	Copper crest (if still available)

Fig 3-240. Typical submarine capstan

c.   **Bollards - Vanguard class.** Vanguard class submarines are fitted with six sets of retractable bollards. They are wound up in a similar fashion to the capstan when required for use and wound down flush with the casing when stowed for sea. Each set is numbered, starting forward and working aft and their positions are as follows:

Ones   A triple set situated on the forward casing adjacent to the fore planes.
Twos   A single set on the centre line aft of the forward escape tower.
Threes   A double set situated aft of the fin.
Fours   A double set aft of the missile casing.
Fives   A single set on the centre line aft of the missile casing.
Sixes   A triple set situated aft of the after escape tower.

Note.   The triple sets forward and aft are designed as towing bollards (although they are also used for berthing) and have a maximum safe pulling load in a forward and aft direction of 75 tonnes. All the other bollards have a maximum safe pulling load of 40 tonnes from any direction.

d.   **Cleats - Trafalgar classes**

(1)   This class of submarine is not fitted with conventional bollards but with hinged cleats (often referred to as bollards). The hinged cleats can be rotated in a forward and aft orientation through 180°. This enables them to be faired off with the casing when not in use. Depending on the modification state of the submarine they are grease or salt water lubricated, the latest being the grease lubricated. At present there is some debate as to the actual loading that the cleats are capable of handling. They are designed to take loads in the horizontal plane only and are liable to damage if the loading angle rises above the horizontal (e.g. when harbour tugs are secured to twos and fours for pulling off the berth). (**Ref BR 45(6) Admiralty Manual of Navigation**). As with the Vanguard Class, each set is referred to by its number, starting forward and working aft. Their positions are as follows:

Ones	A triple set situated aft of the Weapon Loading Trench on the forward casing.
Twos	A single set on the centre line just forward of the fin on the forward casing.
Threes	A single set offset to Port just forward of the ALK buoy doors
Fours	A triple set situated on the after casing in between the engine room hatch and the after capstan.

Note. *Port and starboard hinged cleats are shown in the raised position. The centre line hinged cleats are shown almost in the stowed position but the locking bar has not been applied.*

(2)   The two cleats, which make up one set are locked into position by a rotating bar, which is operated by a key similar to the bollard key. By rotating the locking mechanism, the locking bar can be screwed up or down depending on which way the bollard favours to lock it in either the raised or lowered position. The bar must be locked into position when the cleat is in use, even though the cleat will not turn down with tension upon it. It is possible to rotate the cleat by standing on it, which could cause injury and has caused personnel to fall overboard in the past. When in the stowed position, the locking bar must be screwed tight to prevent the cleats from moving with the flow of water over them and causing a noise short or casing rattle.

Fig 3-241. Typical submarine cleats

e. **Submarine fairlead.** Trafalgar Class submarines are fitted with a fairlead also known as a bullring at the forward and after ends of the casing on the centre line. Vanguard Class submarines are fitted with a centre line fairlead on the forward casing and two fairleads 1 Port and 1 Starboard on the after casing. When required for use the fairleads are turned up through 90° and secured by a large drop-nosed pin. When not required the fairlead is stowed in a self-draining recess that is faired off by a casing plate secured by three casing screws. There is a position for the securing pin to be stowed in the recess but it is normally taken below and stowed in the casing bag along with a spare to minimise the chances of creating a casing rattle should the pin work free when dived.

Fig 3-242. Typical submarine fairleads

f. **Ice rail and 'C' clip.** The Ice Rail is designed to provide an anchor point on the casing for personnel working on the casing in rough weather. It comprises of a recessed 'T' bar, which the ice rail 'C' clips attach to. The clips are attached to a strop by a karabiner Hook which in turn is attached to a safety harness using a second karabiner Hook. The ice rail is designed to take the loading of up to 350kg which is the equivalent of three personnel, two on the casing pulling a third from the water. The disadvantage of this design is that it is extremely difficult to maintain and is prone to failure through corrosion.

Note. *All casing openings and hatches are to be marked with a cyalume light at night and during reduced visibility.*

g.   **Berthing arrangements.** Dutch moor is used when there is a large tidal range on a berth. By using shorter springs this gives greater control.

Fig 3-243. Standard moor

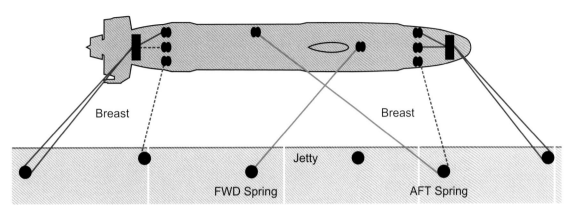

Fig 3-244. Dutch moor

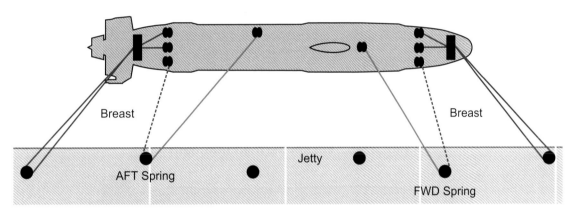

h.   **Precautions associated with berthing submarines:**

(1)   Always stand two metres away from bollards/capstans when working ropes and wires, and never in direct line of recoil (within the snap back zone).

(2)   Always have sleeves buttoned down or rolled up correctly (Irish pennants).

(3)   Never wear any jewellery when working ropes and wires.

(4)   Never pass any working ropes or lines around any part of the body.

(5)   Never straddle ropes or wires.

(6)   Never stand in bites or coils.

(7)   Never stand between ropes and wires and the submarine superstructure.

03079. Submarine berthing – slipping vessels alongside – personnel

a.   The Officer of the day must be piped onto the casing when a vessel is coming alongside. The Duty Senior Rate is to go to the casing and the Duty Leading Hand is to muster the members of the duty watch onto the casing for a briefing.

b.   At least one member of the duty watch should man each bollard with a heaving line. (Each rating is to ensure the berthing rope is passed under the guardrails and the eyes of the ropes are DIPPED through the submarine's ropes).

   (1)   *Equipment*

      Man Overboard Equipment.
      Casing Keys.
      Capstan Keys.
      Heaving Lines (At least one heaving line for each bollard).

      Note.   *Remember to check that external hydraulics is opened up if your capstans are to be used.*

   (2)   *PPE*

      DMS safety boots.
      Correct working rig (as detailed).
      Appropriate headgear.
      Foul weather clothing if required.

Fig 3-245. Vessel berthed outboard

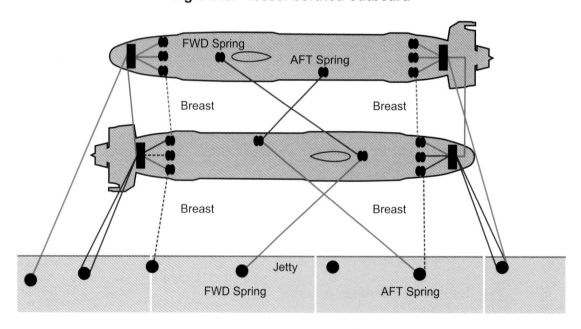

03080. Submarine docking/undocking procedures - personnel

a. **Personnel required**

(1) *VANGUARD CLASS*

Casing Officer I/c of the casing party.
2nd Coxswain 2 I/c of the casing party.
1x Leading Hand and 4x Able Rates on the forward casing party.
4x Able Rates on the missile compartment casing party.
1x Leading Hand and 4 x Able Rates on the after casing.
1x Swimmer of the Watch (second swimmer on standby).

(2) *TRAFALGER CLASS*

Casing Officer I/c of the casing party
2nd Coxswain 2 I/c of the casing (I/c after casing)
2nd Coxswains' Assistant (I/c Forward Casing)
4 x Able Rates on the forward casing party.
4 x Able Rates on the aft casing party.
1 x Swimmer of the Watch (second swimmer on standby).
Civilian riggers/naval qualified.

(3) *ASTUTE CLASS*

2 x Casing Officers I/c of the casing party (cannot transit around the fin, so one fwd and one aft).
2nd Coxswain 2 I/c of the casing (I/c aft casing).
2nd Coxswains Assistant (I/c fwd casing.
4 x AB on fwd casing party.
4 x AB on aft casing party.
1 x Swimmer of the Watch (second swimmer on standby).
Civilian Riggers/naval qualified

Equipment required	PPE required
Man overboard equipment	DMS Boots
Casing keys	Correct working rig (as detailed)
Capstan key	Hazardous duty life jacket
Heaving lines	In data industrial safety helmet
Casing bag	Foul weather clothing if required
Rigging Set	

03081. Submarine emergency casing equipment bag (EMCEB)

a. In the unlikely event of a UK Submarine colliding with a fishing vessel or her trawl there is a requirement for the Submarine to stand by to assist the fishing vessel. This may involve rescue of fishing vessel personnel, the recovery and the clearance of fishing vessel nets and the possible salvage of the vessel. As the submarine will be at Emergency Stations with bulkhead doors shut, access to the second Coxswain's store will be very limited for the duration of the event. Therefore in order for the second Coxswain and his team to be able to man the casing, they must have available casing equipment aft of 29 bulkhead.

The man overboard equipment, stowed on the MAH ladder.
The swimmer of the watch gear stowed in the BWA compartment.
Hazardous duty life jackets, stowed on the MAH ladder.
Harnesses and ice rail clips, stowed in a locker on 59 bulkhead.

b.   The EMCEB is secured in a locked stowage at the main access hatch with a key available in a smash and grab container. All equipment in the EMCEB is painted with an international rescue orange mark for identification. This equipment is not to be used for any other purpose.

c.   **Equipment in the EMCEB**

Casing key	2 x heaving lines
Capstan key	Grapnel hook and line
Bollard key	2 x karabiner Hooks
Axe and chopping block	2 x bow shackles
Crowbar	2 x Straight shackles
Bolt croppers	20 m orange line
Hacksaw and blades	large plastic cable ties (tie wrap)
Large screwdriver	Small plastic cable ties (tie wrap)
Adjustable spanner	2 x rigging sets
2 x hammers	Chisel
Tool bag Roll	
2 x Foul weather jackets	2 x Foul weather trousers
2 x Disposable cameras	4 x Cyalume light sticks and tie wraps
2 x Lifejacket lights	2 x Torches with batteries

The ship's digital camera is also required to take photographic evidence.

d.   All equipment in the EMCEB is to be lightly oiled before being heat-sealed in polythene; the axe and rigging knives are to have a keen edge before stowage. The EMCEB is to be maintained at monthly intervals with the torch batteries changed at this time. If any equipment in the EMCEB is used it is to be replaced or maintained before resealing at the earliest opportunity.

03082. Submarine boat transfer
There are two types of boat transfer (See Fig 3-246, Fig 3-247 and Fig 3-248) depending on the vessel conducting the transfer. This will either be a purpose built transfer vessel such as RMAS Adamant in the Clyde areas, or any other vessel such as a tug; pilot boat; fishing vessel or an inflatable boat. In all cases the concept is similar in that the submarine will rendezvous with the transfer vessel at a predetermined location. Once at the transfer position the submarine will slow down or come to a stop and secure the transfer vessel along side in order to conduct the transfer. In the case of the purpose built transfer vessel a gangway is lowered to the casing and the casing and the personnel and baggage are transferred. For other transfer vessels, the submarine must rig its jumping ladder and personnel transfer via this ladder.

Fig 3-246. SSN conducting a boat transfer

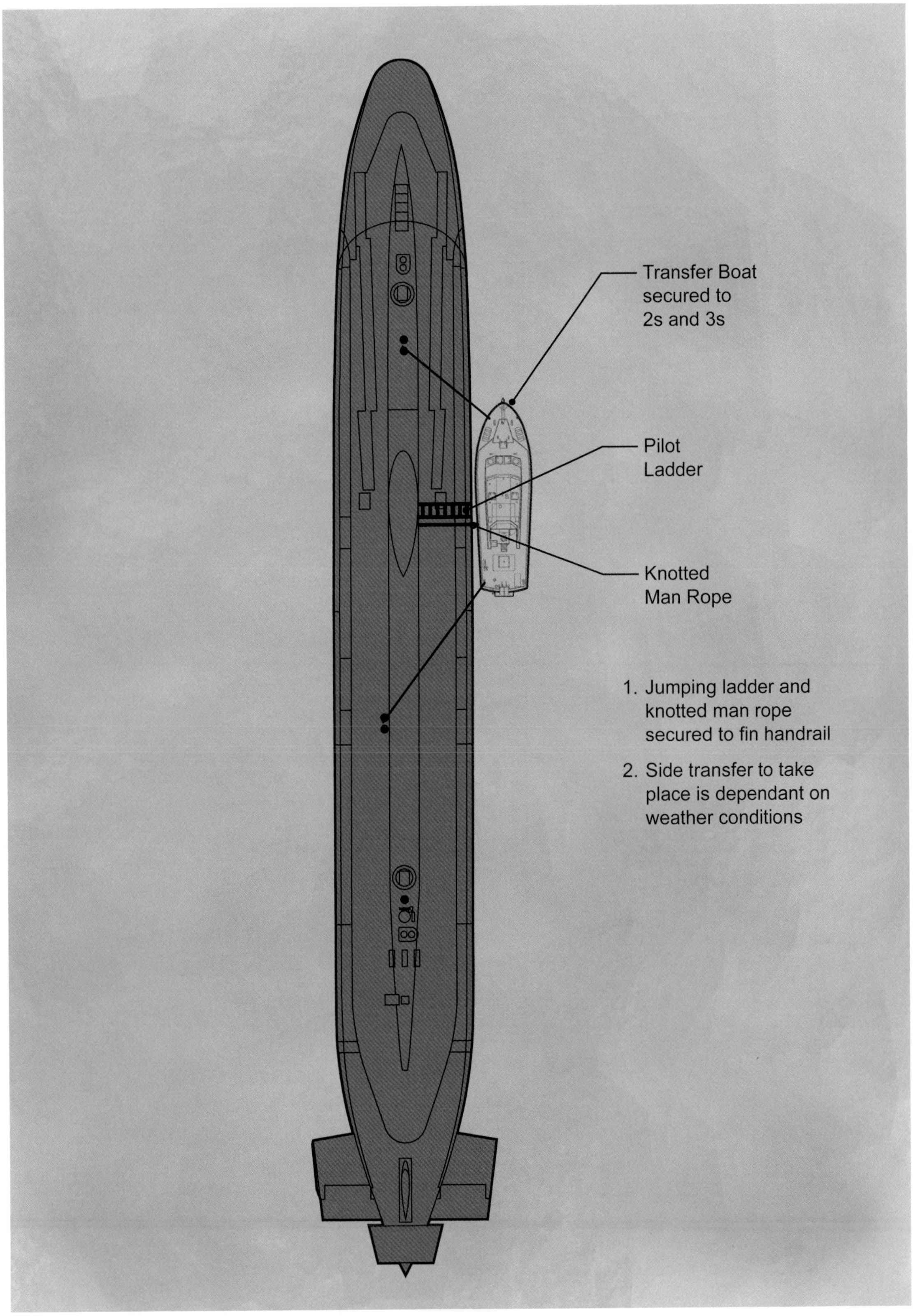

Transfer Boat
secured to
2s and 3s

Pilot
Ladder

Knotted
Man Rope

1. Jumping ladder and
   knotted man rope
   secured to fin handrail

2. Side transfer to take
   place is dependant on
   weather conditions

Fig 3-247. SSBN conducting a boat transfer

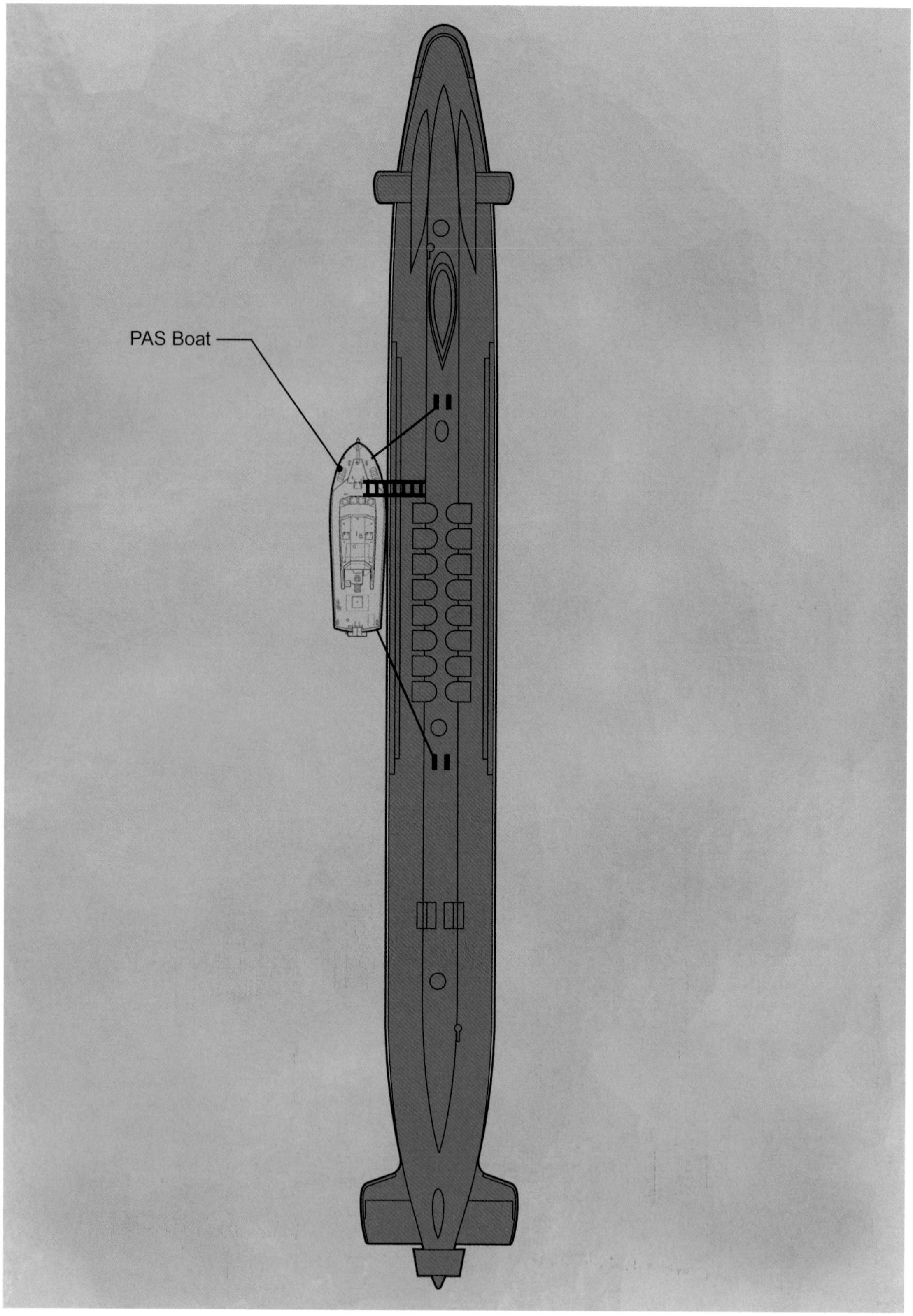

PAS Boat

Fig 3-248. Astute class conducting a boat transfer

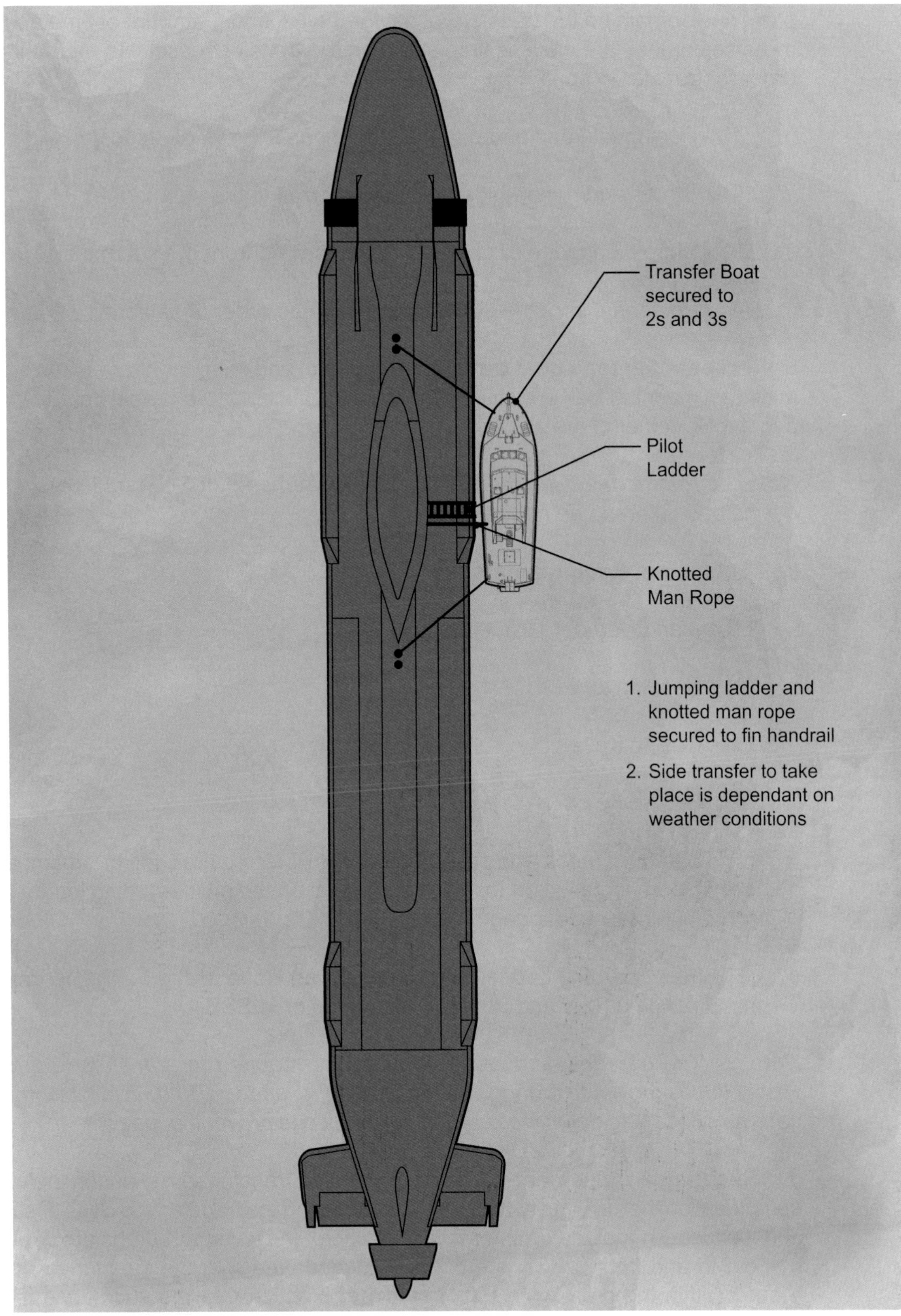

Transfer Boat
secured to
2s and 3s

Pilot
Ladder

Knotted
Man Rope

1. Jumping ladder and
   knotted man rope
   secured to fin handrail

2. Side transfer to take
   place is dependant on
   weather conditions

a. **Order of transfer.** In all transfers the order of proceedings will be the same. This order is dictated by safety concerns and naval tradition. The basic rules are that personnel remain on the transfer vessel for the minimum amount of time and that the more senior they are the less time spent on the transfer vessel. To meet this aim the order for transfer to and from the submarine is:

(1) Personnel transferring to the submarine in order of seniority.

(2) Stores and/or baggage being transferred to the submarine.

(3) Stores; baggage or gash being transferred from the submarine.

(4) Personnel from the submarine in reverse order of seniority.

b. **Preparation for a boat transfer.** Personnel and equipment are made ready. The minimum manning for the casing is the Casing Officer/2nd Coxswain I/c, 3 x Able Rates and the Swimmer of the watch.

Note. *Prior to manning the casing the requirements of SGM 0322 (Access to the casing at sea) are to be adhered to.*

c. **Equipment Requirements are**:

(1) Man Overboard Equipment.

(2) Heaving Lines.

(3) Casing Keys.

(4) Bollard Keys.

(5) Safety harness and restraining lanyard is required for the member of the casing party detailed off to assist personnel on the pilot/boarding ladder and also for transfer stores/baggage.

(6) Pilot/Boarding Ladder and Knotted Man Rope are to be rigged from the fin hand rail on a SSN and from No. 3 bollards on a SSBN.

Note. *The pilot/boarding ladder may not be required for transfers to and from a vessel that is providing a gangway. However the ladder is to be available in case the gangway becomes defective or weather conditions prevent its use.*

d. **Securing arrangements.** The position of the transfer vessel during the transfer is dependant on the size and type of vessel conducting the transfer, the class of submarine and the location that the transfer is taking place. In Devonport, transfers of personnel by boat to and from a SSN are normally undertaken with the submarine moored to a buoy within the breakwater. It is standard practice that the submarine is moored starboard side to and the transfer takes place from the port side of the submarine. The transfer vessel secures alongside the fin with its head rope on No. 2's bollard and the stern rope on No.3's. For SSNs at other locations transferring with vessels other than RMAS Adamant the securing arrangements will be the same using 2's and 3's either side to. When transferring with RMAS Adamant the head rope goes on 2's and the stern rope on 4's, allowing the gangway to be placed on the after casing.

e.   **Safety briefing.** Prior to conducting any transfer of personnel either to or from a submarine a comprehensive briefing to the personnel undertaking the transfer is to take place. This briefing is to be delivered by the person who will be in charge of the casing during the transfer. At the same time he is to ensure that personnel undertaking the transfer are wearing the correct PPE, taking account of current and expected weather conditions/sea state. For personnel departing the submarine safety aspects are to be covered, personnel transferring to the submarine will require coverage of additional security matters (normally given by the coxswain). The briefings are to cover the following areas:

f.   **Safety**

    (1)   The intended sequence of events of the transfer.

    (2)   Route to be taken on the casing by personnel being transferred.

    (3)   Actions to take in the event of an incident or emergency occurring during the transfer.

g.   **Security.** Identification and association of personal baggage to those personnel who are transferring to the submarine, highlight risks of an IED being brought onboard in baggage which has not been packed by the individual or that has been left unattended. Identification of stores/equipment/mail etc to confirm that it is expected and that any packaging/seals are intact and not tampered with.

03083. Submarine – securing a tug alongside

Fig 3-249. Trafalgar class SSN with tug

a.   **Personnel required:**

    (1)   Casing Officer.

    (2)   Second Coxswain.

    (3)   Two members of the casing party per set of bollards that the tug is tying up on.

b. **Equipment required:**

Man overboard equipment   Full set of PPE equipment
Bollard keys   Casing keys
Bollard strop

c. **Procedure for securing a tug.** Captain gives permission for the tug to come alongside. Two members of the casing party per bollard the tug is tying up on. When the tug approaches they will instruct the casing party which bollards they want the ropes to be placed on. The tugs will pass the first ropes to the casing party however the casing party are to have a heaving line ready in case the tug does not reach with the rope. The eye of the rope is placed on the bollards once the first rope is secured the tug will pass the second rope to double up, the casing party are to ensure that the eye is dipped as previously discussed. Another method the tugs may use is a bollard strop and slip they are placed onto the bollards prior to the tug tying up onto the submarine. When the ropes are passed from the tug the ropes are placed into the slip rather than placed onto the bollards. This method is usually used when a more complicated evolution is to be carried out for example going to Loch Goil or going into dock.

03084. Ship movement in dockyards

When ships are being moved by the Dockyard (eg, by tugs or wires, in the charge of a Pilot) certain requirements must be met. These requirements are listed in **BR 9424(1) Fleet Operating Orders Chapter 8 Section 3.**

03085. Designated tug lines

Berthing evolutions require a designated tug line, capable of being rigged easily whilst maintaining their optimum strength characteristics. The use of ship fit berthing hawsers has become unacceptable for the purpose. Therefore, to enable ships to pass standard made up ropes designated for the task; HPMT tug lines are to be used. If there exists a requirement to shorten the tug line to a short lead, then it is to be turned up round bollards and racked. It is imperative that the racking is applied before the weight is taken on the line to avoid the line surging, causing friction and ultimately parting. Cleats or staghorns are not to be used for securing tug lines, also single bollards should have a hawser eye passed over them or use a bollard strop and slip. A tug line should not be tied up on the fitting in a figure-of-eight configuration as this will result in rope or fitting failure due to surging or the load being applied outside of the operational load baring area of the fitting. Designated tug lines are fitted with Blue ICE to provide visual identification of the correct rope being passed.

03086. Seamanship stowages

a. Stowages designated for seamanship equipment are usually only just large enough for their purpose and for this reason it is important that best use is made of the space available by ensuring gear is stowed neatly and logically. A contents board listing all the equipment and compartment layout must be available within the stowage and should be sited adjacent to the access of the compartment, and where necessary individual items of equipment should be tallied to aid identification.

b. **Control of Substances Hazardous to Health (COSHH). JSP 375, Control of Substances Hazardous to Health**, must be consulted and complied with regarding the stowage of substances that may be hazardous to health.

c.   **Acoustic hygiene.** Passive Sonar fitted in modern submarines is able to detect at great ranges noise generated within a ship or other submarines; the process of reducing noise to a minimum within a ship is known as acoustic hygiene. Regarding stowages it involves ensuring that all equipment is stowed securely, and, where necessary, lashed in position. Metal to metal contact should be avoided, and where this is not possible rubber matting should be used to deaden noise.

THIS PAGE IS INTENTIONALLY BLANK

THE NAUTICAL INSTITUTE

ANNEX 3A

SWL BLOCKS IN VARIOUS TACKLE CONFIGURATIONS

MAXIMUM LOAD TO BE LIFTED (TONNES)
(Assuming standing and moving blocks are of the same SWL, and fall is of the required strength)

NATO STOCK No	SWL ON HEAD FITTING (TONNES)	PROOF LOAD (TONNES)	SINGLE WHIP	RUNNER	DOUBLE WHIP (D)	DOUBLE WHIP (A)	LUFF/JIGGER/HANDY BILLY (D)	LUFF/JIGGER/HANDY BILLY (A)
0246/521-2794	1.0	2.0	0.5	1.0				
521-2795	2.0	4.0	1.0	2.0				
190-6915	4.0	8.0	2.0	4.0				
521-0663	2.0	4.0	1.0	2.0				
521-0664	4.0	8.0	2.0	4.0				
521-0665	6.0	12.0	3.0	6.0				
463-3880	0.315	0.63	0.158	0.315				
0246/521-0660	2.0	4.0	1.0	2.0	1.33	2.0	1.5	2.0
521-0661	4.0	8.0	2.0	4.0	2.67	4.0	3.0	4.0
521-06662	6.0	12.0	3.0	6.0	4.0	6.0	4.5	6.0
463-3858	0.375	0.75	0.188	0.375	0.25	0.375	0.28	0.375
521-2797	1.0	2.0	0.5	1.0	0.67	1.0	0.75	1.0
521-2798	2.0	4.0	1.0	2.0	1.33	2.0	1.5	2.0
521-2799	4.0	8.0	2.0	4.0	2.67	4.0	3.0	4.0

Key: (A) – Rigged to Advantage. (D) – Rigged to Disadvantage

SWL BLOCKS IN VARIOUS TACKLE CONFIGURATIONS (Contd.)

MAXIMUM LOAD TO BE LIFTED (TONNES)
(Assuming standing and moving blocks are of the same SWL, and fall is of the required strength)

NATO STOCK No	SWL ON HEAD FITTING (TONNES)	PROOF LOAD (TONNES)	SINGLE WHIP	RUNNER	DOUBLE WHIP (D)	DOUBLE WHIP (A)	LUFF/JIGGER/HANDY BILLY (D)	LUFF/JIGGER/HANDY BILLY (A)
0246/411-9644	0.15	0.3	0.075	0.15	0.10	0.15		
463-3875	2.0	4.0	1.0	2.0	1.33	2.0	1.5	2.0
463-3882	0.5	1.0	0.25	0.5	0.33	0.5		
463-3883	0.5	1.0	0.25	0.5	0.33	0.5	0.375	0.5
463-3884	0.5	1.0	0.25	0.5	0.33	0.5		
463-3885	0.5	1.0	0.25	0.5	0.33	0.5		
463-3891	12.0	24.0	6.0	12.0	8.0	12.0	9.0	12.0
525-0092	0.169	0.337	0.169	0.085	0.113	0.169		
0579/539-4691	1.0	2.0	0.5	1.0		1.0		
539-4693	4.0	8.0	2.0	4.0	0.67			
539-4694	1.0	2.0	0.5	1.0				

(SINGLE WHIP – 1 Sheave; RUNNER – 1 Sheave; DOUBLE WHIP (D) – 1 Sheave, 1 Sheave; DOUBLE WHIP (A) – 1 Sheave, 1 Sheave; LUFF/JIGGER/HANDY BILLY (D) – 2 Sheave, 1 Sheave)

Key: (A) – Rigged to Advantage. (D) – Rigged to Disadvantage

SWL BLOCKS IN VARIOUS TACKLE CONFIGURATIONS (Contd.)

MAXIMUM LOAD TO BE LIFTED (TONNES)
(Assuming standing and moving blocks are of the same SWL, and fall is of the required strength)

NATO STOCK No	SWL ON HEAD FITTING (TONNES)	PROOF LOAD (TONNES)	LUFF/JIGGER/HANDY BILLY (D)	LUFF/JIGGER/HANDY BILLY (A)	TWO-FOLD PURCHASE (D)	TWO-FOLD PURCHASE (A)	3X2 PURCHASE (D)	3X2 PURCHASE (A)
0246/463-3860	0.65	1.3	0.488	0.65	0.52	0.65	0.54	0.65
463-3870	1.75	3.5	1.313	1.75	1.4	1.75	1.458	1.75
463-3876	0.5	1.0	0.375	0.5	0.4	0.5	0.417	0.5
463-3878	1.0	2.0	0.75	1.0	0.8	1.0		
463-3881	0.5	1.0	0.375	0.5	0.4	0.5		
0246/521-2791	1.0	2.0	0.75	1.0	0.8	1.0	0.83	1.0
521-2792	2.0	4.0	1.5	2.0	1.6	2.0	1.67	2.0
521-2793	4.0	8.0	3.0	4.0	3.2	4.0	3.33	4.0
441.9645	0.15	0.3	0.113	0.15	0.12	0.15		
525-0093	0.228	0.456	0.171	0.228	0.182	0.182		
0579/539-9821	1.0	2.0	0.75	1.0	0.8	1.0	0.83	1.0

Key: (A) – Rigged to Advantage. (D) – Rigged to Disadvantage

SWL BLOCKS IN VARIOUS TACKLE CONFIGURATIONS (Contd.)

MAXIMUM LOAD TO BE LIFTED (TONNES)
(Assuming standing and moving blocks are of the same SWL, and fall is of the required strength)

NATO STOCK No	SWL ON HEAD FITTING TONNES	PROOF LOAD TONNES	3X2 PURCHASE (D)	3X2 PURCHASE (A)	THREE-FOLD PURCHASE (D)	THREE-FOLD PURCHASE (A)
0246/521-2725	1.0	2.0	0.83	1.0	0.86	1.0
521-2726	2.0	4.0	1.67	2.0	1.71	2.0
521-2727	4.0	8.0	3.33	4.0	3.43	4.0
525-0094	0.342	0.684	0.285	0.342		

Key: (A) – Rigged to Advantage. (D) – Rigged to Disadvantage

ANNEX 3B

SAFE SYSTEM OF WORK LIFT PLAN

References:

A.   Lifting operations and lifting equipment regulations 1998 (loler 1998)
B.   BR 3027 (1) and (2)
C.   AP 119K-001-01

Give a brief description of the lifting operation and any associated tasks:

....

....

Supervisor:		Name:		Date:	
Assessments:					
Risk:		Serial Number:		Tag out:	
Manual Handling		Serial Number:		Ship Haz:	
Load Characteristics (to be lifted)	Size	Weight*	Shape	Lifting Points Type	Lift Points (qty)
	Moveable contents	Rigid/Fragile contents	Contents security	Headroom available	Centre of Gravity

* Where the Weight or C of G cannot be determined from Markings or Manifests: It may need to be estimated

Environmental Conditions	Location	Lighting	Wind/Tide	Sloping Ground	Ground Strength ok
	Stable Ground	Chemicals Present	Hazardous Equipment	Overhead Obstructions	Lightening Risk
Selection of Lifting Equipment (LE)	Crane Type	Hoist Type	Other Lifting Device (specify)	LE Portable Appliance)s)	Appliance Max SWL
	Accessories Required	Accessories Type	Accessories Qty	Accessories Weight	Weight of 'below hook' LE
Lifting Operation	LE pre Use Check(s)	LE Post Use Check	Guide Ropes Required	Crane/Hoist Sufficient Capacity	Hazards & Obstructions Noted
	Load Free to Lift	Rout Clear	Safety Brief	Agreed Crane Signals to be used	Personnel Required

Responsible Person:	**Slinger (if different):**
Name:.......................Rate/Rank..................	Name:.......................Rate/Rank..................
Signature:...................Date:....................	Signature:...................Date:....................

Special considerations/conditions

Load weight – taken from technical document/manifest/identity plate or estimate

Sling attachment method	Lifting equipment required (approx): (should include swl, length, quantity)

The lift operation setup (photo or sketch)

Total Weight of Load: (including 'below hook LE)	SWL of LE as Rigged on load:	Lifting Capacity of Machine (including any Limits)

Note.   *Complex lifting operations may call for more information to be sought and considered.*

THIS PAGE IS INTENTIONALLY BLANK

ANNEX 3C

SEAMANSHIP EQUIPMENT RECORD SHEET

1.   This Record Sheet is to be completed and retained within the POS Seamanship Log for the in use life of the equipment.

2.   All items of mooring equipment are to have an individual Record Sheet recording details as laid out below.

3.   Before and after surveys are to be recorded on all occasions.

	Comments
Employment ie Head Stern Spring	
Date brought into service	
Stowage	
Certificate of Conformity No	
Local ID No	
Date of First use	

Date of use	**Comments**

Seamanship equipment record sheet (cont'd)

Date of use	Comments

ANNEX 3D

HPMT – SHIPS OUTFIT

Table 3d-1. Hpmt – lpd complete outfit

Product	Size	Uom	Designation	Finished length	Length to make	Make-up	Finished quantity per platform	Total uom
Quantum-12 Black	30Mm dia. Sbl: 53.5 T	Lg	Berthing lines 4020-99-236-1944	200 M	212 M	2M protected mooring eye each end	8 Plus 3 spare	11
Quantum-12 Lime green	32Mm dia. Sbl: 59.5 t	Lg	Picking-up-rope (pur) 4020-99-498-9325	140 M	155 M	St/st thimble eye one end. Pur pendant & hook other end.	1	1
Quantum-12 Black	24Mm dia. Sbl: 53.9 T	Ea	Picking-up-rope pendant 4020-99-471-5118	6 M	-		1	1
Amsteel-blue Lime green	40Mm dia. Sbl: 116 t	Lg	Towing hawser 4020-99-423-1765	200 M	212 M	700Mm served & protected eye each end	1	1
Superstrong parallay nylon	56Mm dia. Sbl: 109 t	Lg	Shock mitigation strop (sms) 4020-99-958-4205	9 M	22 M	Strop configured and served for use with bridles and tow	4	4

PRODUCT	SIZE	UoM	DESIGNATION	FINISHED LENGTH	LENGTH TO MAKE	MAKE-UP	Finished quantity per Platform	TOTAL UoM
Polyester strop P7 pendant	48Mm Sbl: 68.6 T	Ea	Shock mitigation pendant (smp) 4020-99-813-1957	11 M	-	Pendant with 1m & 2m protected mooring eyes. Multi buoy mooring use aft with berthing hawsers	2	2
Quantum-12 black	44Mm dia. Sbl: 109 t	Lg	Bridles/ foul weather pennant/tug assist lines 4020-99-151-5454	110 M	122 M	2M protected mooring eye each end	4	4
Quantum-12 black	44Mm dia. Sbl: 109 t	Lg	Foul weather pendant 4020-99-324-0219	9 M	17 M	2M protected mooring eye one end, 700mm eye other end	2	2
Quantum-12 black	30Mm dia. Sbl: 85.6 T	Ea	Bollard strop, 2.0M 4020-99-739-3890	2 M	8 M	Protected strop configured with thimble and serving	4	4
Mainbrace gard chafe protection for picking up rope	Medium	Ea	Picking-up-rope (pur) 4030-99-846-0641	10 M	11 M	Spliced to 'slip' part of pur	1	1
Stainless steel fairlead shackle	M 120 *Swl: 60 t	Ea	Joining shackle for ropes 4030-99-151-5477	-	-	-	-	8

PRODUCT	SIZE	UoM	DESIGNATION	FINISHED LENGTH	LENGTH TO MAKE	MAKE-UP	Finished quantity per Platform	TOTAL UoM
Buffer's toothbrush st/st tool	Large	Ea	Tool for adjusting fairlead shackle 4030-99-813-1451	-	-	-	-	2
Quantum-12 black	48Mm dia. Sbl: 142 t	Ea	Towing bollard pendant 4020-99-974-2958	8.85 M	19 M	700Mm protected eye each end	1	1
Quantum-12 black	48Mm dia. Sbl: 142 t	Ea	Towing chafe piece 4020-99-524-0748	8 M	16 M	700Mm protected eye with mainbrace gard coating	1	1
Amsteel-blue hmpe with braided jacketed	9Mm Sbl: 8.0 T	Ea	Larne target chafe pendant 6920-99-277-9509	6.5M	8.6 M	St/st thimble eye each end with 3 shock compensators fitted.	1	1
Mooring gard	Size: c	Ea	Hook & loop coated hmpe Chafe protectors 1.5M 4020-99-361-3086	-	-	4 Fitted per berthing hawser – 1 fitted per bridle – 2 fitted on pur	-	28
Splicing tool kit	Medium	Ea	Complete 5120-99-741-2439	-	-	-	-	4

PRODUCT	SIZE	UoM	DESIGNATION	FINISHED LENGTH	LENGTH TO MAKE	MAKE-UP	Finished quantity per Platform	TOTAL UoM
Tech-12 black	14Mm	Ea	Mooring line stopper 4020-99-848-1374	3 M	-	2 Leg stopper with st/st thimble	-	5
Quantum-12 Black	30Mm Sbl 53.5T Obl 140t	Ea	Securing to buoy strop 4020-99-396-2657	9 M	-	Securing to buoy strop method	-	6
Mainbrace ice chafe protection for eyes	Size medium Grey	Lg	Spare eyes protection 4020-99-838-3714	-	23 M	Spare carried onboard for all mooring eyes	-	2
Mainbrace ice chafe protection for eyes	Size medium Blue	Lg	Spare eyes protection 4020-99-581-6606	-	23M	Spare carried onboard for bridles/ foul weather pennant /tug assist lines	-	2

Table 3D-2. HPMT – LPH COMPLETE OUTFIT

PRODUCT	SIZE	UoM	DESIGNATION	FINISHED LENGTH	LENGTH TO MAKE	MAKE-UP	Finished quantity per Platform	TOTAL UoM
Quantum-12 Black	32Mm dia. Sbl: 59.5 T	Lg	Berthing lines 4020-99-813-1955	200 M	212 M	2M protected mooring eye each end	6 Plus 3 spares	9
Amsteel-blue Lime green	40Mm dia. Sbl: 116 t	Lg	Towing hawser 4020-99-423-1765	200 M	212 M	700Mm served & leathered eye each end	1	1
Quantum-12 Lime green	32Mm dia. Sbl: 59.5 T	Lg	Picking-up-rope (pur) 4020-99-498-9325	140 M	152 M	St/st thimble eye one end. Pur pendant & hook other end.	1	1
Quantum-12 Black	24Mm dia. Sbl: 53.9 T	Ea	Picking-up-rope pendant 4020-99-471-5118	6 M	-		1	1
Superstrong parallay nylon	56Mm dia. Sbl: 109 t	Lg	Shock mitigation strop (sms) 4020-99-958-4205	9 M	22 M	Strop configured and served	4	4
Polyester strop P7 pendant	48Mm Sbl: 68.6 T	Ea	Shock mitigation pendant (smp) 4020-99-813-1957	11 M	-	Pendant with 1m & 2m protected mooring eyes. Multi buoy mooring use - aft	2	2
Quantum-12 black	44Mm dia. Sbl: 109 t Mbl: 120 t	Lg	Bridles/ foul weather pennant/tug assist lines 4020-99-151-5454	110 M	122 M	2M protected mooring eye each end	4	4
Quantum-12 black	44Mm dia. Sbl: 109 t Mbl: 120 t	Lg	Foul weather pendant 4020-99-324-0219	9 M	17 M	2M protected mooring eye one end, 700mm eye other end	2	2

PRODUCT	SIZE	UoM	DESIGNATION	FINISHED LENGTH	LENGTH TO MAKE	MAKE-UP	Finished quantity per Platform	TOTAL UoM
Quantum-12 black	30Mm dia. Sbl: 85.6 T	Ea	Bollard strop, 2.0M 4020-99-739-3890	2 M	8 M	Protected strop configured with thimble and serving	4	4
Mainbrace gard chafe protection for picking up rope	Medium	Lg	Picking-up-rope (pur)	10 M	11 M	Spliced to 'slip' part of pur	1	1
Stainless steel fairlead shackle	M 120 Swl: 60 t	Ea	Joining shackle for ropes 4030-99-151-5477	-	-	-	-	8
Buffer's toothbrush st/st tool	Large	Ea	Tool for adjusting fairlead shackle 4030-99-813-1451	-	-	-	-	2
Quantum-12 black	48Mm dia. Sbl: 142 t	Ea	Towing bollard pendant 4020-99-974-2958	11 M	19 M	700Mm protected eye each end	1	1
Quantum-12 black	48Mm dia. Sbl: 142 t	Ea	Towing chafe piece 4020-99-524-0748	8 M	16 M	700Mm protected eye with gard coating	1	1
Mooring gard	Size: c	Ea	Hook & loop coated hmpe Chafe protectors 1.5M 4020-99-361-3086	-	-	4 Fitted per berthing hawser – 1 fitted per bridle – 2 fitted on pur	-	28
Splicing tool kit	Medium	Ea	Complete 5120-99-741-2439	-	-	-	-	4

PRODUCT	SIZE	UoM	DESIGNATION	FINISHED LENGTH	LENGTH TO MAKE	MAKE-UP	Finished quantity per Platform	TOTAL UoM
Tech-12 black	14Mm	Ea	Mooring line stopper 4020-99-848-1374	3 M		2 Leg stopper with st/st thimble		6
Quantum-12 Black	30Mm Sbl 53.5T Obl 140t	Ea	Securing to buoy strop 4020-99-396-2657	9 M		Securing to buoy strop method		5
Mainbrace ice chafe protection for eyes	Size medium Grey	Lg	Spare eyes protection 4020-99-838-3714	-	23 M	Spare carried onboard for all mooring eyes		2
Mainbrace ice chafe protection for eyes	Size medium Blue	Lg	Spare eyes protection 4020-99-581-6606		23 M	Spare carried onboard for bridles/foul weather pennant/ tug assist lines		2
Amsteel-blue hmpe with braided jacketed	9Mm Sbl: 8.0 T	Ea	Larne target chafe pendant 6920-99-277-9509	6.5M	8.6 M	St/st thimble eye each end with 3 shock compensators fitted.	1	1

Table 3D-3. HPMT – T45 COMPLETE OUTFIT

PRODUCT	SIZE	UoM	DESIGNATION	FINISHED LENGTH	LENGTH TO MAKE	MAKE-UP	Finished quantity per Platform	TOTAL UoM
Quantum-12 Black	30Mm dia.	Lg	Breast lines 4020-99-151-5474	85 M	97 M	2.0M protected mooring eye each end	2	2
Quantum-12 Black	30Mm dia.	Lg	Head, stern & springs 4020-99-344-3899	140 M	152 M	2.0M protected mooring eye each end	4 Plus 3 spares	7
Quantum-12 Lime green	30Mm dia.	Lg	Picking-up- rope (pur) 4020-99-670-5380	140 M	152 M	Protected mooring eye each end	1	1
Amsteel-blue Lime green	36Mm dia.	Lg	Towing hawser 4020-99-213-4270	180 M	192 M	700Mm served & leathered eye each end	1	1
Superstrong parallay nylon	48Mm dia.	Lg	Shock mitigation strop (sms) 4020-99-379-2057	9 M	22 M	Strop configured and served	4	4
Quantum-12 black	40Mm dia.	Lg	Bridles/foul weather pennant/ tug assist lines 4020-99-246-6443	85 M	97 M	2.0M protected mooring eye each end	4	4
Quantum-12 black	40Mm dia.	Lg	Foul weather pennant pendant 4020-99-302-1215	9 M	17 M	2.0M protected mooring eye one end, 700mm eye other end	2	2

PRODUCT	SIZE	UoM	DESIGNATION	FINISHED LENGTH	LENGTH TO MAKE	MAKE-UP	Finished quantity per Platform	TOTAL UoM
Quantum-12 black	30Mm dia.	Ea	Bollard strop, 2.0M 4020-99-739-3890	2 M	8 M	Protected strop	3	3
Mainbrace gard chafe protection for picking up rope	Medium 'C'	Lg	Picking-up-rope (pur) 4030-99-173-1091	10 M	11 M	Spliced to 'slip' part of pur	1	1
Quantum-12 Black	24Mm dia.	Ea	Pur pendant 4020-99-471-5118	3 M	10 M	Strop configured with st/st tubular thimble and pu coated areas	1	1
Stainless steel fairlead shackle	M 120	Ea	Joining shackle for ropes 4030-99-151-5477	-	-	-	-	4
Buffer's toothbrush st/st tool	Large	Ea	Tool for adjusting fairlead shackle 4030-99-813-1451	-	-	-	-	2
Turbo-75 black	34Mm	Ea	Bow dome anchoring pendant 4020-99-551-8502	9 M	17 M	Thimble eye one end, joining eye other end. Pu coated areas	1	1
Mooring gard	Size: c	Ea	Hook & loop coated hmpe Chafe protectors 4020-99-361-3086	-	-	-	-	28

PRODUCT	SIZE	UoM	DESIGNATION	FINISHED LENGTH	LENGTH TO MAKE	MAKE-UP	Finished quantity per Platform	TOTAL UoM
Splicing tool kit	Medium	Ea	Complete 5120-99-741-2439	-	-	-	-	4
Quantum-12 Black	30Mm Sbl 53.5T Obl 140t	Ea	Securing to buoy strop 4020-99-396-2657		9 M	Securing to buoy strop method		5
Mainbrace ice chafe protection for eyes	Size medium Grey	Lg	Mooring eyes protection 4020-99-838-3714	-	23 M	Spare carried onboard for all mooring eyes		2
Mainbrace ice chafe protection for eyes	Size medium Blue	Lg	Bridle eye chafe protection 4020-99-581-6606		23 M	Spare carried onboard for bridle/tug assist		2
Tech-12 black	14Mm	Ea	Mooring line stopper 4020-99-848-1374		3 M	2 Leg stopper with st/st thimble		6

Table 3D-4. HPMT – T23 COMPLETE OUTFIT

PRODUCT	SIZE MBL (Spliced)	UoM	DESIGNATION	FINISHED LENGTH	LENGTH TO MAKE	MAKE-UP	Finished quantity per Platform	TOTAL UoM
Quantum-12 Black	24Mm dia. 37.4 T	Lg	Breast lines 4020-99-983-1426	80 M	92 M	2M protected mooring eye each end	2	2
Quantum-12 Black	24Mm dia. 37.4 T	Lg	Head, stern & springs 4020-99-613-4713	130 M	142 M	2M protected mooring eye each end	4 Plus 3 Spare	7
Quantum-12 Lime green	24Mm dia. 37.4 T	Lg	Picking-up- rope (pur) 4020-99-865-9147	130 M	142 M	2M protected mooring eye each end	1	1
Amsteel-blue Lime green	32Mm dia 83.6 T.	Lg	Towing hawser 4020-99-687-2666	180 M	192 M	700Mm served & leathered eye each end	1	1
Superstrong parallay nylon	44Mm dia. 48.5 T (77.6 T)	Lg	Shock mitigation strop (sms) 4020-99-373-9951	8 M	20 M	Strop configured and served	4	4
Quantum-12 black	30Mm dia. 59.4 T	Lg	Bridles/foul weather pennant/tug assist lines 4020-99-246-1912	73 M	85 M	2M protected mooring eye each end	4	4
Quantum-12 black	30Mm dia. 59.4 T	Lg	Foul weather pendant 4020-99-895-9957	9 M	17 M	2M protected mooring eye one end, 700mm eye other end	2	2
Quantum-12 black	24Mm dia. 37.4 T (59.8 T)	Ea	Bollard strop, 1.8M 4020-99-219-8126	1.8 M	7 M	Protected strop configured with thimble and serving	3	3

PRODUCT	SIZE MBL (Spliced)	UoM	DESIGNATION	FINISHED LENGTH	LENGTH TO MAKE	MAKE-UP	Finished quantity per Platform	TOTAL UoM
Mainbrace gard chafe protection for picking up rope	Size d	Lg	Picking-up-rope (pur) 4020-99-891-0799	10 M	10 M	Sliding protection for 'slip-rope' part of pur	1	1
Quantum-12 Black	24Mm dia. 37.4 T (59.84 T)	Ea	Pur pendant 4020-99-696-1091	3 M	10 M	Strop configured with st/st tubular thimble and pu coated areas	1	1
Stainless steel fairlead shackle	M 90	Ea	Joining shackle for ropes 4020-99-958-4133	-	-	-	-	8
Buffer's toothbrush st/st tool	Medium	Ea	Tool for adjusting fairlead shackle 4030-99-316-9347	-	-	-	-	2
Turbo-75 black	34Mm 83.9 T	Ea	Bow dome anchoring pendant 4020-99-551-8501	7 M	12 M	Thimble eye one end, joining eye other end. Pu coated areas	1	1
Mooring gard	Size: b	Ea	Hook & loop coated hmpe Chafe protectors 1.5M 4020-99-151-6871	-	-	4 Fitted per berthing hawser – 1 fitted per bridle – 1 fitted on pur	-	27
Larne target chafe piece	9Mm 8.9 T	Ea	Larne target chafe piece 6920-99-277-9509	5.5 M	-	St/st thimble eye each end with 3 x shock compensators fitted	-	1

PRODUCT	SIZE MBL (Spliced)	UoM	DESIGNATION	FINISHED LENGTH	LENGTH TO MAKE	MAKE-UP	Finished quantity per Platform	TOTAL UoM
Tech-12 black	14Mm	Ea	Mooring line stopper 4020-99-848-1374	3 M		2 Leg stopper with st/st thimble		6
Quantum-12 Black	24Mm Sbl 33.7T Obl 89t	Ea	Securing to buoy strop 4020-99-501-4988	7 M				5
Splicing tool kit	Medium	Ea	Complete 5120-99-741-2439	-	-	-	-	4
Mainbrace ice chafe protection for eyes	Size small Grey	Lg	Spare eyes protection 4020-99-359-6081	-	23 M	Spare carried onboard for all mooring eyes		2
Mainbrace ice chafe protection for eyes	Size small Blue	Lg	Spare eyes protection 4020-99-235-5365		23 M	Spare carried onboard for bridles/spring hawsers/tug assist lines		2

Table 3D-5. HPMT – HUNT CLASS COMPLETE OUTFIT

PRODUCT	SIZE	UoM	DESIGNATION	FINISHED LENGTH	LENGTH TO MAKE	MAKE-UP	Finished quantity per Platform	TOTAL UoM
Quantum-12 Black	22Mm dia. 28.4 T	Lg	Breast lines Nsn 4020-99-219-8143	60 M	70 M	2M protected mooring eye each end	2	2
Quantum-12 Black	22Mm dia. 28.4 T	Lg	Head, stern & springs 4020-99-380-7053	100 M	110 M	2M protected mooring eye each end	4 Plus 3 Spare	7
Quantum-12 Lime green	22Mm dia. 28.4 T	Lg	Picking-up- rope (pur) 4020-99-667-5586	100 M	110 M	St/st thimble eye one end. Pur pendant & hook other end.	1	1
Quantum-12 black	22Mm 28.4 T	Ea	Picking-up- rope pendant 4020-99-813-1436	5 M	12 M		1	1
Amsteel-blue Lime green	22Mm dia. 41.2 T	Lg	Towing hawser 4020-99-434-4829	150 M	160 M	700Mm served & leathered eye each end	1	1
Superstrong parallay nylon	32Mm dia. 25.4 T (40.1 T)	Lg	Shock mitigation strop (sms) 4020-99-273-0329	5 M	13 M	-	4	4
Quantum-12 black	28Mm dia. 47.6 T	Lg	Bridles/foul weather pennant/ tug assist lines 4020-99-707-5400	60 M	70 M	2M protected mooring eye each end	4	4

PRODUCT	SIZE	UoM	DESIGNATION	FINISHED LENGTH	LENGTH TO MAKE	MAKE-UP	Finished quantity per Platform	TOTAL UoM
Quantum-12 black	28Mm dia. 47.6 T	Lg	Foul weather pendant 4020-99-340-8756	6 M	14 M	2M protected mooring eye one end, 700mm sleeved eye other end	2	2
Quantum-12 black	20Mm dia. 21.5 T	Ea	Bollard strop, 1.8M 4020-99-257-8381	1.8 M	7 M	Protected strop configured with thimble and serving	2	2
Mainbrace gard chafe protection for picking up rope	Size c	Ea	Picking-up-rope (pur) 4020-99-813-2480	10 M	11 M	Spliced to 'slip' part of pur	1	1
Stainless steel fairlead shackle M90	M 90	Ea	Joining shackle for ropes 4020-99-958-4133	-	-	-	-	8
Buffer's toothbrush st/st tool	M 90	Ea	Tool for adjusting fairlead shackles 4030-99-316-9347	-	-	-	-	2
Mooring gard	Size: b	Ea	Hook & loop coated hmpe Chafe protectors 1.5M 4020-99-151-6871	-	-	4 Fitted per berthing hawser – 1 fitted per bridle – 1 fitted on pur	-	27
Mainbrace ice chafe protection for mooring eyes	Size small Grey	Lg	Spare eyes protection 4020-99-359-6081	-	23 M		Spare carried onboard for all mooring eyes	2

PRODUCT	SIZE	UoM	DESIGNATION	FINISHED LENGTH	LENGTH TO MAKE	MAKE-UP	Finished quantity per Platform	TOTAL UoM
Mainbrace ice chafe protection for eye	Size small Blue	Lg	Spare eyes protection 4020-99-235-5365	-	23 M		Spare carried onboard for bridles/ foul weather pennant/tug assist lines	2
Quantum-12 Black	20Mm Sbl 20.5T Obl 49.2T	Ea	Securing to buoy strop 4020-99-471-7501	-	7 M		Securing to buoy strop method	5
Tech-12 black	14Mm	Ea	Mooring line stopper 4020-99-848-1374	-	3 M		2 Leg stopper with st/st thimble	6
Quantum-12 Black	28Mm Sbl 42.9T	Ea	Towing bollard pendant 4020-99-384-7681	-	7 M		Bollard pendant	1
Quantum-12 Black	28Mm Sbl 42.9T	Ea	Towing chafe pendant 4020-99-170-5802	-	4.5 M		Towing chafe pendant	1
Splicing tool kit	Medium	Ea	Complete 5120-99-589-8553	-	-	-	-	4

Table 3D-6. HPMT – SANDOWN CLASS COMPLETE OUTFIT

PRODUCT	SIZE	UoM	DESIGNATION	FINISHED LENGTH	LENGTH TO MAKE	MAKE-UP	Finished quantity per Platform	TOTAL UoM
Quantum-12 Black	22Mm dia. 28.4 Tonne	Lg	Breast lines Nsn 4020-99-219-8143	60 M	70 M	2M protected mooring eye each end	2	2
Quantum-12 Black	22Mm dia. 28.4 Tonne	Lg	Head, stern & springs 4020-99-380-7053	100 M	110 M	2M protected mooring eye each end	4 Plus 3 X spare	7
Quantum-12 Lime green	22Mm dia. 28.4 Tonne	Lg	Picking-up- rope (pur) 4020-99-667-5586	100 M	110 M	St/st thimble eye one end. Pur pendant & hook other end.	1	1
Quantum-12 black	22Mm 28.4 Tonne	Ea	Picking-up-rope pendant 4020-99-813-1436	5 M	12 M		1	1
Amsteel-blue Lime green	22Mm dia. 41.2 Tonne	Lg	Towing hawser 4020-99-434-4829	150 M	160 M	700Mm served & leathered eye each end	1	1
Superstrong parallay nylon	32Mm dia. 25.4 Tonne (40.1 T)	Lg	Shock mitigation strop (sms) 4020-99-273-0329	5 M	13 M	Strop configured served & leathered eye each end	4	4
Quantum-12 black	28Mm dia. 47.6 Tonne	Lg	Bridles/foul weather pennant/ tug assist lines 4020-99-707-5400	60 M	70 M	2M protected mooring eye each end	4	4

PRODUCT	SIZE	UoM	DESIGNATION	FINISHED LENGTH	LENGTH TO MAKE	MAKE-UP	Finished quantity per Platform	TOTAL UoM
Quantum-12 black	28Mm dia. 47.6 Tonne	Lg	Foul weather pendant 4020-99-340-8756	6 M	14 M	2M protected mooring eye one end, 700mm sleeved eye other end	2	2
Quantum-12 black	20Mm dia. 21.5 Tonne	Ea	Bollard strop, 1.8M 4020-99-257-8381	1.8 M	7 M	Protected strop configured with thimble and serving	2	2
Mainbrace ice chafe protection for eyes	Small	Lg	All eyes protection 4020-99-359-6081	-	23M	Spliced to all mooring eyes	-	As required
Mainbrace Ice chafe protection for eyes	Size small blue	Lg	Bridles/foul weather eye protection 4020-99-235-5365		23 M	Spliced to bridles and foul weather pendant eyes		As required
Mainbrace gard chafe protection for picking up rope	Size c	Ea	Picking-up-rope (pur) 4020-99-813-2480	10 M	11 M	Spliced to 'slip' part of pur	1	1
Stainless steel fairlead shackle M90	M90	Ea	Joining shackle for ropes 4020-99-958-4133	-	-	-	-	8
Buffer's toothbrush st/st tool	M90	Ea	Tool for adjusting fairlead shackles 4030-99-316-9347	-	-	-	-	2

PRODUCT	SIZE	UoM	DESIGNATION	FINISHED LENGTH	LENGTH TO MAKE	MAKE-UP	Finished quantity per Platform	TOTAL UoM
Mooring gard	Size: b	Ea	Hook & loop coated hmpe Chafe protectors 1.5M 4020-99-151-6871	-	-	4 Fitted per berthing hawser – 1 fitted per bridle – 1 fitted on pur	-	27
Mainbrace ice chafe protection for mooring eyes	Size small Grey	Lg	Spare eyes protection 4020-99-359-6081	-	23 M		Spare carried onboard for all mooring eyes	2
Mainbrace ice chafe protection for eye	Size small Blue	Lg	Spare eyes protection 4020-99-235-5365	-	23 M		Spare carried onboard for bridles/foul weather/tug assist lines	2
Quantum-12 Black	20Mm Sbl 20.5T Obl 49.2T	Ea	Securing to buoy strop 4020-99-471-7501	-	7 M		Securing to buoy strop method	5
Tech-12 black	14Mm	Ea	Mooring line stopper 4020-99-848-1374	-	3 M		2 Leg stopper with st/st thimble	6
Splicing tool kit	Medium	Ea	Complete 5120-99-589-8553	-	-	-	-	4

Table 3D-7. HPMT – MPV (RIVER CLASS) COMPLETE OUTFIT

PRODUCT	SIZE	UoM	DESIGNATION	FINISHED LENGTH	LENGTH TO MAKE	MAKE-UP	Finished quantity per Platform	TOTAL UoM
Quantum-12 Black	22Mm dia. 28.4 Tonne	Lg	Breast lines Nsn 4020-99-219-8143	60 M	70 M	2M protected mooring eye each end	2	2
Quantum-12 Black	22Mm dia. 28.4 Tonne	Lg	Head, stern & springs 4020-99-380-7053	100 M	110 M	2M protected mooring eye each end	4 Plus 3 X spare	7
Quantum-12 Lime green	22Mm dia. 28.4 Tonne	Lg	Picking-up- rope (pur) 4020-99-667-5586	100 M	110 M	St/st thimble eye one end. Pur pendant & hook other end.	1	1
Quantum-12 black	22Mm 28.4 Tonne	Ea	Picking-up- rope pendant 4020-99-813-1436	5 M	12 M		1	1
Amsteel-blue Lime green	22Mm dia. 41.2 Tonne	Lg	Towing hawser 4020-99-434-4829	150 M	160 M	700Mm served & leathered eye each end	1	1
Superstrong parallay nylon	32Mm dia. 25.4 Tonne (40.1 T)	Lg	Shock mitigation strop (sms) 4020-99-273-0329	5 M	13 M	Strop configured served & leathered eye each end	4	4
Quantum-12 black	28Mm dia. 47.6 Tonne	Lg	Bridles/foul weather pennant/ tug assist lines 4020-99-707-5400	60 M	70 M	2M protected mooring eye each end	4	4

PRODUCT	SIZE	UoM	DESIGNATION	FINISHED LENGTH	LENGTH TO MAKE	MAKE-UP	Finished quantity per Platform	TOTAL UoM
Quantum-12 black	28Mm dia. 47.6 Tonne	Lg	Foul weather pendant 4020-99-340-8756	6 M	14 M	2M protected mooring eye one end, 700mm sleeved eye other end	2	2
Quantum-12 black	20Mm dia. 21.5 Tonne	Ea	Bollard strop, 1.8M 4020-99-257-8381	1.8 M	7 M	Protected strop configured with thimble and serving	2	2
Mainbrace gard chafe protection for picking up rope	Size c	Ea	Picking-up-rope (pur) 4020-99-813-2480	10 M	11 M	Spliced to 'slip' part of pur	1	1
Stainless steel fairlead shackle M90	M90	Ea	Joining shackle for ropes 4020-99-958-4133	-	-	-	-	8
Buffer's toothbrush st/st tool	M90	Ea	Tool for adjusting fairlead shackles 4030-99-316-9347	-	-	-	-	2
Mooring gard	Size: b	Ea	Hook & loop coated hmpe Chafe protectors 1.5M 4020-99-151-6871	-	-	4 Fitted per berthing hawser – 1 fitted per bridle – 1 fitted on pur	-	27

PRODUCT	SIZE	UoM	DESIGNATION	FINISHED LENGTH	LENGTH TO MAKE	MAKE-UP	Finished quantity per Platform	TOTAL UoM
Quantum-12 Black	20Mm Sbl 20.5T Obl 49.2T	Ea	Securing to buoy strop 4020-99-471-7501	7 M		Securing to buoy strop method		5
Tech-12 black	14Mm	Ea	Mooring line stopper 4020-99-848-1374	-	3 M		2 Leg stopper with st/st thimble	6
Amsteel-blue Lime green	16Mm Sbl 21.6T Obl 34.56T	Ea	Towing chafe pendant	-	16 M		Aft chafe pendant	1
Amsteel-blue Lime green	16Mm Sbl 21.6T Obl 34.56T	Ea	Towing chafe pendant	-	5 M		Fwd chafe pendant	1
Mainbrace ice chafe protection for mooring eyes	Size small Grey	Lg	Spare eyes protection 4020-99-359-6081	-	23 M		Spare carried onboard for all mooring eyes	2
Mainbrace ice chafe protection for eye	Size small Blue	Lg	Spare eyes protection 4020-99-235-5365	-	23 M		Spare carried onboard for bridles/spring hawsers/tug assist lines	2
Splicing tool kit	Medium	Ea	Complete 5120-99-589-8553	-	-	-	-	4

Table 3D-8. HPMT – HMS SCOTT COMPLETE OUTFIT

PRODUCT	SIZE	UoM	DESIGNATION	FINISHED LENGTH	LENGTH TO MAKE	MAKE-UP	Finished quantity per Platform	TOTAL UoM
Quantum-12 Black	30Mm dia.	Lg	Breast lines 4020-99-151-5474	85 M	97 M	2.0M protected mooring eye each end	2	2
Quantum-12 Black	30Mm dia.	Lg	Head, stern & springs 4020-99-344-3899	140 M	152 M	2.0M protected mooring eye each end	4 Plus 3 spares	7
Quantum-12 Lime green	30Mm dia.	Lg	Picking-up- rope (pur) 4020-99-670-5380	140 M	152 M	Protected mooring eye each end	1	1
Amsteel-blue Lime green	36Mm dia.	Lg	Towing hawser 4020-99-213-4270	180 M	192 M	700Mm served & leathered eye each end	1	1
Superstrong parallay nylon	48Mm dia.	Lg	Shock mitigation strop (sms) 4020-99-379-2057	9 M	22 M	Strop configured and served	4	4
Quantum-12 black	40Mm dia.	Lg	Bridles/foul weather pennant/ tug assist lines 4020-99-246-6443	85 M	97 M	2.0M protected mooring eye each end	4	4
Quantum-12 black	40Mm dia.	Lg	Foul weather pendant 4020-99-302-1215	9 M	17 M	2.0M protected mooring eye one end, 700mm eye other end	2	2
Quantum-12 black	30Mm dia.	Ea	Bollard strop, 2.0M 4020-99-739-3890	2 M	8 M	Protected strop configured with thimble and serving	3	3

PRODUCT	SIZE	UoM	DESIGNATION	FINISHED LENGTH	LENGTH TO MAKE	MAKE-UP	Finished quantity per Platform	TOTAL UoM
Mainbracegard chafe protection for picking up rope	Medium 'C'	Lg	Picking-up-rope (pur) 4030-99-173-1091	10 M	11 M	Spliced to 'slip' part of pur	1	1
Quantum-12 Black	24Mm dia.	Ea	Pur pendant 4020-99-471-5118	3 M	10 M	Strop with st/st tubular thimble and pu coated areas	1	1
Stainless steel fairlead shackle	M 120	Ea	Joining shackle for ropes 4030-99-151-5477	-	-	-	-	8
Buffer's toothbrush st/st tool	Large	Ea	Tool for adjusting fairlead shackle 4030-99-813-1451	-	-	-	-	2
Turbo-75 black	34Mm	Ea	Bow dome anchoring pendant 4020-99-551-8502	9 M	17 M	Thimble eye one end, joining eye other end. Pu coated areas	1	1
Mooring gard	Size: c	Ea	Hook & loop coated hmpe Chafe protectors 4020-99-361-3086	-	-	-	-	28
Splicing tool kit	Medium	Ea	Complete 5120-99-741-2439	-	-	-	-	4

PRODUCT	SIZE	UoM	DESIGNATION	FINISHED LENGTH	LENGTH TO MAKE	MAKE-UP	Finished quantity per Platform	TOTAL UoM
Tech-12 black	14Mm	Ea	Mooring line stopper 4020-99-848-1374	3 M		2 Leg stopper with st/st thimble		6
Quantum-12 Black	30Mm Sbl 53.5T Obl 140t	Ea	Securing to buoy strop 4020-99-396-2657	9 M		Securing to buoy strop method		5
Mainbrace ice chafe protection for eyes	Size medium Grey	Lg	Spare eyes protection 4020-99-838-3714	-	23 M	Spare carried onboard for all mooring eyes		2
Mainbrace ice chafe protection for eyes	Size medium Blue	Lg	Spare eyes protection 4020-99-581-6606		23 M	Spare carried onboard for bridles/ foul weather pennant/tug assist lines		2

Table 3D-9. HPMT – PROTECTOR COMPLETE OUTFIT

PRODUCT	SIZE	UoM	DESIGNATION	FINISHED LENGTH	LENGTH TO MAKE	MAKE-UP	Finished quantity per Platform	TOTAL UoM
Quantum-12 Black	30Mm dia.	Lg	Breast lines 4020-99-151-5474	85 M	97 M	2.0M protected mooring eye each end	4	4
Quantum-12 Black	30Mm dia.	Lg	Head, stern & springs 4020-99-344-3899	140 M	152 M	2.0M protected mooring eye each end	8 Plus 8 spares	16
Quantum-12 Lime green	30Mm dia.	Lg	Picking-up- rope (pur) 4020-99-670-5380	140 M	152 M	Protected mooring eye each end	1	1
Amsteel-blue Lime green	36Mm dia.	Lg	Towing hawser 4020-99-213-4270	180 M	192 M	700Mm served & leathered eye each end	1	1
Superstrong parallay nylon	48Mm dia.	Lg	Shock mitigation strop (sms) 4020-99-379-2057	9 M	22 M	Strop configured and served	4	4
Quantum-12 black	40Mm dia.	Lg	Bridles/foul weather pennant / tug assist lines 4020-99-246-6443	85 M	97 M	2.0M protected mooring eye each end	4	4
Quantum-12 black	40Mm dia.	Lg	Foul weather pendant 4020-99-302-1215	9 M	17 M	2.0M protected mooring eye one end, 700mm eye other end	2	2
Quantum-12 black	30Mm dia.	Ea	Bollard strop, 2.0M 4020-99-739-3890	2 M	8 M	Protected strop configured with thimble and serving	3	3

PRODUCT	SIZE	UoM	DESIGNATION	FINISHED LENGTH	LENGTH TO MAKE	MAKE-UP	Finished quantity per Platform	TOTAL UoM
Mainbrace gard chafe protection for picking up rope	Medium 'C'	Lg	Picking-up-rope (pur) 4030-99-173-1091	10 M	11 M	Spliced to 'slip' part of pur	1	1
Quantum-12 Black	24Mm dia.	Ea	Pur pendant 4020-99-471-5118	3 M	10 M	Strop configured with st/st tubular thimble and pu coated areas	1	1
Stainless steel fairlead shackle	M 120	Ea	Joining shackle for ropes 4030-99-151-5477	-	-	-	-	8
Buffer's toothbrush st/st tool	Large	Ea	Tool for adjusting fairlead shackle 4030-99-813-1451	-	-	-	-	2
Mooring gard	Size: c	Ea	Hook & loop coated hmpe Chafe protectors 1.5M 4020-99-361-3086	-	-	4 Fitted per berthing hawser – 1 fitted per bridle – 2 fitted on pur	-	56
Splicing tool kit	Medium	Ea	Complete 5120-99-741-2439	-	-	-	-	4

PRODUCT	SIZE	UoM	DESIGNATION	FINISHED LENGTH	LENGTH TO MAKE	MAKE-UP	Finished quantity per Platform	TOTAL UoM
Quantum-12 Black	30Mm Sbl 53.5T Obl 140t	Ea	Securing to buoy strop 4020-99-396-2657	9 M	-	Securing to buoy strop method	-	5
Tech-12 black	14Mm	Ea	Mooring line stopper 4020-99-848-1374	3 M	-	2 Leg stopper with st/st thimble	-	6
Mainbrace ice chafe protection for eyes	Size medium grey	Lg	Spare eyes protection 4020-99-838-3714	-	23 M	Spare carried onboard for all mooring eyes	-	2
Mainbrace ice chafe protection for eyes	Size medium blue	Lg	Spare eyes protection 4020-99-581-6606	-	23 M	Spare carried onboard for bridles/foul weather pennant/ tug assist lines	-	2

Table 3D-10. HPMT – ECHO & ENTERPRISE COMPLETE OUTFIT

PRODUCT	SIZE	UoM	DESIGNATION	FINISHED LENGTH	LENGTH TO MAKE	MAKE-UP	Finished quantity per Platform	TOTAL UoM
Quantum-12 Black	24Mm dia. 37.4 T	Lg	Breast lines 4020-99-983-1426	80 M	92 M	2M protected mooring eye each end	2	2
Quantum-12 Black	24Mm dia. 37.4 T	Lg	Head, stern & springs 4020-99-613-4713	130 M	142 M	2M protected mooring eye each end	4 Plus 3 Spare	7
Quantum-12 Lime green	24Mm dia. 37.4 T	Lg	Picking-up- rope (pur) 4020-99-865-9147	130 M	142 M	2M protected mooring eye each end	1	1
Amsteel-blue Lime green	32Mm dia 83.6 T.	Lg	Towing hawser 4020-99-687-2666	180 M	192 M	700Mm served & leathered eye each end	1	1
Superstrong parallay nylon	44Mm dia. 48.5 T 77.6 T	Lg	Shock mitigation strop (sms) 4020-99-373-9951	8 M	20 M	Strop configured and served	4	4
Quantum-12 black	30Mm dia. 59.4 T	Lg	Bridles/foul weather pennant/tug assist lines 4020-99-246-1912	73 M	85 M	2M protected mooring eye each end	4	4
Quantum-12 black	30Mm dia. 59.4 T	Lg	Foul weather pendant 4020-99-895-9957	9 M	17 M	2M protected mooring eye one end, 700mm eye other end	2	2
Quantum-12 black	24Mm dia. 37.4 T 59.8 T	Ea	Bollard strop, 1.8M 4020-99-219-8126	1.8 M	7 M	Protected strop configured with thimble and serving	3	3

PRODUCT	SIZE	UoM	DESIGNATION	FINISHED LENGTH	LENGTH TO MAKE	MAKE-UP	Finished quantity per Platform	TOTAL UoM
Mainbrace gard chafe protection for picking up rope	Size d	Lg	Picking-up-rope (pur) 4020-99-891-0799	10 M	10 M	Sliding protection for 'slip-rope' part of pur	1	1
Quantum-12 Black	24Mm dia. 37.4 T 59.84 T	Ea	Pur pendant 4020-99-696-1091	3 M	10 M	Strop configured with st/st tubular thimble and pu coated areas	1	1
Stainless steel fairlead shackle	M 90	Ea	Joining shackle for ropes 4020-99-958-4133	-	-	-	-	8
Buffer's toothbrush st/st tool	Medium	Ea	Tool for adjusting fairlead shackle 4030-99-316-9347	-	-	-	-	2
Turbo-75 black	34Mm 83.9 T	Ea	Bow dome anchoring pendant 4020-99-551-8501	7 M	12 M	Thimble eye one end, joining eye other end. Pu coated areas	1	1
Mooring gard	Size: b	Ea	Hook & loop coated hmpe Chafe protectors 1.5M 4020-99-151-6871	-	-	-	-	27

PRODUCT	SIZE	UoM	DESIGNATION	FINISHED LENGTH	LENGTH TO MAKE	MAKE-UP	Finished quantity per Platform	TOTAL UoM
Splicing tool kit	Medium	Ea	Complete 5120-99-741-2439	-	-	-	-	4
Tech-12 black	14Mm	Ea	Mooring line stopper 4020-99-848-1374	3 M	-	2 Leg stopper with st/st thimble	-	6
Quantum-12 Black	24Mm Sbl 33.7T Obl 89t	Ea	Securing to buoy strop 4020-99-501-4988	7 M				5
Quantum-12 Black	30Mm Sbl 53.5T Obl 85.6T	Ea	Towing chafe Strop 4020-99-418-8597	5M		Towing chafe strop with dc-gard and soft eye each end		1
Mainbrace ice chafe protection for eyes	Size small Grey	Lg	Spare eyes protection 4020-99-359-6081	-	23 M	Spare carried onboard for all mooring eyes		2
Mainbrace ice chafe protection for eyes	Size small Blue	Lg	Spare eyes protection 4020-99-235-5365	-	23 M	Spare carried onboard for bridles/spring hawsers/tug assist lines		2

Table 3D-12. HPMT – RFA BAY CLASS (LSDA's) COMPLETE OUTFIT *P7 Pennants

PRODUCT	SIZE	UoM	DESIGNATION	FINISHED LENGTH	LENGTH TO MAKE	MAKE-UP	Finished quantity per Platform	TOTAL UoM
Quantum-12 Black	36Mm dia. 86.6 T	Lg	Breast lines/ head & stern/ springs 4020-99-299-1042	200 M	212 M	2M protected mooring eye each end	18 Plus 3 Spare	21
P-7 polyester*	48Mm dia. 101.7 T	Ea	Shock mitigation strop (sms) 4020-99-613-5186	11 M	-	Strop configured and served	12	12
Pro-gard	Size 'c'	Ea	Hook & loop coated hmpe Chafe protectors 1.5M 4020-99-361-3086	1.5 M	-	2 Fitted per in-use berthing hawser	24	24
Quantum-12 black	44Mm Mbl: 120 t		Tug assist lines 4020-99-151-5454	110 M	122 M	2M protected mooring eye each end	2	2
Stainless steel fairlead shackle	M 120 Swl: 60 t	Ea	Joining shackle for ropes 4030-99-151-5477	-	-	-	-	12
Buffer's toothbrush st/ st tool	Large	Ea	Tool for adjusting fairlead shackle 4030-99-813-1451	-	-	-	-	2
Tech-12 black	14Mm	Ea	Mooring line stopper 4020-99-848-1374		3 M	2 Leg stopper with t/st thimble		
Quantum-12 black	44Mm dia. Sbl: 109 t Mbl: 120 t	Lg	Foul weather pennant 4020-99-151-5454	110 M	122 M	2M protected mooring eye each end	2 Plus 1 Spare	3

PRODUCT	SIZE	UoM	DESIGNATION	FINISHED LENGTH	LENGTH TO MAKE	MAKE-UP	Finished quantity per Platform	TOTAL UoM
Mainbrace ice chafe protection for eyes	Size Medium Grey	Lg	All eyes protection 4020-99-838-3714		23 M	Spliced to all mooring eyes		4
Mainbrace Blue-ice chafe protection for eyes	Size medium blue	Lg	Foul weather/tug assist protection 4020-99-581-6606		23 M			4
Splicing tool kit	Medium	Ea	Complete 5120-99-741-2439	-	-	-	-	4
Superstrong	56Mm Mbl: 109 t		Shock mitigation strops (sms) 4020-99-958-4205	9 M	22 M	For use with foul weather pennant	2 Plus 1 Spare	3

Table 3D-13. RFA – FORT VICTORIA COMPLETE OUTFIT

PRODUCT	SIZE	Spliced Break Load (SBL)	DESIGNATION.	FINISHED LENGTH	LENGTH TO MAKE	MAKE-UP	Finished quantity per Platform	TOTAL UoM
Quantum-12 Black 4020-99-299-1042	36Mm 86.6 T Sbl 78 t	78 T	Head/stern lines Primary/secondary breasts	200 M	212 M	2M protected mooring eye each end	7 Plus 3 Spare	10
Quantum-12 Black 4020-99-151-7206	36Mm 86.6 T Sbl 78 t	78 T	Springs Secondary breasts	180 M	192 M	2M protected mooring eye each end	4	4
Superstrong grommet 4020-99-958-4205	56Mm 121 T	109 T	Shock mitigation strops (sms)	9 M	22 M	For use with foul weather pennants	3	3
Quantum-12 black 4020-99-151-5454	44Mm 120 T	109 T	Foul weather pennants	110 M	122 M	2M protected mooring eye each end	2 Plus 1 Spare	3
Quantum-12 black 4020-99-739-3890	30Mm dia. Sbl: 85.6 T	Ea	Bollard strop, 2.0M	2 M	8 M	Protected strop configured with thimble and serving	4	4
Stainless steel fairlead shackle M120 4030-99-151-5477	120 T Swl 65t	Ea	Joining shackle for ropes	-	-	-	-	6
Buffer's toothbrush st/st tool 120M 4030-99-813-1451		Ea	Tool for adjusting fairlead shackles	-	-	-	-	4

PRODUCT	SIZE	Spliced Break Load (SBL)	DESIGNATION.	FINISHED LENGTH	LENGTH TO MAKE	MAKE-UP	Finished quantity per Platform	TOTAL UoM
Mooring gard 4020-99-361-3086	Size: c	Ea	Hook & loop coated hmpe Chafe protectors 1.5M	-	-	2 Fitted per berthing hawser	-	28
Splicing tool kit	Medium	Ea	Complete kit 5120-99-741-2439	-	-	-	-	4
Tech-12 black	14Mm	Ea	Mooring line stopper 4020-99-848-1374		3M	2 Leg stopper with st/st		14
Mainbrace ice chafe protection for eyes	Size medium Grey	Lg	Spare eyes protection 4020-99-838-3714	-	23 M	Spare carried onboard for all mooring eyes		2
Mainbrace ice chafe protection for eyes	Size medium Blue	Lg	Spare eyes protection 4020-99-581-6606		23M	Spare carried onboard for bridles/ foul weather pennant/tug assist lines		2

Table 3D-14. HPMT- RFA – FORT ROSALIE & FORT AUSTIN COMPLETE OUTFIT *P7 Pennants

PRODUCT	SIZE	UoM	DESIGNATION	FINISHED LENGTH	LENGTH TO MAKE	MAKE-UP	Finished quantity per Platform	TOTAL UoM
Quantum-12 Black	32Mm Mbl 66.2 T Sbl 59.5 T		Primary breast lines 4020-99-813-2481	93 M	105 M	2M protected mooring eye each end	4	4
Quantum-12 Black	32Mm Mbl: 66.2 Sbl 59.5 T		Head & stern lines / secondary breasts 4020-99-813-1955	200 M	212 M	2M protected mooring eye each end	6 Plus 3 Spare	9
Quantum-12 Black	32Mm Mbl: 66.2 T		Springs 4020-99-551-8504	153 M	165 M	2M protected mooring eye each end	4	4
Superstrong	56Mm Mbl: 109 t		Shock mitigation strops (sms) 4020-99-958-4205	9 M	22 M	For use with foul weather pennant	2 Plus 1 Spare	3
Quantum-12 black	44Mm Mbl: 120 t		Tug assist lines 4020-99-151-5454	110 M	122 M	2M protected mooring eye each end	2	2
Quantum-12 black	44Mm dia. Sbl: 109 t Mbl: 120 t	Lg	Foul weather pennant 4020-99-151-5454	110 M	122 M	2M protected mooring eye each end	2 Plus 1 Spare	3
Stainless steel fairlead shackle	M-120 Swl: 60 t	Ea	Joining shackle for ropes 4030-99-151-5477	-	-	-	-	6

PRODUCT	SIZE	UoM	DESIGNATION.	FINISHED LENGTH	LENGTH TO MAKE	MAKE-UP	Finished quantity per Platform	TOTAL UoM
Buffer's toothbrush st/st tool	M-120	Ea	Tool for adjusting fairlead shackles 4030-99-813-1451	-	-	-	-	4
Mooring gard	Size: c	Ea	Hook & loop coated hmpe Chafe protectors 1.5M 4020-99-361-3086	-	-	2 Fitted per berthing hawser – 1 fitted per bridle	-	30
Splicing tool kit	Medium	Ea	Complete 5120-99-741-2439	-	-	-	-	4
Tech-12 black	14Mm	Ea	Mooring line stopper 4020-99-848-1374		3 M	2 Leg stopper with st/st thimble		14
Mainbrace ice chafe protection for eyes	Size medium Grey	Lg	Spare eyes protection 4020-99-838-3714	-	23 M	Spare carried onboard for all mooring eyes		2
Mainbrace ice chafe protection for eyes	Size medium Blue	Lg	Spare eyes protection 4020-99-581-6606		23M	Spare carried onboard for bridles/ foul weather pennant/tug assist lines		2

Table 3D-15. HPMT – RFA WAVE CLASS COMPLETE OUTFIT *P-7?

PRODUCT	SIZE	UoM	DESIGNATION	FINISHED LENGTH	LENGTH TO MAKE	MAKE-UP	Finished quantity per Platform	TOTAL UoM
Quantum-12 Black	36Mm 86.6 T	Lg	Head & stern breast/ lines Springs 4020-99-299-1042	200 M	212 M	2M protected mooring eye each end	18 Plus 3 Spare	21
P-7 polyester*	48Mm 101.7 T	Ea	Shock mitigation strop (sms) 4020-99-613-5186	11 M	-	Strop configured and served	12	12
Pro-gard	Size 'c'	Ea	Hook & loop coated hmpe Chafe protectors 1.5M 4020-99-361-3086	1.5 M	-	2 Fitted per in-use berthing hawser	24	24
Stainless steel fairlead shackle	M 120 Swl: 60 t	Ea	Joining shackle for ropes 4030-99-151-5477	-	-	-	-	12
Buffer's toothbrush st/st tool	Large	Ea	Tool for adjusting fairlead shackle 4030-99-813-1451	-	-	-	-	2
Tech-12 black stopper	14Mm	Ea	Mooring line 4020-99-848-1374	-	3M	2 Leg stopper with st/st thimble	-	14
Mainbrace ice chafe protection for eyes	Size medium Grey	Lg	Spare eyes protection 4020-99-838-3714	-	23 M	Spare carried onboard for all mooring eyes	-	4

THE NAUTICAL INSTITUTE

PRODUCT	SIZE	UoM	DESIGNATION	FINISHED LENGTH	LENGTH TO MAKE	MAKE-UP	Finished quantity per Platform	TOTAL UoM
Mainbrace ice chafe protection for eyes	Size medium Blue	Lg	Spare eyes protection 4020-99-581-6606		23 M	Spare carried onboard for bridles/spring hawsers/tug assist lines		4
Quantum-12 black	44Mm Sbl: 109 t Mbl: 120 t	Lg	Foul weather pennant 4020-99-151-5454	110 M	122 M	2M protected mooring eye each end	2 Plus 1 Spare	3
Superstrong parallay nylon	56Mm dia. Sbl: 109 t	Lg	Shock mitigation strop (sms) 4020-99-958-4205	9 M	22 M	Strop configured and served	2 Plus 1 Spare	3
Splicing tool kit	Medium	Ea	Complete 5120-99-741-2439	-	-	-	-	4

Table 3D-16. HPMT – RFA ARGUS COMPLETE OUTFIT

PRODUCT	SIZE	UoM	DESIGNATION	FINISHED LENGTH	LENGTH TO MAKE	MAKE-UP	Finished Quantity per Platform	TOTAL UoM
Quantum-12 Black	32Mm 66.2 T Sbl 59.5 T	Lg	Primary breast Head & stern lines 4020-99-813-1955	200 M	212 M	2M protected mooring eye each end	8 Plus 3 Spare	11
Quantum-12 Black	32Mm 66.2 T	Lg	Springs 4020-99-813-2481	93 M	105 M	2M protected mooring eye each end	4 Plus 1 Spare	5
Quantum-12 black	44Mm dia. Sbl: 109 t Mbl: 120 t	Lg	Tug assist lines 4020-99-151-5454	110 M	122 M	2M protected mooring eye each end	2	2
Quantum-12 black	30Mm dia. Sbl: 85.6 T	Ea	Bollard strop, 2.0M 4020-99-739-3890	2 M	8 M	Protected strop configured with thimble and serving	4	4
Quantum-12 black	44Mm dia. Sbl: 109 t Mbl: 120 t	Lg	Foul weather pennant 4020-99-151-5454	110 M	122 M	2M protected mooring eye each end	2 Plus 1 Spare	3
Superstrong parallay nylon	56Mm dia. Sbl: 109 t	Lg	Shock mitigation strop (sms) 4020-99-958-4205	9 M	22 M	Strop configured and served	2 Plus 1 Spare	3
Tech-12 black	14Mm	Ea	Mooring line stopper 4020-99-848-1374	3 M		2 Leg stopper with st/st thimble		14

PRODUCT	SIZE	UoM	DESIGNATION	FINISHED LENGTH	LENGTH TO MAKE	MAKE-UP	Finished Quantity per Platform	TOTAL UoM
Mainbrace ice chafe protection for eyes	Size medium Grey	Lg	Spare eyes protection 4020-99-838-3714	-	23 M	Spare carried onboard for all mooring eyes		2
Mainbrace ice chafe protection for eyes	Size medium Blue	Lg	Spare eyes protection 4020-99-581-6606		23 M	Spare carried onboard for foul weather pennant/ tug assist lines		2
Splicing tool kit	Medium	Ea	Complete 5120-99-741-2439	-	-	-	-	4
Buffer's toothbrush st/st tool	Large	Ea	Tool for adjusting fairlead shackle 4030-99-813-1451	-	-	-	-	2

Table 3D-17. HPMT – RFA DILIGENCE COMPLETE OUTFIT *P7 Pennants

PRODUCT	SIZE	UoM	DESIGNATION	FINISHED LENGTH	LENGTH TO MAKE	MAKE-UP	Finished quantity per Platform	TOTAL UoM
Quantum-12 Black	30Mm 59.4 Tonne	Lg	Primary breast/ head & stern/ springs Lines 4020-99-236-1944	200 M	212M	2M protected mooring eye each end	19 Plus 3 Spare	22
Superstrong nylon	48Mm Sbl: 80 t	Lg	Shock mitigation strops (sms) 4020-99-379-2057	11 M	22 M	Grommet with seizings & protected mooring eyes	4	4
Quantum-12 black	44Mm 120 T	Lg	Tug assist lines 4020-99-151-5454	110 M	122 M	2M protected mooring eye each end	2	2
Quantum-12 black	44Mm dia. Sbl: 109 t Mbl: 120 t	Lg	Foul weather pennant 4020-99-151-5454	110 M	122M	2M protected mooring eye each end	2 Plus 1 Spare	3
Quantum-12 black	30Mm 85.6 T	Ea	Bollard strop 2m 4020-99-739-3890	-	-	Protected strop	-	4
Stainless steel fairlead shackle M120	60 Tonne Swl	Ea	Joining shackle for ropes 4030-99-151-5477	-	-	-	-	6
Buffer's toothbrush st/st tool 120M	-	Ea	Tool for adjusting fairlead shackles 4030-99-813-1451	-	-	-	-	4

PRODUCT	SIZE	UoM	DESIGNATION	FINISHED LENGTH	LENGTH TO MAKE	MAKE-UP	Finished quantity per Platform	TOTAL UoM
Mooring gard	Size: c	Ea	Hook & loop coated hmpe Chafe protectors 1.5M 4020-99-361-3086	-	-	2 Fitted per berthing hawser – 1 fitted per bridle – 2 fitted on pur	-	30
Splicing tool kit	Medium	Ea	Complete kit 5120-99-741-2439	-	-		-	4
Tech-12 black	14Mm	Ea	Mooring line stopper 4020-99-848-1374		3 M	2 Legged stopper with st/ st thimble		14
Mainbrace ice chafe protection for eyes	Size medium Grey	Lg	Spare eyes protection 4020-99-838-3714	-	23 M	Spare carried onboard for all mooring eyes		2
Mainbrace ice chafe protection for eyes	Size medium Blue	Lg	Spare eyes protection 4020-99-581-6606		23 M	Spare carried onboard for bridles/ foul weather pennant/tug assist lines		2
Submarine capture lines Tutbo-75 Yellow	34Mm 86.6 T	Ea	Winch operated 4020-99-863-5151	100 M	112 M	Finished item.	2 In use, plus 1 spare held onboard.	3

Table 3D-18. HPMT – SUBMARINE MOORING ROPES					
Quantum-12 Black	24Mm dia. 37.4 T	Lg	Breast lines 4020-99-983-1426	80 M	92 M	2M protected mooring eye each end	2 X spare	6
Quantum-12 Black	24Mm dia. 37.4 T	Lg	Head, stern & springs 4020-99-613-4713	130 M	142 M	2M protected mooring eye each end	1 X spare	3

ANNEX 3E

HPMT RAT AND VERMIN GUARDS

Introduction. When a ship is berthed alongside and the Captain deems there is a risk of rat or vermin infestation, rat and vermin guards are to be placed on all berthing hawsers whether singled or doubled up as soon as the ship is secured. These guards are circular discs 360mm, 450mm and 800mm in diameter (see Fig 3E-1), and they guard against rats and vermin from climbing on board the ship along the berthing hawsers.

Fig 3E – 1. HPMT Rat and Vermin Guard Fitted

| (i) | (ii) |

HPMT RAT and VERMIN GUARDS								
Product	**Part no**	**Size**	**Uom**	**Hpmt category**	**To suit hpmt rope diameters (singled up)**	**To suit hpmt rope diameters (doubled up)**	**Make up**	**Finished quantity per platform**
Rat-guard 360 Black Nsn 2040-99-705-3932	Rg360	360Mm	Ea		12-18Mm	12-16Mm	2 Parted disc and core	Small boats & craft not covered within full hpmt categories
Rat guard 450 Black Nsn 2040-99-687-3891	Rg450	450Mm	Ea	Hpmt cat 1 Hpmt cat 2 A class submarines	20-30Mm	20-22Mm	2 Parted disc and core	Cat 1 = 6 Cat 2 = 2 Astute = 6
Rat-guard 800 Black Nsn 2040-99-687-5983	Rg800	800Mm	Ea	Hpmt cat 2 Hpmt cat 3 Hpmt cat 4 T & v class submarines	30-60Mm	24-36Mm	2 Parted disc and core	Cat 2 = 8 Cat 3 = 10 Cat 4 = 10 Rfa = 14

THIS PAGE IS INTENTIONALLY BLANK

CHAPTER 4

TOWING

CONTENTS

Para

CHAPTER 4

TOWING

04001. Introduction

Towing can be defined as either receiving motive assistance from, or rendering it to, another vessel; the assistance can be classed as emergency, when one ship takes another In tow on the high seas, using the gear available in both ships; or planned, when the towed ship is prepared for towing from one place to another. A warship should always be prepared to take another ship in tow at short notice or be taken in tow herself, from either forward or aft. All warships are equipped for towing or being taken in tow and this chapter describes the various arrangements and methods used within the Fleet (including submarine tows) for the preparation, passing and securing of towing gear, the means of communication between the towed and towing vessel, points on safety when working gear, the preparations required before a 'dumb' (unmanned) or 'live' (manned) vessel can be moved from one place to another, and hints and precautions when being moved by tug. The seaman should also be prepared to jury-rig a tow if the types of ship involved, or the condition of the towed ship preclude the use of standard gear and procedures. Equipment, procedures and instructions relating to ship-to-ship towing between NATO units is covered in **ATP-43(D) Ship To Ship Towing. BR 45 Admiralty Manual of Navigation Volume 6 addresses** ship handling aspects of towing and gives guidance on safe towing speeds.

04002. Towing arrangements – RN and RFA ships

The tow should be capable of being slipped at a moment's notice in an emergency, and provision is made for this in the towing ship by securing the towing hawser to a towing slip fitted either on the stern of the ship, or to a towing pendant that is shackled to a special clench and belayed to bollards. The latter arrangement is known as the bollard and clench method. With modern towing arrangements, chafing on bearing surfaces is virtually eliminated because the complete towing hawser is outboard where the towing slip is fitted to the stern or, for the bollard and clench arrangement, a Q-12 chafing piece is incorporated where the tow passes through the towing fairlead. An ASL (AmSteel-Lime) towing hawser is fitted with a Shock Mitigation Strop (SMS) to prevent shock loading and one or two shackles of cable (depth of water permitting) should be included in the tow. A ship may be towed with a towing hawser led through a bower anchor hawsepipe, stem hawsepipe, foremost fairlead or bullring depending on its fo'c'sle arrangements. The preparations for towing or being taken in tow vary slightly with the type of ship and the layout of her quarterdeck, fo'c'sle and upperdeck. Examples of typical towing arrangements in warships are described later in this chapter. Royal Fleet Auxiliary vessels (RFAs) are provided with compatible equipment.

CAUTION

It is important, when towing, that a ship's as fitted drawings are followed to determine the approved layout of towing gear. If unable to comply, other suitable sites may be used for the layout of the gear only. However a form S2022 must be raised. If a safe rig cannot be achieved OPDEF action is to be taken.

04003. Towing equipment – RN and RFA ships

a. **HPMT emergency differential warship towing system (EDWarTS) – Introduction.** AmSteel-Lime Green tow (Fig 4-1) is a lightweight, floating and easily deployed/recovered Emergency Differential Warship Towing System (EDWarTS). This towing system helps increase operational effectiveness in the way of manpower (allowing upperdeck weapon and sensor crews to remain closed-up to fight the ship). The whole system can be deployed and recovered, (providing or receiving at either end), by approximately five persons. There are no heavy parts to the system and stowage space required is vastly reduced, it can also be stowed between decks. The system also allows for the use of all current ships fittings and connecting hardware. The only item to pass between the towing and towed ship's is the main tow line. Deployment of cable length remains unchanged. The EDWarTS System consists of three parts:

(1) A main towing hawser – 180-200 metres x 32-40 mm diameter. 12 strand AmSteel-Lime Green HMPE (Seen in Fig 4-1) with a protected soft eye at each end.

Fig 4-1. AmSteel-Lime green HMPE tow rope

(2) Shock mitigation strop (SMS), 44-56 mm diameter. 2in1 super-strong parallay nylon x 6-11 metres.

(3) M90 or M120 stainless steel fairlead shackles x 1.

Note. Ensure that chafing pieces are fitted to all points of contact on all occasions of use.

b. **Towing hawsers.** The size and length of towing hawsers for the Royal Navy are shown in Table 4-1. Submarine tow ropes are shown in Table 4-4. A towing hawser is designed principally to tow the ship/submarine for which it is provided.

Table 4-1. RN HPMT towing hawsers

Class of ship	No	Size	Length
LPD	1	40 mm	200m
LPH	1	40 mm	200m
Type 45	1	36 mm	180m
Type 23	1	32 mm	180m
SVHO	1	32 mm	180m
Scott	1	36 mm	200m
Protector	1	40 mm	200m
River Class OPV/Clyde	1	22 mm	150m
Hunt class	1	22 mm	150m
Sandown class	1	22 mm	150m

c.   **Towing pendants**. Ships fitted with a Bollard and Clench arrangement are provided with a Quantum-12 Towing Pendant and a Quantum-12 Towing Chafe Piece. River Class and SVHO are provided with Towing Chafe Pieces only. Towing pendants and Towing Chafe Pieces vary in length to suit individual classes of warship and details can be found in Chapter 3.

d.   **Shock mitigation strop (SMS)**. These are provided as part of the HPMT system. The SMS is used in the HPMT Tow system at either end of the ASL tow and are attached by means of the fairlead shackles.

e.   **Towing messengers**. To enable the towing hawser to be passed from one vessel to another, two polypropylene messengers are provided, one of 24 mm (attached to the Tow by a bowline) and one of 12 mm diameter. The smaller and lighter messenger is attached to the 24 mm version when passing the tow by helicopter, or when circumstances make the extra length desirable. A non-rotating Inglefield clip is fitted to the outboard end of the 24 mm messenger and to both ends of the 12 mm messenger.

Table 4-2. Staple polypropylene towing messengers supplied to RN and RFA ships

Class of ship	No	Length	Diameter
Frigates and above	1	220 m	24 mm
	1	220 m	12 mm
All other classes	1	110 m	24 mm
	1	110 m	12 mm

f.   **Recovery rope**. The recovery rope is made up of 16mm polypropylene and is of suitable length to reach, when the tow is rigged, from the bollards on which it is turned up, to a point of the outboard end of the Shock Mitigation Strop. It acts as a recovery rope to haul on deck sufficient towing hawser for it to be manhandled with enough slack for ease of handling and for stopping it to a convenient guardrail stanchion.

g.   **Towing slips**. During towing operations the tow should be capable of being slipped at a moment's notice in an emergency. Provision is made for this in the towing ship by securing the towing hawser to a towing slip. The two types of towing slip used in the Fleet are illustrated in Fig 4-2. Details of slip sizes for individual ships are shown in as fitted drawings and ships' rigging warrants.

Fig 4-2. Towing slips used in the fleet

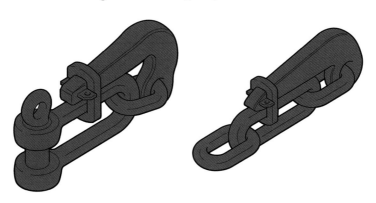

(a)

(b)

(a) Transom fitted towing slip (also used with bollard strop)
Fitted to certain warships as an outboard towing slip, and used by all warships, in conjunction with a bollard strop, for harbour movements that involve the use of tugs. There are three sizes, details as follows:

0263/523-8137 (24 mm)
8138 (32 mm)
8139 (42 mm)

A 42mm AISiBz version for MCMV's (DRG No 03502075) is also available.

(b) Bollard and clench towing slip
Supplied for 'bollard and clench' towing. There are nine sizes, as follows:

0263/523-8143 22 mm
8144 28 mm
8145 32 mm
8147 35 mm
8149 38 mm
8152 48 mm
8154 52 mm
8158 60 mm
8160 70 mm

h.   **Towing shackle**. A towing shackle is an especially long lugged shackle. It is used in bollard and clench towing systems where it is shackled to the chafing piece and takes the tongue of the towing slip. It is also used to connect the Shock Mitigation Strop to the ship's cable.

i.   **Smit bracket.** The Smit bracket is fitted to various RFAs and the SVHO class of ship for securing the towrope. It is used instead of the normal towing slip and deck clench arrangement (see Fig 4-3).

Fig 4-3. Smit bracket and collar

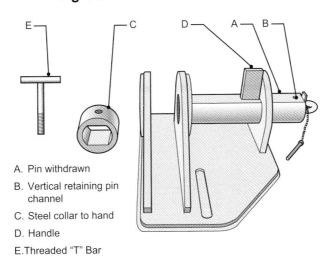

A. Pin withdrawn

B. Vertical retaining pin channel

C. Steel collar to hand

D. Handle

E. Threaded "T" Bar

j.   **Check stopper**. A 14 mm Tech-12 stopper, fitted with a stainless steel thimble eye one end, is provided during preparations to supply a tow and is used to assist in controlling the speed at which the tow is run out. The check stopper should be rigged with both legs passed over the hawser, however if the eye plate used will not allow both legs to be used then a single leg of the stopper should be passed.

04004. Tow forward preparations

a.   **Providing the tow – all ships** (Fig 4-4). The warship to be towed should normally provide the towing hawser and messenger, however, the towing ship should always be ready to provide if required. When the receiving ship is HPMT implemented there is no requirement to pass the Shock Mitigation Strop (SMS) and fairlead shackle. Therefore, break the selected cable abaft the swivel piece and put the Blake slip on the cable as a preventer. Attach the sms to the cable via a lugged anchor shackle/towing shackle with adaptor piece. Connect the inboard end of the Tow via a fairlead shackle to the SMS. Fake down the towing hawser on a shot mat. Lead the other end of the towing hawser forward to a point adjacent to the centreline hawse pipe or bullring and secure the 24 mm messenger to it using a bowline. Fake down the messenger on the fo'c'sle, one end having been secured to the towing hawser as described above, pass the other end down through the centreline hawsepipe and bring it to a position on the fo'c'sle where the gunline can be attached to it in due course. Rig the recovery rope and attach with a bowline to the outboard eye of the SMS.

Note.   *When providing the tow to a NON HPMT implemented vessel a further SMS and fairlead shackle should be passed on the outboard end of the towing hawser.*

b.   **Receiving the tow – all ships**. (Fig 4-5). Break the selected cable abaft the swivel piece; put the Blake slip on the cable as a preventer. Attach the SMS and fairlead shackle to the cable (outboard) using a lugged anchor shackle or a towing shackle in preparation to connect to the towing hawser.

The following diagrams show the EDWarTS in detail.

Fig 4-4. Tow forward – preparations for providing a tow

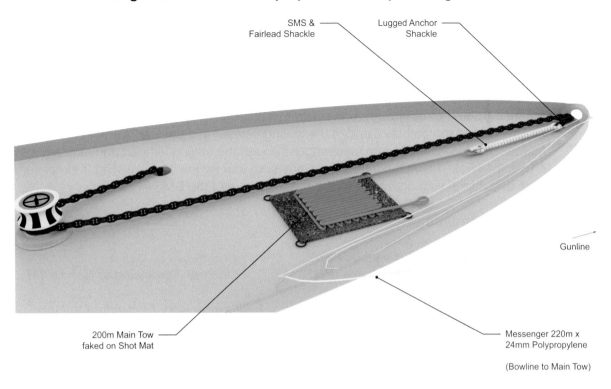

SMS &
Fairlead Shackle

Lugged Anchor
Shackle

Gunline

200m Main Tow
faked on Shot Mat

Messenger 220m x
24mm Polypropylene

(Bowline to Main Tow)

Fig 4-5. Tow forward – preparations for receiving a tow

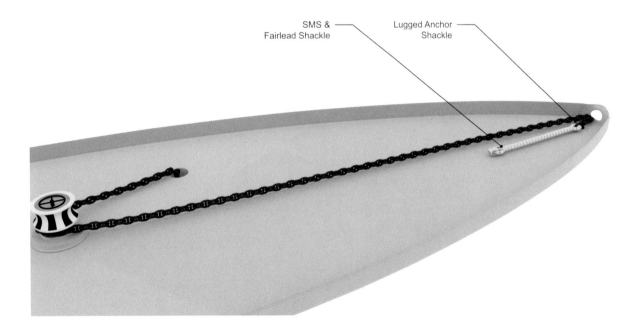

SMS &
Fairlead Shackle

Lugged Anchor
Shackle

04005. Tow aft preparations

a. **Providing the tow – ships fitted with the towing slip outboard**. The preparations for towing and providing the gear for ships fitted with an outboard towing slip are illustrated in Fig 4-6. Attach the SMS direct to the outboard towing slip through the towing fairlead. Fake down the towing hawser on a shot mat and position on the most convenient side of the quarterdeck to ensure a fair lead for the hawser. Attach the inboard end of the towing hawser to the outboard end of the SMS with a fairlead shackle. Lead the outboard end of the towing hawser to a point adjacent to the towing fairlead, then lead the 24 mm messenger through the towing fairlead and attach it with a Bowline. Fake down the messenger similar to that for tow forward. Rig the recovery rope and attach with a bowline to the outboard eye of the SMS.

b. **Gear required**

(1) main tow x 1 (faked down).
(2) shock mitigation strops (SMS) x 1. (2 x required if providing to Non HPMT implemented vessels.
(3) Stainless steel fairlead shackle x 1. (2 x required if providing to Non HPMT implemented vessels).
(4) Messenger 24 mm staple spun polypropylene (faked down).
(5) Gunline party equipment.
(6) Lugged anchor shackle x 1.
(7) Check stopper

Fig 4-6. Tow aft – providing the tow – ships fitted with outboard towing slip

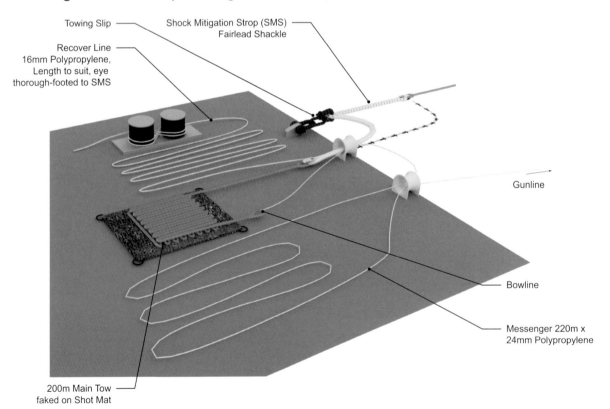

c. **Providing the tow – ships fitted with the bollard and clench towing system**. The preparations in a warship that tows by the bollard and clench method are illustrated in Fig 4-7. Fake down the towing hawser, messenger, easing out/recovery rope and rig the check stopper as described for ships fitted with an outboard towing slip. Shackle one end of the Quantum-12 towing pendant to the deck clench using a lugged joining shackle, belay the towing pendant to the bollards as shown in the inset (Spectacle Turns) and attach the other end to the towing slip screw pin. Attach the towing chafe piece to the towing slip and attach the SMS to the outboard end of the towing chafe piece using a fairlead shackle. Attach the inboard end of the towing hawser to the SMS using a further fairlead shackle.

Fig 4-7. Bollard and clecnh towing arrangement – AX full HPMT towing system

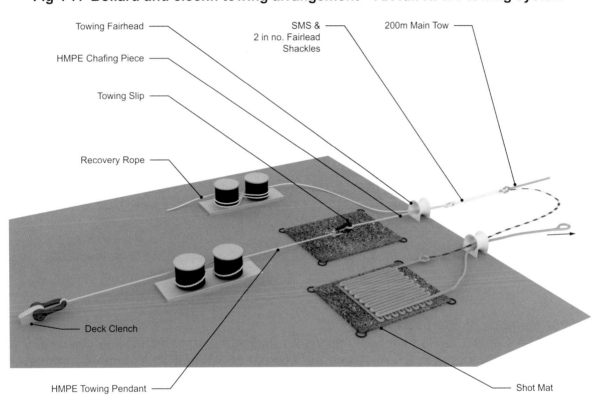

d. **Receiving the tow – ships fitted for bollard and clench towing.** The Q-12 towing pendant, towing slip and chafing piece are rigged as described for providing the tow. An anchor shackle or towing shackle should be provided to connect the chafing piece to the towing hawser and the easing out/recovery rope must be ready to hand.

Note. *The precise configuration and detail of ironwork from deck clench to towing hawser varies by class of ship. Ship's drawings must be checked to ascertain precise arrangements for individual ships.*

e. **Receiving the tow – ships fitted with an outboard towing slip**. Fig 4-8 shows the SMS rigged in a ship fitted with an outboard towing slip. Its purpose is to enable the towing hawser from the providing ship to be connected up safely on deck. A fairlead shackle should be provided to connect the SMS to the towing hawser and the recovery rope rigged on the outboard eye of the SMS.

f.   **Gear required**

(1)   Shot mitigation strop (sms) x 1.
(2)   Stainless steel fairlead shackle x 1.
(3)   16 Mm polypropylene recovery rope (approx. 20 Metre with a 300 mm soft eye one end whipped other end) eye to be thoroughfooted to the outboard eye of the sms.
(4)   Cable bag with addition of 1 in no. 'buffers toothbrush'.
(5)   Tech-12 stopper.

Fig 4-8. Tow aft – receiving the tow – ships fitted with outboard towing slip

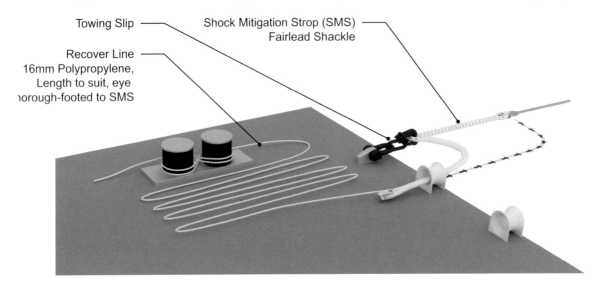

04006. Methods of approach

The Captain has a variety of options for making his approach to the casualty, and these are fully discussed in **BR 45 Admiralty Manual of Navigation Volume 6**. Whatever method is chosen the seaman must appreciate that the optimum position for establishing contact and passing the gear is likely to be difficult to maintain for all but a short period of time. Consequently the tow must be passed and connected as quickly as is safely possible.

Note.   As part of the final preparations before making the approach the end link of the towing hawser should be eased out through the fairlead/bullring to avoid any possibility of the tow snagging during the initial stages of the towing hawser being passed.

04007. Methods of establishing contact

Contact with the ship to be towed may be established by gunline, bolas, helicopter or boat towing a messenger, although if the disabled ship is short-handed or abandoned, boat work should be avoided as an unnecessary complication. If the ship to be towed is drifting fast she may stream a messenger bent to a small buoy or float so that it lies to windward of her and can be grappled by the towing ship; or the towing ship may tow a buoy secured to a messenger across the other ship's bow or quarter for her to grapple as she drifts across it.

a.   **Making contact by gunline.** This is the usual method of establishing contact, and at least three gunlines should be made ready, if possible in both ships. The line is usually fired from the ship providing the tow but in some circumstances it may be easier for the receiving ship to fire; this must be agreed beforehand.

If the towing ship is providing the tow and firing the line it can be fired from the quarterdeck or flight deck so that it is close to the scene of operations, or it can be fired from the fo'c'sle so that the Commanding Officer has an unobstructed view of the proceedings during the critical early stages when he is manoeuvring the ship to get as close as possible. If the latter method is chosen the messenger must be prepared by leading it aft from the fo'c'sle, outboard of all, stopped at intervals to the base of guardrail stanchions, and then inboard through the towing fairlead on the quarterdeck, where it is secured to the towing hawser. Gunline firing procedures are to be in accordance with **BRd 8988**.

b.   **Making contact by bolas.** This method is rarely used but is a useful alternative should the line throwing rifle become defective. A 12 mm cordage monkey's fist with a 0.5-metre tail is Inglefield-clipped to the gunline and used as a bolas.

c.   **Making contact by helicopter**

(1)   *Ships with large flight decks* (ie sufficient space to lay out the gear and range the helicopter). The 12 mm messenger is used because it is much lighter than the 24 mm messenger. The messenger **must not** be made fast to the aircraft but must be held approximately 300 mm from its end by a 10 mm rope stopper, one end of which is secured to the floor mat ringbolt and the other end held by the crewman, with a knife available in case of a jam. For passing the end of the messenger to the vessel to be towed, a heaving line is bent to the messenger with a rolling hitch about 600 mm from the end. The heaving line is coiled up and stopped to the messenger by its own tail, and the monkey's fist is weighed to about two kilograms so that it can be lowered through the downwash of the helicopter rotor (and not wave about).

In the ship about 18 metres of the messenger is faked down on the flight deck (to the quarterdeck) and the remainder led over the edge of the flight deck where it is faked down as for a normal tow aft; the 24 mm messenger is also faked down, ready to bend on. It is advisable to have men, wearing ear defenders, lying on the ends of the flight deck fakes and releasing them as the helicopter rises from the deck. The best flight path for the helicopter is about 185 metres up wind, so the towing vessel must be to leeward of the disabled ship when the helicopter is launched.

(2)   *Ships with small flight decks* are advised if at all possible to use a helicopter operating from another ship. To use one's own helicopter poses more problems than it solves and often leads to the breaking of helicopter safety regulations. It is normally quicker, and certainly quieter, to pass the tow by gunline.

04008.   Passing the tow

a.   **In the towed ship – providing the tow**. After contact is established with the towing ship, pay out the messenger and then the towing hawser. When the towing ship receives the main tow eye safely on deck, the Tech-12 Stopper is applied whilst the SMS is connected via the fairlead shackle, to the towing hawser. The Tech-12 Stopper is removed and the tow and SMS are then passed out of the towing fairlead.

When the towing ship reports that the tow is secured, the towed ship connects up the cable holder, removes the Blake slip and veers (there may be a requirement to man-handle the cable initially using rope hangers) Veer to the desired cable length (one or two shackles of cable - depth of water permitting), then secures the cable in the same manner as for coming to single anchor, ie put the Blake slip on slack, veer until just before the Blake slip has the weight, then on brake hard, on riding slip/compressor/guillotine as an additional preventer, and disconnect the cable holder. This method of securing the cable is the only satisfactory and safe method in most ships. However, in ships built to commercial standards, it is common practice for a centre-line Blake slip to be fitted for towing. In these ships, the weight of the tow is to be taken on the centre-line Blake slip and the windlass brake is to be put on as a preventer.

b.   **In the towing ship – receiving the tow**. Run in the messenger by hand, then, if required, bring to the capstan and heave in until there is sufficient towing hawser on deck to make the connection between the towing hawser and the fairlead shackle attached to the SMS. During this operation hold the weight of the towing hawser on the messenger at the capstan, and pass the Tech-12 Stopper over the towing hawser as an additional preventer. Connect the fairlead shackle to the towing hawser, take-up the slack on the recovery rope and remove the Tech-12 Stopper. Remove the messenger so the recovery rope has the weight. Fake-down the messenger ready to hand for use when the tow is returned. The SMS attached to the tow can now be eased out on the recovery rope. When this has been achieved, the recovery rope is coiled and stopped, outboard of the guardrails.

Note.   *The towing ship must avoid placing weight on the tow until the towed ship has signalled that she is ready to commence the tow.*

c.   **In the towing ship – providing the tow**. The methods employed are similar to those for passing the tow forward. Pay out the messenger and tow until the recovery rope has the weight. The recovery rope is used to ease out the SMS connection so the weight is transferred to the Tow. The recovery rope is coiled and stopped outboard of the guardrails.

d.   **In the towed ship – receiving the tow**. Break the selected cable abaft the swivel piece, and light it forward to a point just abaft, but adjacent to, the centreline hawsepipe or bullring. Attach the SMS to the cable with a towing shackle and provide a fairlead shackle to the outboard end. Provide a Tech-12 Stopper as an additional preventer to hold the towing hawser when the connection is being made. Run the messenger in by hand, bring it to the capstan and heave in until the towing hawser is on deck. Pass the Tech-12 Stopper, then, with the weight of the towing hawser held by the messenger, and the Tech-12 Stopper passed, connect the SMS via the fairlead shackle to the towing hawser. When the connection has been made, veer and remove the messenger, transferring the weight to the Tech-12 Stopper. Connect up the cable holder, remove the Tech-12 Stopper and veer one to two shackles of cable (depth of water permitting). If necessary, manhandle with rope tails the first few metres of cable down the centreline hawsepipe. Secure the cable in the manner previously described.

04009.   Checks before commencing the tow

Before commencing the tow a rating in the towing ship must be detailed off as emergency slipping number; he must be equipped with an axe and a maul/Sharp knife, and sited in a safe position should the tow part, but close enough to be able to react quickly in an emergency. Spare gear must be stowed away, and all personnel other than the emergency slipping number cleared from the area before towing commences.

04010. Commencing the tow

As the towing ship moves ahead and weight comes on the tow, the towed ship may take a sheer. This can make it very difficult to bring her round to the required heading and there is a danger that the tow may be over-stressed in the attempt. Manoeuvring aspects of this problem, and possible solutions, are discussed in **BR 45 Admiralty Manual of Navigation Volume 6**.

04011. Slipping and recovering the tow

Before slipping and recovery of the tow can commence both ships must be stopped. The towing ship must reduce speed gradually, ensuring the towed vessel does not overrun the towing vessel. All personnel involved in recovery of the tow must be fully briefed on the task, with particular emphasis on safety aspects (See Caution Box overleaf).

a. **Slipping**. The method of slipping is similar whatever the rig. If the towed ship has provided the tow, the towing ship must attach recovery rope and heave/haul in until the SMS, fairlead shackle and bight of the tow are on deck. Attach the messenger, transferring the weight to the messenger and pass the Tech-12 Stopper as an additional preventer. Unshackle the fairlead shackle from the main tow. Remove the Tech-12 Stopper then pay back the tow and the messenger to the bitter end. If the towing ship has provided the tow, haul in the recovery rope, then heave/haul in sufficient towing hawser for it to be manhandled and run in (or brought to the capstan and hove in).

Note. *While the weight of the towing hawser is borne by the messenger during the operation of passing the tow back to the supplying vessel, the messenger must be veered under control at the capstan until the weight is off the messenger; turns can then be removed from the capstan and the messenger paid back, hand over hand.*

b. **Recovery**. In the **towed ship** (if the **towed ship** has provided the tow) lead the recovery rope forward to a point adjacent to the centreline hawsepipe, or bullring, ready to bring to on the capstan; provide a Tech 12 Stopper ready to hand. Connect up the cable holder, knock off the riding slip and Blake slip, take off the brake, then heave in the cable until the SMS and main tow are on deck just abaft the broken end of the cable. Pass the stopper, bend the recovery rope to the soft eye then bring the recovery rope to the capstan. Veer the cable until the weight of the tow is on the stopper and recovery rope, unshackle the towing hawser from the cable, and when the tow is slipped in the towing ship, remove the stopper and heave in on the recovery rope until the soft eye of the hawser is close up to the capstan. With several metres of the towing hawser on deck run it in by hand, but if this proves difficult the Tech-12 Stopper must be passed again. If the tow is being returned from the **towed ship** to the **towing ship**, the end of the tow is brought inboard as described above. The messenger is then reattached, brought to on the capstan and hove in until the weight of the tow is transferred to the messenger. The rope stopper is passed, the cable disconnected from the towing hawser. The stopper is removed and the towing hawser paid out on the messenger by veering the capstan. Because the messenger bears the weight of the towing hawser it must be carefully controlled, when veering, until the weight is no longer likely to constitute a hazard.

c. **Emergency breakaway – TOWING SHIP**

(1) Remove the pin from the towing slip – stand by with the maul.

(2) Throw the recovery rope overboard via the towing fairlead

(3) When the weight is off, slip the tow

CAUTION

When the tow is being run in by hand no attempt should be made to assist the process by simultaneously heaving in on the recovery rope. Such action is liable to result in injury to personnel by the bow/roller shackle.

04012. Submarine towing

a. Submarines are not well designed or equipped for towing at sea. The low freeboard in conjunction with lack of proper fo'c'sle arrangements means that a long ocean tow is not feasible without special arrangements and modifications to the structure. There are currently three trialled methods of towing a submarine in an emergency. Tow ropes are supplied as stated in Table 4-3:

Table 4-3. Tow ropes supplied to RN submarines

Class of submarine	No	Size	Length
Trafalgar (HMPE)	1	56 mm	110 m
Rip Out Pendant (HMPE)	1	28 mm	35 m
Messenger (Braidline)	1	25 mm	146 m
Vanguard (Viking Nylon Braidline)	1	72 mm	95 m
Rip Out Pendant (Viking Nylon Braidline)	1	52 mm	55 m
Messenger (Braidline)	1	25 mm	146 m

b. **Use of the fitted rip-out tow (ROT) system**

(1) *Use of the fin harness (FH) system*. The FH system is designed for lassoing the fin of a submarine to enable it to be towed or held with head to wind/sea and prevented from drifting into navigational danger during a breakdown in adverse weather. The procedure for deployment of the FH was developed by S&MO IPT and has been trialled successfully.

(2) *Use of the suitable, approved and accessible fitted mooring bollards.*

(3) *The rip-out tow (ROT) system*. The Rip-out Tow arrangement is stowed in a towing trough situated in the bow of the submarine. The inboard end of the hawser is connected to a slip operated manually from within the submarine and the outboard end of the hawser is spliced to a 'rip-out' pendant. The rip-out pendant is packed in a recess in the casing extending from the towing hawser stowage trough to the top of the bridge fin on the starboard side; when the pendant is stowed the recess is covered with a membrane and tiled over. The outboard end of the pendant, which is positioned behind a portable plate in the bridge fin, is finished with a link and thimble assembly. Submarines are supplied with a line-throwing device called a line thrower 250 L1A1 (see para 04013) this equipment is used to establish initial contact. A diagram of the ROT system is at Fig 4-9.

Fig 4-9. Rip out tow system

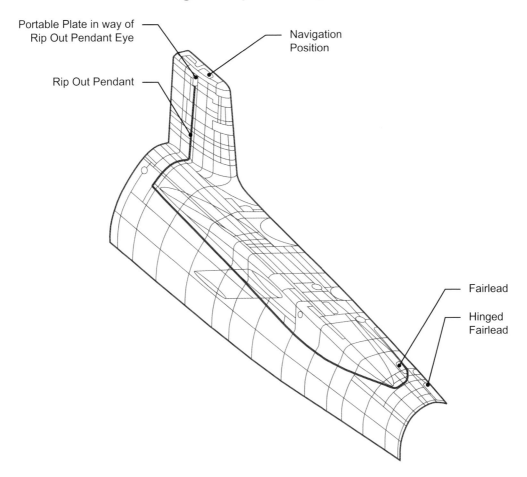

c.   The rip-out tow system enables RN Submarines to be taken in tow using 'limited' specialist manpower on the towing vessel. This means the evolution has to be carefully controlled and coordinated. A breakdown of the various ROT fittings onboard submarines is provided below:

d. ROT fittings onboard submarines

ITEM	TRAFALGAR CLASS	VANGUARD CLASS
Towing slip	The towing slip is sited at the after end of the Tow Trough. The release mechanism is mechanically operated from inboard through mitre gears, a hull gland and connecting linkage. To release the tow approximately 4.5 turns (clockwise) are required using a ratchet spanner and extension.	Holds the towline with facility to release the tow from inside the pressure hull
Tail rope	Not used	Used to bind the line back to the towing line at the link end
Main towline	110 metres of 56 mm, twelve strand HMPE rope (breaking load 193 tonnes). The inboard end is polyurethane coated and spliced to a 100-tonne towing eye or link (See Fig 4-10) for connection to the towing slip (Trafalgar Class only). The link and inboard eye are heavy-duty polyurethane coated 2.75m from the inboard eye for a distance of 4m, the rope is covered with a protective sleeve and is polyurethane coated to prevent chafing on the edges of the tow pack stowage compartment.	Viking Nylon Braidline - 72 mm x 95 m, MBL = 124
Rip out pendant	35 metres of 28 mm twelve strand HMPE (breaking load 57 tonnes). The inboard end is spectacle spliced through the outboard end loop in the main towline. The eye is lashed to form as small a diameter section as possible for stowage in the 'Cricket Bat' area. The outboard end is spliced to a loop and polyurethane coated. The pendant can be replaced independent of the main tow pack.	55 metres x 52 mm Viking Nylon Braidline Rope, MBL= 66 tonnes
Messenger rope	A 146 metre long 25 mm-braidline messenger is provided and stored on the towing vessel. This rope is passed via the submarines speedline 250 for connection to the rip-out pendant.	As per SSN
Portable plate in fin	The bridge fin opening in way of the rip out pendant eye is fared in with the bridge structure with a 7.62 mm thick portable plate. This plate is secured by means of two strong backs and four bolts.	As per SSN but secured in place by six bolts

Fig 4-10. Link assembly at the inboard securing end of the rip-out tow system

Note. *Submarine towing guidance – safe emergency towing pulls and speeds are contained in **BR 45 Admiralty Manual of Navigation Volume 6.***

(1) *Preparations in the submarine.* The portable plate in the starboard side of the bridge covering the outboard end of the rip-out tow pendant is removed (Precautions should be taken to secure this plate and retain on board). The Pains Wessex line throwing equipment is taken to the bridge and prepared for firing and VHF communications/signal bats and rope stops are placed ready to hand.

(2) *Preparations by the towing vessel.* The towing vessel establishes communications with the submarine agreeing the actions to be taken to connect the tow. When ready to commence tow connection, the towing vessel will manoeuvre to a position on the starboard beam of the submarine abreast the bridge fin, maintaining the agreed minimum distance of approach. Submarines do not carry a messenger rope and the towing vessel must therefore provide one. It is advisable to prepare for use both a 12 mm and a 24 mm messenger. Although the 24 mm version must be passed first to the submarine it is possible that the vessels will drift apart during the period the submarine is attaching the messenger to the rip-out pendant; in such circumstances the l2 mm messenger can be tailed to the 24 mm messenger.

Note. *In a minimum distance of approach situation the towing vessel must keep a separation of at least 70 metres from the submarine at all times.*

(3) *Passing the tow.* The towing vessel takes up position at the agreed minimum distance of approach on the starboard beam abreast of the fin of the submarine. The submarine fires the speedline over to the towing vessel. The towing vessel recovers the speedline and attaches it to the soft eye of the messenger. It has been found from experience that the towing vessel may drift away from the submarine during this operation and that the speedline could be in danger of parting. To reduce this risk, every effort should be made to allow the messenger to pay out as quickly as possible. The submarine then hauls over the messenger using the speedline. The submarine then secures the messenger by a rolling hitch to the outboard end of the rip-out pendant below the eye (see Fig 4-11). Once the submarine has secured the messenger to the rip-out pendant, the towing vessel, using her capstan or winch, hauls in the messenger 'starting the release of' the rip-out pendant from the bridge fin (a nominal force of 4.7 tonnes is required to release the pendant). Experience has shown that the towing vessel must not be ahead or astern of the submarine's fin by more than 15° during the initial phase of the rip-out process, otherwise the rip-out tow pendant does not run out smoothly.

The towing vessel then moves slowly forward to a position on the starboard bow, just ahead of the submarine, ripping out the rest of the pendant from its stowage trough in the process. When the outboard eye of the rip-out pendant is to hand on the towing vessel leave it on the pendant until the main tow link assembly as shown in Fig 4-10 is to hand. Attach the towing vessels cable/line to the link assembly, transfer the weight from the pendant to the main towline and pay out until the necessary length (dependant on the weather conditions) is let out before commencing the tow.

Note. *Other methods as laid down for surface ships may be used to pass the tow if the speed line fails.*

Fig 4-11. Messenger attached to rip out pendant with rolling hitch

(4) *Procedure for recovering the tow (ROT system).* A submarine has no facility for recovering the ROT, therefore on completion of the tow, the ROT is slipped by the submarine and recovered by the towing vessel. In the event of failure to slip the ROT from the submarine, communications is to be established with the towing vessel, so that it can shorten the rip-out towline to the minimum possible taking into consideration the sea state conditions. The rip-out towline is to be cut on the towing vessel with an axe and the shortened length passed back to the submarine via a speedline from the submarine. The submarine then secures the remaining rip-out towline to the fin ensuring that it is clear of the water.

(5) *Communications.* Good, reliable communications are essential and need to be established prior to connecting a tow. It is common practice, depending on the EMCON policy in force, to communicate between ships by VHF radio. Propeller flags should be provided on the quarterdeck of the towing vessel and used to indicate immediately to the bridge when there is a danger of the messenger or hawser fouling a propeller. When red is shown it is an immediate indication that a hazard exists near the propeller on the side indicated. Normally white is shown to indicate that no hazard exists.

(6) *Safety.* It is mandatory that a full safety assessment be undertaken prior to commencing any task. Some of the safety precautions that must be observed during any tow operations are provided below, but the list is not exhaustive:

(a) Personnel must be suitably dressed for the task, giving due consideration to the prevailing weather conditions.

(b) Personnel in exposed positions must wear Hazardous Duty Lifejackets and safety harnesses when required to work outboard of guardrails.

(c) All personnel, including the recovery team, must wear DMS boots.

(d) Personnel engaged in handling the tow must be aware of the dangers of handling man-made fibre cordage under tension.

(e) Safety knives are to be worn by all personnel engaged in rigging the tow. An axe and a maul must always be available to cut away the towline in the event of fouling or danger.

(f) Binoculars must be provided at the navigation point on board both the submarine and towing vessel.

Fig 4-12. Submarine being towed with the ROT system tile fragments on casing after deployment

Fig 4-13. Rip-out two – tug leading ahead with submarine following tug's course

e.   **The fin harness system.** The Fin Harness (FH) system (shown in Fig 4-15), which is provisionally earmarked to be held on board each operational UK submarine, consists of a 35 metre length of 40 mm diameter webbing belt and a 100 metre x 44 mm Steelite pendant. A drawing of the Fin Harness is provided below as shown in Fig 4-14. It is designed for use under the following circumstances:

(1)   Emergency tow of a submarine.

(2)   Holding the submarine in position, away from navigational danger in the event of a breakdown at sea.

(3)   Backup for the ROT system when it cannot be used and/or is unavailable for use.

Fig 4-14. Drawing of the fin harness

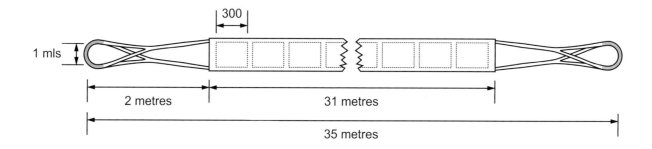

Fig 4-15. Fin harness rigged ready for transfer to tug

(4)   *Procedure for establishing a tow – using the fin harness system*

(a) *Preparations by the submarine.* The fin harness (FH) and one 44 mm diameter x 100 metre Steelite rope are retrieved from their storage position on board the submarine to the casing in front of the fin. The FH is first rove around the fin with the soft eye being passed through the hard eye. The Steelite pendant is then passed through the soft eye of the FH. Both eyes of the Steelite pendant are taken to the upper bridge position on the fin and connected together using a 1.5" Crosby bolt anchor shackle.

(b) *Preparation by the towing vessel.* The towing vessel must provide two messenger ropes for use, a 12 mm and a 24 mm messenger, as submarines do not carry one. The towing vessel establishes communications with the submarine agreeing the actions to be taken to connect the tow.

(c) *Passing the tow.*   When ready to commence tow connection, the towing vessel manoeuvres to a position on the starboard beam of the submarine abreast the bridge fin, maintaining the agreed minimum distance of approach. The submarine fires the speedline over to the towing vessel. The towing vessel recovers the speedline and attaches it to the soft eye of the messenger.

Note.   *It has been found from experience that the towing vessel may drift away from the submarine during this operation and that the speedline could be in danger of parting. To reduce this risk, every effort should be made to allow the messenger to pay out as quickly as possible. It is also possible that both vessels will drift apart during the period the submarine is attaching the messenger to the Steelite pendant. In such circumstances the l2 mm messenger can be tailed to the 24 mm messenger.*

(d)   The submarine then hauls over the messenger using the speedline. The submarine then secures the messenger by a rolling hitch to the 1.5" Crosby bolt anchor shackle. Once the submarine has secured the messenger to the 1.5" Crosby bolt anchor shackle, the towing vessel uses her capstan or winch to haul in the messenger, thereby hauling in the 1.5" Crosby bolt anchor shackle and Steelite pendant from the bridge fin to her towing deck to enable the towing vessel to connect her main towing line to the 1.5" Crosby bolt anchor shackle. Experience has shown that the towing vessel must not be ahead or astern of the submarine's fin by more than 15° during the initial phase of connecting the tow, otherwise the towing hawser could foul the forward planes. The towing vessel then moves slowly forward to a position on the starboard bow as shown in Fig 4-15, just ahead of the submarine, paying out the towing hawser until the necessary length, dependant on the weather conditions, is let out to commence the tow.

Note.   *In a minimum distance of approach situation the towing vessel must keep a separation of not less than 70 metres from the submarine at all times.*

(e)   *Procedure for recovering the tow (FH System).*   Submarines have no facility for recovering the tow, therefore on completion of the tow the Steelite pendant is retrieved by the towing vessel by releasing one end of the Steelite pendant and heaving on the other end, thereby leaving only the FH lassoed around the fin. The FH can then be removed from the fin when the submarine in is calm water.

(f)   *Communications.*   Good, reliable communications are essential and need to be established prior to connecting the fin harness. It is common practice to communicate between the submarine and towing vessel by VHF radio. Propeller flags should be provided on the quarterdeck of the towing vessel and used to indicate immediately to the bridge when there is a danger of the messenger or hawser fouling a propeller. When red is shown it is an immediate indication that a hazard exists near the propeller on the side indicated. Normally white is shown to indicate that no hazard exists.

(g)   *Safety*. It is mandatory that a full safety assessment be undertaken prior to commencing any task. Some of the safety precautions that must be observed during the operation are provided below but the list is not exhaustive:

   i.   Personnel must be suitably dressed for the task, giving due consideration to the prevailing weather conditions.

   ii.   Men in exposed positions must wear Hazardous Duty Lifejackets, and safety harnesses when required to work outboard of guardrails.

   iii.   All personnel, including the recovery team, must wear safety boots.

   iv.   Personnel engaged in handling the FH must be aware of the dangers of handling man-made fibre cordage under tension. A safety knife must be worn by each person engaged in the rigging of the tow. An axe and a maul must always be available to cut away the towline in the event of fouling or danger.

v.   Binoculars must be provided at the towing point of the submarine and towing vessel.

Fig 4-16. Fin harness connected to tug's towline & ready to commence tow

(5)   *Preparation of both the fin harness & rip-out tow systems for use in an emergency.* In suitable sea conditions, if a FH is carried on board the submarine, it would be possible to pre-rig both the FH and ROT systems in readiness for use during an emergency requiring a tow. The FH would be rigged in the usual way as described at Para 04013 sub para d. One soft eye end of a polypropylene rope pendant (10 metres long x 24 mm diameter) is passed underneath the FH and connected to the Rip-Out Pendant eye. The other soft eye end of the polypropylene rope pendant is then taken over the FH to the navigation position on the fin, ready for connecting to the messenger line from the towing vessel.

(6)   *Towing via the use of suitable, approved and cccessible fitted mooring bollards.* Towing of a submarine via the use of her suitable, approved and accessible fitted mooring bollards is feasible as demonstrated during the tow emergency of HMCS CHICOUTIMI in Oct 2004. However, each class of RN Submarine is structurally different and the capabilities of the fitted mooring bollards vary from class to class. Consequently, the Platform Design Authority and S&MO IPT must be consulted prior to use of this tow methodology. The towing rope pendants, shackles, etc required for this tow method are determined on a case-by-case basis and therefore details of the particular rig cannot be provided. Details of the capability of the fitted mooring bollards on RN submarines are provided below:

(a)   *VANGUARD class* – Each bollard on a V class S/M is designed to withstand a maximum of 75 tonnes loading in a fore and aft direction and 40 tonnes in the athwartship direction. However, it is only capable of withstanding 10 tonnes in the vertical plane, therefore care must be exercised to ensure that there is adequate catenary in the towline to prevent lifting of the towline in adverse sea conditions including heavy pitching, surging, rolling, yawing, etc. Additionally, each set of bollards (pair) must be able to withstand a maximum of 125 tonnes in the fore and aft direction and 40 tonnes in the athwartship direction. In view of this load limitation, it is an advantage if the towing vessel is either fitted with a load indicator or a weak-link is designed into the tow rig.

(b)   *TRAFALGAR class* – the mooring bollards on this class of submarine is of inadequate strength to accept any improvised rig for towing purposes.

(c)   *ASTUTE class* – this class of submarine will be fitted with two independent tow rig systems capable of enabling the submarine to be towed in all sea states covering both benign and adverse weather conditions.

Note.   *The fin harness towing facility is unsuitable for the ASTUTE class due to its proximity to the SDV housing.*

F.   **Emergency towing equipment holdings.** The following equipment is held by s&mo ipt as part of an emergency tow pack for submarines:

(1)   Two sets of Fin Harnesses, MBL 144 tonnes

(2)   Three 20 metre x 52 mm diameter Steelite pendants with soft eyes, MBL 147 tonnes

(3)   One 25 metre x 64 mm diameter double Braid nylon stretcher, MBL 160 tonnes

Note.   *The towing vessel requires a minimum of two line-throwing apparatus, each with 250 metre x 16 mm diameter messenger lines on board.*

04013. Line thrower 250 L1A1

a.   **Description**. All submarines are issued with the Line Thrower 250 L1A1 Line Throwing Unit (LTU) (Fig 4-17) as a complete, self-contained unit, pre-loaded and ready for use. It is used for line throwing between vessels during towing operations and is capable of projecting a line over a distance in excess of 230 m in calm weather. Unlike previous line throwing units (eg Speedline 250), it will be stowed in its completed form in approved stowage containers.

b.   **Outline description**. The Line Thrower 250 L1A1 weighs 4.3 kg, is 337 mm long and 316 mm in height, with body diameter 205 mm. It consists of:

(1)   A weatherproof plastic body/launcher incorporating the line chamber, the rocket launch chamber, the striker mechanism and a carrying/firing support handle.

(2)   A rocket with stirrup and bridle for attachment to the line. 275 metres of 4 mm polypropylene (Braided Perlon) line stowed in the line chamber.

Fig 4-17. Line thrower 250 L1A1

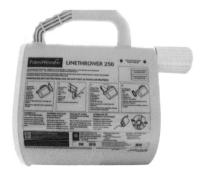 

c.   **Detailed description.** Line Thrower 250 L1A1. consists of the following parts:

(1)   *Launcher.* The launcher consists of yellow plastic (HDPE) moulding that is teardrop shaped in profile. The larger, cylindrical lower chamber is the line stowage chamber and the upper chamber, forming the teardrop profile on the cylindrical lower chamber, is the rocket launcher and also houses the striker mechanism. This upper chamber extends cylindrically backwards beyond the line stowage chamber and forms the twist-grip trigger. An integral handle is moulded onto the top of the launcher and is used in transporting in the unpackaged store and for supporting and aiming the store prior to and during firing. The line stowage chamber contains 275 m of 4 mm braided polyamide line, which has a minimum breaking strain of 2000 N.

One end of the line is attached by a knot to the front of the launcher, whilst the other end, protrudes from the line stowage chamber and attaches to the rocket bridle. The front end of the launcher is fitted with a white low density polyethylene (LDPE) cover for stowage and as protection against any ingress of dirt or moisture. A safety pin inserted into the twist-grip trigger prevents the trigger from inadvertent operation and this safety pin is covered a length of anti-tamper sticking tape. If the tape or the tape and the safety pin are observed to have been removed when the Line Thrower 250 L1A1 is unpackaged, then the integrity of the store cannot be proven and it should not be used.

(2)   *The striker assembly.* The striker assembly forms an integral part of the launcher and consists of a steel firing pin that is forced backwards by the twist in of the twist-grip trigger. The twist-grip trigger is made from ABS resin (acrylonitrile-butadiene- styrene polymer mixed with a property enhancing resin). The movement of the firing pin compresses a spring which reasserts when the twist-grip trigger mechanism reaches the end of its stroke. The released firing pin is forced forwards by the spring and impacts the percussion cap that is positioned at the base of the rocket motor

(3)   *Rocket.* The rocket inside the Line Thrower 250 L1A1 consists of a motor case, with nose and rear nozzle assemblies, a percussion cap, and igniter charge and propellant charge. It is fitted with a stirrup and wire bridle to which the line is attached.

   (a)   *Motor Case.* The motor case consists of a steel tube 122 mm long and 42 mm outer diameter which forms the propellant chamber. At the nose of the chamber tube, the stirrup and wire bridle is attached by a screw and a nozzle containing the percussion cap and ignition system is cannelured just inside the base of the tube, closing it off.

   (b)   *Propellant charge.* The propellant charge is 112.7g of DBE 470/114 Extruded Double Based Propellant.

   (c)   *Ignition composition.* The ignition composition is held within a small foil covered chamber in the rocket, just above the percussion cap. The ignition composition is a boron/potassium nitrate granular composition that is ignited by the percussion cap and provides sufficient stimulus to ignite the rocket propellant efficiently.

   (d)   *Percussion cap.* The percussion cap is a Dynamit Nobel 7003 type percussion cap. The composition and internal build standard are unavailable for commercial reasons

(e) *Stirrup and bridle.* A stirrup, manufactured from metal rod, is located on the nose of the rocket where it is held in place by a small bolt. The legs of the stirrup fit along the side of the rocket. A metal wire bridle is attached to the legs of the stirrup.

d. **Operation**

(1) *General.* Line Thrower 250 L1A1 has been designed for maximum ease of operation. Full pictorial instructions printed on both sides of the unit can be read by either right or left-handed users.

(2) *Preparation.* Preparation prior to use requires only that the white polyethylene protective cover is removed.

(3) *Firing.* Line Thrower 250 is held by the integral handle with one hand and the other hand grips the twist-grip trigger. The launcher should then be aimed over the top of the target at an angle of elevation of 30° to the horizon.

(4) The anti-tamper seal is then broken and the safety pin removed freeing the trigger mechanism. The twist-grip trigger is then twisted in either direction until the store is fired. The twisting motion forces the firing pin backwards against the compression spring via a series of cams. At the end of the stroke (one half-twist in either direction) the retracting cams stop and the firing pin is released from their influence and is pushed forwards by the compression spring energy release. The firing pin then impacts the percussion cap and initiates the explosive train. During the launch of the rocket, gases exhaust from the rear of the rocket giving a "back blast" danger. After the rocket has fired, the launcher is held in the firing position until the line has stopped paying out. The line is then secured to a strong point if possible and a messenger line secured to the thrown line by the personnel of the towing vessel enabling that messenger line to be retrieved.

(5) If a misfire occurs the Line Thrower 250 L1A1 is held in position for five minutes if possible (depending on the situation of use, at the very least the misfire wait time should be one minute) and then dealt with according to local instructions. If the ACA is available and the situation of firing allows, the misfired store should be made safe according to local procedures and repackaged into the ACA (without replacing the white polyethylene protective cover) for transfer to local EOD when possible.

e. **Lifing restrictions**

(1) Lifing restrictions for Line Thrower 250 L1A1 are contained in the JSMCR.

(2) Under the SOLAS regulations the Line Thrower is limited to a maximum of three years life from date of manufacture and therefore no In Service Surveillance (ISS) programme is envisaged. However, a routine periodic inspection programme maintains a watching brief on the continued serviceability of these stores. DGM intend to demonstrate performance against the SOLAS requirements by conducting end of life testing on stores that have been to sea and are over three years old.

04014. SVHO towing

a. Survey vessels HMS ECHO and HMS ENTERPRISE have been constructed to Lloyd's rules. Their towing arrangements (Fig 4-18) differ from other RN ships by the use of a Smit bracket and the cable not having to be broken for attaching the tow. Their system consists of:

(1) Smit bracket

(2) Chaffing piece

(3) Tow rope

b. The remainder of equipment required for the tow is as the current arrangements on RN vessels. Each ship will hold its own SOP and Service Drawing for this method of towing.

Fig 4-18. SVHO – HPMT towing arrangements

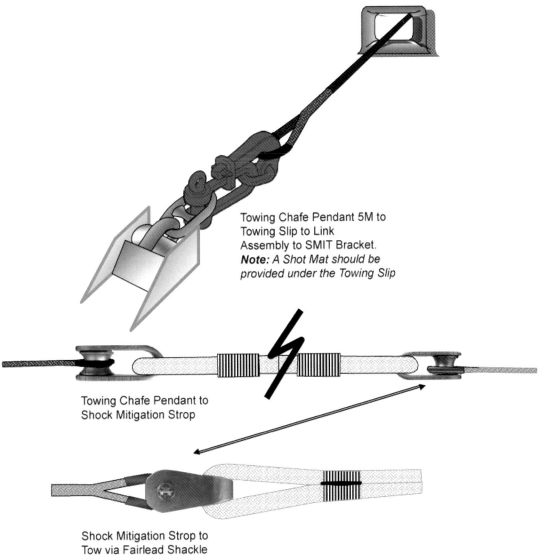

Towing Chafe Pendant 5M to Towing Slip to Link Assembly to SMIT Bracket. *Note: A Shot Mat should be provided under the Towing Slip*

Towing Chafe Pendant to Shock Mitigation Strop

Shock Mitigation Strop to Tow via Fairlead Shackle

04015. River class towing

This arrangement is similar to the deck clench layout on RN vessels with the exception that the Q-12 chafing piece is attached to a bollard strop using a shackle. The remainder of equipment is laid out as with other RN vessels. Each ship will hold its own SOP and Service Drawing for this method of towing.

04016. RFA towing

Unless a real life situation occurs, RFAs normally only carry out towing as part of Basic Operational Sea Training (BOST), usually when acting as a casualty for a warship.

04017. Communications

Good, reliable communications are essential for towing evolutions. The following methods are considered to be most effective:

a. **Bridge to fo'c'sle or bridge to quarterdeck**. Whenever practicable, RICE or sound powered telephone should be used.

b. **Ship to ship**. It is common practice, depending on the EMCON policy in force, to communicate between ships by ship-fitted radio or portable radio. However, communications between the officers-in-charge in the towed ship and in the towing ship should be made primarily by hand signals, using replenishment-at-sea bats by day and wands by night. The signals used are as described in Chapter 7. International flag hoists should be used in the event that language difficulties and ignorance of hand signals hamper communications.

c. **Screw flags.** Should be provided on the quarterdeck and used to indicate immediately to the bridge when there is a danger of the messenger or hawser fouling a propeller. When **red** is shown it is an immediate indication that a hazard exists near the propeller on the side indicated. **White** is shown to indicate that no hazard exists.

04018. Safety

The following safety precautions should be observed during towing operations.

a. Personnel must be suitably dressed for the task, giving due consideration to the prevailing weather conditions. Personnel in exposed positions must wear Hazardous Duty Lifejackets, and safety harnesses when required to work outboard of guardrails. All personnel, including the recovery team, must wear DMS boots and safety helmets.

b. Personnel engaged in handling the tow must be aware of the dangers of handling High Performance Fibre Cordage under tension.

c. When the tow is being passed or recovered, clear visual hand signals must be used to control it. Care must be exercised to prevent the tow from bottoming in shallow water.

d. Sharp knives should be worn by all men, and an axe, a maul and a wooden block must always be available to cut away the tow in an emergency.

e. Binoculars must be provided at the towing point of the towed and towing ship.

04019. Precautions when towing or being towed

a. **Reducing chafe**. Chafing is virtually eliminated with modern towing methods. However, where chafing may occur, the hawsers must be parcelled with a proprietary anti-chafe fitting or any hard wearing material such as leather, canvas or sacking. Cable must be well greased where it is in contact with bearing surfaces such as hawsepipes or fairleads.

b. **Extension in towing hawsers**. HPMT towing hawsers should be fresh water washed down and stowed as they require no recovery time. SMS should be fresh water washed down and left for six hours to recover if stowed on a reel.

c. **Connecting links**. Fairlead shackles should be used as the connecting links for all fibre rope connections. They will pass through fairleads, hawsepipes and over obstructions without opening or being damaged, and they are positively locked by retaining screws.

04020. Planned tows using tugs

Certain basic principles should be applied when preparing a planned tow, because ships vary in size and shape and each has to be treated individually. Several classes of ship have standard towing rigs available on application to the Chief Executive (Marine Services); but these rigs may have to be modified to suit the individual ship, because the positions of bollards, etc may differ in ships of the same class. The method of rigging the towing ship, and the gear used in it, must satisfy the towing master, who is usually master of the tug and responsible for the safe delivery of the tow. If there is lack of uniformity in the preparation of the rig, the towing master will require alterations to be made before he will accept responsibility. Therefore the local naval authority or relevant dockyard department should always be consulted. The towed ship can be a 'live' (manned) tow or a 'dumb' (unmanned) tow; unless the size and condition of the ship are unsuitable for manning, a tow should always be manned. Whether the tow is manned or not, the difference in the rig is slight. When manned, the towed ship should be able to slip the towing hawser from inboard and the tug can then quickly recover it. When the tow is unmanned, the tug should be able to disconnect her towing hawser from a position just outboard of the towed ship; this entails manoeuvring close to the tow, and recovery takes much longer.

*Note. Trim. Excessive weight forward should be avoided, if possible; otherwise a towed ship may have to be ballasted. Ships should normally be trimmed 6-10 decimetres by the stern; the reasons for this are given in **BR 45 Admiralty Manual of Navigation Volume 6**.*

a. **Types of rig**. There are three main types of towing rig; the two-tug rig for ships of LPD size and above, the bridle rig for all other types of ship where there are adequate strong points on the fo'c'sle for securing the rig, and the necklace rig for those small vessels whose fo'c'sle fittings are not strong enough for a bridle rig. The two-tug and bridle rigs should be as simple as possible, using the strongest securing points and the most suitable fairleads. All gear must be sufficiently strong and must have been tested within the established periods for testing. A towing pendant is always included in the rig between the towing hawser and ring, so that the towing hawser need nor pass through and be chafed by a hawsepipe, bullring or fairlead when the ring is inboard, and to make it easier for the tug to shackle on her towing hawser to the end of the pendant, which is always outboard in a manned or unmanned tow. A spare towing pendant should always be provided by a manned tow and unmanned tow when the ring is inboard. It should be secured to the ring, led through the towing lead and stopped outboard to the heels of guardrail stanchions. A slip should never be placed in the catenary of the towrope. A preventer is essential in unmanned bridle or necklace rigs, desirable in manned bridle rigs, and unnecessary in two-tug rigs.

It should be of 6 x 36 or 6 x 41 construction steel wire rope, be secured to a deck fitting or bollard strong enough to take the towing strain, and be shackled to the mooring ring. The preventer should be slack enough to take no strain from the main ring, and it may be used as a recovery wire for the main rig after the tug has unshackled its towing hawser.

(1)   *Two-tug rig.* LPD size ships and above are usually towed by two tugs with separate rigs each side of the fo'c'sle. Each rig is secured to bollards, and the towing pendant, led through a fairlead, is secured to the rig by a slip (Fig 4-19).

Fig 4-19. Towing rig for manned tow – tow tug rig – LPD and above

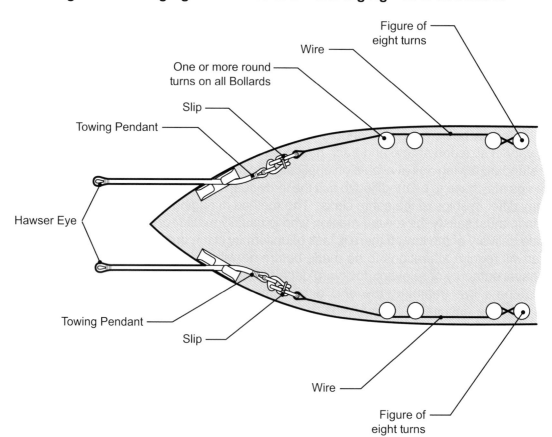

(2)   *Two-legged bridle rig.* This is the rig used for all ships with adequate fo'c'sle securing arrangements, other than LPDs and above. It consists of two wire or chain bridles originating from bollards (two pairs, if possible) on each side of the ship and terminating at a mooring ring. The bridles are of wire rope for MCMVs and below, and of chain cable for larger ships. The mooring ring for a manned tow and unmanned MCMVs, with bullring or stem hawsepipe, is on deck; and a towing slip, shackled to it, takes the tug's towing pendant (Fig 4-20). The mooring ring for a manned tow not fitted with a bullring or stem hawsepipe is outboard, so that it just touches the water when the bridle leads forward at an angle of 45° (Fig 4-21). The rig illustrated at Fig 4-21 is to be used for unmanned tows with the exception of MCMVs.

Fig 4-20. Towing rig for manned tow – with bullring and stem hawsepipe

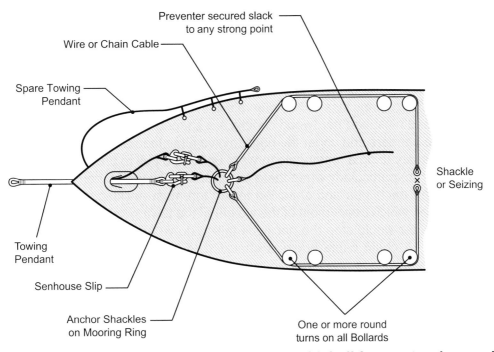

Preventer secured slack to any strong point

Wire or Chain Cable

Spare Towing Pendant

Shackle or Seizing

Towing Pendant

Senhouse Slip

Anchor Shackles on Mooring Ring

One or more round turns on all Bollards

Fig 4-21. Towing rig for manned tow not fitted with bullring or stem hawsepipe

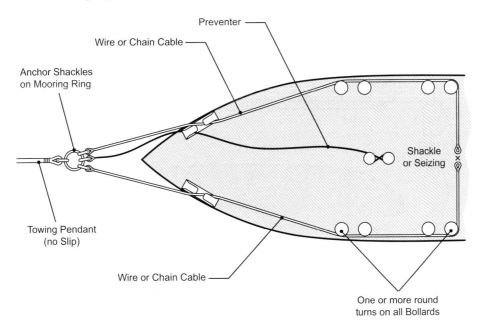

Preventer

Wire or Chain Cable

Anchor Shackles on Mooring Ring

Shackle or Seizing

Towing Pendant (no Slip)

Wire or Chain Cable

One or more round turns on all Bollards

(3) *Necklace rig.* Although most lighters are now fitted with a bullring, deck clenches, bollards and fairleads, the necklace rig is still used for small vessels that lack deck fittings of adequate strength to secure a bridle rig. The rig consists of a necklace of wire encircling the hull of the vessel, supported by wooden chocks or wire pendants (hangers) rigged over the vessel's upper deck so that they support both sides of the necklace.

Certain vessels have towing diagrams from which their rigs can be prepared; other small vessels for which no diagram exists should be rigged in a manner similar to that illustrated in Fig 4-22. The fixed metal plate at the stern prevents the necklace from sliding bodily round the hull, which would give the tow a sheer to one side or the other. In vessels with transom sterns the necklace is secured to plates on each quarter and crossed at the stern so that the port necklace is shackled to the plate on the starboard quarter and vice versa. The hangers are shackled to rings inserted at intervals in the necklace, thereby reducing the chafe and bad nips; and hardwood chocks are shaped over the deck edge in the wake of the hangers and under the rings to give a fair lead and reduce chafe. It may be necessary to rig a martingale forward under the hull to prevent the necklace from riding up, particularly when there is a pronounced tumblehome. A preventer wire is fitted each side and shackled to the foremost necklace rings. If the forward hanger, which bears most of the weight of the towing hawser, parted on deck, the preventer would stop the necklace falling down and act as a secondary towing-point. A chain cable bridle is shackled to each forward ring of the necklace, and the two legs are shackled to the mooring ring. A recovery wire may also be shackled to the ring.

Fig 4-22. Necklace towing rig

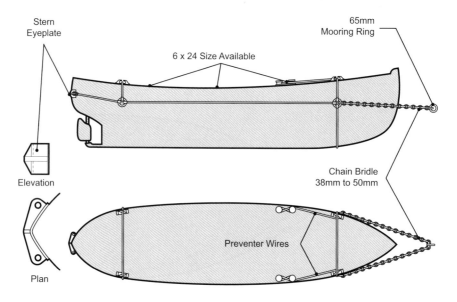

b. **Advice on preparation**

(1)   Ensure that the components of the towing rig are 'in date' with regard to survey and test.

(2)   All wires should be fitted with hawser eyes, so that the thimbles can be changed if they are distorted.

(3)   Adaptor pieces are required when using forged steel cable.

(4)   Demand towing gear by NS Catalogue Number from **BR 2000(91), Manual of Towing Equipment**.

(5)   Have all bollards, fairleads and other strong points surveyed; they may be defective in ships that have lain idle for long periods.

(6)   When rigging the gear, avoid bad nips and foul leads, especially where the bridles pass outboard. In unmanned tows the bridles should lead through fairleads, if possible, otherwise the hawsepipes must be used. Sharp edges play havoc with any rig; therefore no angle of lead should be less than 135°.

(7)   Supply as much hardwood chocking as possible, especially in the way of deck fittings; grease all leads and deck edges.

(8)   When preparing a manned tow at least one anchor should be available for use.

(9)   When securing the rig to bollards, start from forward so that the strain on each set of bollards originates from the bottom of the bollard.

(10) All unmanned, and some manned tows must be fitted with gas navigation lights, which are usually supplied by the tug. Advice on the preparations for fitting gas bottles and lights should be sought from the local naval authority.

04021. Manoeuvring with tugs
    When a ship has to be handled in confined waters there are occasions when the use of tugs is necessary, even by quite small ships. Particulars of the principal types of tug used in HM dockyard ports and naval bases are shown in Table 4-4.

Table 4-4. Principle types of tugs used in HM ports and Naval bases

Class	Bollard pull	Overall length	Draught	Type of propulsion
Damen 2909	43 tonnes	29.14m	4.8m	ATD (Azimuth Tractor Drive)
Damen 2509	40 tonnes	25.14m	4.45m	ASD (Azimuth Stern Drive)
Damen 2009	24 tonnes	21.19m	3.5m	ASD (Azimuth Stern Drive)
TUTT (Twin Unit Tractor Tug)	26 tonnes	38.8m	3.4m	Twin Voith Schneider Propeller
SUTT (Single Unit Tractor Tug)	5.7 tonnes	22.0m	3.4m	Single Voith Schneider Propeller)
Damen 2608	30 tonnes	26.2m	4.0m	Conventional Twin Screw and Bow Thruster

a.   **Securing the towing hawser of a Naval base port tug.** Tugs in Naval base ports have an eye on the outboard end of their towing hawser. The hawser should be brought in through an appropriate fairlead and the eye placed over the barrel of the bollard or to a bollard strop and slip. (The eye of the hawser may have a lanyard attached to ease handling. Care must be taken to ensure this lanyard is not 'pinched' when the eye is placed on the bollard). Towing hawsers fitted in commercial tugs are not always fitted with an eye; in this case the hawsers must be turned up round bollards and racked.

All tugs have arrangements for slipping towing hawsers from their end, but as an additional safety measure, HM ships should have an axe/knife, maul and baulk of timber placed under the hawser ready to cut the towing hawser should it become necessary. Furthermore, whenever tugs are employed, Commanding Officers of HM ships and RFAs must always know exactly how towing hawsers have been secured and they must ensure that the tug masters are informed.

Note. *To enable a safe release when using steel wire rope tug hawsers a bollard strop and slip is to be used.*

WARNING

IT IS IMPERATIVE THAT WHEN TUG LINES ARE TURNED UP ON BOLLARDS A FULL AND COMPLETE RACKING IS APPLIED BEFORE REPORTING THE TUG LINES ARE SECURE.

---

b. **Ships entering port at locations other than Naval base ports**. In some ports bollard strops and slips may be required (Fig 4-23). Ships are to state in their Logreq that bollard strops and slips are available if required. Individual ships must ensure that the strops are of a suitable length that enables them to be placed under tension without straining the seizing of the strop, but not so long that the slip fouls the fairlead through which the towing hawser passes. Where practicable a tommy bar should be lashed to the slip to act as an anti-twist bar.

c. **Tugs positioned for push–pull**. Tugs that are positioned against a ship for push–pull normally pass a bow rope and several other ropes to maintain their position against the effects of tidal stream or ahead or astern movements of the tow. These ropes need not be secured to slips but a seaman must be in attendance to let them go quickly when required.

d. **HMPE bollard strop used in the Royal Navy**

    (1)   *24 mm Quantum-12 with Ice cover x 1.80 m.* MBL 53.86t. SWL 18t.

    (2)   *30 mm Quantum-12 with Ice cover x 2.00 m.* MBL 85.54t. SWL 25t.

Fig 4-23. HMPE bollard strop

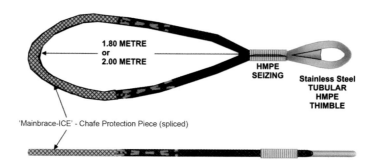

> **WARNING**
>
> IT IS EXTREMELY DANGEROUS TO SLIP A TOWING HAWSER WHILST IT IS UNDER TENSION, AND IT SHOULD NOT BE DONE EXCEPT IN AN EMERGENCY, WHEN THE ORDER 'SLIP THE TUG' WILL BE GIVEN.

e.   **Slipping a tug.** When slipping from a high freeboard ship it must be remembered that if the hawser is in tension it will be flung down on to the crew of the tug. In normal conditions therefore, the tension should be eased before the hawser is slipped or surged round the bollards. Whatever the tension, the seaman knocking off the slip must stand well back and be prepared for either the slip or the towing hawser or both to fly up. If the towing hawser has been turned up round bollards and racked, it must be backed up before the racking is removed, then surged roundly under complete control. When releasing tug lines as ordered particular attention is to be paid to the dangers from bights or fakes on deck or allowing lines to enter the water before the tug crew is ready to recover them safely.

f.   **Girding.** A tug is girded when she is towed broadside by her own towing hawser and is unable to manoeuvre out of this position. The risk is greatest when the tug is towing on the beam and only a small movement of the towed ship can place her in a helpless position and possibly capsize her; many modern tugs are fitted with cycloidal propellers which give exceptional manoeuvrability and greatly reduce the chance of a tug being girded, but propeller driven tugs may be held beam-on by the towing hawser if the ship is moving noticeably ahead or astern. If the ship is putting much weight on the tug, the hawser will have to be slipped quickly to prevent capsize of the tug.

THIS PAGE IS INTENTIONALLY BLANK

CHAPTER 5

BOATS

CONTENTS

SECTION 1 – SMALL BOAT HANDLING

SECTION 2 – WHISKEY CLASS INFLATABLE BOAT

SECTION 3 – HEAVY DUTY MEDIUM INFLATABLE BOAT (HD MIB)

SECTION 12 – GUIDANCE FOR ALL BOAT COXSWAINS

SECTION 13 – MEXEFLOTE - ROYAL FLEET AUXILIARY

Note. *Information and launching procedures for RFA Lifeboats are contained in BR 875(5) Part 2 RFA* **SOLAS** *Training Manual.*

ANNEXES

CHAPTER 5

BOATS

SECTION 1 – SMALL BOAT HANDLING

05001. Introduction

When in harbour a warship's boats are used for embarking, disembarking, and transferring mail, stores, armed parties, force protection, working parties, fire parties, liberty men, passengers and visitors; and also for training and recreation. When at sea a warship's boats are used for rescue, as in man overboard or ditched helicopter; for transferring men and stores to and from another ship, for transferring a boarding party to another ship, or for landing and embarking personnel and stores. Special boats are used for surveying, mine clearance, mine-hunting and other specific duties. Descriptions of the power boats currently carried in warships are given elsewhere in this chapter. Boats are valuable assets, both in turns of cost and capability and they therefore need to be looked after. Equally operating boats at sea is challenging and dangerous and therefore vigorous procedures, practices and training have to be adopted to reduce risks to as low as reasonably practicable. An essential part of ensuring the safe operation of sea boats is the endorsement process.

05002 Boats Coxswain endorsement and AB(1)/(2) (SEA)(HM)(MW) Bowman training

a.   The boat Coxswain, after completing the necessary course, will have to be endorsed by their current unit. Notes for the assessing officers can be found in the boats Coxswain Logbook (S3205). The enclosed *pro forma* is to be completed and inserted into the Logbook. The following criteria should apply when assessing a Coxswain:

(1)   Has a full knowledge of the boat, its equipment and the daily operational checks.

(2)   Is confident in handling and berthing/unberthing the boat in all weather conditions and is aware of the need to reduce the risk of exposure to shock and vibration to ALARP.

(3)   Uses the correct procedure when carrying out Man Overboard recovery.

(4)   Is able to ensure the safety of crew and passengers in prevailing weather conditions.

(5)   Has a working knowledge of BR 453 – Rule of the Road.

(6)   Has a working knowledge of defect procedures and emergency repairs.

(7)   Is First Aid trained iaw the Coxswain's Logbook by the medical branch rating.

(8)   Has a complete knowledge of hoisting and lowering drills and is confident and safe during launching and recovery.

b.   The Senior Rate Seaman Specialist/suitably qualified squadron staff are to carry out the assessment. Authorised endorsing officers are:

Capital Ships	Bosuns
DD/FF	Executive Officers
MM/PP	Commanding Officers

c.   To ensure prospective Coxswains have the necessary skill sets to undertake the RN Coxswains' course successfully, they need to achieve local boat endorsement. This requires the Able Seaman in question to demonstrate the following:

(1)   A thorough understanding of the boat and its associated equipment.

(2)   Work as a coxswain for recovery to the ship on at least two occasions.

(3)   Recover a simulated MOB on at least two occasions as coxswain.

(4)   The ability to re-start the engine after the 'kill cord' has been operated.

(5)   A basic awareness of the IALA buoyage system, including Lateral, Cardinal and Danger Marks.

(6)   Be recommended by the Seamanship Training Officer (as advised by the CBM) as likely to pass the RN Coxswain's course.

d.   The following *pro forma* is to be inserted into the Able Seaman (Specialists)(D) (MW)(HM) On Job Training Media. When the pro forma has been completed and the Able Seaman has been selected for the Coxswain course, a copy is to be forwarded to the Royal Naval School of Seamanship for attention of JPRO. Formal completion of the endorsement process is to be achieved by all Able Seamen (Specialists)(D) (MW)(HM). HMS RALEIGH will only accept students on to the course on receipt of a certificate. This process is aimed at giving the Able Seaman the necessary experience to undertake a RN boat coxswain's course successfully and should avoid wasted training time using valuable resources. This endorsement may be undertaken by Able Seaman 2 (Specialists)(D)(MW)(HM) if operationally required.

Boat coxswain platform endorsement proforma

NAME	RATE	OFFICIAL NUMBER	DATE JOINED	BOAT TYPE

ONBOARD TRAINING			
MOB RECOVERIES			
DAY			
DAY			
NIGHT			
NIGHT			

COXSWAIN DURING LAUNCH AND RECOVERY			
DAY	DAY	NIGHT	NIGHT
REMARKS (weather, brief assessment)	REMARKS (weather, brief assessment)	REMARKS (weather, brief assessment)	REMARKS (weather, brief assessment)
CBM SIG	CBM SIG	CBM SIG	CBM SIG

BOAT AND NAVIGATION BRIEF	
REMARKS (brief assessment)	
DATE	CBM SIG

COXSWAIN PLATFORM ENDORSEMENT	
The above named rating is platform endorsed as a Ships Boat Coxswain.	NAME (Seamanship Training Officer)
	SIGNATURE/OFFICIAL STAMP

Once completed a copy of this form is to be placed in the RN Coxswains logbook

Ab 1 & 2 (sea) (hm) (mw) (d) bowman training and coxswains pre course endorsement proforma

NAME	RATE	OFFICIAL NUMBER	DATE JOINED

ONBOARD TRAINING	
MOB RECOVERIES	
DATE	DATE
REMARKS (weather, brief assessment)	REMARKS (weather, brief assessment)
CBM SIG	CBM SIG
RETURNING THE BOAT ALONGSIDE	
DATE	DATE
REMARKS (weather, brief assessment)	REMARKS (weather, brief assessment)
CBM SIG	CBM SIG
BOAT AND NAVIGATION BRIEF	
DATE	CBM SIG
REMARKS (brief assessment)	

PRE COXSWAIN COURSE ENDORSEMENT	
The above named rating is locally endorsed as competent Bowman and ready to proceed on Boat's Coxswain course.	NAME (Seamanship Training Officer)
	SIGNATURE/OFFICIAL STAMP

05003. Small boat handling – propeller driven – general information

a. **Introduction.** Inflatable boats are fast, inherently seaworthy and easy to deploy. However, a high standard of skill is required to operate them, and in the hands of an inexperienced or poorly trained crew the potential for an accident is high. Training requirements for inflatable boats crews are given in Para 05051. The training programme progresses through the following stages:

    (1)   Acquiring boat knowledge.

    (2)   Handling in harbour.

    (3)   Handling in the open sea.

    (4)   Operating as a sea boat.

b. **Establishing skill sets confidence.** Skill and confidence should go hand in hand. It is important that basic handling skills are acquired in calm water before putting them to the test in more demanding conditions. Coxswains and crew members under training must get the 'feel' of a boat's controls before going on to learn to operate in the open sea. The instructor must concentrate on supervising details of handling performance closely, but at the same time be prepared to inspire confidence when conditions are difficult. The final assessment of a coxswain's competence should be made after he/she has had the opportunity to demonstrate both ability and confidence by taking an inflatable boat away from a ship at sea without immediate supervision in the boat.

CAUTION

Rigid Hulled Inflatable boats are not designed for beaching and damage to the craft can be expected if they are allowed to ground.

05004. Small boat handling – propeller driven – behaviour and seakeeping

a. **On a straight course.** Small inflatable boats are generally powerful and can respond quickly to changes in engine power. When moving slowly an inflatable boat has a tendency to wallow, but on reaching planing speed it adopts a horizontal attitude and becomes directionally stable. At high speed in a seaway the hull will slam into the waves causing the boat to bounce sharply, but without pitching to any great extent. At full speed the 4.7 metre and 5.4 metre rigid hulled inflatable boats may develop a corkscrewing motion which can be controlled by adjusting speed.

b. **When turning.** Inflatable boats lean steeply inwards when turning at speed, but 'lift' from the immersed side of the buoyancy tube keeps the boat stable at a constant angle of heel during the turn. All small inflatable boats can be turned with complete confidence under full power in calm water. It is however unwise to manoeuvre as sharply as this because an inflatable boat will skid in a hard turn and the engine may race due to cavitation. A more effective turn can be made by reducing speed before putting the wheel over and then increasing speed again when the turn is completed. In rough weather altering course across the direction of the waves requires care so that the boat does not expose too much of its underside to a strong gust, risking capsize.

Note. *The coxswain must, whenever practicable, inform all personnel in the boat of imminent course alterations or manoeuvres and any likely impact with significant force.*

c.   **In a seaway**. Manned by an experienced crew, small inflatable boats can operate safely in seas up to sea state 6 (Whiskey Class sea state 4), but loads and speeds may have to be reduced. When running across a beam sea the buoyancy tube on the upwind side absorbs the shock of the waves and the buoyancy tube on the downwind side gives lift contributing to stability. When heading into the sea the buoyancy tube lifts the bows to the oncoming waves and little water will be shipped. At high speed considerable stresses are placed on the bonding between the buoyancy tube and the bow in Rigid Hulled Inflatable boats; in rough weather it is advisable to reduce slamming and exposure to shock and vibration by steering in a series of zigzags across the direction of the sea, and, if the waves are very steep, to reduce speed. When running down sea it is less easy to handle. Constant attention to the boat's speed is required and frequent throttle adjustments are needed. The most important principle to be followed is to present a high bow to the wave which the inflatable boat is about to overtake. The bow of an inflatable boat lifts as it comes off or goes onto the plane, so by slowing down just before the moment of encounter and accelerating quickly to start planing again it can be made to climb a wave rather than to plunge into it. The surfing situation should be avoided if possible as this may lead to burying her bows into the tail of the wave ahead. Lastly it must be remembered that the stern of a small inflatable boat is less buoyant than the bows, so it is inadvisable to allow a steep following wave to overtake and possibly swamp the boat over the transom. This is uncomfortable and the boat will have to be manoeuvred to drain away the water.

d.   **With a payload or passengers**. The distribution of load in a small inflatable boat affects its performance. It is 'bows heavy' when stopped or proceeding at slow speed so the boat should be loaded with the weight towards the stern until it reaches sufficient speed to plane. Tilting the outboard motor to different angles produces the effects shown in Fig 5-1. The coxswain must be sensitive to the boat's performance and trim the propulsion unit to the optimum angle of tilt. An incorrect angle of tilt will reduce both speed and range.

Fig 5-1. Engine rake settings

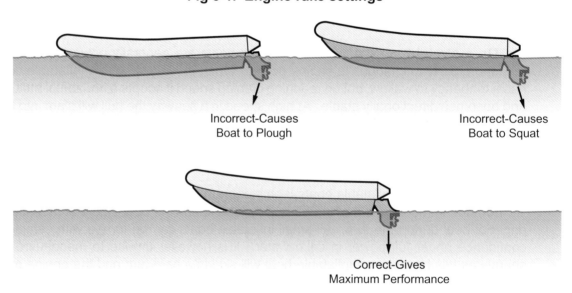

Incorrect-Causes
Boat to Plough

Incorrect-Causes
Boat to Squat

Correct-Gives
Maximum Performance

05005. Small boat handling – propeller driven – boat control

The first step towards learning to handle a small inflatable boat is to acquire a feel for the controls. The helmsman needs to know instinctively when they have moved out of neutral and engaged the ahead or astern gear; they need to know how far they have to move the throttle to produce the power they require. It is worthwhile spending some time in open water to become familiar with these controls before starting to learn how to manoeuvre the boat.

05006. Small boat handling – propeller driven – visual lookout

There is a good all-round view from the helmsman's position. Because these boats are fast, a careful look-out must be kept and bold action taken to prevent close quarters situations developing. At high speed, rain and spray may make it difficult to see ahead and protection such as a visor or goggles should be used.

05007. Small boat handling – propeller driven – manoeuvring

a. **At slow speed.** Small inflatable boats are steered by altering the direction of the thrust or drag of the drive. When the engine is clutched to 'ahead' or 'astern' this has the effect of adding power to the steering, but when the engine is in the neutral position the steering is sluggish (see Fig 5-2). Because the response to the direction of thrust or drag is so quick when engine power is applied, the technique of manoeuvring at slow speeds is different to that required for conventional boats with rudders. The important point for the helmsman to remember is that the wheel must be put over before power is applied. When manoeuvring a small inflatable boat alongside or in a restricted space, it is important to think out the control movements in advance and to make them as a series of distinct steps with the wheel movement always being made before the engine movement.

Fig 5-2. Steering performance of a propeller driven small boat

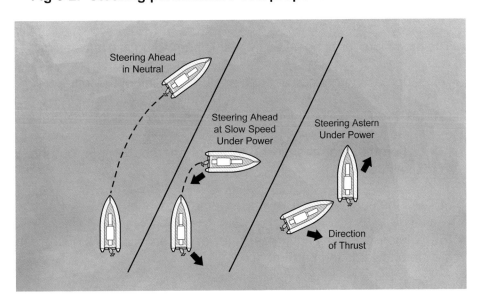

b. **Accelerating.** Once the ahead gear is engaged the throttle can be opened to give a very fast acceleration. A small inflatable boat will gain speed quickly and start to plane in a few seconds. In harbour care must be taken to conform with the speed regulations and to ensure that no damage or disturbance is caused by the wash, which can be considerable. At sea this powerful acceleration is useful when the boat is being operated as a Sea Boat. Speed can be rapidly and accurately adjusted to match the ship's speed and so facilitate returning for hoisting and recovery.

c. **Stopping.** The ability to judge speed and distance in making an approach must be acquired early since it is an essential part of the skill in handling a small inflatable boat effectively. An inflatable boat loses speed quickly when the engine is put into neutral. The distance that it will carry its way is short because they are comparatively light boats. If the speed of approach has been misjudged and the boat is found to be approaching too fast, damage can be prevented by using astern power; but control may be lost and another approach may have to be made.

d.   **Manoeuvring in neutral.** An inflatable boat holds her course well while moving slowly through the water without engine power, but, being a light boat, sufficient allowance must be made for leeway if there is any wind. As soon as the engine is put into neutral a greater amount of wheel will be required and the helmsman must be prepared to work harder at steering the boat. Because of the leeway made at low speeds an experienced helmsman may, if there is a strong wind, decide to hold on under power until a later stage than usual, and then rely on going astern more sharply to take the way off the boat.

e.   **Manoeuvring astern**. There are two important points to be remembered when making a sternboard:

(1)   The stern will move in the direction in which the propulsion unit is pointing as soon as astern power is applied.

(2)   Water will flood over the transom if speed is allowed to build up. The helmsman must therefore be careful to put the required helm on before engaging astern gear and not to go astern too fast. At slow speeds, all inflatable boats can be steered astern very accurately and turned in a tight circle. This is a useful feature which facilitates handling in a confined space.

05008. Small boat handling – propeller driven – going alongside (Fig 5-3)

a.   The procedure for bringing an inflatable boat alongside is as follows:

(1)   Approach under power at an angle to the line of the jetty.

(2)   At three to five boat lengths away, put the engine into neutral.

(3)   When the boat has closed to about one boat length, put the wheel away from the jetty.

(4)   As the boat begins to swing, reverse the wheel.

(5)   Clutch to astern and increase power as necessary to stop the boat and bring the stern towards the berth.

(6)   When alongside and stopped - put the clutch in neutral.

Fig 5-3. Approach to an alongside berth

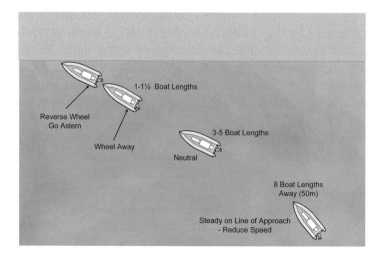

b.   Before starting the approach the coxswain must plan the manoeuvre in advance and decide how he/she is going to carry it out by considering the following three points:

(1)   *Choice of berth*.   It is important to establish early exactly where to lay the boat alongside. In some cases the aiming point may be quite evident and there will be no alternatives. In other cases the coxswain will have to take into account such factors as snags on the side of the jetty, wind and tide, obstructions in the approach, the proximity of ladders and the presence or otherwise of fenders. It can be helpful to sight the berth beforehand so that a last minute decision on the exact position of berthing does not have to be made. If taking the boat alongside an unfamiliar berth remember that the buoyancy tube and hull of an inflatable boat are easily damaged by protruding bolts and bars and also that these types of boats are sufficiently powerful to be held off in the last stage of berthing if in doubt.

(2)   *Selecting the angle of approach*

(a)   The best angle of approach is at about 30° to the line of the ship or jetty. This angle gives plenty of scope to adjust course either way to allow for leeway and set while keeping the boat moving steadily towards the aiming point. It must not however be taken as a hard and fast rule that an approach angle of 30° must be used, as there may be good reasons for adopting a different line. It should be borne in mind that, if a shallow approach angle is adopted, there will be less room available to allow for sideways drift in the latter stages, resulting in rubbing along the jetty. This is not desirable as it wears the buoyancy tube unnecessarily. If an approach is made at a steep angle the inflatable boat closes the jetty much faster, and the coxswain has to place greater reliance on the boat's engine power astern and his own judgement.

(b)   At an approach angle of 30° the lateral rate of closing the jetty is at only half the speed of the boat through the water. The inflatable boat is sufficiently light, powerful and manoeuvrable for a competent coxswain to handle it successfully from a variety of different angles of approach.

(3)   *Judging the speed of approach*.   Judgement of the speed to be used in an approach to a berth will improve as experience is gained. An inflatable boat steers better with the engine clutched in to ahead than in neutral, so, to start with, speed should be reduced to slow at about 50 metres from the berth and the boat driven in at reasonably slow speed until some three to five boat lengths off. The engine should then be put in neutral for the last short stretch. Directional control will become less positive and the speed will fall off fast; if headway or control appear about to be lost, a short burst of ahead power should be given, but it must be remembered that these boats accelerate very quickly.

05009. Small boat handling - propeller driven – leaving from alongside

a.   There are two methods of making a departure from alongside.

b.   **Sternboard method**. The usual method of leaving a jetty is to make a short sternboard to take the boat clear and then, when there is sufficient sea-room for the stern to swing, to go ahead and move steadily away from the berth. This method avoids rubbing the buoyancy tube along the jetty or wall. As in going alongside, leaving requires control of the wheel and engine to be exercised separately; the sequence of control movements should be as follows:

(1)   Put the wheel away from the berth.

(2)   Bear off the bow.

(3)   Engage slow astern to draw the stern away from the jetty.

(4)   When the stern has swung out to an angle of about 20-30º, put the wheel amidships to stop the swing.

(5)   Make a short sternboard to draw clear.

(6)   Put the engine into neutral.

(7)   Put the wheel away from the berth.

(8)   Engage slow ahead, and watch the stern to prevent it swinging in to touch the jetty.

(9)   Steady on a suitable course.

c.   **Proceeding ahead**. The other method of leaving from alongside is to go ahead directly after slipping and bearing off. This is a satisfactory method provided that it is possible to bear off sufficiently to prevent the boat rubbing when being manoeuvred on to her departure course. Precise engine and wheel control is required; small amounts of helm and low engine speeds should be used until the boat is well clear. The control movements required should be in the following sequence:

(1)   Bear off the boat broadside on.

(2)   Put on about 5° of wheel away from the berth.

(3)   Engage slow ahead and watch the stern.

(4)   Steady on a course about 10-15º out from the berth.

(5)   When clear, alter to the required course.

(6)   Increase speed.

Note.   *This method is not advocated if there is an onshore wind or set.*

d.   **Precautions after departure from alongside**. Small inflatable boats gather speed very quickly, so great care must be taken after leaving a jetty not to disturb ships and boats in the vicinity with the wash. The sudden appearance of an inflatable boat accelerating fast round a corner can embarrass other boats and cause a hazardous close-quarters situation to develop quickly. Passengers must be safely settled in the boat (see Para 05052), and the painter and sternfast must be coiled down inboard before accelerating and starting to plane.

05010. Small boat handling – propeller driven – operating in harbour

The coxswain of a small inflatable boat must comply with the local port regulations, particularly those governing the maximum speeds and routes within a harbour. The Rule of the Road must be closely observed. Because of its high speed it will often be the overtaking craft (if the speed restrictions permit); plenty of sea room must be given to any ship or boat being overtaken to allow for unexpected alterations of course by the ship or boat being overhauled. In harbour a good lookout must be kept for logs and baulks of timber floating in the water; these will cause great damage if hit, as there is no protection or fendering on the GRP hull of a Rigid Hulled Inflatable boat. Inflatable boats can create a considerable amount of wash; take care not to upset men working over the side, or to endanger divers or disturb people in small boats.

05011. Small boat handling – propeller driven – operating in the open sea

a. Small inflatable boats are reassuringly seaworthy. They may be lowered with safety at speeds of between five and 12 knots. Before being lowered or leaving the ship for an open sea passage the coxswain is responsible that the boat is fully prepared. Besides making the operator checks listed for the class of boat the coxswain should see that the following preparations are made:

(1) Crew and passengers correctly briefed, dressed and equipped.

(2) Instructions on the objective and method of carrying out the operation are understood by all concerned.

(3) Communications between ship and boat tested.

b. Once at sea the coxswain must continuously assess how the wind and sea is affecting the performance of the boat. He must be prepared to reduce the speed and ease the rates of turn to conform with the weather conditions, and must bear in mind the points made about the sea-keeping behaviour of an inflatable boat. In rough weather an inflatable boat can be driven fast towards or away from the direction of the waves, provided good judgement is exercised and the boat is not allowed to slam dangerously. Considerable care must be taken if the boat is turned across the sea as exaggerated corkscrewing may occur at speed and this could lead to the boat capsizing. The coxswain must be aware throughout of the need to reduce exposure to shock and vibration where practicable and when safe to do so. If caught in very bad weather, speed will have to be brought right down so that the RIB comes off the plane; this is uncomfortable and should only be resorted to if the boat starts to slam unacceptably or beyond the guidance laid down for shock and vibration.

05012. Small boat handling – propeller driven – handling on being lowered at sea

The engines of small boats fitted with appropriate cooling water arrangements should be started while being lowered. Small boats not so fitted should be started as soon as the boat reaches the water. Once the automatic hook has released the coxswain should steer slightly away from the ship's side and move ahead to take the strain off the boatrope. When ordered by the coxswain, the boatrope should be released and recovered on deck. The coxswain must keep the boat clear of the boatrope after it is slipped and then increase speed and move outwards away from the ship. Once clear, turn to the course required, but do not cross close ahead of the ship, as a breakdown or engine failure in this position would prove disastrous.

05013. Small boat handling – recovery of survivors

An Inflatable boat should be stopped several metres upwind of the person in the water; (if propeller driven the engine must be put into neutral so that there is no chance of the propeller injuring the person). The boat should be allowed to drift down on to the survivor who, when close enough, should be lifted into the boat (see Note); if the person is uninjured remember a Manual Line Thrower may be thrown to him/her. If the boat has stopped in the wrong position and is drifting clear of the person it must be manoeuvred upwind and the process repeated. In those small boats manned by a crew of only two personnel, the coxswain may, in exceptional circumstances, have to assist in lifting the casualty over the buoyancy tube. Once inboard the casualty must be protected from exposure, and then positioned with the feet in the bows and the head aft. This position will ease his transfer from boat to ship, and will satisfy the medical requirement for a casualty's posture to be such that the feet are raised higher than the head. The boat's lifting slings ring should be placed on the starboard side of the boat. The crew must be prepared to give basic first-aid if necessary, and in any case must report by radio the condition of the survivor(s). When practicable, the casualty should remain in the boat and be transferred to the care of a medical team after the boat has been hoisted into its stowage. Where this procedure is not workable the transfer should take place with the boat at deck-edge level and bowsed into the ship's side. There are various methods of removing the casualty. A common practice is to provide a door-size board with a batten fixed at a suitable point to its underside. The board is rested athwartships on the centre guardrail and the casualty is slid on to the board, then transferred to a lightweight or canvas stretcher and conveyed to a dry area for treatment.

Note. *Removal of a person overboard from the water when the Jason's cradle is not embarked is best carried out by positioning the victim so the person has their back to the boat. The person carrying out the recovery reaches outboard, passes his/her hands under the victim's armpits and clasps them together on the victim's chest before heaving the casualty inboard. If this is not possible firmly grasp the victim's clothing at the shoulders, push down (to gain momentum), then heave upward and pull the casualty inboard.*

05014. Small boat handling – jet driven – general information

a. **On a straight course.** When moving slowly, a jet driven small boat has a tendency to snake, but on reaching planing speed it adopts a horizontal attitude and becomes directionally stable. At high speed in a seaway the hull will slam into the waves causing the boat to bounce sharply, but without pitching to any great extent. The coxswain must be aware throughout of the need to reduce exposure to shock and vibration where practicable.

b. **When turning.** Although similar to the propeller-driven small boat, the jet-driven boat will only lean slightly inwards when turning at speed.

c. **In a seaway.** When manned by experienced crew, jet driven small boats operate exactly the same as the propeller-driven small boat as already explained in Para 05004 sub para c.

d. **With a payload or passengers.** The distribution of load in a small boat affects its performance. A Rigid Inflatable Boat is 'bows heavy' when stopped or proceeding at slow speed so the boat should be loaded with the weight towards the stern until it reaches sufficient speed to plane.

05015. Small boat handling – jet driven – boat control

The first step towards learning to handle a jet driven small boat is to acquire a feel for the controls. The helmsman needs to know instinctively when they have moved out of neutral and engaged the ahead or astern gear, they need to know how far they have to move the throttle to produce the power they require, and need to know, without looking, where the wheel is. It is worthwhile spending some time in open water to become familiar with these controls before starting to learn how to manoeuvre the boat.

05016. Small boat handling – jet driven – visual lookout

There is a good all-round view from the helmsman's position. Because these boats are fast, a careful look-out must be kept and bold action taken to prevent close quarters situations developing. At high speed, rain and spray may make it difficult to see ahead and protection such as a visor or goggles should be used.

05017. Small boat handling – jet driven – manoeuvring

a. **At slow speed.** Jet driven small boats are steered by altering the direction of the thrust produced by the engine. When the engine is clutched to 'ahead' or 'astern' this has the effect of adding power to the steering, but when the engine is in neutral the steering is sluggish (see Fig 5-4). Because the response to the direction of thrust is so quick when engine power is applied above 1,000 rpm, the technique of manoeuvring at slow speeds is different to that required for conventional boats with rudders. The important point for the helmsman to remember is that the wheel must be put over before power is applied. When manoeuvring a small jet driven boat alongside or in a restricted space, it is important to think out the control movements in advance and to make them as a series of distinct steps with the wheel and the clutch.

Fig 5-4. Steering performance of a jet driven small boat

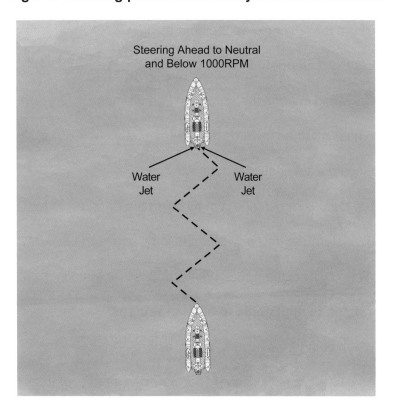

b. **Accelerating, stopping, and manoeuvring in neutral.** These characteristics are exactly the same as the propeller-driven small boat already explained in Para 05007.

c.   **Manoeuvring astern**. There are two important points to be remembered when making a sternboard:

(1)   The stern will move in the opposite direction in which the wheel is pointing as soon as astern power is applied.

(2)   Water will flood over the transom if speed is allowed to build up. The helmsman must therefore be careful to put the required wheel on before engaging astern gear and not to go astern too fast. At slow speeds all inflatable boats can be steered astern very accurately and turned in a tight circle. This is a useful feature which facilitates handling in a confined space.

d.   **Coming alongside.** This manoeuvre should be carried out with the boat heading into the tide:

(1)   Coxswain sets the engine rpm using the throttle, then informs the crew which side to come alongside.

(2)   Approach the pontoon or jetty at approximately 1,000 rpm.

(3)   At half a boat's length away, turn the wheel away from the pontoon/jetty, at the same time the bucket is dropped for a few seconds then returned to neutral.

(4)   As the boat becomes parallel with the pontoon/jetty turn the wheel towards the pontoon to stop the stern swinging into the pontoon/jetty.

(5)   Put the wheel amidships and the boat will slide alongside the pontoon/jetty.

(6)   When alongside, reduce the throttle to the idle position and put the wheel 'away' from the jetty to keep the boat alongside.

e.   **Leaving from alongside**

(1)   Coxswain informs the crew to 'let go all lines'.

(2)   Wheel is turned towards the pontoon/jetty.

(3)   Place bucket control in astern.

(4)   Set the desired engine rpm by using the throttle.

(5)   Boat sternboards away from the jetty.

(6)   When clear of the pontoon/jetty, put bucket ahead.

f.   **General points applicable to all manoeuvres**

(1)   When going astern 'always look astern'.

(2)   As coxswain, always brief your bowman as to your intensions.

(3)   Due consideration should always be given to other water users.

(4)   A kill cord must always be fitted to the coxswain's leg/lifejacket belt.

g.   **Precautions after departure from alongside**.   Small jet driven boats gather speed very quickly, so great care must be taken after leaving a jetty not to disturb ships and boats in the vicinity with the wash.   The sudden appearance of a jet driven boat accelerating fast round a corner can embarrass other boats and cause a hazardous close-quarters situation to develop quickly.   Passengers must be safely settled in the boat and the painter and sternfast must be coiled down inboard before accelerating and starting to plane.

05018. Small boat handling – jet driven – operating in harbour

The coxswain of a small jet driven boat must comply with the local port regulations, particularly those governing the maximum speeds and routes within a harbour.   The Rule of the Road must be closely observed.   Because of its high speed, the boat will often be the overtaking craft (if the speed restrictions permit); plenty of sea room must be given to any ship or boat being overtaken to allow for unexpected alterations of course by the ship or boat being overhauled.   In harbour a good lookout must be kept for logs and baulks of timber floating in the water; these will cause great damage if hit, as there is no protection or fendering on the GRP hull of the boat.   Rigid Hulled Inflatable Boats create a considerable amount of wash; take care not to upset men working over the side, or to endanger divers or disturb people in small boats.

05019. Small boat handling – jet driven – operating in the open sea

Small jet driven boats, like propeller-driven boats, are reassuringly more seaworthy than previously operated craft.   The coxswain must be aware throughout of the need to reduce exposure to shock and vibration where practicable.

05020. Small boat handling – jet driven – handling on being lowered at sea

Small jet driven boats are to be lowered as detailed in Hoisting/Lowering drills at Para 05105.   However, coxswains are to ensure that the bucket control is set to ahead, and the throttle is used to set the engine rpm approximately to match the launching vessel's speed.

05021. Small boat handling – Searider Mk2/Mk3 passenger transfer (RFA Specific)

a.   Prior to authorising the use of the Searider Mk2 for passenger transfers an onboard dynamic risk assessment should be carried out by the XO, supported by the CPO(D) to assess the suitability of the Searider for the required duty and the numbers of personnel being transferred.   Where it is operationally essential that passengers have to be seated on the buoyancy tube (maximum passengers 4) the boats speed is to be kept to minimum to ensure that the boat does not hammer across the sea causing shock or vibration injury to the crew/passengers

b.   Small inflatable boats are reassuringly seaworthy and may be lowered with safety at speeds of between six and 12 knots.   Before being lowered or leaving the ship for an open sea passage the coxswain is responsible that the boat is fully prepared.   Besides making the operator checks listed for the class of boat the coxswain should ensure the crew and passengers are correctly briefed, dressed and equipped.   Coxswains are to ensure the instructions on the objective and method of carrying out the operation are understood by all concerned.

c.   Once at sea the coxswain must continuously assess how the wind and sea is affecting the performance of the boat. He must be prepared to reduce the speed and ease the rates of turn to conform with the weather conditions, and must bear in mind the points made about the sea-keeping behaviour of an inflatable boat.   Considerable care must be taken if the boat is turned across the sea as exaggerated corkscrewing may occur at speed and this could lead to the boat capsizing.

SECTION 2 – WHISKEY CLASS INFLATABLE BOAT

05022. Whiskey Class craft – introduction

a. Inflatable Whiskey Class craft are made in four sizes. The Emergency Rescue Boat (ERB) 310 is for use on submarines and comes with a 20hp engine; the Whiskey 400 replaces the 3.9-metre unit which also comes with a 20hp engine. The W525 (GP) is a direct replacement for the Gemini as we know it, comes with a 40hp engine and is suitable for use as a Sea Boat and dive boat. The W525 (MC/EOD) is used by the Mine Counter Measure Vessels (MCMV) as a Sea Boat, diving and mining operations and comes with a 40hp engine. The Whiskey class hull consists of an inflatable U-shaped buoyancy tube of rubber-proofed fabric. A **transom board**, on which the outboard engine is mounted, is attached to the tube and to the floor. A **butterfly board**, **collapsible keelson** and **floorboards** are used to keep the floor rigid. The buoyancy tube is divided into five airtight compartments, each provided with a combined **inflation/deflation valve** and a **safety-topping-up-valve**. The craft is designed so that it will remain afloat when fully loaded if any two compartments are deflated.

b. **Seaworthiness** of the Whiskey Class is excellent under power. The craft is fast, light to handle and manoeuvrable when unladen, but slow and heavy-handed when laden. The difference between the two conditions is much greater than in the case of a conventional boat.

c. **Hull inflation**. There are four possible methods of inflating the hull. They are **bellows**, **air blower**, **bottle** and **air main**. Bellows are used when there is no great urgency to inflate the craft, and is the method used to top-up the buoyancy tube in normal use. Air-blower inflation is the normal method of inflating the craft. Bottle inflation is available for craft performing specific duties, and air-main inflation may be used where suitable air-pressure systems are available.

05023. Whiskey Class – crewing

The Whiskey class craft carry a crew of two: a coxswain and bowman. The coxswain of the boat must have completed a coxswain course at an authorised training school and, if handling a Whiskey craft as a Sea Boat or crash boat, they must have completed on-board training and be deemed and certified competent by the Seamanship Training Officer before being endorsed and allowed to coxswain the craft unsupervised. They must have a complete working knowledge of their craft and its engine, and be capable of rectifying minor engine defects. The bowman must have completed on-board training to a level where he is capable of taking over from the coxswain, re-starting the engine, manoeuvring the boat safely to recover a man overboard and taking the boat alongside.

05024. W525 – specification

a.   The W525 (See Fig 5-5) is a fully inflatable rubber boat with rigid aluminium deck and plywood transom. It is used for duties in the MCMV roll and by divers. (See Fig 5-6) The boat is supplied in five parts plus the keel and takes approximately twenty minutes to assemble. It is normally inflated and ready to use in ships, but can be stowed away in canvas bags until required.

b.   **Performance**

Capacity	12 persons (including crew) or loads up to 1250kg
Crew	Two
Speed	Approximate performance 10 – 18 knots

c.   **Dimensions**

Length	5.25 metres overall
Width	2.19 metres overall
Tube diameter	0.57 metres

Maximum hoisting weight   900kg

d.   **Weight**

Boat	81kg
Floor	82kg
Total	**163kg**

e.   **Displacement**

Dry	4195kg
Swamped	2400kg

f.   **Propulsion**

Engine	40 hp outboard petrol or 27hp outboard diesel
Fuel	Petrol/Diesel to be contained in the solid plastic fuel tank.

g.   **Slings**. A six-legged webbing lifting sling is used for hoisting and lowering the craft.

h.   **Requirement to fit a propeller guard**. A propeller guard must be fitted unless the subsequent reduction in the speed and power of the boat is inappropriate to the role in which the boat is operating. For example, no propeller guard is required when the boat is used as a Sea Boat, or for boarding operations, or when it is necessary to demonstrate the full capabilities of the craft during training courses.

i.   **Cut-out switch.** A kill cord hooks over the ignition cut-out switch on the front of the cowling; during normal operations the switch is in the 'Run' position. One end of the cord hooked over the switch; the other end is secured to the leg of the coxswain. By tugging on the cord the switch is pulled to the 'Off' position, the ignition circuit is broken and the engine stops. A spare cord must be readily available.

j.   **Boat bag and other onboard equipment.** For normal operations the stores and equipment to be carried in the boat are the same as those given for the 4.7m RIB at Para 05059 standfast the Radar Reflector and Compass, but with the addition of the battery.

Fig 5-5. Whiskey Class craft

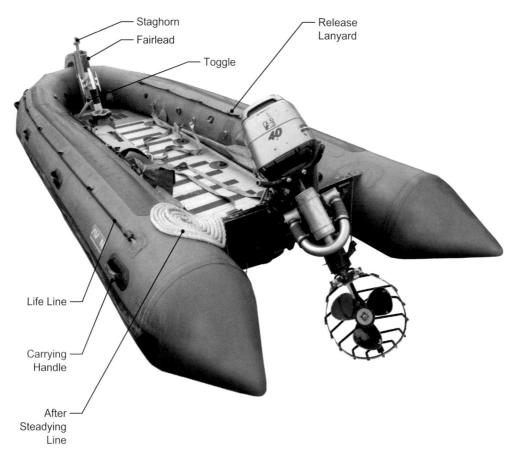

Fig 5-6. Whiskey Class fitted with bow fairlead for mine clearance

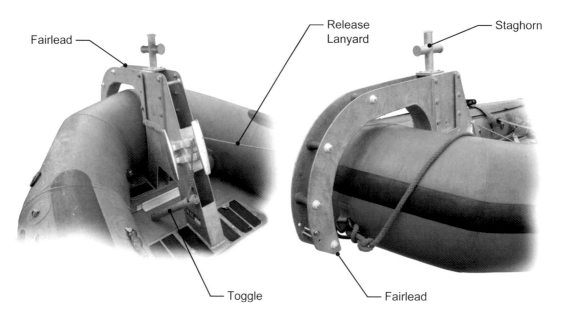

05025. Whiskey Class engine – checks

a.   The coxswain should make the following general checks daily and again on each occasion after the boat has been hoisted. Additionally the Operator's Manual applicable to the engine should be read to ensure any other requirements are met. The following checks are to be completed at the start of each Duty Period:

(1)   Check that the boat is sitting correctly in the chocks. If the boat is in the water ensure that it is sitting correctly, not listing or taking on water.

(2)   Ensure that the towing bridle is correctly in place.

(3)   The steadying lines are rigged correctly.

(4)   The inflation tube from forward to aft is fully inflated.

(5)   Check the boatrope and toggle are correctly rigged.

(6)   Carry out a safety and functional check of the release hook and ensure the chain preventer is correctly rigged, re attach the fall on completion.

(7)   Check contents of boats bag and ancillary equipment (iaw para 05059).

(8)   Carry out functional VHF comms check, test upper deck broadcast and check the availability of flags/wands.

(9)   Instruct crew members on their tasks and check their equipment and dress, ie, Marine safety helmet, immersion suit, automatic hazardous duty lifejacket, safety boots and a sharp knife.

(10) Ensure power to davit/crane is available

b.   **Engine checks**

(1)   Outboard motor firmly clamped to the transom and wire retaining strop in position.

(2)   The motor tilts freely.

(3)   The gear shift lever is in the neutral position.

(4)   No obstructions fouling the propeller.

(5)   Fuel tanks full and shaken well to mix the contents.

(6)   Fuel line connector is correctly snapped on and fuel line is primed.

(7)   Kill cord is fitted to the cut-out switch and a spare Kill cord is readily available.

05026. Whiskey Class engine starting procedures

a.   **Pre-start checks**. Once in the boat the coxswain should carry out the following pre-start checks (these checks are general, the relevant operator's manual for the engine fit should be studied for variations).

(1)   Ensure the fuel tank is filled with unleaded gasoline and the correct grade oil (OMD23) mixed in a gasoline/oil ratio of 50:1.

(2)   Shake the fuel tank to ensure the contents are thoroughly mixed and the tank vent is open.

(3)   Slide fuel connector on to the motor.

(4)   Prime carburettors by squeezing the primer bulb.

(5)   Confirm that the gear shift is in neutral.

b.   **To start.** These procedures are general, the relevant manual for each engine should be studied for variations.

(1)   Attach Kill cord to leg.

(2)   Set the throttle control to 'Start', and, if the engine is cold, press the primer bulb between six and eight times.

(3)   Pull the starting cord slowly out until resistance is felt, then pull it out firmly and sharply to revolve the flywheel. If necessary, repeat until the engine starts.

c.   **Once started**

(1)   Check the flow of cooling water through the tell-tale discharge. (If there is no cooling water, stop the engine immediately).

(2)   Reduce the engine speed to idling. An oil slick may be observed - this is normal. Push the choke in (if fitted).

05027. Whiskey Class engine – running procedures and checks

a.   Once the outboard motor is running the boat is ready to be operated.

b.   **To go ahead**

(1)   Move the gear shift lever smoothly and firmly forward to engage ahead gear.

(2)   Increase speed by twisting the throttle towards the 'Fast' position.

(3)   Do not race the engine, particularly when it is cold.

(4)   When under way, the coxswain must adjust the speed to suit the sea and wind conditions in order to reduce the risk of exposure to shock and vibration where practicable.

c.   **To go astern**

(1)   Throttle back to the slow position; pause until the engine drops to idling speed, then move the gear lever smoothly and firmly backwards to engage astern gear.

(2)   Increase speed by twisting the throttle towards the 'Fast' position until the engine reaches the required speed.

d.   **Changing gear**. Always allow the engine revolutions to drop to idling speed in the neutral position before going on to engage ahead gear from astern gear or vice versa.

e.   **Checks while running**. Periodically check:

(1)   Flow of water through the cooling water discharge.

(2)   Tightness of the engine clamps on the transom.

(3)   Fuel level of the in-use tank.

05028. Whiskey Class engine – stopping procedures

a.   **Normal methods**. There are the following alternative methods of stopping:

(1) Put the engine in neutral and pull off the Kill cord.

(2) Put the engine in neutral, disconnect the fuel line and allow the carburettor to run dry (see Note).

Note.   *Method 2 should be used when the boat is not going to be used for some time, or when it is required to drain the carburettor of fuel for servicing or safety.*

05029. Whiskey Class Engine - Fault Finding

a.   These checks are general and the relevant operator's manual for each engine should be studied for variations.

b.   **If the engine will not start**

Symptom	Remedial action
Engine will not turn over	Check gear shift is in neutral.
Engine will not fire	Check Kill cord is attached.
	Check fuel level.
	Check fuel line lead is primed and tank vent is open.
	Check fuel filter is clear.
	Check spark plugs; change if oiled up.

c. **Lack of power**. Ascertain whether any of the following causes are reducing the power output.

(1) Engine overheating because the cooling system is not operating properly - obstruction at the water intake?

(2) Fuel contamination, water in the fuel?

(3) Fuel pump filter partially blocked?

(4) Plugs dirty?

(5) Damaged propeller or fouling beneath the hull?

(6) Damaged sparking plugs, eg. insulator cracked?

05030. W525 Craft – rigging and operating as a sea boat (minor war vessels)

a. **Fitting an aluminium bow fairlead to a mine clearance W525**. When a Mine Clearance boat is fitted with an aluminium bow fairlead the boatrope is to be led though the fairlead and toggled off allowing the craft to be towed on the boatrope with the bow fairlead taking the strain.

b. **Preparing a W525 as a sea boat**

(1) Place the inflated craft, with the engine secured to the transom on deck under the crane or derrick. Secure the webbing slings to the boat. Lead the boatrope through the aluminium bow fairlead and secure with the toggle then pass the boatrope outboard of the ship's guardrails and other fittings and secure it to bollards or a cleat sited well forward in the ship. The purposes of the boatrope are:

(a) During launching, to keep the boat heading in the same direction as the ship until the RFD hook has released.

(b) If necessary, to tow the boat alongside the ship.

(c) During recovery, to hold the boat directly under the davit while it is being hooked on.

(2) The optimum length of the boatrope is that which allows the boat to ride in the water directly under the fall during launching and recovery. Once the ideal position has been established the rope should be marked with bunting at the point at which it is to be turned up. This length must be regularly checked for accuracy, particularly when the boatrope is new and liable to stretch.

c. **Rigging a W525 sea boat derrick**. If a derrick is to be used to launch and recover the craft it should be rigged with a standing wire topping lift, light tackles for the guys, and a 20mm polyester fall. The fall must be fitted with an RFD hook and preventer.

d. **Crew and lowerers**. The crew of a W525 Sea Boat consists of a coxswain and a bowman. A Petty Officer or Leading Seaman is in charge of the lowerers and is responsible for the operation of lowering and launching the Sea Boat. The lowerers should comprise a Winch Driver, two hands to back up on the fall and, depending on the weather conditions, from one to three hands to man each guy.

e. **Launching**. Drills for launching a W525 rigged as a Sea Boat are similar to those given for RIBs except that during the launch and recovery of a W525 the ship should maintain a speed of between two and five knots, depending on the prevailing weather conditions and the experience of the crew. In the mine countermeasures W525, the coxswain swings the engine into the down position whilst the boat is at deck-edge level and before the lowering sequence has commenced. Once the boat is in the water and the RFD has released and clear the coxswain starts the engine before embarking the crew. The craft is then moved ahead to take the weight off the boatrope before giving the bowman the order to slip the boatrope.

f. **Handling a W525 on the open sea**. The handling characteristics of a W525 in sheltered waters will be well understood by a qualified coxswain. However, it should be borne in mind that handling a W525 on the open sea can present additional difficulties; they are:

(1) *Overturning*. An unladen W525 is easily overturned when heading into a strong wind or heavy sea, and in such conditions the coxswain and bowman should sit as far forward as possible. The boat must be kept well balanced and speed must be reduced when making a turn.

(2) *Going alongside*. The most significant factors in bringing a W525 alongside in the open sea are the considerable drift caused by wind and the effect of the overtaking stern wave. The angle of approach is not too critical and the best line to minimise the effects of sea and wind can therefore be selected. The buoyancy tube acts as a large fender, but the fabric must not be allowed to chafe on abrasive surfaces or be torn by any projections.

g. **Recovery**. Drills for recovering a W525 rigged as a Sea Boat are similar to those laid down for RIBs. The boatrope is always used in the first stage of the recovery. After any passengers have disembarked from the craft the engine is cut and the boat hoisted. At deck-edge level the engine is housed. After hoisting and placing on deck, the boat is prepared as a Sea Boat and a check is made of the Sea Boat's equipment and the derrick's rigging.

05031. Whiskey Class – safety and transportation procedures

a. **Safety procedures**. The following safety procedures are to be observed in Whiskey craft on all occasions:

(1) Smoking in the boat is never permitted. A **NO SMOKING** notice should be clearly displayed when the boat is 'fuelled up' ready for use. When the craft is not required for use fuel tanks must be taken out of the boat and stowed in a designated stowage.

(2) The painter must be 0.6 metres shorter than the length of the boat in order not to risk fouling the propeller. It is not to be used as a steadying line for passengers embarked or for riding the painter by the crew, ie bowman standing up leaning back on the painter whilst the boat is underway.

(3) Outboard motors must be secured with a safety line when being moved or placed in the boat. Whenever a motor is shipped it must be secured to the transom by a 6mm SWR safety strop.

(4) In strong winds the boat should be kept well balanced and speed should be reduced when making a turn.

(5)   Whiskey craft should not be used for painting operations. If paint is accidentally spilled on any part it is to be removed immediately with a clean rag. Solvents are not to be used.

(6)   The side manned by the coxswain in a Whiskey is optional. However, in a Sea Boat launch or recovery the coxswain is best seated on the outboard side and adjacent to the toggle release lanyard.

b. **Transportation procedures**

(1)   The Whiskey 525 can be transported, inflated or deflated provided there is adequate protection from a boat cover or polyethylene wrapping.

(2)   Fuel tanks and battery must be removed and the engine secured according to the manufacturer's instructions.

(3)   The boat must be well supported on either a trailer or cradle and chocks adjusted to fit the hull correctly.

(4)   The boat must be secured to the trailer or chocks with suitable webbing straps.

(5)   If the boat is to be transported in an enclosed vehicle, it is to be deflated, dismantled and stowed in its respective valises before being loaded.

SECTION 3 – HEAVY DUTY MEDIUM INFLATABLE BOAT (HD MIB)

05032. Heavy duty medium inflatable boat (HD MIB) Mk 2 – introduction

a. **The heavy duty medium inflatable boat (Fig 5-7).** The HD MIB has been developed as a replacement for the Gemini Boat, which has given excellent service to the Royal Navy for many years. The HD MIB consists of an inflatable U-shaped tube, manufactured in a proofed fabric which forms the sides and bow, the bow being double skinned on the bottom quadrant. A transom board of marine plywood, on which the engine is mounted, is bonded to the tube and floor panel. The buoyancy tube is divided into five compartments, plus keel, each provided with a combined inflation/deflation valve and a safety top-up-valve. The craft is designed so that it will remain afloat when fully loaded if any two compartments are deflated. A roll-away slatted deck with three thrust boards' forward forms a semi-rigid deck, below which is the inflatable keel and fabric floor assembly. The HD MIB may be equipped with a long-shafted Mariner 40 HP min mag outboard engine for use in the mine clearance role or a Yanmar D27 (diesel) outboard engine for general use. By fitting the appropriate equipment the general service HD MIB may be used as a general purpose boat capable of fulfilling the following roles:

(1) Mine clearance.

(2) Clearance diving.

(3) General purpose diving boat for bottom search, deep diving, etc.

(4) Patrol and assault.

(5) Communications at sea.

(6) Boom defence maintenance.

b. **Seaworthiness.** Once at sea, the coxswain must continuously assess how wind and sea are affecting the performance of the boat. He must be prepared to reduce the speed and adjust the rate of turn to suit the weather conditions and the sea- keeping characteristics of the boat. In rough weather a HD MIB can be driven fast towards and away from the direction of the waves, provided good judgment is exercised and the boat is not allowed to slam dangerously. Considerable care must be taken if the boat is turned across the sea as exaggerated corkscrewing may occur at speed and this may lead to capsizing. If caught in very bad weather, speed must be reduced until the boat comes off the plane. This can be extremely uncomfortable and should only be used as a last resort should the boat begin to slam exceptionally hard. The coxswain should also be aware of the dangers of the boat flexing in higher sea states and when being hoisted or lowered, if not fully inflated.

WARNING

THE HD MIB MUST NOT BE USED AS A QUICK REACTION SEA BOAT OR CRASHBOAT AND SHOULD ONLY BE LAUNCHED AND RECOVERED IN AN UNMANNED CONDITION WHEN THE SHIP IS STOPPED IN THE WATER.

Fig 5-7. Medium inflatable boat (MIB)

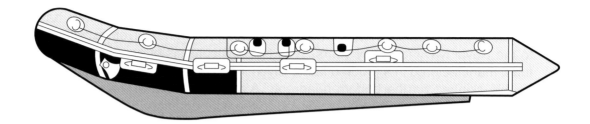

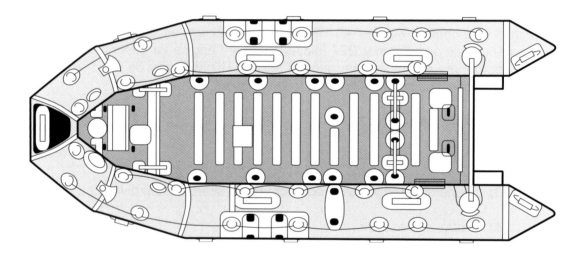

05033. HD MIB – specification

a. The HD MIB General Service NSN 1940-99-169-0738 is a fully inflatable rubber boat with a rigid plywood transom. The boat is packed away in its canvas valise and inflated as and when required, normally by ships diving teams. **BR 7909 Inflatable Raiding Craft Mk2 and Heavy Duty Medium Inflatable Boat - General Service** is the authoritative publication for this craft.

b. There are three variations of the HD MIB, these are:

    (1) HD MIB High Transom
    (2) HD MIB Assault
    (3) HD MIB EOD (Superseded by the W525 MC/EOD).

c. **Environmental Conditions**

    Maximum Sea State   4
    Maximum Wind Force   5
    Operating Temperatures   -30 to + 45ºC

d. **Dimensions**

Inflated

Length	5.20 metres
Beam	2.18 metres
Tube diameter	0.57 metres
Maximum engine size	1 x 40 hp (30 kW)

Stowed in Valise

Length	1.60 metres
Breadth	0.78 metres
Height	0.50 metres

e. **Weight**

Weight of boat with engine and fuel	393 kg (engine weight 94 kg)
Crew of two	150 kg
Boat bag	10 kg
Total weight	553 kg

Maximum Hoisting Weight - 700kg

f. **Boat assembly time**

Manual inflation – 10 minutes
HP Air inflation – approximately one minute

g. **Performance**

Speed	10-18 knots
Capacity	12 (including crew)
Crew	Two

h. **Requirement to fit a propeller guard**. A propeller guard must be fitted unless the subsequent reduction in the speed and power of the boat is inappropriate to the role in which the boat is operating. For example, no propeller guard is required when the boat is used as a Sea Boat, or for boarding operations, or when it is necessary to demonstrate the full capabilities of the craft during training courses.

05034. HD MIB – crewing

The HD MIB carries a crew of two: a coxswain and bowman. The coxswain of the HD MIB must have completed a boat coxswains course at an authorised training school and must have completed on-board training and be deemed and certified competent by the Seamanship Training Officer before being allowed to coxswain the craft unsupervised. He must have a complete working knowledge of his craft and its engine, and be capable of rectifying minor engine defects. The bowman must have completed on-board training to a level where he is capable of taking over from the coxswain, re-starting the engine, manoeuvring the boat safely to recover a man overboard and taking the boat alongside. Dress in the HD MIB must conform to that given for RIBs.

05035. HD MIB – assembly

a.   The HD MIB is designed for simplicity of assembly. When the boat is initially assembled, everything is a tight fit. This is normal, as during the first few hours of service the boat is inclined to stretch a little and the fabric will become more flexible. After a small amount of use the boat will be easier to assemble, to use and to pack into its valise. The boat is to be manually inflated in the following manner:

(1)   Open the valise by releasing the quick release buckles.

(2)   The valise is now free to open, allowing the boat to be unrolled, exposing the manual inflation valves.

(3)   Inflate the boat through the "B5" valves in the buoyancy tubes and the "A7" valve in the keel, using the inflate/deflate bellows.

(4)   The boat must be inflated to full working pressure for optimum performance. This pressure of 4 pounds per square inch (psi) in the buoyancy tubes and 6 psi in the keel, is reached when air can be heard escaping from the relief valves.

05036. HD MIB general service packing details

Fig 5-8. HD MIB packing details

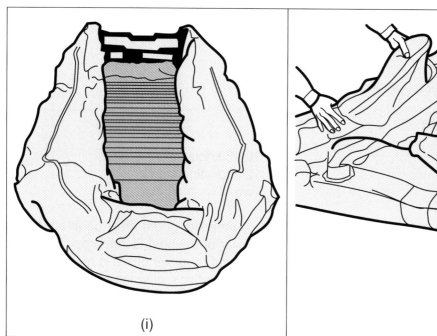	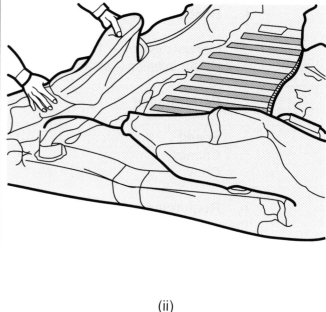
(i)	(ii)
Stage 1. With the tubes deflated but not "sucked out", pull the port and starboard buoyancy tubes inboard against the sides of the deck.	**Stage 2.** Fold the cone ends of the buoyancy tube to the same width as the transom and inboard to lay flat on the transom face.

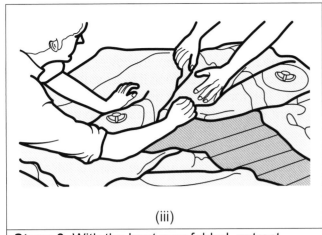

(iii)

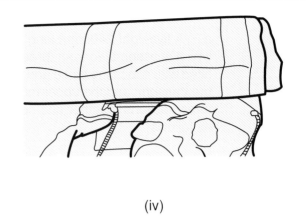

(iv)

Stage 3. With the boat now folded, extract any remaining air from the stern chambers using the bellows and ensure that the valve diaphragms are in the reset positions and caps are correctly fitted.

Stage 4. Roll the folded boat from the transom forward. Roll the stern squarely and tightly towards the bow (twice). Extract the air from the bow chambers and keel.

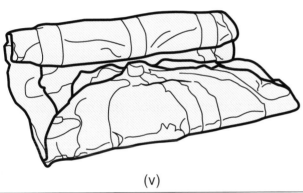

(v)

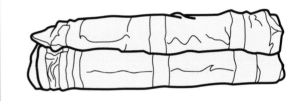

(vi)

Stage 5. Fold the bow towards the stern using the forward edge of the stern thrustboard as a fold line.

Stage 6. Fold the bow section on top of the pack.

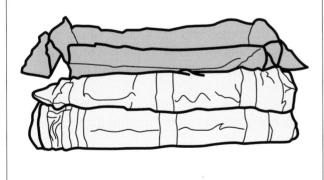

(vii)

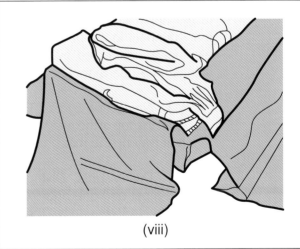

(viii)

Stage 7. Place the boat into the valise. The pack must fill the full area of the valise and sit squarely.

Stage 8. Fold the straps of the valise over the pack and secure the quick-release buckles. Fold the side flaps of the valise over and secure the quick-release buckles

05037. HD MIB – lighting mast and assembly

a.   A five-light 2400mm long mast (Fig 5-9) is fitted to the General Service HD MIB which is assembled from three sections: the mounting clamp, the lower mast section, fitted with a locating pintle and clamp arrangement for securing it to a locating block on the transom, and the upper mast section. The mast is to be assembled by mating the three sections together and securing them with Protex over-centre fastening devices as follows:

(1)   Fit the upper and lower sections together using the 'over-centre' latch.

(2)   Secure the lower section to the mounting clamp using the 'over-centre' latch.

(3)   Place the mast on the transom, positioning the mast spigot on the transom location. For single engine installations the mast must be fitted on the starboard location, and for twin engine installations the mast must be fitted on the central location.

(4)   Secure the mast firmly in position with the hand clamp.

(5)   Connect the waterproof plugs and sockets between the mast sections and connect the lower plug to the battery box.

Notes:

1.   Care must be taken with the plugs and sockets to ensure that mating surfaces and threads are kept clear of sand and grit.

2.   A radar reflector can be fitted at the top of the mast. An internally threaded aluminium insert welded into the top section receives an M12 bolt fitted to the reflector.

b.   The mast has a three-position, single pole, centre-off switch to select the navigation lights (switch up) and diving lights (switch down). Two in-line, double pole plugs and sockets connect the middle and upper mast sections, to provide the electrical supply to the upper lights. A cable from the switch box terminates in a double-pole plug that connects to the battery box socket. The centre and top section of the mast are electrically connected by two double pole connectors, one in each circuit. All light fittings are Aqua Signal 25 Series and are fitted to the mast as detailed below.

(1)   *Navigation lights.* The masthead light is all round white, mounted 360mm from the top of the mast and a bicolour light, red and green, mounted approximately half way up the mast.

(2)   *Diving lights.* Diving lights are two all round red, mounted one at the top of the mast and one approximately 660mm above the transom, and one all round white, 1455mm above the transom. Navigation and diving lights all face forward.

Fig 5-9. Light mast, HD MIB – general service

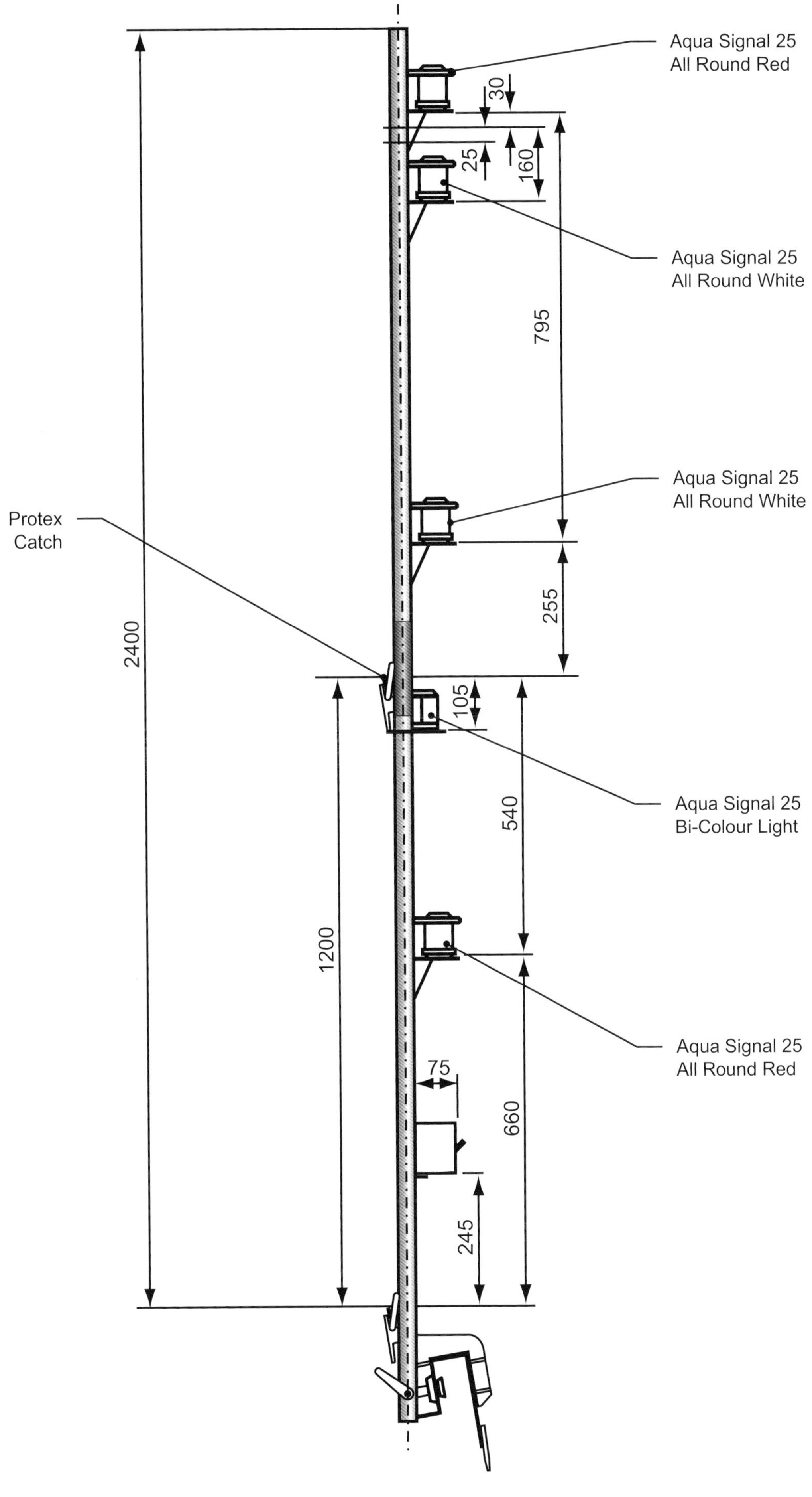
Aqua Signal 25
All Round Red
30
25
160
Aqua Signal 25
All Round White
795
Aqua Signal 25
All Round White
Protex
Catch
255
2400
105
Aqua Signal 25
Bi-Colour Light
540
1200
Aqua Signal 25
All Round Red
75
660
245

05038. HD MIB – battery box

The battery box, which is manufactured from high impact plastic, holds a 12V, 55Ah battery packed in closed-cell PVC foam. Fitted to the front of the box are two 12 A Niphan sockets which mate with the plugs on the mast lighting cable. Adjacent to the sockets are two 20 A waterproof toggle switches which switch the battery power. The lid is retained by two Protex catches and is hinged at the rear. Two webbing handles are provided for lifting and carrying the box which are secured on the boat by two strap locators fitted to the front and rear of the lid. At the rear of the sockets and switches is a small waterproof enclosure on top of which are mounted two fuse holders. Two fuse holders which carry spare fuses are also enclosed in the battery box.

Fig 5-10. Battery box

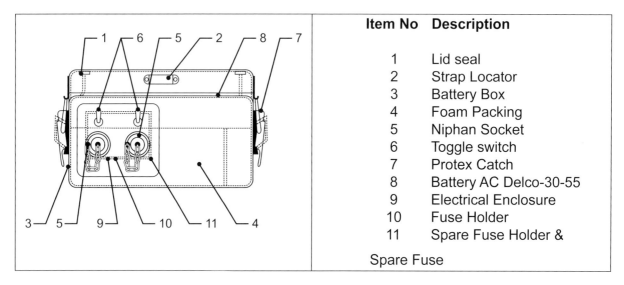

Item No	Description
1	Lid seal
2	Strap Locator
3	Battery Box
4	Foam Packing
5	Niphan Socket
6	Toggle switch
7	Protex Catch
8	Battery AC Delco-30-55
9	Electrical Enclosure
10	Fuse Holder
11	Spare Fuse Holder & Spare Fuse

05039. HD MIB – boat rope towing arrangement

a. Details of the bridle, its components and fitting instructions are similar to those given for the 6.5m RIB, with the following exceptions:

(1) The HD MIB towing bridle consists of a stainless steel ring to which are attached three lengths of 2 metres x 14mm dia, three-strand, black nylon rope. Each rope is soft spliced to the ring with a 75mm long eye into a 120mm long splice. The second end of each rope is similarly eye spliced to a karabiner hook with a screw down collar locking device, for securing the central main bridle leg to the "D" ring on the stern thrustboard and the port and starboard bridles to the tow patches fitted on top of the tube.

(2) When towing with the HD MIB, the towline is attached to a bridle fitted to the two U bolts that face outboard on the transom.

Note. *A bow fairlead can be fitted to the HD MIB (similar to the W525 shown in Fig 5-6) when used in the Mine Clearance Role. Further details will be found in* **Category three of BR 7909.**

05040. HD MIB – lifting arrangements

a. **Lifting points.** The HD MIB lifting points are: two stainless steel U bolts, mounted on the transom and facing inboard, one lifting patch port and starboard midships and one lifting patch port and starboard forward are provided as attachments for a six-legged sling.

b.   **Lifting slings.**   The HD MIB six-legged lifting sling consists of an oval forged steel ring which carries three mild steel slotted shackle plates fitted to the ring before closure. Each shackle plate carries two 50mm wide webbing straps; each pair indelibly stencilled FORWARD LEG, MID LEG OR AFT LEG. Each strap terminates in a single "snap-on" hook. The lifting sling strap lengths for use with the HD MIB using a diesel engine differ from those used when a gasoline engine is fitted. The two lifting slings are not interchangeable; each must only be used for its designated purpose. If a boat is to be hoisted when a gasoline engine is fitted then the sling used must be coloured Drab Green. When a diesel engine is fitted a Bright Orange sling is used. Lengths of sling legs are listed below.

Boat type	NSN	Fwd leg	Middle leg	After leg
Standard (gasoline)	3940-831-1986	1.913m	1.113m	1.523m
Diesel	3940-500-8690	2.31m	1.40m	1.50m

Fig 5-11. Hoisting the boat

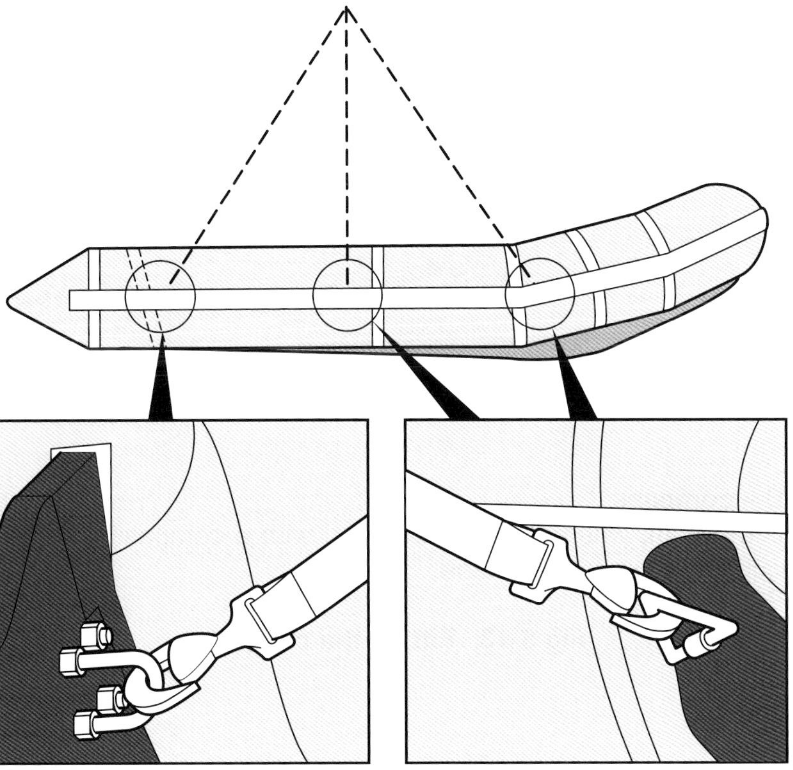

c.   Each lifting sling has a stainless steel chain tag engraved or stamped containing the following details:

(1)   Safe working load
SWL = 0.70 tonnes.

(2)   Test load: 1.40 Tonnes.

(3)   Test certificate serial number.

(4)   Date of test.

(5)   Test authority: eg manufacturer.

> *Note.* *Should no chain tag be fitted, or if more than 12 months has passed since the last proof test, then the appliance is considered unserviceable and must not be used.*

05041. HD MIB – fuel

Diesel fuel used for the Yanmar (D27) or petrol used in the 40 hp outboard engine is to be contained in five-gallon Flexible Fuel Tanks NSN 0479-99-642-2317. These tanks are designed to be attached to the inside of the boat as shown in Fig 5-12. This method of stowage ensures that the bag maintains its shape and reduces the risk of damage. When not in use the bayonet fuel connector should always have the protection plug fitted to prevent damage to the bayonet socket (Now supplied with push fit connectors). The flexible fuel tank should be used iaw BR 7977.

Fig 5-12. The flexible fuel tank

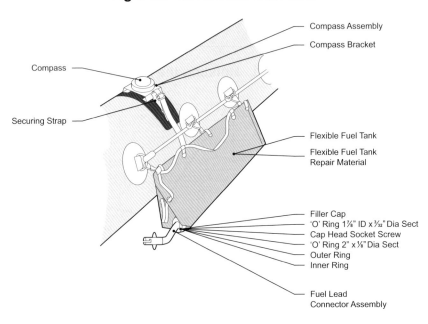

05042. HD MIB – compass

The HD MIB can, when required, be fitted with a compass. This is mounted on a bracket and secured to the buoyancy tube.

Fig 5-13. Fitting the compass

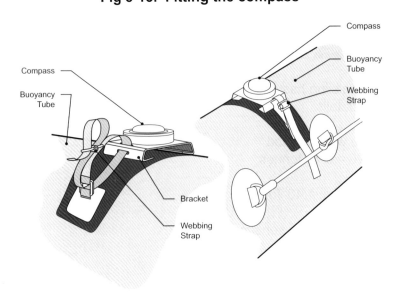

05043. HD MIB – operating checks and procedures

a. **First deployment checks**. The Following checks are to be made at first deployment following removal from the valise and at regular intervals if the boat is to remain inflated and rigged for any length of time to ensure availability for immediate use.

(1) Inspect the hull to ensure that it is free from abrasions or damage to the fabric.

(2) Ensure that the buoyancy chambers are completely inflated to the correct working pressure and that the valves, including the caps and valve inserts are tightened correctly to prevent air loss.

(3) Ensure that the grab line fixings are secure.

(4) Check that all shackles are in place and secure: pin heads must face away from the inflation chambers.

(5) The outboard engine is to be checked to ensure it is firmly clamped to the transom and secured by a 6mm wire retaining strop. The propeller guard is to be inspected for damage and security.

Notes:

1. Avoid leaving a fully inflated boat in direct sunlight as this can cause premature wear of the valves.

2. Do not use the carrying handles for towing or mooring the boat. The "D" rings specifically designed should be used.

3. Do not inflate the boat using an air line without pressure reduction equipment.

b. **Pre-start checks.** The coxswain should make the following general checks daily and again on each occasion after the boat has been hoisted. Additionally the Operators Manual applicable to the engine should be read to ensure any other requirements are met. The following checks are to be completed at the start of each duty period:

(1) Check that the boat is sitting correctly in the chocks. If the boat is in the water ensure that it is sitting correctly, not listing or taking on water.

(2) Ensure that the towing bridle is correctly in place.

(3) The steadying lines are rigged correctly.

(4) The inflation tube from forward to aft is fully inflated.

(5) Check the boatrope and toggle are correctly rigged.

(6) Carry out a safety and functional check of the release hook and ensure the chain preventer is correctly rigged, re attach the fall on completion.

(7) Check contents of boats bag and ancillary equipment (iaw para 05059).

(8)   Instruct crew members on their tasks and check their equipment and dress ie, Marine safety helmet, immersion suit, automatic hazardous duty lifejacket, safety boots and sharp knife.

(9)   Ensure power to davit/crane is available.

(10) Carry out functional VHF comms check, test upper deck broadcast and check the availability of flags/wands.

c.   **Engine checks**

(1)   Outboard engine firmly clamped to the transom and wire retaining strop in position.

(2)   The engine tilts freely.

(3)   The gear shift lever is in the neutral position.

(4)   No obstructions fouling the propeller.

(5)   Fuel tanks full and shaken well to mix the contents.

(6)   Fuel line connector is correctly snapped on and fuel line is primed.

(7)   Kill cord is fitted to the cut-out switch and a spare Kill cord is readily available.

HD MIB engine starting procedures

d.   **Pre-start checks**. Once in the boat the coxswain should carry out the following pre-start checks (these checks are general, the relevant operator's manual for the engine fit should be studied for variations).

(1)   Ensure the fuel tank is filled with unleaded gasoline and the correct grade oil (OMD23) mixed in a gasoline/oil ratio of 50:1 or diesel for the D27 Yanmar engine.

(2)   Shake the fuel tank to ensure the contents are thoroughly mixed and the tank vent is open.

(3)   Slide fuel connector on to the engine fuel connector.

(4)   Prime carburettors by squeezing the primer bulb.

(5)   Confirm that the gear shift is in neutral.

e.   **To start**. These procedures are general; the relevant manual for each engine should be studied for variations.

(1)   Attach Kill cord to leg.

(2)   Set the throttle control to 'Start', and, if the engine is cold, press the primer bulb between six and eight times.

(3)   Pull the starting cord slowly out until resistance is felt, then pull it out firmly and sharply to revolve the flywheel. If necessary, repeat until the engine starts.

f.   **Once started**

(1)   Check the flow of cooling water through the tell-tale discharge. (If there is no cooling water, stop the engine immediately).

(2)   Reduce the engine speed to idling. An oil slick may be observed - this is normal. Push the choke in (if fitted).

HD MIB engine – running procedures and checks

g.   **Checks while running**. Periodically check:

(1)   Flow of water through the cooling water discharge.

(2)   Tightness of the engine clamps on the transom.

(3)   Fuel level of the in-use tank.

Whiskey Class engine – stopping procedures

h.   **Normal methods**. There are three following alternative methods of stopping:

(1)   Put the engine in neutral and pull off the Kill cord.

(2)   Press the red button on the end of the throttle grip.

(3)   Put the engine in neutral, disconnect the fuel line and allow the carburettor to run dry.

Note.   Method 3 should be used when the boat is not going to be used for some time, or when it is required to drain the carburettor of fuel for servicing or safety.

05044. HD MIB – maintenance

a.   **HD MIB.** Maintenance schedules have been prepared for the HD MIB; these can be found in **Category 5 of BR 7909**, the authoritative publication for this type of boat.

b.   **Yanmar D27 engine.** There are no reference books for this type of outboard engine but Manufacturer's Workshop Manuals and Parts Books may be ordered using the engine type correct description of Yanmar D27AXLE Build standard 0183, NSN 0482-99-957-4638.

05045. HD MIB – boat bag and other onboard equipment

For normal operations the stores and equipment to be carried in the boat are the same as those given for the 4.7m RIB at Para 05059 standfast the Radar Reflector and Compass but with the addition of the battery.

05046. HD MIB – launch and recovery procedures

Drills for launching and recovering a HD MIB when rigged as a Sea Boat are similar to those given for RIBs in Para 05097.

SECTION 4 – RIGID INFLATABLE BOATS (RIB) INTRODUCTION

05047. Rigid inflatable boats (RIB) – introduction

Top weight is a key factor in warships. In the mid 1970s an urgent need to reduce top weight caused a critical review to be made of the boats borne in HM ships. Conventional boats with GRP or wooden hulls slung on twin davits contributed a considerable amount to the top weight of a ship, so it was decided to try to find a lighter design of ship's boat which could be hoisted on a lighter type of davit or crane. The Gemini inflatable craft, which the Royal Navy had considerable experience in operating, was considered not to have sufficient strength or directional stability to provide a satisfactory replacement for standard ship's boats, but a development of the Gemini – the Rigid Inflatable Boat – seemed to possess the lightness and sea-keeping qualities which were required; this type of boat had been used as a small lifeboat by the RNLI for several years. The 5.4 metre Searider was introduced into service with the Offshore Patrol Vessels and ships of the Fishery Protection Squadron in the late seventies. This craft proved its versatility and seaworthiness in operations around the world. Since then water-powered 6.5 metre and 7.8-metre RIBs have been introduced to replace some of the older types of ship's boat. A 5.4 metre Searider with an inboard diesel engine has now been procured for use in ships with insufficient available deck space to accommodate either a Pacific 22 or 24.

05048. RIB – operating features

As already mentioned the key factor hastening the introduction of the RIB as a ship's boat was the saving in ship's top weight, but this type of craft has other advantages. The RIB is fast and seaworthy and can reach the scene of an incident quickly. The single-fall davit or hydraulic crane is simple to operate and lowering and recovery is quick and efficient. The coxswain has a good all-round view from a powerful and easily manoeuvred boat. These features make the RIB an excellent sea boat. The drawbacks of the Rigid Inflatable design are that this type of boat has a smaller carrying capacity than a traditional boat and provides little protection from wind and spray. However the reduced carrying capacity is compensated for by the RIB's high speed. The RIB is not a comfortable means of transport between ship and shore; this disadvantage of RIB operation must be recognised and passengers must be properly briefed and equipped before embarking. The coxswain must be aware throughout of the need to reduce exposure to shock and vibration where practicable and when safe to do so.

05049. RIB – general construction

The term rigid inflatable boat is derived from the manner of its construction. RIBs are built with a V shaped hull surmounted by an inflatable U-collar to form the gunwale. They have a wide square transom suitably strengthened to provide a mounting for an outboard motor in the smaller craft or a water-jet drive unit for the Pacific 22 and 24. RIBs are designed for speed and stability. All non-essentials have been dispensed with: there are no canopies or cabins, the controls are simple and there is no rudder. All RIBs have a high power-to-weight ratio and a planing type of hull. They start to plane at about 15 knots and once on the plane will achieve a considerably higher top speed, depending on the type of RIB, weather and load.

05050. RIB – design features

a.　**Hull.** The deep 'V' hull of a RIB is derived from offshore racing boat designs. It provides a very stable platform when the boat is stopped and draws sufficient depth under water to give reasonable control at slow speed in a wind. The shape of the bow deflects the force of the waves when the boat is planing; this reduces deceleration and slamming in a rough sea. The buoyancy tube, which adds to the freeboard of the hull, produces lift while the RIB is heeling inwards when turning under power. The combination of lift from the buoyancy tube and the inherent stability in the hull design makes the RIB safe to turn at high speed; there is little danger of capsizing. The bonding of the buoyancy tube to the hull is very strong as it is subjected to high stresses at the sides and in the bow.

b.　**Propulsion**. The smaller types of RIB are currently propelled by gasoline driven outboard motors. Fuel is a fire and explosion hazard so a **'No Smoking'** sign must be displayed adjacent to the boat when fuel is embarked: the portable fuel tanks must be removed from the boat and stowed in the designated gasoline tank stowage when the boat is not being used as a Sea Boat or operated in harbour. The Pacific 22-metre and 24-metre RIBs are fitted with an internally mounted diesel engine located behind the coxswain's position. Drive is transmitted from the engine via a driveshaft through a water-jet mounted reinforced transom.

c.　**Control.** The coxswain's control is from a seated position. The simple controls consist of a steering wheel and a combined gearshift/throttle lever. The number of instruments and switches on the control panel vary depending upon the type of engine and the electrical installations fitted in the boat, but are sufficient to allow the coxswain to monitor the performance of his engine when under way. Battery power is used for starting the RIB engines and electrical outlets are provided for navigation lights, the radio and the signalling lamp.

05051. RIB – crewing

The minimum crew for a RIB is two: a coxswain and a crewman, but the Pacific 22 and 24 RIB is more easily worked with a crew of three. The coxswain of a RIB must have completed the appropriate RIB coxswain course at an authorised training school and, if handling a RIB as a Sea Boat or crash boat, must have completed on-board training and be deemed and certified competent by the Seamanship Training Officer. The coxswain must have a complete working knowledge of the boat, its engine and its electrical system, and be capable of rectifying minor defects. Crew members other than the coxswain must have received on-board training to a level where they are capable of taking over from the coxswain, re-starting the engine, manoeuvring the boat safely to recover a man overboard and taking the boat alongside. Because all RIBs bounce and slam when under way, the crew must be physically fit and have the necessary stamina and endurance needed to handle and man the boat effectively for several hours. All crew members are to be first-aid trained to Level 1 by the Senior Medical Branch rating ashore/afloat every three months, and also be familiar with casualty handling procedures. Common sense dictates that the judgement of the crew of any boat must not be affected by alcohol; this is particularly true with regard to RIBs, where fast reflexes are required to handle these high performance craft. Therefore personnel called upon, or liable to be called upon, to crew a RIB must not consume alcohol for a period of at least ten hours before the event.

05052. RIB – dress and safety

a.   RIBs are fast and provide no shelter from wind or sea; these add considerably to the dangers of exposure or of being accidentally thrown overboard in a rough sea or during a violent manoeuvre (see Note). To minimise this possibility all crew and passengers must use toe straps, although this requirement can be relaxed for passengers in the following circumstances:

   (1)   When conducting diving operations.

   (2)   In an emergency.

   (3)   During supervised operational sea training.

b.   On occasions when there are insufficient toe straps, handholds must be used and personnel must not sit on the inflatable collar forward of the coxswain's console.

c.   **Immersion suit**. To avoid the danger of hypothermia or drowning if personnel are thrown out of the boat, the crew and passengers must be dressed appropriately. Crew members are to wear an Immersion suit or similar garment with appropriate undergarments to suit the prevailing conditions. This is mandatory when operating in water temperatures up to and including 15°C but is left to the discretion of the Commanding Officer in water temperatures between 16°C and 20°C, giving due consideration to the nature of the task and the risk of cooling from wind-chill, spray and wave splash. When the water temperature is above 15°C and suits are not worn then sufficient foul weather clothing must be carried in the boat for all crew and passengers. Above 20°C there are very few circumstances in which the wearing of such clothing is of value, and the penalties from overheating are likely to outweigh any benefits. A hazardous duty lifejacket and DMS boots are to be worn. Properly sheathed seaman's knives are to be carried. When personnel from other nations or navies are being carried as passengers they must conform to the dress requirements outlined above. They must carry a properly sheathed seaman's knife. Naval store numbers for the Immersion suits are as follows:

Boat's crew (two toned)	Passengers/boarding party (black)
8415-99-573-7213 (S)	8415-99-765-4968 (S)
8415-99-573-7214 (M)	8415-99-765-4969 (M)
8415-99-573-7215 (L)	8415-99-765-4970 (L)
8415-99-573-7216 (XL)	8415-99-765-4971 (XL)
8415-99-765-4967 (XXL)	8415-99-765-4972 (XXL)

d.   **Lifejackets for passengers**. All passengers must be instructed in the operation of lifejackets. Passengers in RN RIBs are to wear a manual lifejacket when embarked in accordance with the SE Matrix DIN. Where crew and passengers equipment exceed the buoyancy of the HDLJ, then the ATLJ or Maritime Counter Terrorism Life-jacket (MCTLJ) may be used. LCLJs fitted with spray caps over the operating head are **not** to be used in RIBs under any circumstances, because of the risk of uncontrolled inflation leading to entrapment in the case of capsize. Armed troops and boarding parties are to wear an appropriate manual lifejacket which will provide adequate buoyancy for the equipment that they are wearing. Ties and belts should be loosened and collars unbuttoned by all personnel.

e.   **Marine safety helmet.** Marine Safety Helmets (MSHs) are designed for cranium protection and are to be worn during launch, recovery and transiting in RIBS, MIBs, and Whiskey-class small craft operation.   The MSH is fitted with removable plastic ear comfort pieces; these can be used as required and are not mandatory. Comfort pieces are patternised items and can be demanded through Naval Stores to maintain the in service life of the helmets.   The correct ear defender to use with the MSH is NSN 6515-99-126/3570; their use is mandatory in all RIBs when transiting but may be removed, at the coxswain's discretion, on arrival at the operational area where clear communication is important.   Ear defenders are not required to be worn in boats powered by outboard engines of 40 hp or below. Specialist communications-fitted boats will have MSHs fitted with the appropriate communications in the helmet.   The wearing of the helmet is mandatory whilst the craft is underway.   However, this rule can be relaxed at the discretion of the craft's coxswain if:

(1)   The craft is in a waiting station during boarding operations (motionless).

(2)   The craft is motionless.

(3)   At a dive site conducting diving operations.

(4)   In extreme hot weather conditions if the craft is loitering (2 - 3 knots) in the patrol area for long periods of time to prevent the wearer from overheating.

However,

(a) If the craft is called into a chase scenario then the helmet is to be replaced immediately before the craft is powered up onto the plane.

(b) At no time is the helmet to be relaxed for transits or long insertions into rivers or estuaries.

(c) The coxswain is to risk assess the likelihood of head injury against heat exhaustion in each instance.

Note.   *The coxswain must, whenever practicable, inform all personnel in the boat of imminent course alterations or manoeuvres.*

f.   **Requirement to fit a propeller guard**.   A propeller guard must be fitted unless the subsequent reduction in the speed and power of the boat is inappropriate to the role in which the boat is operating.   For example, no propeller guard is required when the boat is used as a Sea Boat, or for boarding operations, or when it is necessary to demonstrate the full capabilities of the craft during training courses.

g.   **Control of vibration**.

(1) *Background.*   The Control of Vibration at Work Regulations 2005 and the Merchant Shipping & Fishing Vessel (Control of Vibration at Work) Regulations 2007 stipulates that nothing shall exonerate operating authorities, line management, boat coxswains, crews and passengers from the consequences of neglect in the application and implementation of the Regulations.   It is therefore incumbent on all MoD employees when planning, ordering or executing boat missions to do so whilst considering the effect of Whole Body Vibration (WBV) on the personnel undertaking any boat mission.   This is particularly so for the operation of small high speed craft (RHIB) which are often subjected to greater shock to the hull when planning at high speeds.

(2) *Management.* Regulation 4 which stipulates the exposure dosage of WBV which should not be exceeded is currently not always achievable to the MoD boat missions without unacceptable impact on Operational Capability.

An exemption from this Regulation has been approved by the Secretary of State for Defence until July 2015 whilst the MoD undertakes a programme of work to reduce the Risk of Harm from Maritime WBV (MWBV) to As Low As is Reasonably Practicable (ALARP). Therefore it is imperative that individuals are honest and accurate with any discomfort being caused by MWBV. Using Form S3205 Boats Crew & Regular Users Logbooks and the Small Craft Mission and Health Monitoring Database as historical evidence, individuals can request a meeting with their Chain of Command (CoC) and/or sick bay in order to discuss current exposure to WBV both in the short and long term. Any aspirations for reduced exposure to WBV can be recorded on their personal preferences in order to inform the relevant Specialisation Advisor for future appointments. The earlier individuals bring issues and concerns to light the more credibility they will carry and the earlier Command can put controls in place.

(3) *Responsibility.* In order for Line Managers to manage exposure to WBV and manage the rehabilitation of anyone who is injured through WBV, individuals are required to honestly and accurately appraise their physical state throughout their career. The implementation of this policy is both a personal responsibility and a sub unit responsibility that will be checked via any FOST/Squadron Inspection.

(4) *Training.* A thorough understanding of WBV is essential if individuals and Command are to effectively manage exposure.

> (a) A standard (Institute of Naval Medicine (INM) approved) MWBV presentation will be produced and owned by NAVY SSM-AW SEA WO1 in NCHQ; it will be delivered to all seamanship vocational courses and the CODC/XODC.

> (b) The MWBV presentation will also be delivered to all boat crews annually, this will be recorded with the Command; this will checked annually as part of FOST/Squadron Inspections.

> (c) All line managers and coxswain students will attend a one-day WBV Managers course (currently under development by the INM) to allow them to effectively manage the exposure to WBV of individuals in their charge.

> (d) Physical Training. All Commands should generate and encourage unit level physical training in conjunction with RM/RN RI's in order to target and develop core body strength and flexibility.

(5) *Governance.* Individuals and Squadrons are to ensure that:

> (a) Anyone joining the branch is to be issued with Form S3205 Boats Crew & Regular Users Logbook, BR98 Boat Signal Book and Coxswains Aide Memoire, and complete a pre-exposure questionnaire (MOD 5055) as part of their joining routine and record this with the Command; this will be checked annually as part of the FOST/Squadron Inspection.

> (b) Individuals will complete and submit annually to sick bay the WBV exposure form MOD Form 5056; this will be checked annually as part of the FOST/Squadron Inspection.

(c)   The WBV exposure form MOD Form 5056 will also be completed and submitted when drafted on arrival at the gaining unit; this will be checked annually as part of the FOST/Squadron Inspection.

(d)   Individuals will complete their passage in the Boats Crew & Regular Users Logbook, paying attention to operating conditions and any injuries sustained in the remarks columns. This logbook will be used as the reference and historical evidence when completing the annual WBV exposure form (MOD 5056) or presenting to Sick Bay for treatment.

(e)   SNCO's are to pay particular attention to WBV entries when signing off passages during their normal checks. Regular entries are to be discussed with the individual and mitigation put in place where required.

(f)   Operating Authorities are to ensure that a pre-mission is conducted and the effects of WBV on the crew are considered.

(g)   Post mission debriefs are to ensure that WBV data is collected and the designated crew member completes the entry into the Small Craft Mission and Health Monitoring Database.

(h)   Any injury sustained during boat missions should be reported to sickbay with the individual clearly ensuring the cause of the injury is included in their medical documentation.

(i)   Any dynamic injury will also be reported to the Command as soon as reasonably practicable so that an incident or near miss form can be raised.

05053. RIB – seaworthiness

RIBs have excellent sea-keeping qualities and perform well in bad weather. They are extremely stable and unlikely to capsize, but certain precautions must be taken in handling RIBs in bad weather. A RIB should not be driven at high speed into a steep head sea, instead it should be steered on a diagonal course or series of courses across the direction of the waves. In a strong wind, a RIB should not be turned tightly at high speed across the wind, instead speed should be reduced before entering the turn and a gentle turn made. If the waves are short and steep, speed must be adjusted to prevent the RIB slamming too hard; in some circumstances this may require the boat to come off the plane. The coxswain must be aware throughout of the need to reduce exposure to shock and vibration where practicable and when safe to do so. Coxswains must also appreciate right from the beginning that RIBs carry very little headway and are almost totally dependent upon their engines for manoeuvring.

In order to be able to handle a RIB well, a coxswain must acquire a deft and precise 'feel' for the controls so that they know, without looking down, the direction and power that they are applying from the propulsion. A RIB is very responsive and can be manoeuvred with great accuracy while its engine is running and engaged.

05054. RIB – requirement to fit radar reflectors

a.   To enhance the radar signature of RIBs operating as Sea Boats (or whenever required), radar reflectors are provided; one reflector and mounting kit per RIB. The pattern numbers are as follows:

Radar reflector	0480-225-7922	EA	P
Mounting bracket	0480-490-4034	EA	P

b.   The same size reflector is supplied for each type of RIB, with a mounting bracket capable of adaption to each RIB. Detailed fitting instructions are provided with each reflector. Reflectors are to be placed in a readily accessible stowage and rigged when the boat is to be deployed outside the range of visibility of the ship, and/or at the Commanding Officer's discretion.

05055. RIB – returning for hoisting in the open sea

The ship should make a lee so that passengers can leave the RIB in shelter. A Pilot/ Boarding ladder or davit hoist can be used for disembarking passengers depending on the weather conditions. As soon as the RIB has been unloaded and is ready for hoisting, the ship's speed should be increased to at least five knots and the RIB sent round under the Sea Boat fall. The coxswain must manoeuvre to pick up the boatrope and keep the RIB away from the ship's side. Once the boatrope has been secured, reduce speed and allow the RIB to lie back on the boatrope (for propeller-driven craft and the Pac 24) then hook on to the fall. For Pac 22 only the weight is to remain off the boatrope. When hooked on, the coxswain indicates to the Leading Seaman on deck that the RIB is 'hooked on and ready for hoisting'. The engines of the 5.4 metre and 4.7-metre RIB must be stopped before the boat is hoisted since they must not be run without cooling water. The engine of the Pacific RIB has an internal cooling system and may be allowed to run for a short time until the boat is clear of the water.

05056. RIB – emergencies

a.   An emergency may occur occasionally as the result of mechanical faults - such as engine failure - bad handling or inattention to correct procedures by the crew. The coxswain and crew must be aware that these incidents can happen and know what action to take in the event.

b.   **Engine failure**. The immediate result of a sudden engine failure will be that the RIB stops suddenly and may fill with water over the transom. The coxswain should try to find out the cause of the engine stopping; the immediate checks to be made are:

(1)   Inadvertent operation of the emergency cut-out switch.

(2)   Fuel tank empty or fuel supply cut off.

(3)   Ignition failure.

c.   Subsequent action if engine is not re-started. If the cause cannot be found quickly, the sea anchor should be streamed to prevent the RIB drifting fast downwind and a more detailed investigation made to find the fault. The ship should be informed of the time and position of stopping and the direction and rate of drift. The crew should then take the following action:

(1)   Tend the sea anchor line to stop it snubbing and to reduce the rate of drift.

(2)   Bale out any water on deck.

(3)   Try paddling (if likely to be effective in the prevailing weather).

(4)   Have the distress signal flares available.

(5)   Maintain radio contact with the ship.

d.   **Steering jammed.** If this occurs in narrow or crowded waters, slow down and stop immediately.

e. **Deflation of the buoyancy tube**. RIBs have buoyancy tubes with either five or seven compartments and it is unlikely that the whole buoyancy tube will become deflated. If one or more compartments are deflated the height of the gunwale will be lowered and, in the open sea, the boat should be manoeuvred to prevent water being shipped. It is preferable to bring a RIB alongside with the damaged part of the buoyancy tube outboard. Losing air out of the buoyancy tube does not affect the immediate buoyancy of a RIB. The RIB with a defective buoyancy tube is, however, much less seaworthy and repairs should be made without delay.

f. **First aid inflation tube repair**

(1) *Leak stoppers*. Temporary repairs to punctures and tears in the buoyancy tubes may be carried out in an emergency by using leak stoppers. These stoppers (size 2, 3, 4 and 5) are rubber cones with a right handed thread moulded to the exterior. They are intended for temporary repair of small clean-cut holes only and a proper repair must be carried out as soon as possible. Suitable holes must be repaired as follows:

(a) Select a stopper, the greater diameter of which is larger that the hole.

(b) Insert the stopper into the hole until ther threads grip the edge of the hole.

(c) Screw the stopper into the hole until the hole is sealed.

(2) *Repair clamps*. These clamps are colloquially known as Oyster Clamps and are useful for carrying out temporary repairs to small ragged holes or tears to the buoyancy tube. The clamp consists of two oval, dish-shaped metal plates, the flat edges of which can be held firmly together by means of a bolt which passes through the centre of the plates and is secured with a wingnut. The clamp is used as follows:

(a) Loosen the wingnut so that the plates can be separated.

(b) Insert the clamp through the hole so that one plate is inside the tube and the other plate and wingnut are on the outside.

(c) Ensuring that the clamp lies along the direction of the tear and that there are no wrinkles around the clamp, tighten the wingnut until the fabric around the hole is firmly gripped between the edges of the clamp plate.

(d) Carry out a permanent repair as soon as possible.

g. **Fire**. Fire in a RIB must be dealt with quickly. Identify the area, isolate the cause and extinguish.

(1) *Pacific RIBs*. If fire breaks out in the engine compartment or below deck:

(a) Shut down all machinery.

(b) Close fuel supply valve.

(c) Operate fire extinguisher through the access port.

(d) Allow heat to dissipate before removing cover from the engine.

(2) *Petrol engined RIBs*. Fire is most likely to be caused by an electrical fault. If this is the cause:

(a) Stop the engine.

(b) Disconnect fuel leads.

(c) Isolate the battery.

(d) Extinguish fire.

(e) Re-start engine when the cause has been identified and the boat has been made safe.

h. **Swamping**. This may occur if the boat slows down suddenly and is overtaken by a following sea. A burst of power ahead will clear the RIB of water provided the scupper hoses - (in boats so fitted) - are streamed. The Pacific RIB must never be allowed to fill with so much water that the engine casing is flooded. Minor swamping is not dangerous, but can affect the handling of a RIB. As a matter of principle water on deck should be discharged as quickly as possible.

i. **Corkscrewing**. This may occur - particularly in the 5.4 metre RIB - if a RIB is being driven too fast across the sea in unfavourable weather conditions. If it starts to corkscrew a RIB is out of control and the coxswain must act immediately by reducing the speed and altering the course to bring the boat under control again.

j. **Man Overboard**. In the event of someone going overboard, the coxswain must bring the boat round by the shortest possible way to a point about five metres upwind of the man in the water; then carry out the recovery procedure given in Para 05013. If the coxswain is accidentally jerked overboard the engine will be stopped by operation of the emergency cut-out switch. A member of the crew must then take over as helmsman. After resetting the emergency cut-out switch and securing the Kill cord to his leg, he should re-start the engine and manoeuvre the RIB as described above.

05057. RIB – towing

a. **Taking in tow**. RIBs are not designed for towing and should be employed in this role only for short periods. In the Pacific RIB the weight of the tow should never be taken by the transom; when taking a tow astern the towing line must draw clear on the quarter so that it does not foul the sterndrive or outboard motor. Sufficient length of towrope must be streamed to prevent snatching and the speed of tow should be kept low. When towing alongside, fenders must be placed in suitable positions to prevent damage to the GRP hull if the object under tow is low in the water. If the craft under tow bears on the buoyancy tube it must be firmly secured to reduce rubbing and great care must be taken to see that there are no projections which might tear the fabric.

b. **Being towed**. All RIBs may be towed for short periods on the boatrope bridle, but care must be taken to prevent the bridle from chafing the buoyancy tube. The crew should insert a wooden or canvas Scotchman to absorb any wear from the movement of the towrope. The Pacific and Searider RIB have a towing eyeplate fitted on the forefoot. If possible the tow should be connected to this eyeplate if it is likely that either of these RIBs may be towed for a long distance. The eyeplate is not easily reached and in rough weather in the open sea it may be less hazardous to connect the tow to the towing bridle instead. The coxswain of the RIB under tow should try to keep the boat steering as steady as possible.

SECTION 5 – 5.4 metre RIGID INFLATABLE BOAT – WITH OUTBOARD ENGINE

05058. 5.4 metre RIB – specification

a.   **Introduction.** The 5.4 metre RIB Mk 2 (Fig 5-14), also known as the Searider, is a fast medium-sized RIB. In addition to its normal crew of two it has a carrying capacity of eight passengers or a payload of 600 kg. The boat is powered by a gasoline driven Mariner 75 outboard motor bolted to the transom. Fuel is supplied from a portable gasoline tank, and there is space for two tanks to be strapped into position between the transom stays. The coxswain controls the Searider from a console amidships which is fitted with a steering wheel, combined gearshift/throttle lever and a switch and instrument panel. A 12V battery, housed beneath the coxswain's jockey seat, provides power for starting the engine. There are three mechanical control cables leading from the console housing to the outboard motor for the remote control of the steering, gear selection and engine speed; a loom of electrical cables connects the starting, lighting and charging services. The authoritative maintenance publication for this craft is **BR 3970 - 5.4m Searider Maintenance Manual**. The dimensions of the Searider are:

Length overall	5.46 metres
Beam	2.06 metres
Height	1.45 metres
Internal width	1.07 metres

b.   **Performance.** In calm conditions, lightly loaded, the boat will start to plane at about 15 knots and reach a top speed of approximately 38 knots. In conditions up to sea state 4 (wave heights 1.25 – 2.5 metres) or with heavier loads the boat will still plane, but the maximum speed attained will drop by up to 12 knots. In higher sea states the engine power must be reduced to give a safe speed according to the strength and direction of the wind and sea. Two portable fuel tanks are normally carried with a combined capacity of 50 litres. With consumption of 25 litres an hour at maximum continuous engine rating the two tanks give an endurance of approximately two hours. The limiting distance of operation will depend upon the speed attainable with the payload that the Searider is required to carry under the prevailing weather conditions. For certain roles additional fuel tanks may be embarked.

Fig 5-14. 5.4 metre RIB Mk 2

c. **Weight and capacity**. The following table gives the weights of the boat, personnel and other items, and should be used when calculating hoisting out and recovery weights. The maximum Safe Working Lift for this craft is 1.5 tonnes, thus assuming the lifting device is capable of this lift there is a spare capacity of 475 kg when the boat is loaded as shown below. It is necessary on occasions to utilise this spare capacity, for example when conducting boarding operations or recovering survivors, but whenever possible stores or additional personnel should be embarked or disembarked when the boat is in the water to reduce unnecessary stress on the boat when it is suspended on its slings. The weight of the boat includes the weight of the water ballast that automatically enters the hull when the boat slows down and comes off the plane.

Weight of boat with 75hp engine	800 kg
Two tanks of fuel	40 kg
Boat bag	10 kg
Crash bag	25 kg
Crew of two	150 kg
Passengers x 8	600 kg
Total	1625 kg
Carrying capacity in the water	600 kg or eight Passengers

d. **Hull**. The hull of the 5.4 metre RIB is constructed of moulded GRP with a nominal thickness of 9mm. The deck of GRP coated marine ply is bonded in place to form an inner skin. The space between the deck and the hull is free-flooding and draining except for two foam-filled buoyancy tanks sited forward and aft. The remainder of this space is free to fill with 160 kg of seawater (134 kg in the 4.7-metre RIB) as ballast through two flooding ports on either side of the bow. Seawater ballast flows into the bottom compartment when the Searider comes off the plane, and flows out again through the large port in the centre of the transom when speed is increased.

e. **Transom**. The transom (Fig 5-15) is constructed of two sheets of marine ply coated with GRP. It is braced for extra strength by two sloping stainless steel stays which also provide an anchorage for the fuel tank securing straps. Viewed from astern (Fig 5-16), there are three drainage ports in the transom. The ballast drain port is on the centreline; this is open to the sea and is designed to allow the ballast water to flow out of the boat as it gathers speed. At deck level on either side are the two deck scuppers for draining away sea water shipped over the gunwale or stern. These are fitted on the outboard side with scupper hoses made of light rubber tubing. The purpose of these is to prevent water flowing back on board when the boat is stopped and lying low in the water. The scupper hoses should be triced up by their lanyards when the boat slows down and should be allowed to trail when the boat is gathering speed to go on the plane. The transom provides the mounting for the outboard motor and there are four holes drilled through the upper part to take the securing bolts. Fitting the engine is a delicate operation which requires suitable lifting gear, and the process should normally be carried out by the maintainer.

Fig 5-15. 5.4 metre RIB – side view of transom

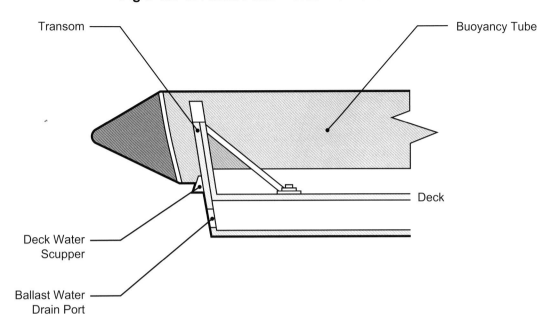

Transom

Buoyancy Tube

Deck

Deck Water Scupper

Ballast Water Drain Port

Fig 5-16. 5.4 metre RIB – transom from astern

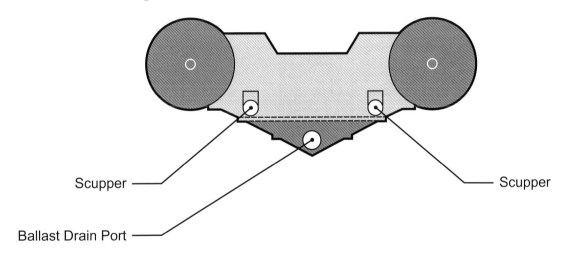

Scupper

Scupper

Ballast Drain Port

Fig 5-17. 5.4 metre RIB – buoyancy tube – compartments and valves

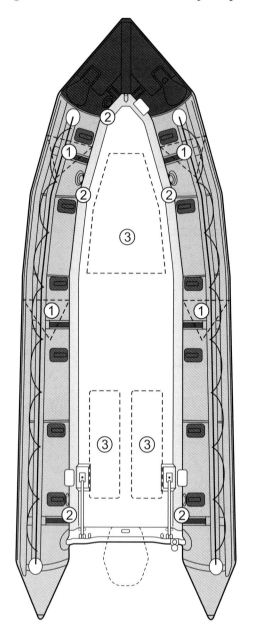

1   Baffles Between Compartments

2   Inflation Valves

3   Positions of Buoyancy Boxes
     Below the Deck

Fig 5-18. 5.4 metre RIB – buoyancy tube valve assembly

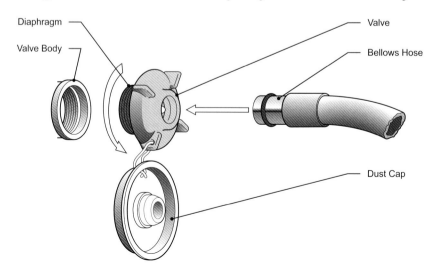

f.   **Buoyancy tube**

(1)   The buoyancy tube of the Searider has five separate compartments, each of which is inflated through its own valve. The layout of the compartments and the positions of the valves are shown in Fig 5-17. Either an electric blower or the foot pump provided with the boat may be used to inflate the buoyancy tube. The design of the valve is shown in Fig 5-18 and the procedure is simple:

(a)   Remove the dust cap.

(b)   Ensure that the valve is screwed tightly into the buoyancy tube.

(c)   Insert the air supply hose, taking care not to damage the valve diaphragm by forcing it in too far, then pump.

(d)   When the tube feels firmly inflated at a pressure of between $0.14 - 0.2$ bar (2 - 3 lbf/in^2), remove the air hose and replace the dust cap.

(2)   The bonding of the buoyancy tube to the top edge of the GRP hull is reinforced by a number of webbing straps passed around the tube from anchorages on the hull. In spite of the additional reinforcement, damage may be caused to the tube if it is allowed to drop below its operating pressure and the bonding (to the hull) may be strained in rough weather or when the boat is brought alongside. The coxswain should check that the buoyancy tube is always kept inflated so that it feels taut and firm. There are the following fittings on the buoyancy tube:

(a)   Metal 'D' rings, one on either side forward. These are secured by patches to the top of the tube.

(b)   Six steadying handles on top of the tube each side.

(c)   Eight lifeline handholds on each side for supporting men in the water.

(d)   Manual Line Thrower.

(3)   Any defects to the buoyancy tube or its fittings must be repaired quickly to prevent further deterioration. The coxswain should watch the following points for signs of damage:

(a)   Tapes covering seams becoming unstuck.

(b)   Abrasion or cracks.

(c)   Patches and labels lifting.

(d)   Valves leaking.

(e)   Loss of pressure.

g.   **External design and fittings**. A stainless steel eyeplate is fixed to the sharply raked stem to act as a towing point; this should be used for prolonged tows. Four longitudinal chines run along the outside of the hull. These act as spray deflectors but, because of their angular shape, they are susceptible to chipping. If any damage to the chines or the outside of the hull is found, it must be repaired quickly. This will prevent water penetrating the protective external gel coat of the GRP hull.

h.   **Slinging points** (Fig 5-19). There are three slinging points – one forward and two aft – in the Searider. A three-leg polyester webbing sling, naval stores number 0479/761-2880, is shackled to these slinging points by bow screw shackles. The bolts of these shackles must always be moused to prevent them working loose. The sling has a safe working load of 1.5 tonnes and an in-use life of two years, commencing from the date the sling is removed from its bag. A history card giving instructions for surveying the sling comes with each set. The sling is designed to place the RIB horizontally in the water. During lowering or hoisting, the coxswain should be seated at the console and the bowman should sit on the seat directly behind him. Any additional load in the boat should be positioned to give the boat a slight nose up attitude. Fig 5-19 also shows the chocking points for stowage on crutches.

Fig 5-19. 5.4 metre RIB – slinging arrangements

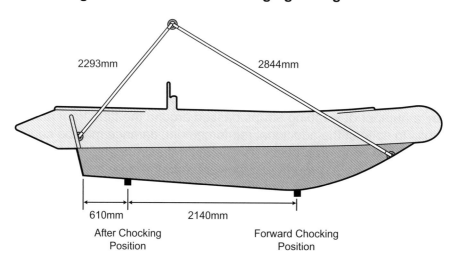

i.   **Navigation lights and masts**. All the navigation lights are fitted to a removable 'A' frame that slots into metal tubes fitted on the transom. The lights are connected to a socket on the transom.

j.   **Toe straps.** Provided for the coxswain and two other persons to sit astride the jockey seat. Additional toe straps in the form of webbing straps run forward to aft either side of the console are provided for passengers.

k.   **Boatrope and boatrope towing bridle** (Fig 5-21). When operated as a Sea Boat the craft must be fitted with a boatrope towing bridle to provide a means of attachment to the boatrope. In principle the bridle is similar to that described for the inflatable boat, although certain component parts differ. The purposes of a boatrope are explained in Para 05030. The procedure for fitting a towing bridle to a 4.7-metre RIB is as follows:

    (1)   *Bridle components*

Ring: mild steel 102mm inside diameter	(0263/549-1963)
Main bridle leg 16mm polyester	(0350/923-7144)
Thimble, ms	(0263/441-2980)
Shackle, bow	(0263/721-6104)
Port and starboard bridle legs: 12mm polyester	(0350/923-7143)
Boatrope: 24mm HL polypropylene	(0350/375-2994)
Boatrope recovery line, 16mm HL polypropylene	(0350/571-3172)
Toggle, beech wood, with hole for release lanyard	(2090/834-8106)
Toggle release lanyard: 8mm HL polyethylene	(0350/543-0141)

Fig 5-20. Boatrope toggle

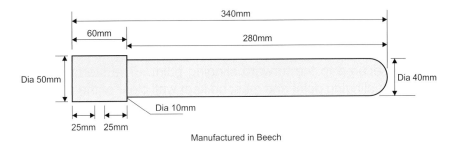

Manufactured in Beech

Fig 5-21. 5.4m RIB – boatrope towing bridle

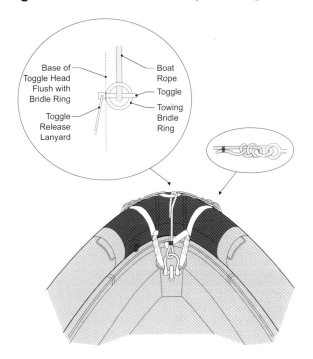

(2)   *Fitting and operation*

(a)   Splice the thimble into one end of the main bridle leg, then shackle that end to the forward slinging point of the boat. Now place the ring well forward on the nose of the boat and splice the outboard end of the main bridle leg to the ring.

(b)   Splice the port and starboard 12mm polyester bridle legs to the ring, centralise the ring, and tie off the port and starboard legs through the D rings on the port and starboard bow of the craft using a round turn and two half hitches. Whip or stitch the fag ends back to the standing part. (Rigged in this manner the towing bridle is portable and can be easily transferred from one boat to another).

(c)   Splice a 150mm soft eye in one end of the boatrope, then splice in the 16mm polypropylene recovery line close to the eye. This allows the recovery line to also be used when necessary as a steadying line.

(d)   Drill a hole in one end of the toggle and attach the polyethylene release lanyard using a soft eye splice (see Fig 5-20 above). Run the toggle releasing lanyard through the hand holds on the outboard buoyancy tube to a position abreast the console. This will enable the boatrope to be slipped without the crew going forward.

(e) Pass the soft eye of the boatrope up through the bridle ring, insert the toggle.

l.   **Painter and sternfast**. The painter and sternfast are made of 12mm polyester rope. The painter is five metres in length to prevent any risk of fouling the propeller; it should be secured to the forward slinging point. The sternfast is secured to the starboard after slinging point and must be kept well clear of the control cables and the outboard motor.

m.   **Anchor and cable**. When carried, the anchor is stowed on deck in the starboard bow. The 12mm polyester rope anchor cable is secured to the forward slinging point.

05059. 5.4 metre RIB – boat bag and other on-board equipment

a.   For normal operations the following items should be carried in the boat.

Equipment	Naval stores number
2 x paddles	2040-99-923-0423
Manual Line Thrower (Balcan Bell)	0472-781-0504
Horn	0268/407-9681
Bailer	0479/923-0770
4 x Distress Flares (to be removed in harbour)	
Bellows	2090-99-794-3813
Spare Kill Cord (ready to hand)	0482/250-0801
Compass (fitted in console)	0671/525-2105
Boat bag	0479/531/8185
(containing)	
Leak stopper S1	0468/923-0767
Leak stopper S2	0472/923-0768
Leak stopper S3	0472/923-0769
Repair clamp	4220-12-192-6151 or 4220-99-923-0770
Sea anchor	0468/GX0003965
Torch (with a signalling capability)	
First Aid Kit	6545/211-1573
Blanket in waterproof bag (if rigged as a Sea Boat)	
Radar Reflector (See Para 05054)	
Boat Ensign Size 2	8345/571-3296
CO2 2Kg Fire Extinguisher	4210-99-729-0440

b.   Additional equipment required for the engine. (These item to be stowed in a separate container)

Emergency starting cord
Fuel lead, and fuel lead adaptor if required
Fuel filter, cable snips and tie-wraps
Spark plug
Spare fuses
Socket and torque handle for spark plug removal
Pliers
Screwdriver
Spare propeller, nyloc nut and special tab washer
Suitable sockets for propeller removal

05060. 5.4 metre RIB – hull – operator checks

a. **Preparations at the start of the watch**. The coxswain should:

(1) Confirm that power is available at the crane or davit.

(2) Confirm that the boatrope and steadying lines are rigged and ready for use.

(3) If the guardrails are to be lowered for hoisting out the boat, check that a temporary guardrail is available and that hazardous duty lifejackets are provided for the hoisting and lowering party.

(4) Carry out a safety and functional check of the release hook and ensure the chain preventer is correctly rigged, re-attach the fall on completion.

(5) Ensure safety helmets are provided for the hoisting and lowering party.

(6) Check the boats bag and ancillary equipment is correct (iaw para 05059).

(7) Carry out pre-start checks.

(8) If an umbilical connection is being used, confirm that a cooling water supply is available for ship's services.

(9) Instruct crew members on their tasks and check their equipment and ensure they are dressed correctly ie Marine safety helmet, immersion suit, manual hazardous duty lifejacket, safety boots and a sharp knife.

(10) To prevent the risk of RADHAZ shocks the crew member that operates the release hook is to wear PPE gloves.

(11) Carry out a functional VHF comms check, test upperdeck broadcast and check the availability of flags and wands.

b. The coxswain should also make visual checks of the hull, buoyancy tube and equipment each day, and again after the boat has been hoisted.

c. **External**

(1) Drain hoses open to allow drainage of rain/spray.

(2) No damage to hull or outside of the buoyancy tube.

(3) Buoyancy tube firmly clamped to the hull.

(4) Nothing fouling the outboard motor or propeller.

d. **Internal**

(1) Slings clear of obstructions and not worn or frayed. Slinging points secure and shackle pins in place and moused.

(2) Boatrope strop securely attached and toggle ready for use.

(3) Painter and sternfast secured and coiled down.

(4) Equipment safely and securely stowed.

e. **Buoyancy tube**

(1)   Inflated so that it is taut to the touch.

(2)   All patches, tapes and bonding strips firmly stuck down.

(3)   No signs of abrasion cracks or damage.

05061.   5.4 metre RIB – propulsion and electrical system

a.   **The engine**. The engine for the 5.4 metre RIB is the 75hp 'longshaft' Mariner outboard motor. Gasoline is supplied unmixed from a 25 litre portable fuel tank fitted with a snap or bayonet connector on its flexible fuel line which allows it to be connected quickly to the outboard motor; two portable fuel tanks are normally embarked in the boat. The carburettors on the outboard motor hold sufficient fuel for the supply to be exchanged from one tank to the other without stopping the engine.

CAUTION

An operation and maintenance manual is available for this engine and its associated equipment. Users must read the manual and follow the procedures laid down.

---

b.   **Requirement to fit a propeller guard**. A propeller guard must be fitted unless the subsequent reduction in the speed and power of the boat is inappropriate to the role in which the boat is operating. For example, no propeller guard is required when the boat is used as a Sea Boat, or for boarding operations, or when it is necessary to demonstrate the full capabilities of the craft during training courses.

c.   **Cooling system**. The engine will seize up within a period of a few seconds if run without cooling water. There is a tell-tale discharge on the starboard after side of the powerhead which, if water is flowing from it, indicates that the cooling system is functioning. The coxswain must always turn round to check the discharge as soon as the engine has been started; he should also make further checks while the engine is running. A warning horn is fitted to indicate if the cooling water temperature rises above the permitted limit. If this alarm (a continuous tone) is heard or the flow of water through the tell-tale stops, the coxswain must cut the engine immediately. There are two sources of supply for cooling water: from the sea, after the boat has been lowered, or from the ship's fresh or salt water services through a polythene hose known as the 'umbilical connection'.

(1)   *Normal circulation*. When the boat is in the water, sea water for cooling is drawn in through the cooling water intake low on the exhaust housing above the gear case, pumped through the cooling system and finally discharged through an outlet in the propeller boss with the exhaust. There are bypass and relief valves to regulate the temperature and pressure of the cooling water as the speed of the engine increases.

(2)   *Umbilical connection*. To permit starting the outboard motor when the boat is out of the water, a modification has been made to allow the ship's fresh or salt water main to supply cooling water. A polythene hose is connected to the outboard motor cooling system by a pull-break coupling fitted on the transom of the boat. A suitable access point from the ship's fresh or salt water services is then used to supply cooling water through this 'umbilical connection'. The pressure range should be between 0.3 – 7.0 bar. A recovery line, shorter in length than the hose, is secured between the ship and the coupling so that when the boat moves away the coupling is disconnected before the hose is parted.

Cooling water is drawn in through the normal intake on the outboard motor once the boat has been lowered into the sea. The umbilical cord only supplies a small volume of cooling water to the engine; the outboard motor must therefore be kept at idling speed until the boat is in the water.

d.   **Cut-out switch**. See Operator's Manual

05062. 5.4 metre RIB – electrical installation
See Operator's Manual

05063. 5.4 metre RIB – engine and electrical – operator checks

a.   The coxswain should make the following checks daily and on each occasion after the Searider has been hoisted. (These checks are general. The Operator's manual should be read to ensure any other requirements are met.)

b.   **Engine checks**

(1)   The four bolts securing the motor to the transom are fully tightened.

(2)   The motor tilts freely, and is down in the 'Run' position.

(3)   The steering wheel swivels the motor easily between the port and starboard stops.

(4)   There are no obstructions resting on the control cables.

(5)   The gear shift/throttle lever is in the neutral position. It should never be forced out of neutral when the engine is stopped.

(6)   There is nothing fouling the propeller.

(7)   The fuel tanks are full and the fuel line is primed.

(8)   The fuel tanks are strapped tightly into position.

(9)   The fuel line connector is correctly snapped on.

(10) Integral oil tank is topped up.

(11) When required: the umbilical connection is properly coupled to the engine and the recovery line secured.

(12) Water supply for the umbilical connection available and at the correct pressure.

c.   **Electrical checks**

(1)   Leads to battery terminals tight and uncorroded, and the lid to battery box firmly in place.

(2)   Battery isolating switch closed.

(3)   Caps on the electrical power sockets on the forward and after ends of the GRP console housing in place, but free to be taken off.

(4)   Navigation lights functioning correctly.

(5)   Kill cord fitted, and spare readily available.

05064. 5.4 metre RIB – controls at the console

a.   The Searider controls and instruments are mounted on the console in front of the coxswain; the layout is shown in Fig 5-22. The gear shift and throttle control box is mounted on the starboard side of the console housing. Three mechanical cables lead aft from the console for steering, gear shift and throttle control. An electrical loom containing cables for the starting, ignition control and charging circuits also leads aft, together with a supply to the navigation lights.

b.   **Gear shift and throttle control**. A single lever controls both the gear shift and the engine speed through a linkage contained in the throttle control box. In the central position the lever is locked, the gears are in neutral and the engine is idling. To move from neutral to ahead, squeeze the grip beneath the handle to unlock the catch, then move the throttle lever forward. Ahead gear will have been engaged when a spring-loaded catch is felt to fall into a small recess. Moving the lever further forward opens the throttle and increases the engine speed. Similarly, to go astern, unlock the throttle lever from neutral and move it backwards until the catch falls into the astern gear recess, then increase speed as required by pulling the lever steadily aft.

Fig 5-22. 5.4m RIB – controls at the console

c.   **Fast-idle control**. The engine can only be started when the gear shift/throttle control lever is in neutral. In this position the throttle opening is set to idling speed. Because this may not be sufficiently fast for the engine to warm up satisfactorily, a separate engine speed control, called the fast-idle control, is provided. This is operated by the fast-idle lever which is fitted flush with the top of the throttle box. This lever should always be raised when starting the outboard motor from cold, and the coxswain must remember to return it to the housed position once the engine has warmed up. It is not required if the engine has just been running.

d.   **Fuel injection primer**. This pumps fuel directly into the engine to assist starting. A three-way key switch for the fuel injection pump is operated by pushing the key inwards against a spring for a few seconds before turning it to the second position to operate the starter motor.

05065. 5.4 metre RIB – engine starting procedures

a.   **Pre-start checks**. Before getting into his seat the coxswain should carry out the following pre-start routine:

(1)   Ensure the fuel tank is filled with unleaded gasoline and the correct grade of oil is in the integral tank.

(2)   Slide the fuel line connector onto the outboard motor.

(3)   Prime the carburettor by squeezing the fuel bulb.

(4)   Check that the engine is firmly bolted to the transom.

(5)   Check that the kill switch is in the 'Run' position.

(6)   Confirm that the pull-break coupling of the umbilical cord is firmly connected (if in use) and that the water supply is available.

(7)   Confirm that the gear shift/throttle lever is in neutral and raise the fast-idle lever.

b.   **To start**. After getting into his seat the coxswain should:

(1)   Ensure the Kill cord is secured to the cut-out switch, then secure the other end of the Kill cord to his leg.

(2)   If using the umbilical connection - order the cooling water to be turned on and then check the flow of water from the motor.

(3)   Switch on the ignition switch.

(4)   Operate choke or primer pump, but only if the engine is being started from cold.

(5)   Depress starter motor switch (turn key in models where fitted) and run starter motor for not more than ten seconds. If the engine fails to start - stop and repeat after a short pause.

(6)   As the engine starts, release both switches.

c.   **Once started**

(1)   Check the cooling water flow through the tell-tale discharge.

(2)   Reduce the engine speed to idle by housing the fast-idle warm up lever.

05066. 5.4 metre RIB – running procedures and checks

    a.   Once the outboard motor is running and the boat is in the water, the Searider is ready to be operated.

    b.   **To go ahead**

        (1)   Release the 'neutral safety lock' on the underside of the throttle handle and move the gear shift/throttle lever smoothly and firmly forward about 30° to engage the propeller drive in ahead gear.

        (2)   Increase speed by continuing to move the gear shift/throttle lever forward. When the weight is off the boatrope the coxswain orders it to be released.

        (3)   Once the Searider is on the plane, throttle back to the required operating speed. The engine must not be allowed to race, particularly when it is cold.

        (4)   The coxswain should keep his hand on the gear shift/throttle lever all the time the boat is underway in order to be able to change speed quickly to adjust to wind and sea.

    c.   **To go astern**

        (1)   Move the lever to the neutral position, pause until the engine is at idling speed, then release the neutral safety lock and pull the lever smoothly and firmly back to the recess to engage astern gear.

        (2)   Increase speed as required by pulling the lever further back until the required astern power is obtained.

    d.   **Checks while running**. Periodically check:

        (1)   Flow of cooling water through the tell-tale discharge.

        (2)   Tightness of the engine bolts on the transom.

        (3)   Fuel level of the in-use tank.

05067. 5.4 metre RIB – stopping procedures

    a.   **Normal methods**. There are the following alternative methods of stopping:

        (1)   Put the engine in neutral and turn the ignition switch to 'off'.

        (2)   Put the engine in neutral and disconnect the fuel line to allow the carburettor to run dry. This method should be used to ensure reliable restarting after being stopped for a period or if the engine is to be serviced.

    b.   **Emergency method**. The cut-out switch is actuated by a pull on the Kill cord attached to the coxswain's leg. The coxswain should not employ this as a routine method of stopping the engine, but may, however, test it from time to time provided that the gear shift/throttle lever is put in neutral first.

05068. 5.4 metre RIB – fault finding on the engine

a.   These checks are general.   The relevant manual for each engine should be studied for variations.

b.   **If The engine will not start**

Symptom	**Remedial action**
Engine will not turn on starter	Check battery charge level and battery terminals.
	Check throttle/gear shift is in neutral.
	Check 20-amp fuse.
	Check all electrical connections.
Engine will not fire	Check cut-out switch is attached.
	Check fuel level.
	Check fuel line lead is primed and tank vent is open.
	Check fuel filter is clear.
	Check spark plugs; change if oiled up.

c.   **Lack of power**. Ascertain whether any of the following causes are reducing the power output.

(1)   Engine overheating because the cooling system is not operating properly, obstruction at the water intake?

(2)   Fuel contamination, water in the fuel?

(3)   Fuel pump filter partially blocked?

(4)   Plugs dirty?

(5)   Damaged propeller or fouling beneath the hull?

(6)   Damaged sparking plugs, eg. insulator cracked?

d.   **Alarms.** There is a possibility of one of two alarms being activated:

(1)   Intermittent – Low oil.

(2)   Constant – Engine overheating.

SECTION 6 - 5.4 metre RIGID INFLATABLE BOAT MK3 – WITH INBOARD DIESEL ENGINE

05069. 5.4 metre Searider Mk3 with inboard diesel engine

a.   **Introduction.** The 5.4 metre Searider Mk3 is a fast medium-sized RIB. (See Fig 5-23, Fig 5-24 and Fig 5-25). In addition to its normal crew of two it has a carrying capacity of four passengers or a payload of 450 kg. The boat is powered by a 75hp Yanmar Diesel Engine (4JH3-TE). Fuel is supplied from two 21.4-litre fuel tanks located under the console seating. The coxswain controls the Searider from a console amidships which is fitted with a steering wheel, combined gearshift/throttle lever and a switch and instrument panel. Two 12V batteries, housed in a battery box situated within the console provide power for engine starting and navigation lights. The authoritative maintenance publication for this craft is the **Operating and Maintenance Manual VC940131 Issue 2 dated 05-02-07.**

b.   **5.4 metre Searider Mk3 with inboard diesel engine – dimensions**

Overall length	5.43 metres
Inside Length	3.9 metres
Overall Beam	2.03 metres
Inside Beam	1.09 metres

c.   **Performance**. The 5.4 metre Searider Mk3 Diesel variant in calm conditions and lightly loaded will start to plane at about 15 knots and reach a top speed of approximately 16-18 knots. In conditions up to sea state 4 (wave heights 1.25 – 2.5 metres) or with heavier loads the boat will still plane, but the maximum speed will drop considerably. In higher sea states the engine power must be reduced to give a safe speed according to the strength and direction of the wind and sea. Two diesel fuel tanks with a combined capacity of 43 litres are fitted. The limiting distance of operation will depend upon the speed attainable with the payload that the Searider is required to carry under the prevailing weather conditions.

d.   **Weight and capacity**. The following table gives the weights of the boat, personnel and other items, and should be used when calculating hoisting out and recovery weights. The maximum Safe Working Lift for this craft is 1.5 tonnes, thus assuming the lifting device is capable of this lift there is a spare capacity of 445 kg when the boat is loaded as shown below. It is sometimes necessary to use this spare capacity, for example when recovering survivors. Whenever possible stores or additional personnel should be embarked or disembarked when the boat is in the water to reduce unnecessary stress on the boat when it is suspended on its slings.

Weight of boat, fuel & standard equipment	1015 kg
Boat bag	10 kg
Crew of two	150 kg
Four passengers	300 kg
Total	1475 kg
Carrying capacity in the water	450 kgs or four passengers

e.   **Hull**. The hull of the 5.4 metre Searider Mk3 Diesel variant is constructed of fire retardant glass re-enforced plastic (GRP), a buoyancy tube topsides and a two seater console amidships. The deep 'V' GRP hull has a transom and deck constructed of marine plywood both of which are bonded to the hull moulding and overlaid with GRP. The deck has a thickness of 9mm and the transom is made up of two thicknesses, one of 12mm and one of 18mm bonded together. Viewed from astern there are three drainage ports in the transom. The ballast drain port is on the centreline; this is open to the sea and is designed to allow the ballast water to flow out of the boat as it gathers speed. At deck level on either side are the two deck scuppers for draining away sea water shipped over the gunwale or stern. These are fitted on the outboard side with scupper hoses made of light rubber tubing. The purpose of these is to prevent water flowing back onboard when the boat is stopped and lying low in the water. The scupper hoses should be triced up by their lanyards when the boat slows down and should be allowed to trail when the boat is gathering speed to go on the plane. The buoyancy tube collar is foam filled and bonded to the hull and transom around the flange. The tube contains an inflatable bladder which runs down the centre and is inflated to tension the external skin of the collar, secondary strapping is secured around the circumference of the buoyancy tube for additional security.

f.   **Self-righting equipment.** The boat is fitted with self-righting equipment to right the craft after capsize. The self-righting bag is inflated with CO_2 gas from a cylinder secured to the self-righting frame and is operated by pulling the operating handle positioned on the outside face of the transom. The righting frame itself is mounted into sockets on the outboard face of the transom and is removable. The frame also supports the navigation lights, radio aerial and radar reflector. Wiring runs from the frame to the rear of the console where the navigation lights are connected to the supply via plug and socket.

Fig 5-23. 5.4 metre Searider Mk 3 with diesel inboard engine – plan view

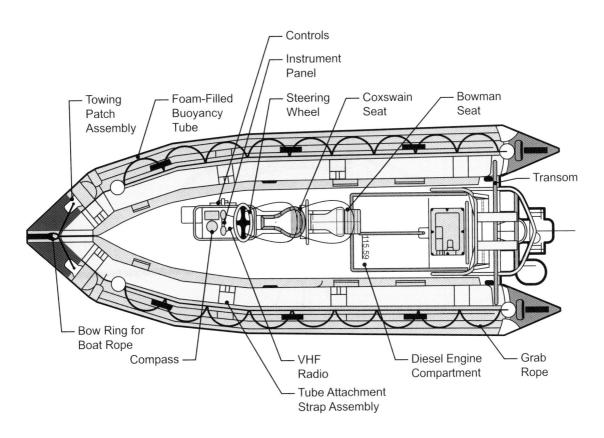

Fig 5-24. 5.4 metre Searider Mk 3 with diesel inboard engine – side view

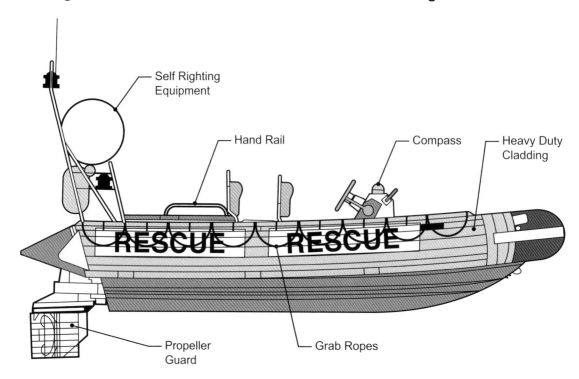

Self Righting
Equipment

Hand Rail

Compass

Heavy Duty
Cladding

Propeller
Guard

Grab Ropes

Fig 5-25. 5.4 metre Searider Mk 3 with diesel inboard engine – front view

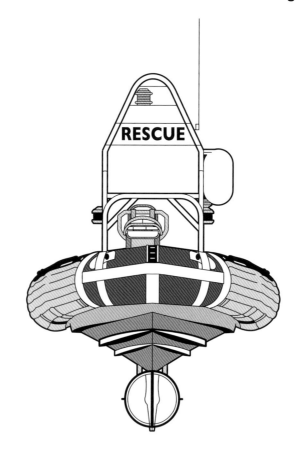

SECTION 7 – 6.5 metre PACIFIC 22 MK 2 RIGID INFLATABLE BOAT – JETPAC

05070. 6.5 metre RIB Pacific 22 Mk 2 – jetpac – introduction

a. **Introduction.** The 6.5 metre RIB Fast Rescue Boat (FRB) (Fig 5-26, Fig 5-27 and Fig 5-28) is constructed in accordance with SOLAS requirements for Life-saving Appliances for a Fast Rescue Boat and is approved for six passengers and two crew. The boat is also built in compliance with MoD(N) specifications. It comprises a deep V hard chine-planning hull, constructed from GRP, surmounted by a mechanically inflated tube (flotation collar). One diesel engine is mounted inboard within an enclosure located behind the coxswain's position. Drive is transmitted from the engine via a drive shaft through a water jet mounted reinforced transom. The coxswain is provided with a straddle type seat and backrest aft of the console and bench-type seats are provided either side of the engine cowling for passengers. Toe straps and grab-rails provide added support. The RIB incorporates a tubular frame, with integral lifting ring, situated between the coxswain's seating position and gearbox, for specific use with a single point lifting system. At the stern a manually operated, gas- inflated, self-righting bag is fitted on a dedicated framework. Also fitted at the stern is a set of rollers to assist in recovery of casualties, and secured to the transom is a tubular water jet guard with a ladder to assist in recovery of personnel/divers from the water.

Fig 5-26. 6.5 metre Pacific 22 Mk 2 RIB – plan view

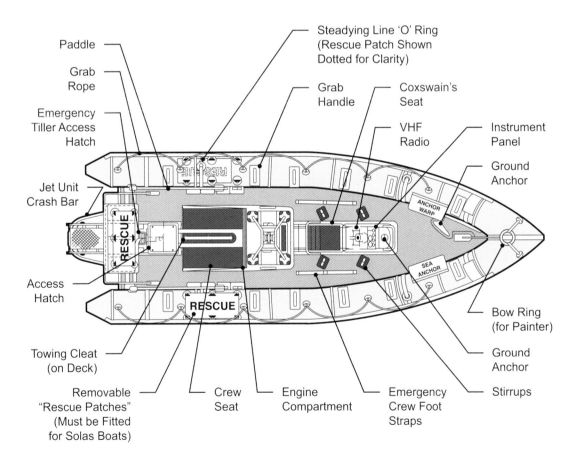

Fig 5-27. 6.5 metre Pacific 22 Mk 2 – jetpac – side view

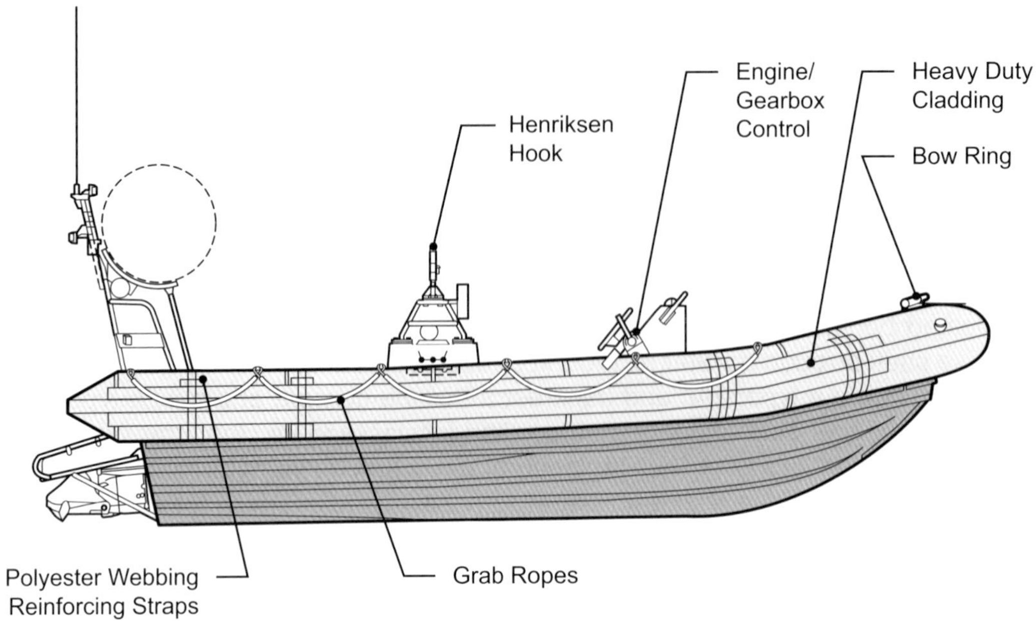

Engine/
Gearbox
Control

Heavy Duty
Cladding

Bow Ring

Henriksen
Hook

Polyester Webbing
Reinforcing Straps

Grab Ropes

Fig 5-28. 6.5 metre Pacific 22 Mk 2 – jetpac – stern view

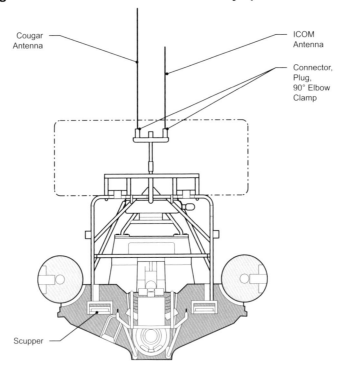

Cougar
Antenna

ICOM
Antenna

Connector,
Plug,
90° Elbow
Clamp

Scupper

b. **Dimensions of the 6.5 metre Pacific 22 Mk 2 – jetpac**

Length overall	7.10 metres
Length rigid hull	6.12 metres
Beam overall	2.44 metres
Beam rigid hull	2.03 metres
Draught (operational)	0.50 metres
Fuel	150 litres
Crew x 2	
Passengers x 4	

c.   **Performance.** The 6.5 metre RIB - Pacific Mk 2 handles safely in rough weather and may be operated with a full load in a sea state 5. In higher sea states than this the load and speed may have to be reduced. It is capable of achieving 28 knots (approximately) under optimum sea conditions and a full load. At 20 knots with eight persons and a full load, the fuel tank with a capacity of 142 litres will give an endurance of approximately 4.5 hours.

d.   **Extreme operating conditions**

(1)   Sea water temperature above 30ºC.

(2)   Air temperature at the turbo inlet of the engine 45º C. This should not be confused with ambient outside air temperature. It is the air temperature at the turbo inlet having picked up waste heat from the engine bay. This as a general rule can be seen with air temperature of 30 to 35º C. The practice of running the boat with the watertight access doors open to reduce temperature in the engine bay is not endorsed or advised. If the boat were to capsize then it could not be self-righted if the doors are open.

e.   **Operating limitations**.   Operating Limitations are essential to maintain the capability of the boat. Operating in the NAG during the summer months has proven to be very costly in engine failures.

(1)   To assist in maintaining the capability of the boat ships have in the past operated their boats successfully in the following manner:

(a) It is critical that boats are not overloaded with excess boarding personnel or equipment.

(b) On launching the boat the engine should be allowed to warm up before heavy engine loading is applied. Engine exhaust cooling is achieved via the header tank. Until the engine warms sudden high loads and resulting exhaust gas temp can overheat the header tank resulting in boiling of the tank or even fracture of the cooler and loss of water via the exhaust.

(c) The boat can then be allowed to achieve planing speed. The throttle MUST be reduced back to just keep the boat on the plane.

(d) On completion of transits the boat must be run at low powers (engine revs not exceeding 2600 rpm) to allow the cooling system to remove the heat soak from the engine.

(2)   If the boat is operated as above, evidence suggests that improved availability of the asset and operational capability could be achieved. If the boat's crews continue to use the boat at full throttle with a boat fully loaded, engine failure will quickly occur due to carry over of unburnt fuel.

(3)   Mentoring of the engine by fresh water temperature alone is not supported, the fresh water temperature can be at or less then 85º and the boat operating on the plane with the throttle being over used. This will result in excess fuelling of the engine and unburnt fuel being passed into the cylinders. The air temperature at the turbo inlet is one of the major influences on engine combustion; reliance on fresh water temperature only does not reflect the loss of power due to air density and temperature. Bass recommend operating the boats as detailed at sub para (e) above.

f.   **Weight and capacity**. Before attempting to lift the RIB, ensure that adequate lifting capacity is available. The maximum hoisting weight of the boat is to be no greater than 2500 kg. The following table gives the weight of the boat, personnel.

Fast Rescue Craft/Sea Boat/Crashboat

Weight of boat, fuel and two crew	2050 kg
Boat bag	10 kg
Crash bag	25 kg
Total	2085 kg

g.   **Boatrope and boatrope towing arrangement.** Like the Searider the Pacific 22 and Pacific 24 when operated as a Sea Boat or deployed while the ship is underway must be fitted with a boatrope towing bridle (Fig 5-29) for attaching the boatrope. The purposes of the boatrope are explained in Para 05030.

Fig 5-29. Boat rope and toggle arrangement

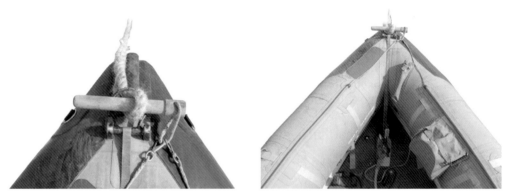

h.   **6.5 metre Pacific 22 Mk 2 – jetpac – boats roles**

   (1)   Compliant Boarding Operations. (In accordance with Annex 5A).

   (2)   Force Protection.

   (3)   Life-saving.

   (4)   Passenger/Stores Transfer.

05071. 6.5 metre RIB Pacific 22 Mk 2 – jetpac – propulsion and control

a.   The Pacific Mk 2 Jetpac is powered by a single Yanmar 4LH-STE turbo-charged inboard diesel engine producing 190hp at 3100 rpm (continuous rating) and giving a maximum speed of 30 knots. The engine is longitudinally aligned and is connected via a flywheel and drive shaft to the waterjet.

b.   **Fuel system**. The fuel tank has a capacity of approximately 142 litres. The tank is housed centrally in the hull sited immediately below the console. The fuel-filling position, with removable gauze filter, is located at the forward end of the console. A cover plate fitted in the deck provides access to the tank for maintenance. A dipstick, stowed on the outside of the engine case, facilitates sounding of the tank contents.

c.   **Steering system**. The boat is fitted with a Wagner hydraulic steering system operated by the console steering wheel. The system works in conjunction with the waterjet forward and astern thrust control for manoeuvring.

d.   **Waterjet**. A single Hamilton HJ 241 waterjet unit is fitted. The unit is transom mounted and comprises a jet tube with an internally mounted impeller. The water intake is located below, and flushes with, the stern of the boat. The jet impeller is shaft mounted, with thrust bearing and transom seal, and is directly driven through a cardan shaft by the engine. From the impeller the water passes through the rear of the jet tube, where its velocity is greatly increased, and then forced through the steering nozzle.

05072.   6.5 metre RIB Pacific 22 Mk 2 – jetpac – electrical installation
See relevant Operator's Manual.

05073.   6.5 metre RIB Pacific 22 Mk 2 – jetpac – engine and electrical – operator checks
See relevant Operators Manual.

05074.   6.5 metre RIB Pacific 22 Mk 2 – jetpac – controls and switches
The majority of these are mounted on or in the console in front of the coxswain. The precise layout varies slightly depending on the year the craft was manufactured. Consult the Operator's Manual.

05075.   6.5 metre RIB Pacific 22 Mk 2 – jetpac – deadman's switch operation

a.   The Deadman's Switch is located on the console in front of the coxswain.

b.   Prior to starting the engine and until the engine is stopped, the Switch Key must be fitted into the switch and physically connected to the coxswain by its lanyard.

c.   In the event of the coxswain falling overboard, or otherwise moving away from the helm, the Switch Key will be pulled off and the engine will automatically stop.

d.   To re-start the engine, insert the key back into the Deadman's Switch and start the engine in the normal way as described above. Ensure the lanyard is again secured to the coxswain.

05076.   6.5 metre RIB Pacific 22 Mk 2 – jetpac – engine start procedures

a.   **Pre-start checks**. These checks are general; the manual for the particular engine fit should be studied for variations.

b.   **Normal start – in the water**

WARNINGS
1. BEFORE STARTING THE ENGINE ENSURE THAT THE WATERJET CONTROL IS SET TO THE NEUTRAL POSITION AND THE THROTTLE LEVER TO THE LOW REVS POSITION AND, IF ALONGSIDE, THAT THE BOAT IS SECURELY MOORED. THERE IS EFFECTIVELY NO INTERLOCK ARRANGEMENT TO PREVENT THE ENGINE BEING STARTED WITH AHEAD OR ASTERN MOTION ENGAGED.
2. INHALATION OF EXHAUST FUMES IS DETREMENTAL TO HEALTH. IF RUNNING THE ENGINE WHEN OUT OF THE WATER THE RUNNING TIME MUST BE KEPT TO NO MORE THAN FIVE MINUTES, OR LESS IF THERE IS INDICATION OF A HIGH FRESHWATER TEMPERATURE. SUITABLE PRECAUTIONS MUST BE TAKEN, WHERE PRACTICABLE, TO AVOID THE FUMES COLLECTING AROUND THE BOAT.

c. Following completion of the sea checks:

Note. *The waterjet is fitted with a dry-run thrust bearing enabling the engine to be started and run for short periods (up to five minutes) whilst out of the water. It should be noted however, that the more this facility is used, especially in dirty water environments, the more rapid will be the wear on the plastic bearing and the more frequent checking and replacement will be required.*

(1) Remove the self-righting gas cylinder arming pin from the head of the gas cylinder and place in its stowage at the console to ready the system for operation.

(2) Ensure that the boat is securely moored (if already in the water).

(3) Ensure that there is no loose debris in the immediate vicinity of the waterjet and intake.

Note. *The engine will not start unless the Deadman's Switch is inhibited by inserting the fork (key) and consequently the engine air intake valve is set to the open position.*

(4) Check that the throttle lever is set to the half full position and the waterjet control lever to the Neutral position.

(5) Set the Ignition Switch to the IGNITION position. Verify that the gauges now operate.

(6) Press the engine Start Push button. Release the button as soon as the engine starts.

(7) As the engine fires, control the boat position with the helm and bucket controls. The maximum engine revs for approximately one minute is 1000 rpm.

(8) After starting the engine, check all engine indicators for any incorrect readings. Stop the engine immediately if audible or visual warnings are apparent. Investigate and rectify before attempting to restart.

(9) Move the waterjet control lever to Ahead, then Astern, to confirm the waterjet responds. Return the control lever to the Neutral position. Similarly move the throttle lever forward and then to astern and verify the engine revs respond in both directions.

(10) The boat is now ready for operation.

d. **Starting out of the water.** Following completion of the sea checks:

(1) Follow the procedures in Para 05086c sub para (1) to sub para (6) for Normal Start.

(2) The maximum run time is five minutes.

(3) Continuous engine speed (out of water) should be 800 rpm with intermittent 1000 rpm maximum.

(4) The minimum time delay between runs in air, except in an emergency, is one hour.

05077. 6.5 metre RIB Pacific 22 Mk 2 – jetpac – manoeuvring and running

    a. **running checks while the boat is running:**

        (1) Periodically monitor the engine instrumentation for abnormal readings.

        (2) Check the engine parameters are within the following recommended limits:

            (a) Engine lubricating oil pressure - 2.72 – 4.5 bar (40 – 65 psi)

            (b) Engine coolant temperature   - 78 - 91°C (172 - 196°F)

            (c) Turbo boost pressure   - 1.0 – 1.5 bar (14.5 – 21.75 psi) at CR

        (3) Check all system pipework for signs of leakage.

        (4) Check for abnormal noise or vibration.

        (5) Regularly run the fuel tank to a low level to ensure fuel turn-over in order to reduce the risk of microbiological growth. (Fuel additives must only be used in accordance with MoD directives).

05078. 6.5 metre RIB Pacific 22 Mk 2 – jetpac – stopping the engine

---

CAUTION

To prevent damage to the Solenoid Switch, do not leave the ignition key on and the Deadman's Switch disengaged for extended periods.

---

    a. The procedure for stopping the engines is as follows and is dependent upon the prevailing conditions:

        (1) Ensure that the throttle lever is set to the low speed position and the waterjet control to the Neutral position.

        (2) When stopping briefly, press the Stop Push Button and when the engine has stopped turn the Engine Ignition Switch to the OFF position. When stopping the boat after running at high speed for a long time, allow the engine to idle and cool for three to five minutes before stopping the engine (this also allows lubrication oil to the turbo as it 'spins down').

        (3) Periodically stop the engine by operation of the Deadman's Switch to verify its operation.

        (4) Switch the Battery Isolation Switches OFF prior to leaving the boat and connect the external battery charging cables as necessary.

        (5) Prior to leaving the boat, remove the self-righting gas cylinder arming pin from its stowage at the console and re-install it in the head of the gas cylinder.

05079. 6.5 metre RIB Pacific 22 Mk 2 – jetpac – general manoeuvring

The fitment of a waterjet makes the boat extremely manoeuvrable by individual or combined use of the throttles, waterjet control and the steering. As there is no change of waterjet impeller rotation, the boat direction can be set from full ahead to full astern without reducing the engine revolutions. However, for passenger comfort and safety, this manoeuvre should be considered only an emergency procedure. Due to the large amount of power available to pass through the jet from a standing start, the power should not be applied too rapidly otherwise cavitation will occur.

WARNING
THE MANOEUVRABILITY AFFORDED BY THE WATERJET ALLOWS RAPID CHANGES IN THE SPEED OF THE BOAT, POSSIBLY FROM FULL AHEAD TO STOP OR FULL ASTERN. THE COXSWAIN MUST BE AWARE OF THE POTENTIAL SAFETY HAZARD TO CREW MEMBERS OF SUCH ACTIONS, PARTICULARY IF CARRIED OUT UNEXPECTEDLY AND WITH THE CREW NOT PROPERLY SEATED.

SECTION 8 – 7.8-metre PACIFIC 24 RIGID INFLATABLE FAST RESCUE/BOARDING CRAFT

05080. General description

a.   The Pacific 24 Rigid Inflatable fast rescue craft (FRC)/boarding boat (See Fig 5-30 to Fig 5-33) is designed and built, where practicable, in accordance with the MCA requirements for Fast Rescue Boats under SOLAS regulations and is approved for six passengers and two crew. It is also built in compliance with MoD(N) specifications. It comprises a deep 'V' hard chine planing hull, constructed from glass/carbon reinforced epoxy resin with the gel coat incorporating a fire retardant resin instead of a separate fire retardant layer. The hull is surmounted by a mechanically attached inflatable buoyancy tube (flotation collar). One diesel engine is mounted inboard, aft, within an enclosure located ahead of the Coxswain and Navigator seating positions. Drive is transmitted from the engine via a gearbox and driveshaft through a waterjet mounted reinforced transom. The Coxswain and Navigator are provided with adjacent straddle type seats with backrests, aft of the console. Four similar straddle type seats for passengers are provided forward of the engine/console enclosure. In order to maximise the equipment carrying capability the passenger seats are removable. Toe straps and grab rails provide extra support. There are two further passenger seats mounted on the forward end of the engine/console enclosure, secured side by side on the battery box lid. The console moulding incorporates a Henriksen Hook Assembly, situated amidships and aft of the two rear passenger seats for use with a single point lifting system. At the stern a manually operated, gas inflated, self-righting bag is fitted on a dedicated framework integral with a goal post frame. A reinforced base is provided in the foredeck for the mounting of a GPMG mount pedestal and gun.

Fig 5-30. Pacific 24 RIB – general arrangement profile

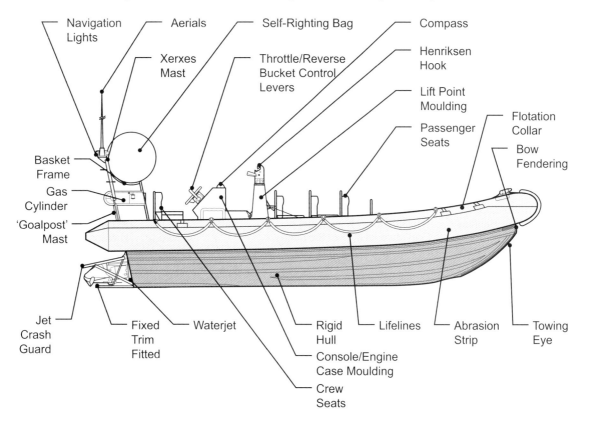

Fig 5-31. Pacific 24 RIB – general arrangements – plan view

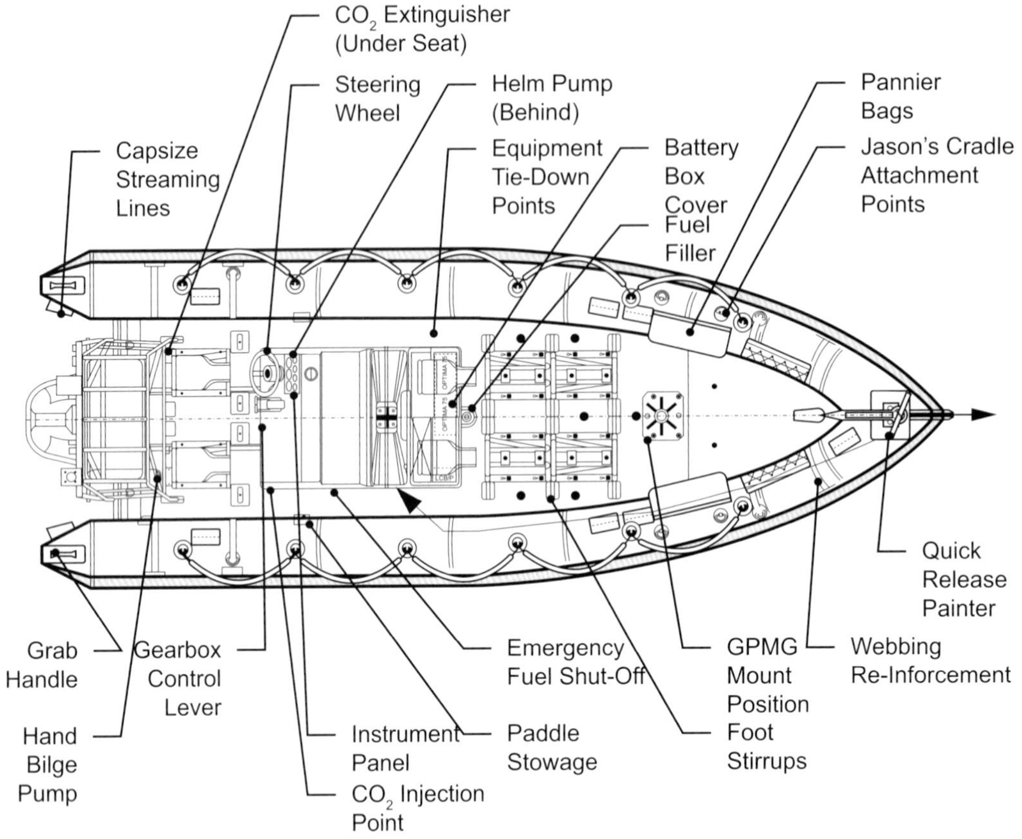

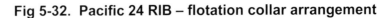

- CO₂ Extinguisher (Under Seat)
- Steering Wheel
- Helm Pump (Behind)
- Pannier Bags
- Capsize Streaming Lines
- Equipment Tie-Down Points
- Battery Box Cover
- Jason's Cradle Attachment Points
- Fuel Filler
- Grab Handle
- Gearbox Control Lever
- Emergency Fuel Shut-Off
- GPMG Mount Position Foot Stirrups
- Quick Release Painter
- Webbing Re-Inforcement
- Hand Bilge Pump
- Instrument Panel
- Paddle Stowage
- CO₂ Injection Point

Fig 5-32. Pacific 24 RIB – flotation collar arrangement

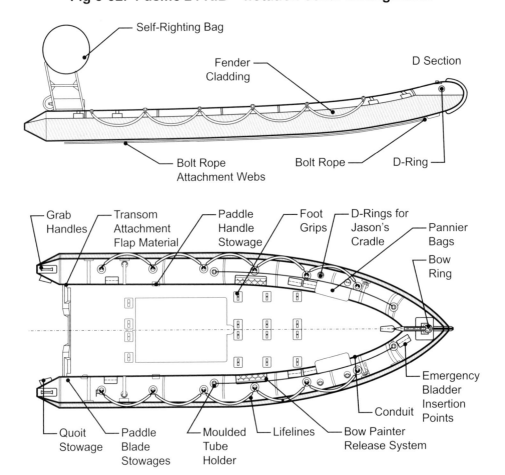

- Self-Righting Bag
- Fender Cladding
- D Section
- Bolt Rope Attachment Webs
- Bolt Rope
- D-Ring
- Grab Handles
- Transom Attachment Flap Material
- Paddle Handle Stowage
- Foot Grips
- D-Rings for Jason's Cradle
- Pannier Bags
- Bow Ring
- Quoit Stowage
- Paddle Blade Stowages
- Moulded Tube Holder
- Lifelines
- Bow Painter Release System
- Conduit
- Emergency Bladder Insertion Points

Fig 5-33. Pacific 24 RIB – mast arrangement and capsize righting system

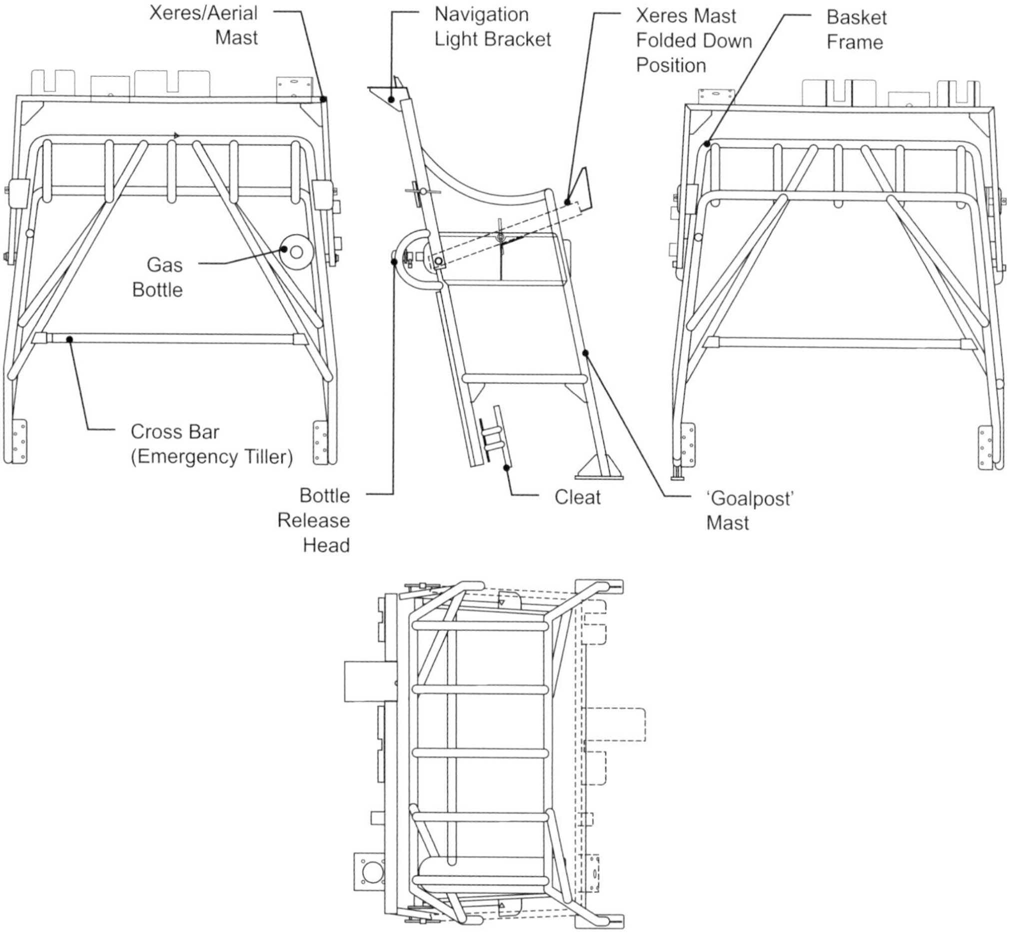

b. **Weight and principle dimensions of the Pacific 24 RIB**

Operationally loaded (c/w Full Fuel, XERES fit 2 crew + 6 passengers 240Kg Equipment	3.19 tonnes
Length overall	7.8 metres
Length Moulded	6.625 metres
Beam overall	2.67 metres
Beam Moulded	2.234 metres
Draught (full fuel + 2 crew)	0.54 metres
Displacement, dry	2030kg
Displacement, full load	3130kg

c. **Performance.** The Pacific 24 RIB handles safely in rough weather and may be operated with a full load in a sea state 5. In higher sea states than this the load and speed may have to be reduced. It is capable of achieving 40 knots under optimum sea conditions and with a full load. At 20 knots with eight persons embarked, a full load and a full tank the boat will have an endurance of approximately 4 hours 20 minutes (86 nautical miles). At speeds under ten knots with the revs set, the bucket can be used to turn the boat in its own boat length without any forward or astern motion.

d. **Weight and capacity.** The following table gives the weight of the boat, personnel and other equipment and should be used when calculating hoisting and lowering weights:

(1) *Fast rescue craft/sea boat/crashboat (Xeres fitted)*

Weight of boat, fuel and two crew	2470 kg
Boat bag	10 kg
Crash Bag	25 kg
Total	2505 kg

(2) *Force protection craft GPMG mounted (Xeres Fitted)*

Weight of boat, fuel and two crew	2470 kg
Boat bag	10 kg
Unloaded GPMG	11 kg
Ammunition – three boxes of 200 rounds	18 kg
GPMG Fenlow Mount	40 kg
Total	2549 kg

(3) *Boarding craft Xeres fitted (GPMG not fitted)*

Weight of boat, fuel and two crew	2470 kg
Boat bag	10 kg
GPMG Fenlow Mount	40 kg
Boarding ladder 3m	10 kg
Boarding ladder 2m	10 kg
One Stihl Saw	10 kg
Spare fuel for Stihl Saw	5 kg
Total	2555 kg

(4) *Boarding craft Xeres fitted (GPMG not fitted) utilised as a sea boat/crash boat*

Weight of boat, fuel and three crew (SOW)	2545 kg
Boat bag	10 kg
Crash Bag	25 kg
GPMG Fenlow Mount	40 kg
Total	2620 kg

Note. When the forward four seats are removed for stores transfer or the fitting of the GPMG mount the weight of the boat is reduced by 44 kg. The weight of the boat, fuel and two crew then becomes 2426 kg.

e.   **Boats roles.** The Pacific 24 can be role-changed to provide the command with a versatile platform for ever-changing world-wide tasking. The legacy statement that the Sea Boats primary role was life-saving has now changed to the following:

    (1)   Boarding Operations.

    (2)   Force Protection.

    (3)   Life-saving.

    (4)   Passenger / Stores Transfer.

f.   **Boarding operations**. The Pacific 24 is configured to carry XERES communication and tracking equipment in support of boarding operations. The following equipment is fitted to the craft:

    (1)   Oceana Sea Boat Computer.

    (2)   KY 100 Secure communications radio.

    (3)   Harris military radio.

    (4)   Man overboard alarm facility.

g.   **Boarding role/XERES fit.** (Further information is contained in BR1920). Current concept of operations requires a two-boat capability to board targets over the horizon, more than ten to twelve nautical miles away, with the mother ship and the Sea Boats maintaining tracking and secure communications. A two-boat deployment gives the command an extra capability:

    (1)   Personnel and equipment can be inserted to the target vessel in one operation.

    (2)   Gives the command the flexibility to board multiple target vessels whilst in congested waters (fishing fleet/estuaries).

    (3)   XERES-fitted equipment allows the command to vector both boats to a specific target area/vessel whilst tracking both boats on the mother ship's bridge.

    (4)   Secure communications to both boats allows for an element of surprise.

    (5)   Two boat deployment allows a safety boat coverage whilst conducting boarding operations. One boat proceeds alongside the target vessel whilst the second boat sits in the waiting station. This allows the second boat to act as a safety boat, in case of man overboard or loss of equipment.

    (6)   Due to the distances being deployed and the Pacific 24 being single engined, deployment in pairs gives the crews' confidence of recovery or assistance if the craft suffers from mechanical or technical problems.

h.   **Force protection role.** When deploying in the Force Protection Role the craft will be fitted with a General Purpose Machine Gun (GPMG) and Fenlow Mount. The Bowman will be the GPMG aimer when in the Force Protection Role.

i.   **Armed RIB.** Use of the GPMG during Boarding Operations is limited in that the weapon may be rigged during the transit of personnel. However, no current clearance is available for it to be manned other than those occasions listed in BRd 8988 Chapter 23. During the transit, when rigged, the weapon is to remain in the stowed position with the Bowman seated accordingly. When laying off having delivered the Stick, the armed RIB may be used as required by the Command.

Notes:
*1.   The instructions for the operation procedures for RIB Mounted GPMGs are contained in **BR 8295 Chapter 6B**; **for safety reasons, the procedures are not for interpretation.***

*2.   The Tactical Guidance when a RIB is tasked in the Force Protection Role is contained in **BRd 8988 Chapter 23.***

j.   **Mk 6A and mark 7 combat helmet for boarding operations in potential threat areas.** It is a requirement for all members of Boarding Teams to wear Mk6A and Mk 7 combat helmets when tasked into potential threat areas. During boarding operations the requirement to change from Gecko Marine Safety Helmet (MSH) to the Mk 6A and Mk7 Helmet in the final approach could threaten the effectiveness of the boarding team. Until the Officer In Charge is able to don Bowman communications (not compatible with the MSH), boarding teams are unable to communicate. To improve the operational effect RM and RN boarding teams including boats crews are to conduct operational boarding in Mk 6A and Mk 7 Combat helmets. Training exercises are to continue to use Gecko Marine Safety helmets to a point immediately prior to the boarding iaw current FOST policy.

k.   **Preparations at the start of the watch.** The coxswain should:

(1)   Confirm that power is available at the crane or davit.

(2)   Confirm that the boatrope and steadying lines are rigged correctly on deck and ready for use.

(3)   If the guardrails are to lowered for hoisting out the boat, check that a temporary guardrail is available and that hazardous duty lifejackets are provided for the hoisting/lowering party.

(4)   Carry out a safety and functional check of the release hook and ensure the chain preventer is correctly rigged, re attach the fall on completion.

(5)   Ensure safety helmets are provided for the hoisting/lowering party.

(6)   Check the boats bag and ancillary equipment is correct (iaw para 05059).

(7)   Carry out pre start checks.

(8)   Instruct crew members on their tasks and check their equipment and dress, ie marine safety helmet, immersion suit, manual hazardous duty lifejacket, safety boots, sharp knife.

(9)   To prevent the risk of SHIPHAZ shocks the crew member that operates the release hook is to wear PPE gloves.

(10) Carry out functional VHF comms check, test upper deck broadcast and check the availability of flags/wands.

I.   **Pre-start checks**

(1)   To be completed at the start of each duty period.

(a) Check that the boat is sitting correctly in the chocks (also check that the intake and exhaust is clear). If the boat is in water ensure that it is sitting correctly, not listing or taking on water.

(b) Ensure that the D-ring is intact, double patch is in good condition and webbing strong back is in place.

(c)   The flotation collar from forward to aft is fully inflated.

(d)   Check fuel (max 165 litres).

(e)   Steering bypass valve is in the shut position.

(f)   Water inlet valve on the transom is open.

(g)   Breaker Switch.

(h)   Steering fluid, check that the steering oil reservoir is full (OM 15).

(i)   There is full movement of both throttle and bucket.

(j)   The back flush control is in the ahead position.

(k)   The Deadman's lanyard is fitted and operational.

(l)   Fuel shut-off valve is in the open position.

(m) Check the boatrope, toggle and steadying lines are rigged correctly.

(2)   Open engine compartment and battery compartment.

(a) Check the sand trap (port side of engine compartment). The sand trap can only be cleared when the engine is running.

(b) Check that the bucket hydraulic pump reservoir has sufficient oil (OX 75).

(c)   Check alternator belt for tension.

(d)   Check drive belt tension.

(e)   Pump out both bilge and hydraulic space.

(f)   Engine oil (Shell Rimula 15W 40 grade).

(g)   Coolant level (AL39) + fresh water 50/50 mix).

(h)   Check back flush oil (Shell Rimula X30).

(i)   Back flush set to ahead position.

(j)   Remove safety/arming pin on self-righting gear and place in stowage on the console.

(k)   Check that the bucket is in the neutral position and that the throttle is set to the idle position.

(l)   Navigation lights.

(m) Communications.

(n) Ensure battery isolation switch is on (be aware that there is an emergency battery facility).

m. **Running checks**

(1)   Check the gauges.

Engine oil pressure	2.7-4.5 bar (40-65 psi)
Engine coolant	78-91°C (172-196°F)
Turbo boost pressure	1.0-1.5 bar (14.5-21.75 psi)

(2)   Check for abnormal noises/vibrations.

(3)   Sand trap should be checked if running in shallow water.

n. **Normal stopping procedure**

(1)   Check that the throttle is set to idle.

(2)   Check that the bucket control is in neutral.

(3)   After high speed running allow the engine to idle for three to five minutes before stopping.

(4)   Press engine stop button/emergency stop on the top of the engine.

(5)   Isolate batteries.

(6)   Switch ignition off.

Note.   *If XERES fitted, it must be turned off prior to engine stop.*

o. **Emergencies**

(1)   *Emergency stop.* Coxswain's actions:

(a) Drop the bucket control and fully throttle back.

(b) Gradually increase throttle until the boat has stopped.

Note.   *The coxswain should be aware of carrying out this manoeuvre whilst in the turn as there is a danger of throwing passengers out of the boat.*

(2) *Steering failure*

(a) Revs are to be reduced and the bucket placed in neutral.

(b) Coxswain opens the bypass valve under the console.

(c) Bowman removes the crossbar from the A-frame, opens the watertight hatch in the stern of the boat and inserts the crossbar into the emergency steering point.

(d) Coxswain puts the bucket to the ahead position and increases slowly to minimum revs needed to maintain steerageway.

Note.   *If the revs are too high, the bowman will not be able to steer (not above 2000 rpm). Do not attempt recovery to a moving ship.*

(3) *Stern hydraulics failure.* The first indication of stern hydraulics failure is that the bucket will drop into the astern position. The following action is to be carried out:

(a) Reduce revs immediately.

(b) Open up the engine cover.

(c) Check the drive belt to the hydraulic pump hasn't parted. If it is intact then there is probably a failure in the hydraulic line and the following actions are to be taken:

(d) Remove crossbar from the 'A' frame.

i   Bowman reaches over the transom and with the use of a rope's end, secures the bucket in its uppermost position.

ii   Bowman replaces the crossbar in the stowage on the A frame.

iii   Coxswain moves ahead.

iv   Coxswain contacts the ship and reports the situation.

v   With close liaison between the Coxswain and the command the boat is recovered alongside.

Note. *With the bucket lashed in the uppermost position, the boat will not be able to go astern. Therefore the ship must maintain headway and not be stationary in the water for recovery.*

(4) *Loss of power through the water*

(a) Put the engine revs to minimum.

(b) Manoeuvre to safe water.

(c) Operate the back flush lever.

(5) *Engine cuts out*

    (a) Check the Kill Cord has not operated inadvertently

    (b) Ensure the fuel shut of valve is correctly opened.

    (c) Check for leaks/blockage in the fuel line.

    (d) Dip the fuel tank.

Note.   *The coxswain must be aware of how to prime the engine if the boat has run out of fuel.*

(6) *Engine overheats*

    (a) Has the boat ingested any mud or silt as a result of grounding?

    (b) Operate the back flush.

    (c) Consider operating the sand trap by opening the valves, setting the engine rpm and flushing.

    (d) If the problem is still present. Stop the engine.

    (e) Check the cooling water header tank is full (the tank must be left to cool before removing the filler cap).

    (f) Restart the engine and monitor the temperature gauge.

(7) *Fire in the inboard diesel engine*

    (a) Radio the ship.

    (b) Close the emergency fuel shut of valve. Shut down the engine.

    (c) Close the air inlet flap.

    (d) Place the CO_2 fire extinguisher nozzle into the injection port and inject two thirds of the extinguisher capacity.

    (e) Save the remaining contents in case of re-ignition.

    (f) Lift the engine cover when the fire is out.

    (g) Check for damage and serviceability of the boat.

(8) *Capsizing.* In the event of a capsize, passengers and crew are to take a deep breath and brace, wait until movement has ceased, then exit as soon as possible.

    (a) The Coxswain is in charge of the crew and passengers and anyone trapped under the boat.

    (b) In the event of the Coxswain being unconscious then the bowman is to take charge.

(c)   Nobody is to let go of the boat and as soon as the boat has settled the Coxswain will do a head count.

(d)   If anyone is missing the Coxswain may have to duck under the boat to assist anyone who is trapped.

(e)   The Coxswain will lead all personnel to the stern of the boat with each person holding the belt of the lifejacket of the person in front of them and using the grab handles on the tube to assist.

(f)   Once all crew and passengers are at the rear of the boat, the Coxswain will stream the quoit and line/stern line and again account for all personnel.

(g)   The Coxswain will then operate the self-righting lanyard ensuring that no-one is in danger of getting injured by the boat as it self-rights.

(h)   Once the boat has self righted, the Coxswain is the first man aboard.

(i)   The Coxswain will then assist the bowman into the boat.

(j)   The Coxswain will operate the electric bilge pump while the bowman assists all passengers to board.

(k)   The bowman operates the manual bilge pump whilst the Coxswain conducts another head count.

(l)   Allow all the oils time to settle for about five minutes, then carry out a complete set of engine checks and attempt to restart the engine.

(m) Return to the ship giving a situation report en-route.

Note.   *The self-righting gear is to remain inflated until back at the ship or establishment. Care is to be taken when returning to the ship with regard to the sail effect of the inflated self-righting bag on the handling characteristics of the boat.*

SECTION 9 – RECOVERY OF A PERSON FROM THE WATER USING THE JASON'S CRADLE

05081. Recovering a person from the water using a Jason's Cradle

a. **Introduction.** The Jason's Cradle lifting frame (See Fig 5-34) has been introduced into RN service to improve rescuer safety, reduce the risks to the health of the casualty, and facilitate recovery of a casualty from the sea into a rescue boat. It is a ladder-like device constructed from a number of units (rungs). The inboard end of the device is secured to the inflation tube of the rescue craft. When used for man overboard recovery, the outboard end of the cradle is kept in hand and the bight is lowered into the water. This action automatically forms an articulating non-collapsible loop. The casualty is floated into the loop and lifted from the water (horizontally) as the cradle is pulled aboard. The device is to be available for fitting to most Sea Boats as required. The cradle is not necessary for the Searider due to limited space. It is assumed that the Pacific RIB has a crew of three; all the other craft operate with a crew of two. The operation of the cradle in the Pacific RIB is two-handed. In the other craft the operation is single-handed unless prevailing conditions are such that the coxswain can assist.

b. **Description.** The Jason's Cradle is four rungs wide by fifteen rungs long and has a deployment strop that is adjustable to a maximum length of 1.1 metres. The cradle, which has a carrying strop fitted to the outside of the stowage bag, can be fitted to either the port or starboard inflation tube. It is fitted forward of the coxswain's console in a RIB, but because the coxswain is positioned in the stern of an Inflatable boat, the cradle must be positioned slightly further aft. Naval stores numbers of the equipment are as follows:

Jason's Cradle (complete unit)	0472-709-0889
D-Ring Patch Assembly	0472-723-0441
Bag for Stowage and Transport	0472-348-9911
Carbine Clip	0472-327-9614
Strap Webbing	0472-862-3287
End Nut	0472-864-6877

c. **Training.** Rescue boat crews must be trained to use the equipment safely and effectively. The procedures outlined in this guide should assist in meeting this objective.

d. **Installation into the rescue boat**

(1) Ascertain the fitting positions for the various rescue craft, then attach the cradle to the appropriate port or starboard tube D-rings using the attachment clips. The attachment clips should protrude from the two holes in the stowage bag. The cradle should be attached with the bag flap uppermost, see Fig 5-39(a).

(2) Open the bag and fold the flap over the inflation tube.

Note. *Even when the cradle is tightly rolled-up in its stowage bag, it is relatively bulky (approximately 710mm long by 330mm in diameter) and heavy (approximately 17kg). Therefore, due care should be taken when placing the cradle into the boat, to minimise the manual handling risks.*

Fig 5-34. Installing a Jason's Cradle

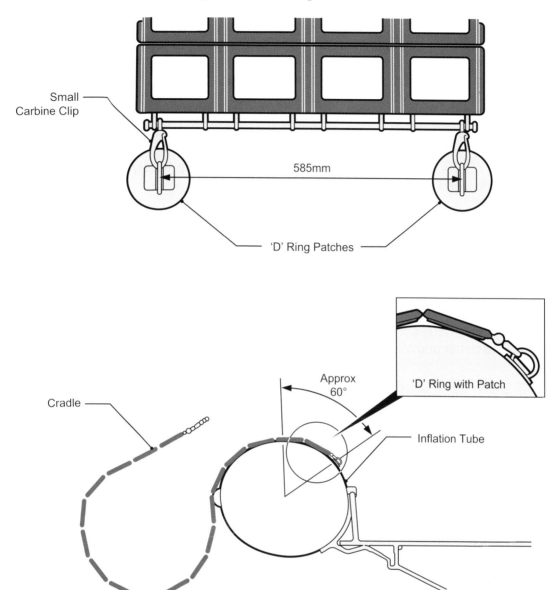

Small Carbine Clip

585mm

'D' Ring Patches

Cradle

Approx 60°

'D' Ring with Patch

Inflation Tube

05082. Safety considerations and general guidance for all users

a.   **Minimising the risk of manual handling injury**. Care should be taken when carrying out the rescue procedures using a Jason's Cradle. The rescuers must maintain stable postures during the recovery of the casualty to minimise the risk of falling overboard. To reduce the risk of incurring a manual handling injury when the casualty is being pulled aboard in the cradle, the rescuers must maintain an upright stance and avoid either leaning forward or flexing the spine excessively. Additionally, the rescuers should take care to avoid minor finger injuries when using the cradle (fingers can be nipped in the hinged joints of the cradle). Finally, the rescue must be conducted in a methodical, controlled manner to reduce the risk of injury and to ensure that the casualty's injuries are not exacerbated.

b.   **Use of gloves**. The use of suitable gloves will improve the rescuer's grip whilst using the cradle, and reduce the risk of minor finger injuries. In extreme cold conditions the use of gloves is strongly recommended.

c.   **Stowing the Jason's Cradle**. Preparing the cradle for stowage is more easily achieved on the ship's deck. Therefore the cradle should be removed from the rescue boat before it is placed into its stowage bag. Care should be taken when removing the cradle from the boat to minimise the manual handling risks.

(1)   After use the cradle should be washed with fresh water.

(2)   The following steps describe the easiest method for placing the cradle into its stowage bag:

(a) Stand the cradle on its edge and coil up tightly with the free end (the end not attached to the bag) innermost.

(b) Fit the bag around the cradle, ensuring that the attachment clips protrude from the holes in the bag, and seal the VELCRO® brand flap.

(c) Fasten the buckle and tighten (the VELCRO® brand may need to be re-sealed).

Note.   *The cradle should not be lifted by the carrying strop until the buckle fastener and VELCRO® brand flap are fully secure.*

(3)   Store in a dry location close to the boat deck(s) or in the designated rescue boat.

Note.   *The basic sequence for deploying the Jason's Cradle is shown pictorially in Fig 5-35.*

05083. RIB recovery procedure – two-handed operation

a.   The cradle strop should be adjusted to its maximum length of approximately 1.1 metres for use with this type of RIB. This ensures that when the cradle is deployed, the deployer does not have to lean out excessively.

b.   **Approach to the casualty.** The approach should be at low speed, with the cradle and casualty on the leeward side of the boat. During heavy seas (and high winds) it may be safer to position the casualty on the windward side of the boat. This will ensure that the boat does not drift over or land on top of the casualty as it is lifted on the swell. The two crew position themselves on either side of the cradle, Crewman 1 forward and Crewman 2 aft, Crewman 2 being the first-aider.

(1)   During the final stages of the approach, Crewman 2 begins to deploy the cradle. This can be partially achieved by unrolling the cradle on the deck of the boat. To deploy the cradle, guide it over the side of the inflation tube whilst holding onto the strop, and lower it towards the water. The cradle will form a non-collapsing loop. A normal hand-grip on the strop will suffice. The strop should not be wound around the hand or secured to Crewman 2 in any way. The cradle should be fully deployed before reaching the casualty, with the cradle submerged in the water so that approximately one rung of the free end is above the water surface. This will ensure that the loop is deep enough to allow the casualty to float in. The strop adjustment ensures that Crewman 2 does not have to lean out excessively to perform this task.

(2)   Crewman 1 should establish verbal contact with the casualty (if conscious) and explain the basic rescue procedure.

c.   **Placing the casualty in the cradle**.   Prior to starting the recovery, the crew should assume kneeling postures against the inboard side of the inflation tube. This will place the crew close to the water and casualty, in a safe and stable posture.

(1)   On reaching the casualty the Coxswain is to put the engine into neutral; Crewman 1 prepares to guide the casualty into the cradle. The casualty should be guided into the cradle head first, to ensure a feet towards bow attitude once the casualty is in the boat. This may require the casualty to be turned in the water. If the local conditions are such that turning the casualty in the water is not feasible, then the recovery should be made with the feet aft and if possible the casualty turned in the boat. Crewman 2 is to ensure that the loop is wide enough to accommodate the casualty and help Crewman 1 with the casualty when within reach. The casualty's arms should remain in the cradle during the recovery.

(2)   When the casualty's shoulders are slightly overhanging the edge of the cradle (torso fully contained in the loop) Crewman 2 should pull on the strop to close the loop and secure the casualty in the cradle.

(3)   If the sea conditions are heavy, 'slamming' of the bow of the rescue boat may occur. In these conditions it may be safer to guide the casualty into the cradle from aft. The most effective way to achieve this is for Crewman 1 to deploy the cradle and Crewman 2 to guide in the casualty. Again, the casualty's arms should be inside the cradle prior to the recovery commencing.

d.   **Recovering the casualty**

(1)   Both crew take hold of the free end of the cradle (with one hand) and pull until the free end is over the inflation tube. Crewman 1 should then adopt a standing posture, with the lower leg/knee braced against the inboard side of the inflation tube, Crewman 2 should then do the same. During these posture changes a firm grip should be maintained on the cradle. To ease this change of posture the free hand should be used to push off the inflation tube. Placing a knee against the inflation tube will also assist in securing the casualty on top of the inflation tube, as this will prevent the casualty dropping onto the deck of the boat.

(2)   To complete the recovery task, the cradle should be pulled in at an angle of approximately 45° to the horizontal. This is the optimum pull angle for the cradle, therefore the rescuers can fully benefit from the cradle's two-to-one mechanical lifting advantage. Attempting to pull at a lower angle will make the recovery task difficult to complete and will increase the risk of a manual handling injury occurring.

(3)   To assist in the co-ordination of the shared lift, instructions should be shouted by Crewman 1 during the following steps. To ease the recovery when pulling the cradle (and casualty) aboard, the rescuers should adopt a palm-down grip.

(4).   Both crew should pull in the cradle (at approximately. 45°) with one hand, whilst the other hand reaches under the cradle for the next hand-hold. This new hand-hold should be two rungs down, and once located, the first two rungs should be folded over the top of the cradle.

(5)   The cradle should be pulled in again, another hand-hold located (a further two rungs down the cradle), and the excess rungs folded over the top again.

(6)   After another short pull on the cradle, the casualty should be lying face-up on the inflation tube. Crewman 1 may have to pull in the legs, and then keep a firm grip on the casualty. Crewman 2 should find a suitable hand-hold on the upper torso of the casualty.

(7)   Once the casualty is securely held on the top of the inflation tube, the free end of the cradle should be released to allow the cradle to hang over the side of the boat. Conscious casualties should be instructed to remain horizontal and should not be allowed to sit up until an initial first aid assessment has been conducted.

(8)   The crew should now take up positions at the head and foot of the casualty and conduct a controlled lift to place the casualty on to the deck of the boat immediately adjacent to the inflation tube. This will place the head and shoulders of the casualty next to the coxswain's console, with Crewman 2 further aft.

e.   **Preparation for return to ship**

(1)   Crewman 2 should immediately proceed with an initial first aid assessment, the priority task being to check the casualty's breathing. The first aider (Crewman 2) is in a good position to perform mouth-to-mouth resuscitation if required.

(2)   Whilst Crewman 2 is assessing the casualty, Crewman 1 can retrieve the cradle. This can be achieved by pulling in the cradle in a controlled manner and laying it across the casualty to the other side of the boat. The weight of the cradle on the casualty is minimal and should not cause distress. Once the cradle is on board, it can be unclipped from its anchor points and temporarily stowed along the opposite side of the coxswain's console. Alternatively, if moving the cradle elsewhere causes an obstruction, it can be left lying across the casualty (if this does not cause problems for the casualty). The cradle stowage bag has been designed to remain attached to the cradle.

(3)   Once the first aider has stabilised the casualty, the rescue boat can return to the ship.

05084. RIB recovery procedure – single-handed operation

a.   If the rescue conditions are such that the Coxswain cannot assist in the recovery of the casualty, the recovery must be conducted single-handed. The cradle strop is to be adjusted to a length suitable for these type of rescue craft. The optimum length of strop should allow the cradle to be fully deployed (cradle submerged in the water so that approximately one rung of the free end is above the water surface) without the deployer leaning out excessively.

b.   **Approach to casualty.** The final approach should be at low speed, with the cradle and casualty on the leeward side of the boat. During heavy seas (and high winds) it may be safer to position the casualty on the windward side of the boat. This will ensure that the boat does not drift over the casualty or land on top of the casualty as it is lifted on the swell.

(1)   During the approach, the Bowman should begin to deploy the cradle. This can be partially achieved by unrolling the cradle on the deck of the boat. To deploy the cradle, guide it over the side of the inflation tube whilst holding on to the strop, and lower it towards the water.

The cradle will form a non-collapsing loop. A normal hand-grip on the strop will suffice. The strop should not be wound around the hand or secured to the Bowman in any way. The cradle should be fully deployed before reaching the casualty, with the cradle submerged in the water so that approximately one rung of the free end is above the water surface, this will ensure that the loop is deep enough to allow the casualty to float in.

(2)   The Bowman should establish verbal contact with the casualty (if conscious) and explain the basic rescue procedure.

c.   **Placing the casualty in the cradle.** Prior to starting the recovery, the Bowman should assume a kneeling posture against the inboard side of the inflation tube. This will place the Bowman close to the water and casualty, in a safe and stable posture.

(1)   On reaching the casualty, the Coxswain puts the engine into neutral and the Bowman prepares to guide the casualty into the cradle, having checked that the loop is wide enough to accommodate the casualty. The casualty should then be guided into the cradle head first, to ensure a feet-towards-bow attitude once the casualty is in the boat. This may require the casualty to be turned in the water. If the local conditions are such that turning the casualty in the water is not feasible, then the recovery should be made with the feet aft and if possible (due to the restricted space) the casualty turned in the boat. The casualty's arms should remain in the cradle during the recovery.

(2)   When the casualty's shoulders are slightly overhanging the edge of the cradle (torso fully contained in the loop) the Bowman pulls on the strop to close the loop and secure the casualty in the cradle.

(3)   If the sea conditions are heavy, 'slamming' of the bow of the rescue boat may occur. Under these conditions, it may be safer to guide the casualty into the cradle from aft. Again, the casualty's arms should be inside the cradle prior to the recovery commencing.

d.   **Recovering the casualty**

(1)   The Bowman should take hold of the free end of the cradle (with one hand) and pull until the free end is over the inflation tube. The Bowman then adopts a standing posture, with the lower leg/knee braced against the inboard side of the inflation tube. During this posture change a firm grip should be maintained on the cradle. To ease this change of posture the free hand should be used to push off the inflation tube. Placing a knee against the inflation tube will also assist in securing the casualty on top of the inflation tube, as this will prevent the casualty dropping onto the deck of the boat.

(2)   To complete the recovery task, the cradle should be pulled in at an angle of approximately 45° to the horizontal. This is the optimum pull angle for the cradle and ensures the rescuer fully benefit from the cradle's two-to-one mechanical lifting advantage. Attempting to pull at a lower angle will make the recovery task difficult to complete and will increase the risk of a manual handling injury. To ease the recovery when pulling the cradle (and casualty) aboard, the Bowman should adopt a palm-down grip.

(3)   The Bowman pulls in the cradle (at approximately. 45°) with one hand, whilst the other hand reaches under the cradle for the next hand-hold. This new hand-hold should be two rungs down, and once located, the first two rungs should be folded over the top of the cradle.

(4)   The cradle should be pulled in again, another hand-hold located (a further two rungs down the cradle), and the excess rungs folded over the top again.

(5)   After another short pull on the cradle, the casualty should be lying face-up on the inflation tube. The Bowman may have to pull in the legs, and then keep a firm grip on the casualty.

(6)   Once the casualty is securely held on the top of the inflation tube, the free end of the cradle should be released to allow the cradle to hang over the side of the boat. Conscious casualties should be instructed to remain horizontal and should not be allowed to sit up until an initial first aid assessment has been conducted.

(7)   The Bowman should then take up a position at the head of the casualty and conduct a controlled lift to place the casualty onto the deck of the boat immediately adjacent to the inflation tube.

e.   **Preparation for return to ship**

(1)   The Bowman should immediately proceed with an initial first aid assessment, the priority task being to check the casualty's breathing. If the Coxswain is the first aider, they must swap places. The first aider is in a good position to perform mouth-to-mouth resuscitation if required.

(2)   Once the first aider has stabilised the casualty, the cradle can be retrieved. This can be achieved by pulling in the cradle in a controlled manner and laying it across the casualty to the other side of the boat. The weight of the cradle on the casualty is minimal and should not cause distress. Once the cradle is onboard it can be unclipped from its anchor points and temporarily stowed along the opposite side of the coxswain's console. Alternatively, if moving the cradle elsewhere causes an obstruction, it can be left lying across the casualty (if this does not cause problems for the casualty). The cradle stowage bag has been designed to remain attached to the cradle. The rescue boat can then return to the ship.

05085. Searider, Whiskey and MIB recovery procedure – two-handed operation

a.   When the rescue conditions allow, the Coxswain should assist in the recovery of the casualty. The cradle strop should be adjusted to a length suitable for these type of rescue craft. The optimum length of strop should allow the cradle to be fully deployed (cradle submerged in the water so that approximately one rung of the free end is above the water surface) without the deployer leaning out excessively.

b.   **Approach to casualty**

(1)   The approach should be at low speed, with cradle and casualty on the leeward side of the boat. During heavy seas (and high winds) it may be safer to position the casualty on the windward side of the boat. This will ensure that the boat does not drift over the casualty or land on top of the casualty as it is lifted on the swells.

(2)   The Bowman should establish verbal contact with the casualty (if conscious) and explain the basic rescue procedure.

c.   **Placing the casualty in the cradle**. Prior to starting the recovery, the Bowman should assume a kneeling posture against the inboard side of the inflation tube. This will place the Bowman close to the water and casualty, in a safe and stable posture.

(1)   On reaching the casualty, the Coxswain puts the engine into neutral and the Bowman secures the casualty. Once the casualty is secured, the Coxswain should join the Bowman to complete the recovery. The current design of boat cut-out switch uses a 'Kill Cord' system which stops the engine when the cord is pulled. Therefore, the only way to allow the Coxswain to assist without stopping the engine is to detach the Kill Cord from the Coxswain.

(2)   The Crewman who is first aid trained should take up a kneeling posture aft of the cradle (Crewman 2), with the other crewman forward (Crewman 1). If the Bowman is the first-aider, the crew must change places. Care is to be taken to ensure the casualty remains secure during the hand-over.

(3)   Crewman 2 deploys the cradle. This can be partially achieved by unrolling the cradle on the deck of the boat. To deploy the cradle, guide it over the side of the inflation tube whilst holding onto the strop, and lower it towards the water. The cradle will form a non-collapsing loop. A normal hand-grip on the strop will suffice. The strop should not be wound around the hand or secured to Crewman 2 in any way. The cradle should be submerged in the water so that approximately one rung of the free end is above the water surface, this will ensure that the loop is deep enough to allow the casualty to float in.

(4)   Crewman 2 should ensure that the loop is wide enough to accommodate the casualty. The casualty should then be guided into the cradle head first (to ensure a feet-towards-bow attitude once the casualty is in the boat), this may require the casualty to be turned in the water. If the local conditions are such that turning the casualty in the water is not feasible, then the recovery should be made with the feet aft and if possible (due to the restricted space) the casualty turned in the boat. The casualty's arms should remain in the cradle during the recovery.

(5)   When the casualty's shoulders are slightly overhanging the edge of the cradle (torso fully contained in the loop) Crewman 2 should pull on the strop to close the loop and secure the casualty in the cradle.

(6)   If the sea conditions are heavy, 'slamming' of the bow of the rescue boat may occur. Under these conditions, it may be safer to guide the casualty into the cradle from aft. Again, the casualty's arms should be inside the cradle prior to the recovery commencing.

d.   **Recovering the casualty**

(1)   Both crew should then take hold of the free end of the cradle (with one hand) and pull until the free end is over the inflation tube. Crewman 1 then adopts a standing posture, with the lower leg/knee braced against the inboard side of the inflation tube, Crewman 2 does the same. During these posture changes a firm grip should be maintained on the cradle. To ease this change of posture the free hand should be used to push off the inflation tube. Placing a knee against the inflation tube will also assist in securing the casualty on top of the inflation tube, as this will prevent the casualty dropping onto the deck of the boat.

(2)   To complete the recovery task, the cradle should be pulled in at an angle of approximately 45° to the horizontal. This is the optimum pull angle for the cradle and allows the rescuers to benefit fully from the cradle's two-to-one mechanical lifting advantage. Attempting to pull at a lower angle will make the recovery task difficult to complete and will increase the risk of a manual handling injury occurring.

(3)   To assist in the co-ordination of the shared lift, instructions should be shouted by Crewman 1 during the following steps. To ease the recovery when pulling the cradle (and casualty) aboard, the rescuers should adopt a palm-down grip.

(4)   Both crew should pull in the cradle (at approximately. 45°) with one hand, whilst the other hand reaches under the cradle for the next hand-hold. This new hand-hold should be two rungs down, and once located, the first two rungs should be folded over the top of the cradle.

(5)   The cradle should be pulled in again, another hand-hold located (a further two rungs down the cradle), and the excess rungs folded over the top again.

(6)   After another short pull on the cradle, the casualty should be lying face-up on the inflation tube. Crewman 1 may have to pull in the legs, and then keep a firm grip on the casualty. Crewman 2 should find a suitable hand-hold on the upper torso of the casualty.

(7)   Once the casualty is securely held on the top of the inflation tube, the free end of the cradle must be released and allowed to hang over the side of the boat. Conscious casualties should be instructed to remain horizontal and should not be allowed to sit up until an initial first aid assessment has been conducted.

(8)   The crew then take up positions at the head and foot of the casualty and conduct a controlled lift to place the casualty on to the deck of the boat immediately adjacent to the inflation tube. In the Searider, this will place the head and shoulders of the casualty next to the coxswain's console, with Crewman 2 further aft.

e.   **Preparation for return to ship**

(1)   Crewman 2 must immediately proceed with an initial first aid assessment, the priority task being to check the casualty's breathing. The first aider (Crewman 2) is in a good position to perform mouth-to-mouth resuscitation if required.

(2)   Whilst Crewman 2 is assessing the casualty, Crewman 1 can retrieve the cradle. This can be achieved by pulling in the cradle in a controlled manner and laying it across the casualty to the other side of the boat. The weight of the cradle on the casualty is minimal and should not cause distress. Once the cradle is on board, it can be unclipped from its anchor points and temporarily stowed along the opposite side of the coxswain's console (in Searider). Alternatively, if moving the cradle elsewhere causes an obstruction, it can be left lying across the casualty (if this does not cause problems for the casualty). The cradle stowage bag has been designed to remain attached to the cradle.

(3)   Once the first aider has stabilised the casualty, the rescue boat can return to the ship. The Kill Cord must be re-attached to the Coxswain soon as possible after the casualty has been recovered.

Fig 5-35. Recovering a casualty using the Jason's cradle

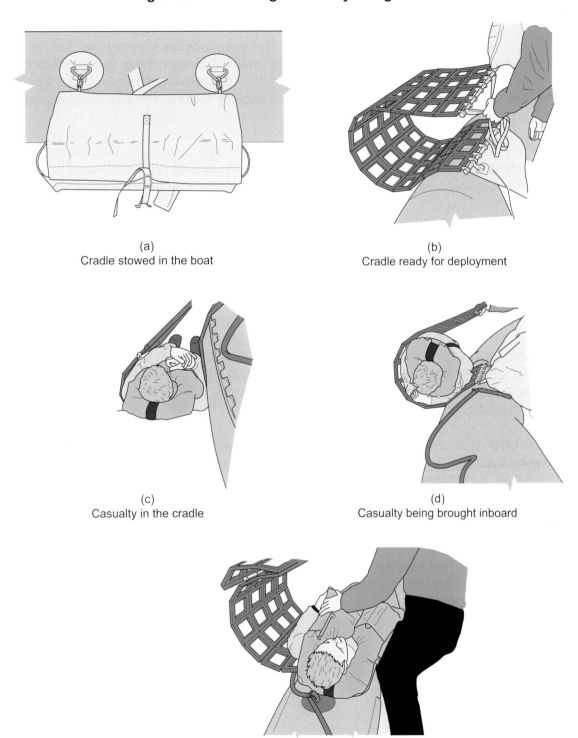

(a)
Cradle stowed in the boat

(b)
Cradle ready for deployment

(c)
Casualty in the cradle

(d)
Casualty being brought inboard

(e)
Causualty recovered into the boat

05086. Boat handling for jet driven RIBs during launch and recovery

a.   The Pacific Mk 2 Jetpac and the Pacific 24' are prone to directional instability at slow speeds. (See warning box below). If slow speeds are unavoidable, the handling of the boat is completely different. The boat will always move in the direction the wheel is turned whether ahead or astern. The command needs to be aware of the potential for instability and to ensure that the Coxswain takes special care with particular reference to the trim.

b.   To aid the Coxswain in positioning the craft correctly under the falls, a small visual reference mark should be made on the ships side to enable the Coxswain to maintain steerageway and prevent him from putting too much weight on the boatrope.

c.   To prevent an unexpected boatrope release during the recovery phase, I/C's are to ensure that whilst the weight is not on the boatrope , the boatrope stray line is kept taught at all times.

WARNINGS

1.   JETPAC BOATS ARE POTENTIALLY DIRECTIONALLY UNSTABLE AT VERY LOW SPEEDS, THUS INCREASING THE RISK OF CAPSIZE WHEN OPERATING ALONGSIDE A SLOW MOVING PLATFORM. DURING LAUNCH/RECOVERY, THE IDEAL SHIP'S SPEED SHOULD BE BETWEEN 6-12 KNOTS AND SHOULD NOT REDUCE BELOW SIX KNOTS WITHOUT COMMAND APPROVAL AND ACKNOWLEDGMENT OF CHANGES IN THE JETPAC HANDLING CHARACTERISTICS.

2.   DURING RECOVERY THE BOAT SHOULD CAPTURE THE BOATROPE IN THE NORMAL MANNER, WITH THE COXSWAIN REDUCING POWER BUT STILL MAINTAINING STEERAGE, ALLOWING THE WEIGHT OF THE CRAFT TO TRANSFER ONTO THE BOAT ROPE AND ENABLING CORRECT POSITIONING UNDER THE FALL FOR HOISTING. THE BUCKET IS TO REMAIN IN THE AHEAD POSITION (UP) AND SPEED IS TO BE REDUCED GRADUALLY. THE COXSWAIN WILL HAVE TO STEER THE BOAT AS THE BOAT ROPE WILL CAUSE THE CRAFT TO SEEK THE SHIPS SIDE. COXSWAINS ARE TO AVOID USING THE BUCKET IN THE ASTERN OR NEUTRAL POSITION AS THIS WILL CAUSE THE BOW TO DIP ALLOWING INGRESS OF WATER, RESULTING IN A POSSIBLE CAPSIZE SITUATION.

SECTION 10 – BOAT LIFTING DEVICES

05087. Boat lifting devices

a.   **Introduction**. A variety of davits and cranes are fitted in HM Ships for hoisting RIBs; an example of a 'C' Type Davit is shown in Fig 5-36. Cranes used for hoisting RIBs have an elevating jib that enables them to be operated in a more confined space; the jib can be raised before being slewed and so controlled to hoist the RIB clear of obstructions. Some cranes are designed with folding jibs; this type is likely to be found in ships where space on deck is very limited.

b.   **Operation of lifting devices**. The requirement to train and qualify crane operators is laid down in Chapter 3; a similar criterion is to be applied to the training of davit operators. It is important to ensure that detailed operating procedures are produced on board for each type of crane or davit in the ship. These procedures should be produced by the Seamanship Training Officer in conjunction with the equipment maintainer and must comply with the equipment manufacturer's instructions. Copies of procedures are to be held in the Seamanship Data Book.

c.   **Use of hanging pendants.** The practice of hanging boats outboard for extended periods on hanging pendants is considered bad practice and may cause wear on the slings where they are attached to lifting shackles and intermediate links. Ship's boats therefore, are not to be suspended outboard. However, to overcome hoisting/ lowering difficulties during those periods when ships of the Fishery Protection conduct consecutive boarding operations and Mine Counter Measure Vessels (MCMVs) conduct Flying, Mine Warfare and Diving operations, a relaxation is granted for their boats to be suspended outboard for limited periods in suitable weather conditions. On these occasions, frequent checks of a boat's slinging arrangements are to be conducted with particular regard to chafing of the webbing. When the boat is recovered inboard and the weight is off the sling, the area of the sling attached to the lifting shackles and intermediate links should be checked for chafing.

Fig 5-36. Examples of the 'C' type davit in use

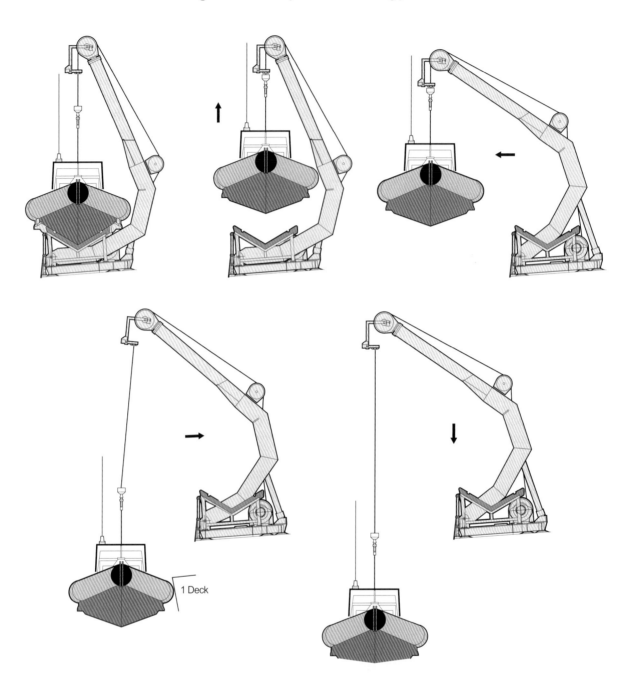

THE NAUTICAL INSTITUTE

05088. Henriksen release hook – lowering and hoisting

a.   Procedures for lowering and hoisting are to be carried out in accordance with normal boat launch and recovery operations with the following additional procedures when using the Henriksen Hook:

b.   **Lowering**

(1)   Engage the lifting ring into the Henriksen hook. Make sure that the handle is in the high position and that the locking pin is inserted according to Fig 5-37(A).

(2)   Hoist, and then train the davit outboard and down to deck edge level.

(3)   When ready the Coxswain starts the engine ensuring that the bucket control is set to ahead.

(4)   When lowering, once the RIB has left deck edge, the Coxswain directs the Bowman to 'Remove the locking pin', by twisting it clockwise.

(5)   As the RIB passes a point approximately two metres from the water, the Coxswain directs the Bowman to 'cock the hook', by squeezing the handle and moving it to the low position. In the PAC 22 Mk 2 RIB where the Coxswain cannot easily see the hook, the Bowman should tap the Coxswain firmly on the shoulder and report 'HOOK COCKED'.

WARNING

THIS SYSTEM OPERATING PROCEDURE SHOULD PROVIDE A SMOOTH AND SEAMLESS LOWERING PROCEDURE, HOWEVER, IF FOR WHATEVER REASON THE HOOK IS NOT GOING TO BE COCKED PRIOR TO ENTERING THE WATER, THE COXSWAIN IS TO RAISE HIS HAND AND SHOUT 'STOP'. UPON WITNESSING THIS, THE LOWERING OF THE RIB IS TO BE CEASED. LOWERING IS ONLY TO CONTINUE WHEN THE COXSWAIN IS CONTENT THAT THE HOOK IS COCKED. IF THERE IS DOUBT AS TO THE STATE OF THE HOOK THE RIB IS TO BE RECOVERED.

---

(6)   Once the hook is cocked, the Bowman should stand well back. When the boat touches the water, the weight of the fall on the hook will reduce, causing the hook to open automatically and release the lifting ring. On witnessing this the lowering party should immediately haul the lifting ring clear of the boat using the 'Bowsing in Line'.

(7)   The I/C of the lowering party is reminded of direction at Para 05094 to check that the lowering device/davit is operating correctly prior to lowering. This should include checking the fall wire for riding turns etc where possible.

(8)   Care is to be taken not to get caught in the ship's bow wave as this causes disturbance in the water which has an affect on the handling characteristics of the Pacific 24.

(9)   If the Henriksen Hook has been cocked and the launch is aborted, the hook is to be disarmed by putting the handle to the high position and the locking pin re-inserted. Only then is the RIB to be hoisted to deck edge level.

Fig 5-37. Henriksen hook operation during launch

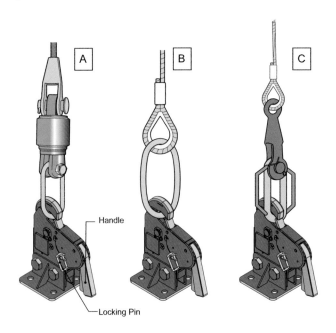

Note. *Fig 5-37 above shows different styles of lifting ring that may be presented to the boat from different NATO ships.*

c. **Hoisting**

(1)   The bucket is to remain in the full ahead position at all times for recovery. The revs throttle is to be used to adjust the speed for coming alongside and not the bucket.

(2)   Once the boatrope is attached, reduce the revs as required. Revs as required will have to be kept on to maintain steerageway until the boat is clear of the water.

(3)   Make sure that the handle is in the high position and that the locking pin is inserted as shown in Fig 5-37A above.

Note.   *The lifting frame is positioned and designed so that the RIB will adopt an even trim when lifted.*

(4)   The Bowman catches the lifting ring and inserts it into the jaw of the hook as shown in Fig 5-38D below then stands back during the hoisting of the boat.

(5)   Check the trim of the boat; the boat must be on an even trim.

CAUTION

Do not lift the boat if the trim is uneven. Lower the boat back into the water. Investigate the cause and redistribute the weight as necessary before attempting to repeat the lifting operation.

---

(6)   When the trim is even, carry on hoisting to deck edge level.

(7)   Stow the boat in accordance with normal boat operations.

Fig 5-38. GBR Henriksen hook operation during recovery

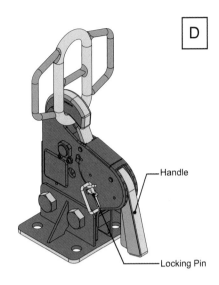

05089. **RFD release hook**

a. **Introduction**. The RFD Automatic Release Hook Mk 5, Naval stores No F218-513-8208 (Fig 5-39), is designed to trip automatically when the weight of the boat comes off the fall. It has two operating positions: 'Safe' and 'Cocked'. The ring of the boat's sling is engaged by lateral pressure on the back of the hook; this sets a pointer on the cheek-plate to 'safe' and makes the release mechanism inoperative. The Coxswain sets the automatic release mechanism by giving a pull on the cocking lanyard after the boat has been lowered to a approximately one metre above the top of the waves, this moves the pointer to the 'cocked' position. The hook then trips when the tension in the hoist falls below 9 kg as the RIB enters the water.

Fig 5-39. RFD automatic release hook

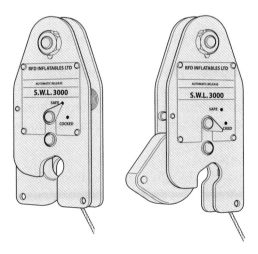

b. **Load specification and test requirements**. The RFD Automatic Release Hook has a safe working load (SWL) of three tonnes and is only to be used for the W525 and Searider operations. Each hook is supplied in a sealed package and is accompanied by a history card.

On receipt the history card is to be checked, and if not signed by the Naval Stores then it is to be signed on receipt in the Naval stores section. The hook must not be dismantled on board. If a fault occurs it must be returned to stores for inspection by the manufacturer. The hook has an on-board life of two years and an in-service life of one year, after which it must be returned to the manufacturer with history card via naval stores for servicing and retesting. If the hook remains 'on the shelf' for more than a year, the in-service life is reduced accordingly, ie, if the hook has been 'on the shelf' for eighteen months the in-service life of the hook is reduced to six months before it must be returned to the manufacturer via naval stores for inspection and retesting.

Note.   *The in-service life commences once the sealed package containing the hook has been broached.*

c.   **Fitting the RFD hook to the fall** (Fig 5-40). A visual inspection is to be carried out first by the maintainer, then; fit the cones (1) in the eye of the fall and insert between the cheek plates of the RFD block. Thread the washers on to the bolt so that the right-angled tabs (2) on the washers engage in the recesses on the cheek plates, then screw on and tighten the nut; finish by knocking down the locking tabs onto the flats of the nut. The washers are essential to prevent the nut and bolt from working loose.

Fig 5-40. Fitting the RFD hook to the fall

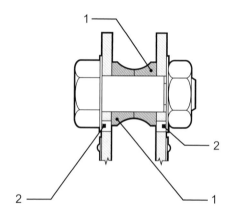

d.   **Maintenance**. Maintenance of the RFD Hook must be in accordance with the MMS.

05090. RIBs/displacement boats – lifeline requirement

Modern methods of davit launch and recovery including MCA Fast Rescue Craft requirements negate the use of lifelines. Therefore, when operating RIBs, lifelines are not to be rigged or used. However, for displacement boats, lifelines are to be rigged and used at all times.

05091. RIBs – safety preventer

A preventer consisting of a length of chain fitted with a spring hook one end and a shackle the other is available for use as an added safety measure whenever a RIB, Whiskey class or MIB is lowered or hoisted with an RFD hook. Two sizes of preventer are issued: one with a SWL of 2.5 tonnes, NSN 0263/796-5046, for the Pacific 22 Mk 2, the other with a SWL of 1.5 tonnes, NSN 0263/798-3984, for the 5.4 metre and 4.7-metre RIB. The preventer is attached to the fall by a shackle resting on top of the RFD hook (Fig 5-41).

Although inadvertent release when the RFD hook is in the 'SAFE' position cannot occur, it is possible for release to take place following snagging or jerking when the hook is in the 'COCKED' position. Rules for the use of the preventer are given in the notes following the RIB hoisting and lowering drills.

Fig 5-41. Preventer rigged and hooked back to fall

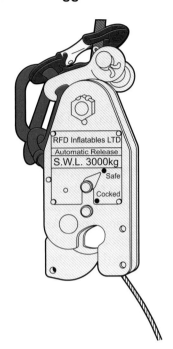

05092. RIBs – used as a sea boat

When at sea all ships must have a boat, known as the Sea Boat, ready for lowering at a moment's notice; most warships and RFAs use a RIB for this duty. A Sea Boat may be used for rescuing a person who has fallen over the side, communicating with another ship or the shore, or for any other occasion when a boat is required at short notice at sea. The necessary personnel must be detailed, and all involved must know their duties. The Coxswain of the Sea Boat is responsible for checking that the boat is correctly secured, equipped and ready for immediate use until the ship returns to harbour. When leaving harbour and at the beginning of each watch or period of duty the Coxswain musters and briefs the crew, inspects the boat, functionally checks the Automatic Release Hook, then reports to the Officer of the Watch that all is correct, or whether there are any deficiencies he is unable to rectify. When leaving harbour and at the beginning of each watch or period of duty the Leading Seaman of the watch on deck musters and briefs the lowerers and handlers, and checks that the lowering device is operating correctly and then reports to the Officer of the Watch that all is correct, or whether there are any deficiencies he is unable to rectify.

05093. RIBs – preparations and personnel required for lowering and hoisting a RIB

 a. **The deck team** must consist of the following as a minimum:

  (1) Safety officer.

  (2) I/c of evolution.

  (3) Competent davit/crane operator.

  (4) Boatrope handler.

  (5) After steadying line handler.

  (6) Flag/wand person.

b. In rough weather if the ship is rolling the number of handlers may have to be increased. Many ships are able to utilise cleats/fittings to facilitate the handling and control of the boat steadying lines; in ships without such fittings, up to three persons at each end of the craft may be required to manhandle the RIB safely while it is being turned out from its stowage. The i/c of the lowering party is responsible for the safe conduct of the whole evolution to the point where the boatrope is slipped and must supervise preparations being made beforehand for hoisting out and recovery, and he must be in good communication with the bridge throughout the evolution.

Note. *Davits are to be marked with training limit marks to assist the i/c when turning boats outboard/inboard.*

c. **The crew** consists of a Coxswain and at least one crewman who must be capable of driving the boat in an emergency (See Para 05051). The Coxswain is responsible for making all preparations within the boat and ensuring that the RIB is fully fuelled and equipped and is in charge of the crew members and must check that they are properly dressed for manning the boat. The coxswain must also ensure that they know how to handle and slip the boatrope, how to operate the Automatic Release Hook and how to clip on and release the steadying line. As a general rule during lowering/hoisting operations, only the Coxswain should sit in the centre of the boat, the remainder of the crew should sit on the outboard tube then transfer to nominated seats when the boat is in the water. However, during Searider lowering operations the Coxswain and Bowman should sit on the centre console.

d. **Preparations at the start of the watch**. The i/c should:

(1) Confirm that power is available at the davit or crane.

(2) Confirm that the boatrope and steadying line are ranged ready for use.

(3) If the guardrails have to be lowered for hoisting out the boat check that a temporary guardrail is available and hazardous duty life-jackets are provided for lowerers.

(4) Test communication with the bridge, and check that flags and wands are available as secondary methods of communication (see sub para f. below).

(5) Ensure Safety Helmets are provided for the lowering party.

e. The Coxswain should:

(1) Check Boat bag and all other ancillary equipment is correct.

(2) Make the pre-start checks for the RIB.

(3) Check that the boatrope and toggle are rigged ready for use.

(4) Carry out a functional check and ensure that the Automatic Release Hook.

(5) If an umbilical connection is being used, confirm that a cooling water supply is available from ship's services.

(6) Test radio communications (if applicable).

(7) Instruct crew members on their tasks and check their dress and equipment.

> **CAUTION**
>
> To prevent the risk of Shiphaz Shock the boats crew members who operate the Hook are to wear PPE gloves.

f.   **Bridge/boat-deck communications**. Communications between the bridge and the boat deck are usually achieved either by upperdeck broadcast or flag/wand signals; the most suitable of these two methods will vary ship to ship. Wherever practicable both methods should be made available for all boat evolutions/transfers but using a combination of the two should be avoided. The flag/wand signalling system is shown below. All personnel involved must be aware that if a flag or wand is not showing, no action is to be taken.

Note.   *Certain ships are fitted with a dedicated system of boat control lights similar to those fitted for Flying Operations.*

g. **Sea boat lowering/hoisting – flag/wand signals – non type 45**

(1) *Lowering*

Position	Flag or wand	meaning
Boat deck	Green	Ready to lower boat to deck-edge level
Bridge	Green	Lower boat to deck-edge level
Bridge	Red	Hold boat at deck-edge level
Boat deck	Red	Preparing boat
Boat deck	Green	Ready in the Boat
Bridge	Green	Carry on with the Sea Boat

(2) *Hoisting*

Position	Flag or wand	Meaning
Bridge	Red	Boat lay off
Boat deck	Red	Preparing for recovery
Boat deck	Green	Ready to recover Sea Boat
Bridge	Green	Recover Sea Boat
Boat deck	Red	Sea Boat at deck-edge level
Boat deck	Green	Ready to hoist Sea Boat inboard
Bridge	Green	Hoist the Sea Boat inboard

h. **Sea boat lowering/hoisting – flag/wand signals – type 45 specific**

(1) *Lowering.* **Pipe "launch STBD/PORT seaboat" Rpt.**

Position	Stop/go lights	Meaning
Boat Bay	Red	Preparing Boat and Crew
Bridge	Red	Ship Manoeuvring
Boat Bay	Green	Ready in the Boat
Bridge	Green	Move Boat to Ready State
Boat Bay	Red	Boat at Ready State
Bridge	Red	Standby
Boat Bay	Green	Ready to Lower Boat
Bridge	Green	Carry on and Lower Boat

(2) *Hoisting.* **Pipe "standby to recover STBD/PORT seaboat".**

Position	Stop/go lights	Meaning
Boat Bay	Red	Prepare to Recover
Bridge	Red	Boat Lay Off
Boat Bay	Green	Ready to Recover
Bridge	Green	Recover the Boat
Boat Bay (MOBEX)	Red	Boat at Deck Edge
Bridge (MOBEX)	Red	Hold at deck Edge
Boat Bay (MOBEX)	Green	Ready to Move to Crutches
Bridge (MOBEX)	Green	Move Boat to Crutches
Boat Bay (MOBEX)	Red	Seaboat in Crutches

Note. *For type 45 launch and recovery SOP refer to Para 05094 sub para d and sub para e.*

05094. RIBs – hoisting and lowering drills

a.   The following procedures are to be used for the launch and recovery of a RIB when being used as a Sea Boat. During launching the ship should maintain a speed of between eight and 12 knots, taking into account prevailing weather conditions and the experience of the crew.   In heavy weather it is advantageous to turn the ship slowly to provide a calm slick of water into which the boat can be launched.

CAUTION

Gravity Lower is only to be used in emergencies

---

b.   **Launching the sea boat.**   The following drills are written for the launch of a Sea Boat when using the Henriksen Hook to recover a man overboard. The initial pipe must be modified as appropriate if the Sea Boat is being launched for any other purpose.

	Bridge		**Boatdeck**
OOW	Pipe 'Man overboard, Man overboard, Man overboard, Away Sea Boat, Away SOW'. (When the quickest method of recovery has been determined, Pipe:) 'Recovery will be by Sea Boat/SOW'.		This pipe is the authority from the OOW to the i/c of the boat deck to prepare the boat and slip the gripes. <u>If using flags, the boat deck should at this stage show a GREEN flag once they are ready to move the boat to deck edge level.</u>
OOW	<u>Lower the Sea Boat to deck edge level.</u>		<u>If using flags, the bridge should at this stage show a GREEN FLAG</u> when content to lift the load However, should conditions not be suitable the bridge may order 'Hold the Boat in the Crutches' or show a <u>RED FLAG.</u>
		i/c	I/c establish comms with bridge on Upperdeck broadcast or flags/wands.
		i/c	Lowering Party close up, check steadying lines and power to davit/crane. 'Slip the gripes'.
			Sea Boat's crew dresses at full speed and establishes comms with bridge.
		i/c	'Man the steadying lines'. 'Hoist'. (The handlers must keep the RIB firmly under control whilst it is being hoisted clear of its stowage and turned outboard). When RIB is clear of crutches/ guardrail,
		i/c	'Avast hoisting, slew outboard'. When RIB is clear of ship's side.
		i/c	'Avast slewing, lower to deck level'.
		i/c	'Avast lowering, slew inboard'. When buoyancy tube rests on ship's side at deck level:
		i/c	'Avast slewing'.
		i/c	Reports to bridge: 'Boat at deck level' <u>RED FLAG.</u>

	Bridge		Boatdeck
OOW	'Roger' <u>RED FLAG</u>		
OOW	Report on upperdeck broadcast relative bearing and range of MOB.		
		Coxswain i/c	Crew man the boat. Coxswain conducts checks and starts engine, then checks cooling water and that boatrope is correctly toggled in. I/c confirms brief with Coxswain who reports: 'Ready in the boat'. GREEN FLAG
OOW	'Carry on with the Sea Boat' <u>GREEN FLAG</u>		Steadying lines are removed.
		i/c	'Roger, carry on with the Sea Boat'.
		i/c	'Slew outboard, lower away'. Use the ship's side to steady the boat during lowering. Boats using the Henriksen Hook are to follow the procedure in Para 05098 and boats fitted with RFD Hooks are to see Note below.
		Crew i/c	Hook automatically releases when boat enters the water and weight comes off the hook. (For RIB operations where the Coxswain cannot easily see the hook, the crewman taps the Coxswain's shoulders firmly and reports loudly to Coxswain:) 'Hook Released'. When hook has released from the lifting point 'Avast lowering'.
		i/c	'Hoist roundly' or 'Bowse in' (Bowsing in the fall to the ship's side is quicker than hoisting but may not always be practicable). When fall is clear of the boat, Coxswain engages throttle using the boatrope to clear ship's side, moves ahead and, when appropriate, orders the bowman to slip the boatrope.
		i/c	Report to bridge: 'Sea Boat clear of ship's side'. RED FLAG Rigging for recovery.
		i/c	'Ready to recover the Sea Boat' GREEN FLAG

Note. *Ships fitted with RFD hooks will 'avast' at one metre above the water. Remove the preventer (if used), umbilical cord and cock the RFD. Then 'lower away'. If the launch is aborted once the RFD is cocked re-attach the preventer and recover to deck level.*

WARNING

IF THE BOATROPE IS INADVERTENTLY RELEASED BEFORE THE BOAT FROM THE FALL THE BOAT MUST BE HOISTED CLEAR OF THE WATER IMMEDIATELY AND THE BOATROPE RE-ATTACHED. ATTEMPTING TO LAUNCH THE BOAT WITHOUT A BOATROPE RIGGED WILL ALMOST CERTAINLY RESULT IN THE BOAT CAPSIZING.

---

c.   **Recovery and hoisting.** The ship should provide a lee for the boat and maintain a minimum speed of eight knots to facilitate hoisting the returning boat. In heavy weather it is advantageous to turn slowly towards the boat to create a calmer slick for hoisting. After approaching, the Coxswain should assess, then match, the ship's speed, keeping his craft on a parallel track before steering in to capture the boatrope. The boatrope is captured, secured to the bow of the boat and the RIB allowed to lie back on the boatrope while the Automatic Release hook is hooked on. As soon as the fall has been attached the Coxswain reports: 'Hooked on in the boat', the RIB is hoisted at full speed until clear of the crests of the waves. The RIB should be hoisted with the boat touching the ship's side to check adverse movement. The boatrope strayline should be manned and used as the forward steadying line throughout the hoisting procedure.

	Bridge		Boatdeck/Sea Boat
OOW	'Recover the Sea Boat' GREEN FLAG		
			I/c calls RIB alongside. Coxswain matches ship's speed, places craft parallel to boatrope and then steers in to capture the boatrope. Toggle in and haul in tight on the strayline to prevent inadvertent release. When the boatrope is secured the Coxswain reduces speed to allow the RIB to lie back gently on the boatrope, coming to rest directly under the fall.
		i/c	'Lower roundly' or 'Pass the fall'. Davit operator lowers or passes the fall.
			Crew hook on the fall. Coxswain checks and reports: 'Hooked on in the boat'.
		i/c	'Hoist roundly'. Davit/crane operator moves control lever to fastest hoist position. Boatrope handlers tend boatrope and maintain tension to ensure that the toggle does not slip out.
			When boat is clear of the water, Coxswain stops the engine.
		i/c	I/c reports to bridge: 'Boat clear of the water'. When boat clear of the water,
		i/c	'Hoist handsomely'. When Sea Boat is at deck level or high enough to safely evacuate passengers/casualties:
		i/c	'Avast hoisting, slew inboard'. Davit/crane is slewed inboard until the RIB's buoyancy tube rests gently on the ship's side or guardrail stanchions, clear of all protrusions.
		i/c	'Avast slewing'. I/c reports to bridge:
OOW	'Roger, boat at deck level'. RED FLAG	i/c	'Boat at deck level'. RED FLAG
		i/c	Steadying lines are passed.'Clear the casualty from the boat' (See Para 05013), crew assist in casualty evacuation, then clear boat.
			'Permission to recover the Sea Boat inboard' GREEN FLAG

	Bridge		Boatdeck/Sea Boat
OOW	'Hoist the Sea Boat inboard'. GREEN FLAG		
		i/c	'Man the steadying lines, slew outboard'. The davit/crane is slewed outboard until the boat is clear of the ship's side.
		i/c	'Hoist handsomely'. Boat is hoisted until it is clear of the guardrails. 'Avast hoisting, slew inboard'.
		i/c	Davit/crane is slewed inboard until boat is directly above crutches. 'Avast slewing, lower away'. Boat is lowered gently into its crutches, line handlers preventing swinging. When boat is firmly in crutches the gripes are passed. I/c reports to bridge 'RIB in crutches and rigged as a Sea Boat'
		i/c	
		i/c	
OOW	'Roger, Sea Boat secured'.		

Notes:

1.   Although inadvertent release when the RFD hook is in the 'SAFE' position cannot occur, it is possible for release to take place following snagging or jerking when the hook is in the 'COCKED' position. For normal operations - the preventer is to be available and remain shackled to the whip, but hooked back on itself or to the whip.

2.   Ships should be aware that instances have occurred when it has been found impossible to cock the RFD hook with the weight of the boat on the hook. With design adjustments and improved machining of the hook this problem has virtually been eliminated, but coxswains should be briefed that if it does occur the hook should be cocked when the boat is in the water. The hook will then release.

    d.   **Launch seaboat – type 45 boat specific**

	Bridge		Boatbay/sea boat
OOW	Launch the Port/Stbd Seaboat		
		i/c	Power up hydraulic power unit. Check: Lamp/Hook Lock clear
OOW	Permission from Bridge GREEN LIGHT		
		i/c	Boat Bay and Boat Crew ready. GREEN LIGHT Hoist Boat Wave Compensation on Slacken rope to engage wave compensator Chocks down Guardrails down Boom out clear of chocks 'Avast' Rig Boatrope Boom out until outboard of guardrails Guardrails up Wave compensator off Tension wire-hoist Ready state RED LIGHT 'Ready' GREEN LIGHT Hook lock off
OOW	GREEN LIGHT		Arms Release – off steadying lines Lower

e. **Recover seaboat – type 45 specific**

	Bridge		Boatbay/sea boat
OOW	Standby to recover the Seaboat		
		i/c	Power up hydraulic power unit Lamp check
OOW	Permission from Bridge GREEN LIGHT		
		i/c	Boat Bay ready. GREEN LIGHT Lower Davit Wire and Boatrope Hoist when the boat is hooked on Pass aft steadying line when clear of the water Arms in Hook lock on Wave compensation on Slacken rope to engage compensator Guardrails down Boom in – Slip boat rope Guardrails up Chocks up Wave compensator off Tension wire hoist Hook lock off Lower boat to chocks RED LIGHT

Note. *Where compensators are fitted it is advisable that they are used on all occasions for recovery of the seaboat.*

05095. Maritime realistic surface target (MRST) – sprite target

a. **Introduction.** The MRST (SPRITE) (Fig 5-42) is a two-stroke petrol (ULGAS) powered autonomous target system, designed as a disposable gunnery target. It is a compact lightweight inflatable catamaran that is easily deployed from and recovered on to ships at sea and is capable of operating beyond visual range to provide realistic FIAC representative attack profiles and defence training.

Fig 5-42. Maritime realistic surface target (MRST) – sprite target

b. **Hoisting and lowering MRST**

(1) *Equipment required*:

(a) Two-tonne spring hook or RFD Hook.

(b) Suitable length hook ropes to be provided in the Seaboat.

(c) Suitable length Steadying lines x 2.

(d) Safety Helmets, HDLJ and Communications.

(e) Portable Marpol equipment available (Fuel tank leakage).

(f) AFFF Fire extinguisher to be available (Fuel tank leakage).

(g) Wooden hand spike.

(h) Local manufactured righting strap. (Secured and lashed in the MRST before deploying).

(2) *Preparations.* Standard safety precautions contained within Chapter 3 para 03014 are to be observed. Communications with the bridge and Seaboat are to be checked prior to commencing the evolution. A full brief is to be given to the hoisting and lowering party and boats crew on the points below.

(3) *Points to be briefed:*

(a) Righting drill in the event of target capsizing.

(b) Righting strop to be rigged prior to launching.

(c) All personnel to be correctly dressed iaw para 05052.

(d) Target is not to be entered at anytime while afloat this is due to weak decking and entrapment danger.

(e) Boat crew Coxswain and Bowman, plus two working hands to assist launching and recovery procedure.

(f) Lifting appliance: Unit to hold valid test certification and all equipment to be subject to a thorough examination as appropriate by a competent person before and after use examinations to be recorded in Ships lifting register.

(g) All shackles to be moused.

(h) Ship to be stopped in the water to launch and recover the target.

(i) Damaged target recovery routine to be briefed to all personnel.

(j) Standard Seamanship safety brief to be give iaw Chap 3 para 03014.

(4) *Holed fuel tank:*

(a) Retrieval of the MRS until confirmed otherwise, it is to be assumed that (on retrieval of MRST vehicle post firing serial) the MRST fuel tank has sustained damage and is leaking. The fuel tank is to be removed and examined for damage and/or signs of fuel leakage.

(b) Ship's boat is to approach 'up wind' of the MRST vehicle and remove the fuel tank. Removal of the fuel tank is achieved by releasing the fuel tank bungee securing chords, disconnecting the engine fuel supply line and manually lifting the fuel tank clear of the MRST vehicle.

(c) An undamaged fuel tank is to be stowed on board the ship's boat. Ship's boat crew may then resume RF transmissions and escort the MRST vehicle to the ship. Undamaged partial or full MRST fuel tank is then to be transferred to ship for storage in authorised petrol stowage facility.

(d) A damaged/leaking fuel tank is to be purged of fuel by removal of the filler cap and submerging and filling with sea water. The tank is then to be drained and the process repeated, as necessary, to ensure complete removal of residual fuel. The fuel tank is then to be drained and filler cap replaced. Damaged fuel tank is then to be transferred to ship for storage in authorised petrol stowage facility and subsequent disposal.

(5) *Turning out and lowering MRST*

Bridge	I/C lowering party	Target ops
When safe to do so Bridge orders 'turn out and lower target to deck edge level'.	Man the steadying lines and 'Hoist'. When the target is clear of the guardrails 'Avast'. Slew outboard".	The target must be kept firmly under control by the handlers Whilst it is being hoisted and turned outboard.
	When the Target is clear of the ships side 'Avast slewing'. 'Lower away to deck edge level.'	Line handlers control the swing.
	'Avast lowering slew inboard'	
	When the buoyancy tube rests gently against the ships side at deck edge level, 'Avast slewing.'	
	I/C reports 'Boat at deck edge level.'	(If RFD Hook used this is to be cocked at deck edge level)
'Carry on with the target'	'Slew outboard, lower away.'	
	'Avast' once target in the water and the weight comes off the hook	(If RFD used this should release as the weight comes off the hook)
	Seaboat called in to remove the fall.	Bowman removes hook
	'Hoist away.' It is important to hoist the hook immediately in order to clear it from the personnel working in the boat.	
	Seaboat secure along side the target	Seaboat to be used to tow vessel clear to exclusion zone once the steadying lines have been removed.
	Remove the steadying lines	Handlers remove steadying line, Seaboat tow vessel to exclusion zone.
	'Start the target engine.'	Target Operator starts the targets engine once outside the exclusion zone.

(6) *Recovery of MRST*

Bridge	I/C Lowering Party	Seaboat
When safe to do so, Bridge orders stand by to recover target.	Man the fwd and aft steadying lines.	Seaboat approach towing the target
	Lower steadying lines	Steadying lines to be lower to the target and connected by the Bowman
	The target to be positioned under the falls	Seaboat then position the target under the falls
	'Lower the hook.'	Once hook at the required height Bowman to hook on
	'Hook on in the target.'.	Once hook is attached report Coxswain reports "Hooked on in the target." Seaboat to move clear before hoisting.
	'Hoist.' Hoist until the target is at deck edge	(The Target must be kept firmly under control by the handlers whilst being hoisted and turned inboard).
	'Hoist' when the target is clear of the guardrail 'Avast hoisting' 'Slew inboard' slew crane inboard once in required position above the target trolley 'Avast slewing'.	
	'Lower away.' Lower target to trolley, once in the trolley 'Avast lowering'.	Remove the hook from the slings
		Remove the target from the area using the trolley.

c. **Emergency recovery of MRST using the sprite recovery cargo net (SRCN)**

(1) *Equipment required:*

(a) Sprite Recovery Cargo Net Part Number 84-400074 and SRCN Frame made from HE30 Aluminum and 4 legged Webbing Sling.

(b) two-tonne spring hook or RFD hook.

(c) Suitable length steadying lines x 4 (2 in boat).

(d) Temporary Guardrail.

(e) Boat Hook to be carried in the boat.

(f) Shot Mats for deck protection.

(2) *Preparations.* Standard safety precautions contained within Chapter 3 para 03014 are to be observed. Communications with bridge and Seaboat are to be checked prior to commencing the evolution. A full procedural brief is to be given to the deck team and boats crew on the procedure for recovery. Seaboat to be launched with additional equipment and SRCN rigged.

(3) *Points to be briefed:*

(a) All personnel to be correctly dressed iaw para 05052.

(b) Target not to be entered at anytime while afloat weak decking and entrapment danger.

(c) Boat crew of Coxswains and Bowman plus two working hands to assist in recovery procedure.

(d) Lifting appliance: unit to hold valid test certification and to be subject to a thorough examination as appropriate by a competent person before and after use and be recorded on ship's lifting register.

(e) All shackles to be moused.

(f) Ship to be stopped in the water to recover the target.

(g) Damaged target recovery routine to be briefed to all personnel.

(h) Standard Seamanship safety brief to be given iaw Chapter 3 para 03014.

(4) *Recovery Procedure*

Bridge	I/C Lowering Party	Deck Team/Seaboat
When safe to do so, Bridge orders standby to recover target.	Man the fwd and aft steadying lines on the SRCN.	Deck team man steadying lines.
	Hook on SRCN to the fall 'Lower the temporary guardrail.'	Temporary guardrail to be taken in hand and manned throughout the evolution.
	'Hoist' hoist recovery net to the required height then slew outboard (Derrick height may need adjusting)	
	Once recovery net outboard raise temporary guardrail 'Avast slewing, lower away.'	
	Once recovery net submerged Avast lowering.	Seaboat approach towing the target
	Lower steadying lines this is so the Ship has control of the target.	Steadying lines to be lower to the target and connected by the Bowman. Disconnect the towing ropes from the target once the ship has control.

Bridge	I/C Lowering Party	Deck Team/Seaboat
	The target to be positioned into the recovery net with assistance from the Seaboat.	Seaboat help position the target into the net then to move clear before hoisting.
	Once the target is in the net 'Hoist.'. Hoist until the target high enough to bring inboard.	Steady the recovery net as it is being hoisted. (Target must be kept firmly under control by the handlers whilst being hoisted and turned inboard).
	'Lower temporary guardrail.' Slew inboard using the aft guy (Derrick height may need adjusting to recovery).	Lower guardrail to allow target to be trained inboard, raise once inboard.
	Once over the required position inboard 'Avast slewing.' 'Lower away' Lower target to shot mat on the deck 'Avast lowering.'	Remove the hook from the slings, unshackle the slings from the recovery net, remove target as required.

d.   **MRST righting procedure.** Should the MRST capsize and become inverted in the water the following procedure is to be conducted to right the craft.

(1)   *Equipment.* Designated righting rope (Fig 5-43) is manufacture from 12 mm polypropylene two legged recovery rope with soft eyes spliced in each leg, length of each leg 1.3 meters with a finished length of 5 m.

Fig 5-43. Designated righting rope

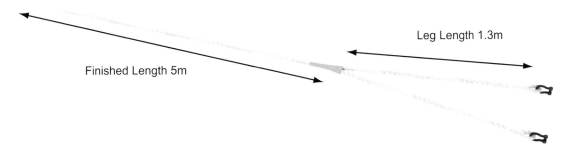

Leg Length 1.3m

Finished Length 5m

(2)   *Rigging.* Righting strap to be rigged prior to deploying the craft, shackled to the lifting point both fwd and aft and lightly lashed to the tubing.

(3)   *Righting Procedure*

   (a)   Seaboat to go alongside leeward side of the inverted craft.

   (b)   Break free the designated righting rope from under the craft.

   (c)   Pass the line right over both hulls.

(d) Secure the recovery line at the stern of the Seaboat.

(e) Gently motor away to pull the craft up to the 90 degree position. Once at this position stop motoring away and pull craft to the up right position by hand.

(f) Once re-righted take the craft in tow and recovery iaw current SOP's.

05096. Petrol (gasoline) tanks and stowages

a. **Outboard engine gasoline tanks**. Outboard engine gasoline tanks, Pattern No 0482-234-3346, are manufactured in a light grey plastic material. They must be marked in accordance with **BR 1754, Safety Regulations for Storing and Handling Petroleum Oils, Lubricant and Certain Other Hazardous Stores in HM Ships**. The number of tanks carried by a ship is not to exceed the number that can be stowed in the ship's gasoline tank stowage.

b. **Gasoline tank stowages**. Ships with a requirement to carry gasoline for outboard engines are fitted with gasoline tank stowages that permit the tanks to be jettisoned in an emergency. The stowages are to be painted to match the ship. They are to be locked at all times and the key kept on the Important Key Board.

SECTION 11 – DISPLACEMENT BOATS

05097. Displacement boats – introduction

The phrase 'Displacement Boats' has come to be accepted as the generic term applied to all motor-powered service craft other than RIBs and inflatable craft. With the need for ships to reduce topweight and decrease the maintenance load, the numbers of such craft in use in the Service have reduced in the last few years, and this trend is likely to continue. However, displacement boats are still required for certain tasks and duties.

Note. *"Owing to their age these boats have not achieved MCA certification as passenger boats. Passenger capacities should therefore be limited to a maximum of 12 unless clearance is given by NCHQ"*

05098. Displacement boats – davit arrangements

a. **Introduction**. Displacement boats are usually stowed in ships on a pair of gravity davits. Each davit consists of a **cradle**, which supports the boat, moving on rollers up or down an inclined track called a **skid.** This skid is angled so that the cradle and boat will operate under gravity when the ship is heeled up to 30° away from the boat. There are two types, the main differences being the positions of the hydraulic or electric motors and rope drums, and the rig of the wire falls. The falls may be of the **ball-weight** (single-part fall) type or **floating-block** (two-part fall) type. The floating-block type of fall is generally incorporated into davits used for the stowage of the heaviest displacement boats. The gravity davit of the ball-weight type consists of a trackway of two channels curving inwards from the deck edge, and a cradle fitted with rollers running inside the trackway. The davits operate in two stages: the movement of the cradle down or up the trackway, and the movement of the boat, down or up, when the cradle is at the lowering position. Both stages are controlled by the wire falls. Regardless of the position of the rope drums and electric or hydraulic motor, all of which are mounted on the trackways, the single wire fall passes round an intermediate sheave, and then through a tube and over the top sheave which are both inside the cradle. The fall then passes through a **stirrup,** hinged at the end of the cradle, and terminates in a tapered **ferrule.** Shackled to the ferrule is an end fitting (ball weight and linkage) which has a **swivel-ring shackle** for attachment of the boat's slings. Two **tusks,** projecting from the underside of the cradle end, fit underneath the ferrule when the cradle is raised. The cradles are locked in the raised position by **trigger levers** mounted on the trackways. These levers engage with pins on the cradles when the **gripe wires**, shackled to the ends of the levers, are in tension. The boat is carried on the **keel rests** and it lies against the gunwale chocks. In this position the tension in the falls can be released. Pointers on the trackway and cradle indicate the stowed position. The cradles can also be locked to the trackways by passing **harbour stop pins** through holes in both of them.

b. **Lowering action**. When the gripes are slipped, the triggers automatically release the cradles, allowing them to be lowered by power or gravity (power for light falls only, eg. without a boat slung). When the cradle head moves outboard to swing the boat clear of the ship's side, the boat leaves the cradles and hangs on the ferrules supported by the tusks. When the cradles are near the outermost position, the ferrules leave the tusks and the weight of the boat is transferred to the falls. Further movement of the falls lowers the boat, because the cradles have now reached their lower stops.

c. **Raising action**. The boat is raised until the ferrules strike the stirrups and further movement of the falls moves the cradles inboard until the pin on the cradles engages with the trigger lever. The hydraulic or electric motor is stopped. The boat is then secured at the davits by passing the gripes when at sea or inserting the stop pins in harbour. Gravity davits fitted with floating blocks are very similar in operation, the principle difference being the two-part instead of the single-part falls.

05099. Displacement boats – slinging arrangements

The slings in displacement boats consist of two sets, one forward and one aft. The precise arrangements vary depending on the type of boat and details can be found in the relevant Book of Reference (BR). Boats slings are fitted in the dockyards by experienced shipwrights so that the weight of the boat will be correctly distributed between the legs. The slings are carefully adjusted to conform to the span of the davits; a boat should therefore be hoisted by her own slings at her own davits whenever practicable. When lowered, her slings should always remain in the boat.

05100. Displacement boats – anti-shock strops and SWR hanging pendants

Anti-shock strops and steel wire rope (SWR) hanging pendants are provided for all displacement boats hung at davits. The anti-shock strops are attached to the boat's falls prior to hoisting the boat to prevent shock-loading when the weight of the boat is first taken up, and the SWR hanging pendants, one fitted to each davit cradle head, are provided to take the weight of the boat at the end of the hoisting sequence so that the anti-shock strops may be removed from between the falls and the slings, and the falls then re-attached to the slings. Fig 5-44 & Fig 5-45 show the arrangement of the anti-shock strop and steel wire hanging pendant at the point in the boat-hoisting procedure when both are attached to the lifting gear.

Note. *The precise arrangements for attaching the anti-shock strops and SWR hanging pendants to the slings vary depending on the type of boat being hoisted. The relevant BR for the type of boat must be referred to.*

Fig 5-44. Anti-shock strop   **Fig 5-45. SWR hanging pendant and anti-shock strop**

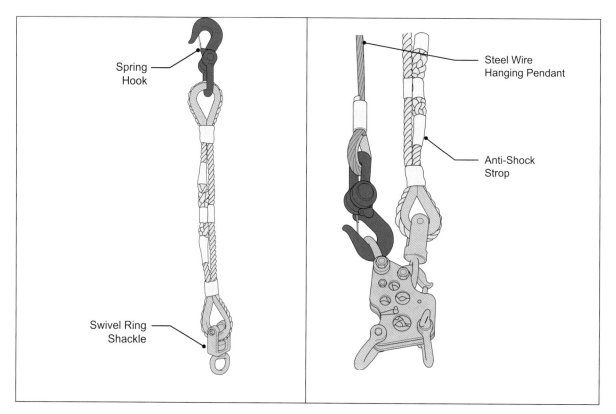

05101. Displacement boats – general stores and equipment

For normal operations the following list of equipment, in addition to the Boat bag, should be carried in all displacement boats. Other equipment is specified in the relevant paragraph on each type of boat.

Equipment	Naval stores number
VHF hand held radio (Cougar)	
Boat hook	0262/16895
(With stave)	0472/923-0765
Bailer	0255/320-4496
Manual Line Thrower	0472-781-0504
Four Distress Flares	
Horn	0268/407-9681
Hand signalling lamp	0558/527-7235
First aid kit	6545/211-1573
Fire extinguishers (2)	
Compass (if required)	
Boat's Lead Line (if required)	
Boat Ensign Size 2	8345/571-3296

05102. Displacement boats – boat bag

A boat bag should always be carried in the boat. It is made of PVC cloth and contains sufficient equipment to repair a damaged hull or fittings. The contents of the Boat bag should be: hand drill and two 3.8mm twist drills, crosspoint screwdriver, rasp, hand axe, marline spike, two repair clamps, three assorted leak stoppers and roping twine. Four locally manufactured 'patch packets' should be included, each containing copper sheets in sizes from 75 x 50mm to 300 x 230mm, tallow-coated fearnought in sizes from 100 x 75mm to 330 x 250mm, and self-tapping screws, in boxes, of 9, 11, 21 and 31. Each patch packet should contain instructions for fixing.

05103. Displacement boats – crewing

The criteria regarding the training and qualifying of a displacement boat coxswain and crew is similar to that laid down in para 05023 for RIB coxswains and crew. However, certified displacement boat coxswains are permitted to train potential coxswains locally. To gain certification, once the potential coxswain is deemed competent, he/she must either undergo a formal assessment at HMS Raleigh, or it can be requested of HMS Raleigh that a qualified assessor visits the parent ship/establishment to carry out the assessment.

05104. Displacement boats – securing a displacement boat for sea

a. When securing a displacement boat for sea the following points should be followed:

(1) The boat should be hoisted close up to the davit head with harbour stop pins in.

(2) The gripes should be shackled to the trigger levers of the davits and well set up around the boat so that she is firmly bowsed-in to her griping pads.

(3)   The guys (if fitted) and davit span should be set up.   The two **lizards** (fitted only in some high-sided ships and only required if lowering the boat in a seaway) should be rove on two **sea jackstays.** The lower ends of the jackstays are secured to recessed eyeplates at the waterline on the ship's side; the upper ends are secured to an eyeplate at the base of each davit trackway. Whenever possible the jackstays should be secured in harbour from a boat. The lizards should be lightly stopped inboard in the ship, and passed into the boat when at the deck edge. Lizards when kept in hand enable the boat's crew to steady the boat during hoisting and lowering when in a seaway.

(4)   The lifelines, one for each crew member, (one lifeline fitted to each davit head and any others free running on the davit span) should be coiled down free for running in the boat.

(5)   The steel wire hanging pendants should be shackled to each davit head and stopped back along the davit cradles **clear of the falls and the boat**, until required for boat hoisting.

(6)   The anti-shock stops should be available in the vicinity of the davits.

(7)   Bottom boards should be secured, but those in the way of the slings should be removed and secured inboard.

(8)   The hooks of sling steadying chains should be hooked, bill uppermost. The slings must be free of twists.

(9)   The boat should be dry with the plug in place.

(10) The boat's outfit of stores and equipment should be complete.

(11) When not required for use the boat should be covered.

05105.   Displacement boats – preparations and personnel required for lowering and hoisting

a.   **Introduction**. Displacement boats stowed in gravity davits sit on their keel rests, with gripes and the harbour stop pins inserted into the trackways to prevent movement of the cradles. Whenever power-operated davits are to be used it is essential to check that power is available to the system. As a check before lowering with davits the boat should be inched up under power when stowed in the davits.

CAUTIONS

1. It is inadvisable unless in an emergency to lower a displacement boat if the swell exceeds 0.5 metres.
2. When hoisting a displacement boat in even a slight sea or swell anti shock stops are mandatory.
3. If lowering/hoisting in a seaway a boatrope should always be rigged.

---

b.   **Safety**

(1)   No-one in a boat is allowed to place their hands on the falls, and everyone in the boat must hold a lifeline during hoisting and lowering. Whenever a boat is being manned, lowered or hoisted no-one is allowed **before the foremost fall** or **abaft the aftermost fall** because, if one fall were to part, personnel in either of these positions would be crushed between the other fall and the bow or stern of the boat.

(2)   The steel wire hanging pendants must always be shackled with pin and forelock shackles to the head of the davits. They must be stopped in such a way that they can be released easily without need to climb on the davits. When a boat is being hoisted or lowered the rating operating the control handle **must not direct the hoisting or lowering operation**. The boat should not normally be lowered under power. Power-operated davits are potentially dangerous except when in the stowed position with the harbour stop pins inserted. The following points must be adhered to:

(3). Personnel are to be warned to keep clear of davits whilst they are being operated.

(4)   No-one is allowed on the davits unless the davits are in the stowed position with harbour stop pins inserted.

(5)   The access holes in the davits are never to be used as hand or foot-holds.

c.   **The lowering and hoisting party**

(1)   The Lowering and Hoisting Party is to consist of the following as a minimum:

Leading Seaman in Charge.
Davit Control Operator.
Ratings to remove harbour stop pins and to tend fenders at the ship's side.
Boatrope Handler (if required)/Headfast tender.
After Steadying Line Handler.

(2)   In marginal conditions the number of handlers may need to be increased. The seaman in charge of the lowering party is responsible for the safe conduct of the whole evolution to the point where the boat is released from the falls and must supervise preparations for hoisting and recovery, and must be in good communication with the bridge throughout the evolution.

d.   **The crew** usually consists of a coxswain and two crewmen (a boat stoker dependant on the boat tasking). The Coxswain is responsible for making all preparations within the boat and ensuring that the boat is fully fuelled and equipped and is in charge of the crew members and must check that they are properly dressed before manning the boat. The coxswain must also ensure that they know how to handle and slip the boatrope; how to unhook the falls safely; and how to clip on and release the steadying line(s). At least one member of the crew must be capable of taking over from the Coxswain, and be fully prepared to do so in an emergency.

e.   **Preparations for lowering**. The leading seaman in charge is to:

(1)   Brief the lowering party.

(2).   Confirm that power is available at the davit or crane.

(3)   Have the steadying line(s) ranged ready for use.

(4)   Test communication with the bridge.

f.   The Coxswain is to:

(1)   Make the pre-start checks for the boat.

(2)   Check the boat's stores and equipment are correct for the task.

(3)   If required, check that the boatrope is rigged ready for use.

(4)   See that lifelines are rigged.

(5)   Test radio communications.

(6)   Instruct crew members on their tasks and check their dress and equipment.

05106. Displacement boats – lowering and hoisting drills

a.   When lowering or hoisting a boat in harbour a boatrope will not normally be required.   However, if lowering or hoisting a boat in a seaway a boatrope should always be rigged.

b.   **Lowering brocedure**

Order	Action/remarks
'Away...crew, hands detailed close up'	Crew muster abreast the boat, dressed for the conditions (always wearing safety helmets and DMS boots) then man the boat. The boat is to be inched up to establish there is power on the davits. Lowerers then remove harbour pins.
'Slip the gripes'	Lowerers knock off the slips and recover the gripes inboard. Because of the tendency for a boat to swing out this order must not be given before the boat is fully manned and lifelines have been passed over the side of the boat (outboard) and are in hand.
'Lower to the deck edge'	Rating manning the control puts lever to **lower** until the boat is level with the deck edge. The boat can now be checked.
'Lower away'	Rating manning the control puts lever to lower. When the boat is waterborne the lowerer selects **Power Lower**.
'Avast lowering'	Rating manning the control puts lever to **stop**. This order is given when there is enough slack to unhook the boat.
'Unhook the falls'	Crewman unhooks after fall and reports loudly, 'After fall released'. The bowman then releases for'ard fall and reports loudly, 'For'ard fall released'. Coxswain moves the boat ahead and, when appropriate, orders the bowman to slip the boatrope.

c.   **Preparations before hoisting**. Whilst the boat is away from the ship the following preparations for her recovery are to be made. The procedures below assume that a boatrope and anti-shock strops are being used.

(1)   The davits are to remain in the outboard position unless ordered to be fully recovered. (This will be governed by time and the ship's movements.)

(2)   Hoist the falls until their bottom ends are level with the deck edge.

(3)   Recover the falls inboard with a boat-hook. Hook the anti-shock strops into the ends of the falls then lower the falls over the side, taking care to leave a clear run for the boat beneath them.

(4)   Release the hanging pendants and pass them outboard to hang free from the davit head. (If allowed to swing outboard they are likely to foul the falls.)

(5)   If required, hold the boatrope outboard on its strayline with the eye about one metre clear of the water.

(6)   Prepare fenders.

d.   **Summary of hoisting procedure**. If underway the ship should, if possible and necessary, manoeuvre to provide a lee. When the boat comes alongside it is steered to a position slightly forward of the falls. The bowman recovers and secures the boatrope. When the boatrope is secured, the Coxswain drops the boat astern until it is under the falls. The falls are then lowered and the anti-shock strops hooked to the boat's lifting arrangements (forward fall first). The Coxswain reports 'Hooked on in the boat'. When this report is received the boat is hoisted roundly clear of the water. At the same time a sternfast (if necessary) is passed to the Coxswain who secures it aft; the sternfast is tended inboard to prevent the boat surging. When the boat is clear of the water, the order 'Handsomely' is given and the boat continues to be hoisted until she is high enough for the steel wire hanging pendants to be hooked on to the lifting arrangements. The pendants are hooked on and the boat is lowered until the pendants take the weight. The anti-shock strops are removed, the falls are lowered and hooked direct to the lifting arrangements and the hoisting of the boat is then continued. The hanging pendants are unhooked and passed outboard for safety when the weight is taken on the falls. After the gripes have been passed the pendants are stopped to the davits with parting stops and the boat is re-secured. Detailed hoisting drills are given on the following page.

e.   **Hoisting procedure**. On receipt of the report 'Hooked on in the boat', the boat is hoisted using the following procedures.

Order by I/C	Action/remarks
'Hoist roundly.'	Rating manning the control puts lever to **fastest hoist** position. The sternfast is manned inboard and tended to reduce the boat's surging. The Coxswain stops the engine. Hands on deck man their fenders and follow up the boat as she is hoisted.
'Hoist handsomely.'	Rating manning the control puts lever to a **slower hoist** position.
'Avast hoisting. On hanging pendants.'	Rating manning the control puts lever to **stop**. This order is given when the boat is high enough for the wire pendants to be hooked on. The Coxswain and Bowman hook on their respective pendants to the lifting arrangements, raising a hand when the hook is properly engaged. Coxswain reports 'Hanging pendants hooked on in the boat'.
'Lower to the hanging pendants.'	Rating manning the control puts lever to **lower** until the pendants take the weight of the boat and the falls slacken.
'Off anti-shock strops.'	The anti-shock strops are removed and the falls hooked on to the lifting arrangements. Coxswain reports 'Falls hooked on in the boat.
'Stand clear of the davits – hoist away.'	Rating manning the control lever puts lever to hoist. The hanging pendants are unhooked and passed outboard.
'High enough.'	Rating manning the control puts the lever to stop. This order is given just before the cradle reaches its stops. The gripes are then passed and set up, and the boat is re-secured. The hanging pendants are re-stopped to the davits and the crew clears the boat.

    f.   The Coxswain thoroughly checks the boat and then reports to the OOW/OOD that the boat is correct, or otherwise if any defects or deficiencies exist.

05107. 10.6m survey motor boat (SMB)

a.   The 10.6 metre Survey Motor Boat (SMB) (Fig 5-46) is a single-skinned moulded GRP hull with an all-round rubber 'D' fender. It is divided into five sections. The layout of the boat provides a forward section which contains all the domestic facilities, this includes: various stowages for equipment, a galley area containing microwave cooker, water heater, sink and stowages for utensils, an enclosed head which can discharge overboard or to an on-board tank, and an eating area with stowable bunks. A wheelhouse located in the centre of the boat is directly above the engine room which is accessed by two hatches in the deck of the wheelhouse. Further aft is a generator space which is accessed by a hatch from the after well deck and a Tiller Flat which is situated furthest aft.

Fig 5-46. Survey motor boat (SMB)

b.   **Performance**

Capacity	Fair weather 9
	Foul weather 6
Speed	15 knots
Endurance	300 miles at 8 knots

c.   **Dimensions**

Length	10.6 metres
Beam	3.5 metres
Draught	1.5 metres
Displacement	10.25 tonnes

d. **Propulsion**

Engine	2 x 6-cylinder Perkins Sabre 185C turbo-intercooled.
Fuel	800 litres of Diesel
Shafts	2 shafts, 2 rudders. (Each propeller is fitted with a rope cutter)

e. **Slinging arrangements**. The slinging arrangements for these craft when carried in davits are given in Service Drawing numbers 002641823.

f. **Boatrope securing arrangements**. If the boat is being lowered in a seaway a boatrope should be secured to one of the cleats on the forward decking of the boat.

g. **Anchor and cable**. The anchor for the boat is an 18 kg CQR (naval stores number 0232/21026), fitted with a 16mm x 37m polyester cable.

h. **Painter and sternfast**. The painter and sternfast are made of 16mm polyester and are 11 metres and 7 metres long respectively.

i. **Stores and equipment**. See Para 05101

j. **Boat bag**. See Para 05102.

k. **Propulsion and electrical system**. The propulsion and electrical system fitted in these craft is described fully in **BR 7837**. Also included in that publication are details of engine starting and stopping procedures and a guide to fault finding should the equipment not operate correctly.

l. **Crewing**. See Para 05103

m. **Dress for crew and passengers**. The boat provides shelter for crew and passengers; consequently the requirement to wear suitable foul weather clothing is left to the discretion of the CO. However, because on occasions the crew are required to move around the boat outside the confines of the cabin areas they must wear Hazardous Duty Lifejackets at all times. Passengers are not normally required to wear lifejackets but may be ordered to do so by the CO if deemed necessary. It is prudent to suspend passenger boat operations in all but emergency situations if the prevailing or forecast weather conditions indicate a possible hazard to personnel.

05108. HMS PROTECTOR 10.5m survey motor boat (ice variant) (SMB)

a.   The 10.5m Survey Motor Boat (Ice Variant) (SMB) (Fig 5-47) is an all-welded aluminium construction with a foam-filled collar. The wheelhouse and superstructure are generally of welded aluminium construction. The hull is fitted with two transverse and two longitudinal bulkheads which provide seven watertight compartments. The layout of the boat provides a forward section/wheelhouse which contains various equipment stowages; an enclosed portable chemical head attached to a 20-litre onboard black water tank, and is accessed via after access door. Further aft is the engine compartment located under the port and starboard flush engine hatches.

Fig 5-47. Survey motor boat (ice variant) (SMB)

b.   **Performance**

Capacity Fair weather	12 people
Foul weather	6 people
Speed	10-12 knots
Endurance	100 nm 16hrs at 6 knots

c.   **Dimensions**

Length	10.5 metres
Beam	3.8 metres
Draught	0.75 metres
Displacement	5.5 tonnes to 7.26 tonnes

d.   **Propulsion**

Engine	2 x Yanmar 315 hp @ 3800 rpm
Fuel	1000 litres of Diesel
Twin Jet Drive	

e.   **Slinging arrangements**. The slinging arrangements for this craft carried in a VESTDAVIT are via forward and aft eight-tonne Henriksen Hooks (Fig 5-48).

Fig 5-48. Slinging arrangements

f.   **Boat rope securing arrangements**. If the boat is being lowered in a seaway a boat rope should be passed through the forward bullring and secured to the centre bollard on the bow of the boat and is to be released by hand.

g.   **Anchor and cable**. The anchor for the boat is a galvanised Hi holding power 15 kg anchor fitted with 8mm x 10m galvanised chain a 14mm x 30m Nylon multi plait rope.

h.   **Painter and sternfast**. The painter and sternfast are made of 16mm polyester and are 12 metres long.

i.   **Stores and equipment**. See Para 05101

j.   **Boat bag**. See Para 05102.

k.   **Propulsion and electrical system**. The propulsion and electrical system fitted in these craft is described fully in Mustang marine hand book.

l.   **Crewing**. See Para 05103.

m.   **Dress for crew and passengers**.   The boat provides shelter for crew and passengers; the requirement to wear suitable foul weather clothing is at the discretion of the Commanding Officer. However, because on occasions the crew are required to move around the boat outside the confines of the cabin areas they must wear Crew Saver Elite Twin 275n lifejackets. All personnel proceeding forward of the main cabin are to be attached via safety lanyard connected to both lifejacket and safety railing system. It is prudent to suspend passenger boat operations in all but emergency situations if the prevailing or forecast weather conditions indicate a possible hazard to personnel.

05109. HMS ECHO/ENTERPRISE 10.5m Survey Motor Boat (SMB)

a.   This is an all-welded aluminum construction SMB based upon the proven design already in service of the SMB (Ice Variant) onboard HMS PROTECTOR. The wheelhouse and superstructure are generally of welded aluminum construction with a foam filled collar fitted at the vessel's sides. The hull is fitted with two transverse and two longitudinal bulkheads which provide seven watertight compartments. The fuel tank is located amidships under the main deck. The vessels are propelled by twin marine diesel engines driving water jet propulsion units.

Fig 5-49. HMS ECHO/ENTERPRISE Survey Motor Boat (SMB)

b.   **Performance**

Capacity Fair weather	12 people
Foul weather	6 people
Speed	Max 22 knots
Endurance	100 nm 34hrs at 6 knots

c.   **Dimensions**

Length	10.5 metres
Beam	3.8 metres
Draught	0.70 metres
Displacement	6.92 tonnes to 9.27 tonnes

d.   **Propulsion**

Engine	2 x Yanmar 315 hp @ 3800 rpm
Fuel	1000 litres of diesel
Twin Jet Drive	

e.   **Lifting arrangements.** Lifting arrangements are by a twin-armed Vest davit with each hook rated at eight-tonne giving a total of 16 tonne spread across the twin arms. The SWL of the davit is actually rated at 13 tonnes.   Henriksen release hooks rated at eight-tonne SWL are fitted on the centre line forward and aft.   The hooks are the off-load type with local release handles mounted adjacent to, but slightly away from the lifting hooks on the starboard side of the vessel.   Each hook incorporates a swivel joint allowing limited rotation of the hook to avoid side loading as the vessel swings during launch and recovery.   Removable weather proof covers are provided for each lifting hook.

f.   **Boat rope securing arrangements**.   If the boat is being lowered in a seaway, a boat rope should be passed through the forward fairlead and secured to the centre bollard on the bow of the boat and is to be released by hand.

g.   **Anchor and cable**.   The anchor for the boat is a galvanised Hi-holding power 15 kg anchor fitted with 8mm x 10m galvanised chain and a 14mm x 30m Nylon multi-plait cable.   A second anchor with a holding power nine kg is also carried with 6mm x 10m galvanised chain and a 10mm x 30m Nylon multi plait rope.

h.   **Painter and sternfast**.   The painter and sternfast are made of 16mm polyester and are 12 metres long.

i.   **Stores and equipment**.   See Para 05101

j.   **Boat bag**.   See Para 05102.

k.   **Propulsion and electrical system**.   The propulsion and electrical system fitted in these craft is described fully in Mustang marine hand book.

l.   **Crewing**.   See Para 05103.

m.   **Dress for crew and passengers**.   The boat provides shelter for crew and passengers; the requirement to wear suitable foul weather clothing is at the discretion of the Commanding Officer.   However, because on occasions the crew are required to move around the boat outside the confines of the cabin areas they must wear Crew Saver Elite Twin 275n lifejackets. All personnel proceeding forward of the main cabin are to be attached via safety lanyard connected to both lifejacket and safety railing system. It is prudent to suspend passenger boat operations in all but emergency situations if the prevailing or forecast weather conditions indicate a possible hazard to personnel.

05110. 11.0 metre work boat — specification

a.   The 11.0 metre work boat (Fig 5-50) is carried in the CVS and certain RFAs for the carriage of stores or personnel. It is of GRP construction with a shallow V hull and spoon bow suitable for beaching. Layout provides a large open deck forward, the steering position aft, and a single diesel engine mounted aft with 'Vee' drive to the propeller. The authoritative publication for this craft is **BR 6595 (007) 36 Ft Work Boat.**

Fig 5-50. 11.0m work boat

b.   **Performance**

Capacity	12 persons (excluding crew)
Crew	Three
Speed	9 knots
Endurance	180 nautical miles

c.   **Dimensions**

Length	11.22 metres
Width	3.48 metres
Height	3.1 metres
Weight (Max Hoisting)	7.2 tonnes

d.   **Propulsion**

Engine	1 x Perkins 130hp
Fuel	405 litres of diesel

e.   **Slinging arrangements**. The slinging arrangements for this boat are given in Service Drawing numbers 002549685/25.

f.   **Boatrope securing arrangements**. If the Workboat is being lowered in a seaway a boatrope should be secured to one of the staghorns on the forward decking of the boat.

g. **Anchor and cable**. The anchor for the boat is a 11 kg CQR (naval stores number 0232/21026), fitted with a 16mm x 37-metre polyester cable.

h. **Painter and sternfast**. The painter and sternfast are made of 16mm polyester and are 11 metres and 7 metres long respectively.

i. **Stores and equipment**. See Para 05101.

j. **Boat bag**. See Para 05102.

k. **Propulsion and electrical system**. The propulsion and electrical system fitted in these craft is described fully in **BR 6595 (007)**. Also included in that publication are details of engine starting and stopping procedures and a guide to fault-finding should the equipment not operate correctly.

l. **Crewing**. See Para 05103.

m. **Dress for crew and passengers**. Dress requirements for passengers and crew are identical to those laid down for the SMB at Para 05107 sub para m. It is prudent to suspend passenger boat operations in all but emergency situations if the prevailing or forecast weather conditions indicate a possible hazard to personnel.

n. **Davit arrangements**. See Para 05099.

o. **Lowering and hoisting**. See Para 05106.

CAUTION

Owing to the age of the Work Boats in use, they have not achieved MCA certification as passenger boats. Passenger capacities should be limited to a maximum of 12 persons unless clearance is given by Navy Command HQ.

05111. Handling displacement power boats – general information

a. **Introduction**. The handling of any type of power boat is governed in general by the common-sense rules of seamanship, but the method of manoeuvring one boat may differ considerably from that of another owing to differences in the shape of their hulls, the number of propellers and the type of rudders. The rotary movement of a boat's propeller (or propellers) exerts a considerable effect on the directive powers of her rudder, not only when she is moving through the water but also when she has stopped or lost steerage way. The extent to which the steering of a boat is affected by the movement of her propellers depends upon their number and size, the direction in which they revolve, the speed of their revolution, the distance from the rudder and the shape of the boat's hull. The particular handling characteristics of propeller-driven boats, which are steered by altering the direction of the thrust or drag of the propeller, were explained earlier in this chapter. Although these types of boats are generally slower than the RIB, the coxswain must be aware throughout of the need to reduce exposure to shock and vibration where practicable and when safe to do so.

b.   **Hull forms**. The hull form of a Rigid Inflatable Boat, known as a Deep-Vee, is described earlier in this chapter. Hull forms for other types of service power boat are of two main types, one where the athwartship section is round-bilge (Fig 5-51(i)) and the other where it is hard-chine (Fig 5-51(ii)). The hard-chine boat planes at speed and is therefore faster than a round-bilge boat, but it has inferior sea-keeping qualities.

Fig 5-51. Hull forms – conventional boats

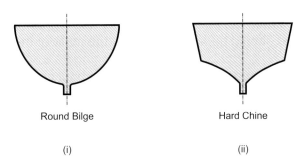

Round Bilge   Hard Chine

(i)   (ii)

c.   **Direction of rotation of a propeller**. The direction of rotation of a propeller is described as being either right-handed or left-handed; a right-handed propeller is one that turns in a clockwise direction when driving the boat ahead and viewed from astern, and a left-handed propeller is one that turns in a counter-clockwise direction under the same conditions. Single-screw service boats or vessels have right-handed propellers. In general twin-screw service boats have outward-turning propellers (right-handed on the starboard side and left-handed on the port side), but a few have propellers turning the same way.

d.   **Use of the rudder.** The turning effect of the rudder when the boat is underway increases with speed as well as the angle between the rudder and the fore-and-aft line of the boat, and it reaches its maximum value when the latter is about 35°. Beyond 35° the turning effect begins to decrease and the retarding effect of the rudder on the speed of the boat increases rapidly. The rudder angle of a boat is therefore limited to 35°. When the boat turns under the effect of her rudder, she turns about a pivoting point which is usually about one-third of her length from the bow in round-bilge boats, and farther forward or aft in hard-chine boats. This pivotal point should be borne in mind when leaving an accommodation ladder or landing-place, because if the rudder is put over to swing the bow outwards, the stern may swing in towards the ladder or landing-place and so damage the boat or the ladder. When turning at speed, particularly if the rudder is put hard over, the boat skids over the water broadside-on and outwards as she turns before gathering way in the direction in which her bow is pointing. This is more marked in a shallow-draught or a hard-chine boat than in a deep draught or round-bilge boat. As the boat skids, the resistance of the water to the hull heels the boat outwards to an angle depending on the type of boat, her speed and loading. It is more marked in a round-bilge than in a hard-chine boat, and in a boat laden with top-weight than in a normally loaded boat. **The rudder should therefore never be used drastically, particularly in boats laden with men or gear, or in a heavy sea, on which occasions the speed of the boat should be reduced before altering course**. When proceeding at full speed a boat is very sensitive to even a slight touch of wheel, so a large amount of rudder should then only be used in an emergency. Except in emergency or at low speed, drastic use of the rudder shows lack of foresight, and is therefore bad seamanship. When proceeding slowly, however, or when manoeuvring a boat in a confined space, it will often be necessary to use full wheel, ie to put the rudder hard over. The trim of the boat has a great effect on steering; if she is down by the head or stern she will be difficult to manoeuvre, and men or weights should therefore be kept distributed evenly amidships as far as possible.

e. **Handling in a seaway**. When running before a sea, or when towing, the boat should be trimmed by the stern to keep her propeller immersed and improve her steering qualities. When running before a swell which appears to be moving at the same speed as the boat reduce speed immediately, if necessary by streaming a drogue; otherwise your boat may be carried along on the front of a wave and may broach-to and capsize. When running before a quartering sea or swell be on your guard against a wave bearing under the weather counter and so broaching the boat to. When sea or swell are on the bow, meet the larger waves head on and reduce speed as necessary. Alteration of speed in a seaway has a great effect on the behaviour of the boat, so speed should be adjusted to suit the state of the sea.

f. **Regulation of speed.** When underway in harbour proceed with due consideration for others. The wash made by a boat at high speed can damage boats alongside ladders or jetties, and cause great inconvenience to small boats and men on painting catamarans; so reduce speed or give a wide berth in these circumstances, and always keep a good lookout for diving operations.

g. **Going alongside**

(1) *Accommodation Ladder*. When going alongside an accommodation ladder in a tideway, avoid overshooting and getting the stream on the outer bow; otherwise the boat may be jammed by the stream under the forward side of the ladder and may even be heeled over and swamped. When lying alongside a ladder in a tideway, secure the boatrope over the inner bow, and steer the boat so that she rides by the boatrope with her side about one-third of a metre clear of the ladder.

Fig 5-52. Faults in handling a boat alongside

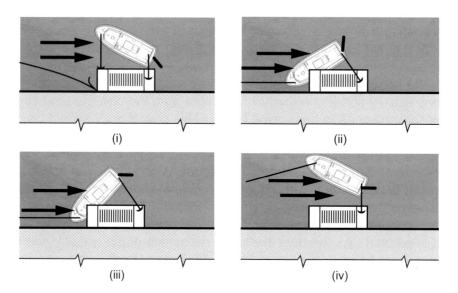

(i) (ii)

(iii) (iv)

(a) In Fig 5-52(i) the Bowman has failed to secure the boatrope, the Sternsheetsman has griped the stern to the ladder and the bows have swung out, the stream bearing on the inner bow. The remedy is to let go forward and aft, go ahead and come alongside again.

(b) In Fig 5-52(ii) the boat has overshot the ladder, the Bowman has griped-in the bows and the stream on the outer bow has forced the boat under the ladder; the Sternsheetsman cannot haul the stern into the ladder. The remedy is to let go aft, go full astern and come alongside again.

(c) In Fig 5-52(iii) the Bowman has secured the boatrope, but the boat is too far ahead and the Coxswain has forgotten to use his rudder, thereby allowing the bows to swing into the ship's side. The Sternsheetsman cannot haul the stern into the ladder. The remedy is to put on starboard rudder until the bows swing out, then steer the boat so that she remains parallel to the ship's side. If the bows will not swing out, the boat must be worked astern a short distance.

(d) In Fig 5-52(iv) the Bowman has secured the boatrope and the Sternsheetsman has griped the stern to the ladder, but the Coxswain has failed to use his rudder to keep the boat parallel to the ship's side. The remedy is to let go aft, put on port rudder until the boat is riding head to stream and clear of the ladder; then steer her gently in until she lies alongside.

(2) *Landing-place*. When going alongside a landing-place take into account the direction and strength of the wind and tidal stream; whenever possible go alongside head-to-wind or stream, whichever has the most effect on the boat. A one-knot stream is about equivalent to a wind of Force 3 to 4, and a two-knot stream to a wind of force 5 to 6. If the landing-place lies across wind or stream and there is a choice of sides, choose the lee side. Always approach at slow speed and keep the boat heading in a safe direction in case her engines fail to go astern. If manoeuvring space near the landing-space is limited, it may be an advantage to leave bows first, particularly in single-screw boats; the approach must then be made stern first, or the boat turned when alongside. When going alongside a strange landing-place in suspected shallow water, approach slowly, taking soundings with a boat-hook.

h.   **Use of springs**. In Fig 5-53(i) a headrope has been made fast and the boat can be brought alongside either by going slow astern or by allowing the wind or stream to do the work. In Fig 5-53(ii) a headspring has been made fast on the jetty and is secured abreast the pivoting point of the boat. By going slow ahead with the rudder to starboard, the stern will be brought into the jetty. Once alongside, particularly when lying head to wind or stream, the head and stern ropes should be secured as springs (Fig 5-54(i)); they will be more effective in holding the boat alongside and are ready for springing off (described below).

Fig 5-53. Use of springs when going alongside

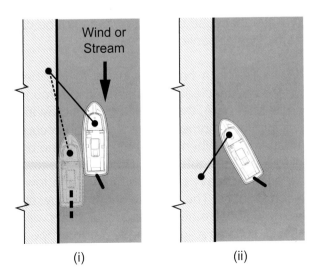

(i)   (ii)

i. **Casting off**

(1) *From a landing-place.* When leaving a landing-place always shove the boat well off before using the engines; if the boat is too heavy to shove off, cast her off on her springs with the help of the wind or the stream, or by using the engines.

(2) *Springing off.* When there is a head wind or stream, the bows can be sprung off by putting the rudder to starboard and letting go the head spring. When the bows have swung out far enough, go slow ahead with rudder amidships and let go the backspring (Fig 5-54(ii)). When there is little or no wind, the stern can be sprung off by letting go the backspring, putting the rudder to port and going slow ahead (Fig 5-54(iii)); or the bows may be sprung off by holding on to the backspring and going slow astern until the bows have paid off far enough (Fig 5-54(iv)).

Fig 5-54. Use of spring when casting off

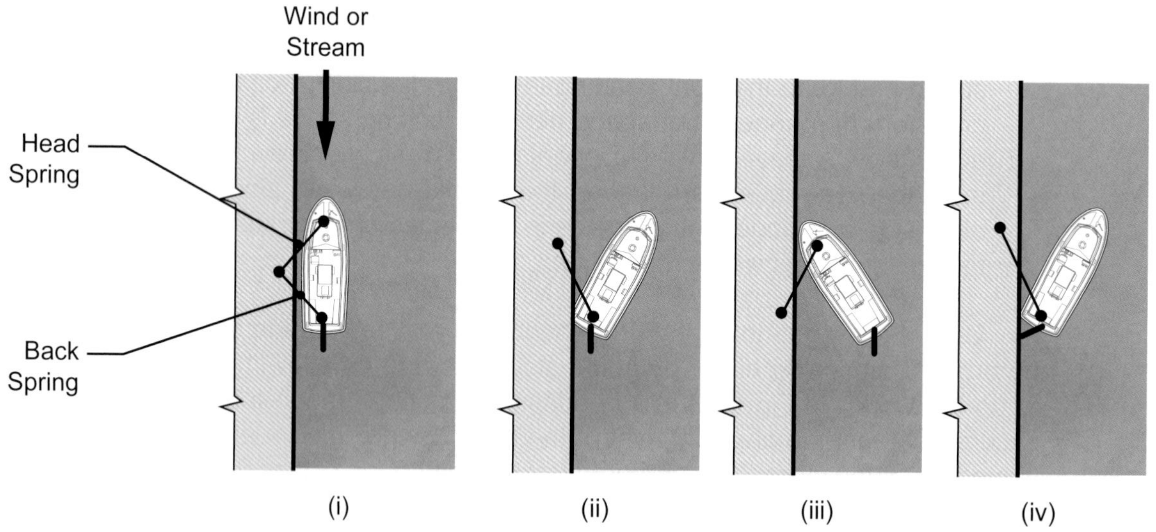

j. **Shallow water**. A boat running into shallow water at speed settles deeper in the water and trims by the stern. At the same time as her hull wash increases, a stern wave builds up and the hull vibrates. If these signs become evident, stop immediately and go astern into deep water on the opposite course. Avoid taking a boat into shallow, muddy or sandy water, because the mud or sand will be churned up and may choke the cooling system of water-cooled engines.

k. **Towing**. When towing a boat, it is usual to use her painter as the towrope, bringing it to your lee quarter cleat with one round turn round the stem of the cleat and half a turn round its after horn, the end being tended by the Sternsheetsman so that the tow can be slipped at a moment's notice. On no account should a hitch be made or the end left unattended. When towing more than one boat the heaviest should be first in the line of tow and the lightest last. Boats may be towed in calm water at a fairly short stay, but in a lop or heavy sea, the length of the tow should be increased until both boats ride comfortably. The total weight of the tow should not normally exceed the weight of the towing boat, otherwise an unfair strain will be put on her engines. To tow a heavier vessel, such as a lighter, make her tow rope fast as near to the pivoting point of your boat as possible; this may necessitate removing the after canopy. If the tow rope is made fast to the quarter cleat, the weight of the tow will gird the stern of the boat so that she will not answer the helm readily.

l.   If the tow yaws badly pass another tow rope from one quarter of the towing boat to the opposite bow of the tow (Fig 5-55(i)) and equalise the strain on both ropes. Another method is to tow the vessel on a bridle, one leg of which is shorter than the other (Fig 5-55(ii)). To tow a lighter alongside secure the boat to her quarter, as shown in Fig 5-55(iii). The rudder and propeller are not blanketed by the lighter's wash, and the rudder exerts a far better turning moment about the combined pivoting point of the two craft than it would if the boat were made fast to the lighter amidships.

Fig 5-55. Methods of towing

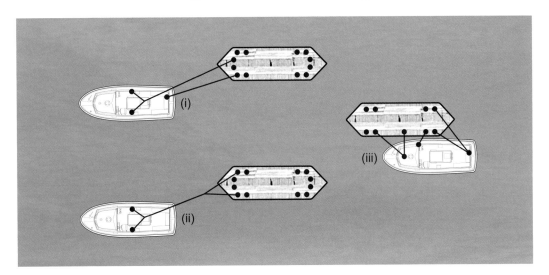

05112. Handling power boats – round-bilge, single-screw boats

a.   **Introduction**

(1)   A revolving propeller exerts a sideways thrust on the after part of the hull, and the extent of this thrust and its effect on the boat depends upon:

(a) Whether the boat is at rest or moving;

(b) Whether she is moving ahead or astern;

(c) The speed at which she is moving;

(d) The rate at which the propeller is turning.

(2)   It is not necessary for the Coxswain to understand the theory underlying the effects of a revolving propeller, but he/she should know what effects it has on the steering of the boat under various circumstances. The most important of these effects in a boat with a single right-handed propeller are described here (there are no boats in service with a single, left-handed propeller). The faster the propeller is revolving and the slower the boat is moving, the greater will be these effects.

b.   **Boat at rest, propeller going ahead.** If the rudder is amidships or to port, the stern kicks to starboard, but if the rudder is to starboard the kick is counteracted (Fig-5-56(i)).

Fig 5-56. Right-handed single-screw boat; from rest

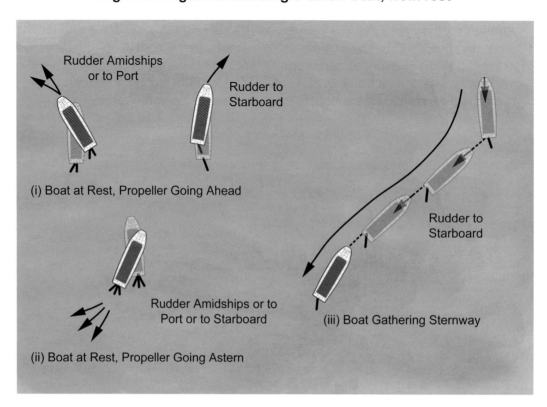

c. **Boat gathering headway**. As the boat gathers headway, the side thrust of the propeller diminishes and becomes imperceptible as soon as the boat gets steerage way.

d. **Boat at rest, propeller going astern**. The stern kicks to port whatever the position of the rudder, but the kick is more pronounced if the rudder is to port (Fig-5-56(ii)).

e. **Boat gathering sternway**. As the boat gathers sternway, the stern continues to swing to port to a lesser or greater degree, according to the setting of the rudder (Fig 5-56(iii)). But as the speed of the boat increases, so the turning effect of the rudder increases, and with starboard rudder the swing is reduced and, in some boats, may be checked completely. Very few right-handed single-screw boats can be made to swing stern to starboard when going astern, even with the engine at full speed, but if the propeller is stopped when the boat has good sternway, the rudder exerts its full effect.

f. **Boat going ahead, propeller going astern**. This is in some respects the most important reaction, because it occurs in emergency and when going alongside. As soon as the propeller starts to turn, the boat fails to obey in the normal manner and her subsequent behaviour depends on the position and size of her rudder. In the following examples (Fig 5-57), it is assumed that the engine is suddenly reversed to full speed astern when the boat is going full speed ahead, but the slower the boat is going ahead and the faster the propeller is turning, the more marked will be her behaviour.

(1)   *Rudder amidships* (Fig 5-57(i)). The boat's head falls off to starboard and the boat gains ground to starboard before losing her way.

(2)   *Rudder to port* (Fig 5-57(ii)). The boat's head usually goes to port first, but not far; it then begins to swing to starboard.

(3)   *Rudder to starboard* (Fig 5-57(iii)). The boat's head pays off to starboard because both rudder and propeller tend to turn the boat that way.

**Fig 5-57. Right-handed single-screw boat: engine full astern
when boat is going full speed ahead**

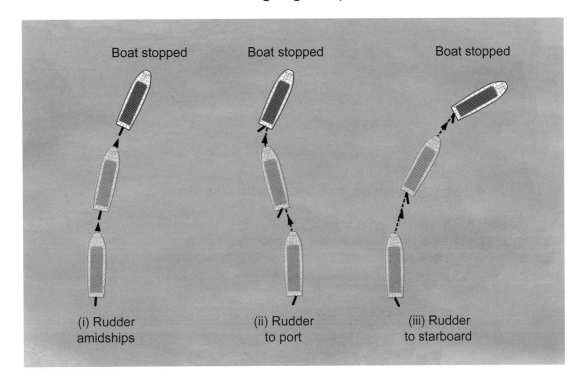

g.   **Boat going astern, propeller going ahead**. Here again, the behaviour of the boat depends on the position and size of her rudder, her speed and the engine speed. If the engine is put to full speed ahead when the boat is going full speed astern, the boat reacts as illustrated in Fig 5-58.

(1)   *Rudder amidships*. No definite forecast of the boat's behaviour can be given, because so much depends on the type of boat.

(2)   *Rudder to starboard* (Fig 5-58(i)). The boat's head pays off to starboard - slowly at first, then more rapidly as the wash of the propeller impinges on the rudder.

(3)   *Rudder to port* (Fig 5-58(ii)). The boat's head pays off to port.

Fig 5-58. Right-handed, single-screw boat:
engine full ahead when boat is going full astern

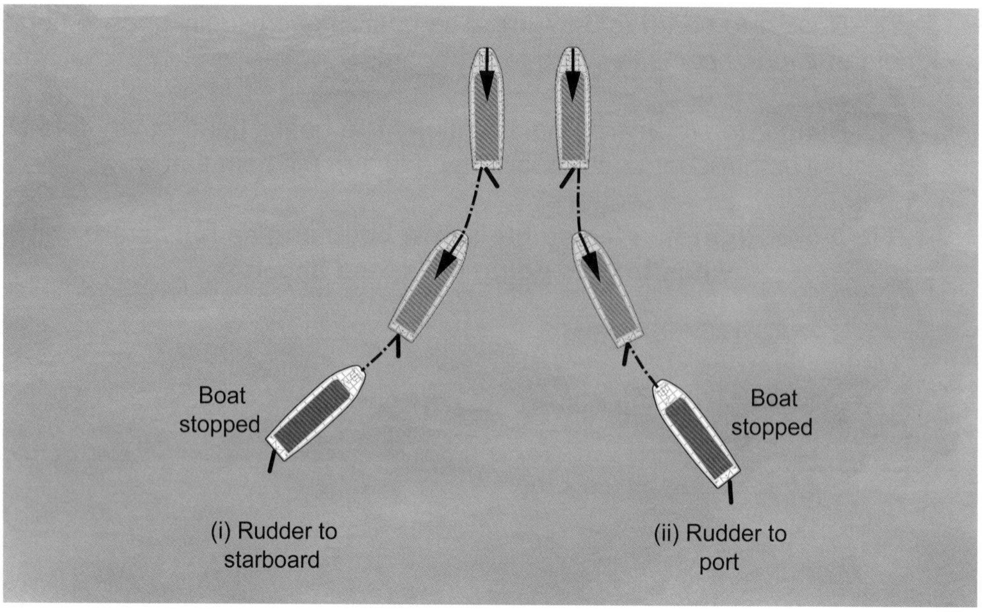

Boat
stopped

Boat
stopped

(i) Rudder to
starboard

(ii) Rudder to
port

h.   **Turning a right-handed, single-screw boat in narrow waters**

(1)   It will now be seen that the best way to turn a right-handed single-screw boat in narrow waters is to starboard, as follows (Fig 5-59):

Fig 5-59.   Right-hand, single-screw boat; turning in narrow waters

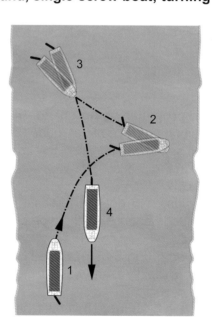

(a) Put the rudder to starboard and go ahead; the stern immediately kicks to port and will swing more rapidly as she gathers headway.

(b) Reverse the engine and put the rudder to port; the stern continues to swing to port.

(c) Go ahead and put the rudder to starboard; continue the movement of (2) and (3) as necessary until the vessel can achieve position 4.

(2)   If it is more convenient to go astern first, begin by going astern with the rudder to port. If there is a strong breeze from the starboard side, avoid going astern too far or the vessel will tend to back into the wind. If the breeze is from the port side it will be advantageous to continue the sternboard until the stern is into the wind, if there is room to do so. If there is sufficient room to go ahead and astern at fair speed for some distance it may be possible to turn to port, but the turn to starboard is always more easily and rapidly made.

i.   **Going alongside in a right-handed, single-Screw boat**.   When going alongside port side to, the boat can approach on a steady course at a small angle to the jetty or ladder, and when her engine is put astern to reduce her way, the action of the propeller kicks her stern in towards the ladder so that she brings up squarely abreast of it (Fig-5-60).

Fig 5-60. Going alongside in a right-handed, single-screw boat

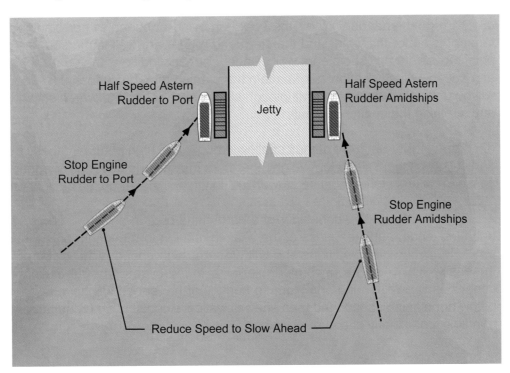

05113. Handling power boats – round-bilge, twin-screw boats

Manoeuvring a twin-screw, round-bilge boat is much easier than manoeuvring a similar single-screw boat. All such service boats have out-turning propellers. When both propellers are going ahead or astern at the same rate, the sideways thrust of one cancels that of the other, and the boat answers her rudder in the normal manner provided she has steerage way. The boat can be turned at rest on her heel with her rudder amidships by going ahead with one propeller and astern with the other, and by adjusting their rates of revolution so that the boat does not gather way either ahead or astern. But, if manoeuvring space allows, the boat can be turned more quickly if she is given a little headway or sternway with the rudder set in the direction of the turn. Some boats turn better when going ahead and some when going astern. If there is a wind blowing, some turn better if manoeuvred head to wind, and some stern to wind. Each boat has its own peculiarities so no hard and fast rules can be laid down, but when the boat is at rest, or moving slowly ahead or astern, she answers to the thrust of her propellers rather than the setting of her rudder.

05114 Handling power boats – hard-chine boats

a. **Introduction.** A hard-chine boat is designed to plane on the surface of the water at comparatively high speed, and therefore has a shallow draught, a flat bottom, and a greater beam than a round-bilge boat of similar length. The trim of the boat and her steering qualities are very different at high and low speeds. All hard-chine boats in use in the service have twin, out-turning propellers and handling is similar to that of twin-screw round-bilge boats, but because of the shallow draught the kick of the propellers is more marked.

b. **At high speeds.** The boat has a hull of V-shaped cross-section forward and of rectangular cross-section aft. When at rest or moving slowly the draught is greater forward than aft, the pivoting point is at or near the bows and the boat tends to skid when under wheel. Because she is trimmed by the head, the boat answers her rudder sluggishly and, when at rest, the rudder has little or no effect.

c. **At higher speeds.** When the boat is moving at speed in her planing trim the forefoot is out of the water and the stern and rudder are well immersed; the pivoting point moves aft, and she steers well. Under normal conditions the boat should be run at a speed which will allow her to attain her planing trim, but if she is overloaded she will be unable to attain it and will plough sluggishly through the water, shipping water and straining the engine and hull.

d. **Topweight.** Because of their shallow draught and high freeboard these boats are particularly susceptible to top-weight; therefore they should never be overloaded, and passengers and stores must be stowed within the hull, never on the deck or canopies.

e. **In heavy sea.** The behaviour of a hard-chine boat in a heavy seaway depends upon the length and steepness of the seas in relation to the length and speed of the boat. In favourable conditions she will plane at high speed with comparative ease in seas which would be uncomfortable for a round-bilge boat; but in unfavourable conditions she will pound and slam so badly that her speed will have to be reduced below her planing speed, and then she will wallow sluggishly and require very careful handling, particularly in a quartering sea.

SECTION 12 - GUIDANCE FOR ALL BOAT COXSWAINS

05115. Guidance for all boat coxswains

a.   **Introduction.** It is an old Service saying that a ship is known by her boats; when away in a boat remember that you are in charge of the boat and the reputation of your ship depends partly on you. Check the gear and equipment regularly. This should be done when the boat is being cleaned, or before she is called away for the first trip of the day, or before she is lowered, or when you take over a watch or period of duty. Make good defects between trips; report any which you cannot make good to the Officer of the Watch and the Boat Officer. After the last trip of the day make sure that the boat is ready in all respects for the first trip of the following day.

b.   **Briefings for trips**. (see Annex 5C)

c.   **Dress and behaviour in the boat**. Always check that your crew is properly dressed in the correct rig; if caps are being worn chin-stays must be down. The crew and passengers should not be allowed to stand up, except when necessary to carry out their duties. Nobody should be allowed to place their arms or hands on the washstrakes or gunwales, especially when the boat is alongside or about to go alongside. Do not allow skylarking in a boat; even in a recreational environment the potential for an accident is high. **Smoking is forbidden in all service boats**.

d.   **Unhooking.** When unhooking a boat from her falls, always unhook the after fall before the foremost fall. If the foremost fall is unhooked first, the boat may swing out, and in a strong tideway may broach-to. For the same reason, when hooking a boat to her falls, the foremost fall should always be hooked on before the after fall.

e.   **Carrying passengers and stores**. You must know the maximum number of persons and the maximum weight your boat is allowed to carry in calm weather (see the relevant paragraphs in this chapter); remember that these are maximum limits for calm weather, and that you must reduce them according to the conditions and sea which your boat will encounter. Passengers must embark and disembark one at a time as directed by the Coxswain to keep the boat stable; the sequence for embarking passengers is Junior Rates first, followed by Senior Rates, then Officers; this sequence is reversed when disembarking. When embarking stores they should be placed as near as possible amidships and low down in the boat. If the centre of gravity of the stores is above the gunwale the boat will be top-heavy and tender; if weights are placed right forward she will not rise to the waves and will be in danger of broaching-to, and if placed right aft she will be in danger of being pooped by a following sea. When loaded, your boat should have an even trim and no list, but when running before a heavy sea it is best to trim the boat slightly by the stern. If you are carrying top-weight alter course carefully, and if you are heavily loaded remember that the boat will carry her way for a much greater distance than when she is lightly loaded.

f.   **Carrying money or valuable stores**. Before a large sum of money or a valuable item of stores is embarked, the bag containing it should be secured to a buoy-rope which should be long enough easily to reach the bottom at any point on your passage back to the ship; should any accident then occur the item can be recovered later by picking up the buoy and buoy-rope. When disembarking the item the buoy and buoy-rope should be passed first into the ship.

g.   **When underway**. In setting your course make due allowance for leeway or the set or current of any tidal stream. If your course lies beam-on to a heavy sea or swell it is better to steer a dog-leg course to windward than to steer a direct one. Meet the wash of passing craft bows on, and do not pass under the bow or stern of a ship at anchor. Do not cross the bows of your superiors. Be thoroughly conversant with the Rule of the Road.

h.   **Gangway hand signals**. Fig 5-61 shows the code of gangway hand signals. If you have to wait before going alongside another ship, lie off well clear on her quarter and keep a lookout for the signal or hail to call you alongside.

Fig 5-61. Code of gangway hand signals

Carry On   Lie Off

Make Fast   Come Alongside

i.   **Securing a boat**

(1)   *To an accommodation ladder*. Pass the end of the gangway boatrope through the eyeplate on the boat's bow and secure it around a cleat. Do not remain alongside an accommodation ladder unless ordered to do so.

(2)   *To a buoy*. Secure the boat's painter to the buoy ring by a round-turn-and-two-half-hitches.

(3)   *To a jetty or alongside another boat*. Ensure the craft is well fendered. The securing lines should be led down through a ring or around a bollard on the jetty or boat to which you are making fast, then back into your boat and secured to a cleat.

j.   **Care and protection of craft when secured away from parent ship.** Craft that are routinely tied up alongside jetties, pontoons, catamarans or stowed in cradles on the jetty for minor repairs or maintenance periods, but remain in Fleet time continue to be a ship's responsibility for its care and protection. As a minimum, the following routines are to be conducted at the end of the working day by a responsible member of staff from the parent ship/unit:

(1)   Full line check, with additional lines rigged in preparation for inclement weather iaw local weather forecasts.

(2)   Security checks to include secure compartments (CO_2 and Pyro lockers etc, and access into the craft).

(3)   Draft marks to be checked for to ensure stability and watertight integrity.

(4)   Correct stowage of all equipment and tools.

(5)   Completion of any extant permits to work, hot-work rounds, or maintenance.

(6)   That the craft is ready in all respects to be left overnight without undue risk to the craft or personnel.

(7)   Boats that are stowed in cradles on the jetty are to be covered at all times. Covers can be removed for maintenance on boats but must be refitted at the end of each working day.

(8)   Record the rounds in the ship's Log.

Where craft are left in the water in other locations, the parent ship is to assess the increased risk to the craft posed by exposed locations, including tidal streams, jetty construction and security and is to enhance the above requirement to a suitable level in order to discharge their duty. Should there be any doubt then advice should be sought from Navy Command Seamanship.

k.   **Boat cradle.** Pacific 22 and 24 RIB Collapsible Cradle Assembly Instructions (See Annex 5D).

05116. Guidance for sea boat coxswains

a.   **Use of the automatic release hook and preventer (where fitted).** Ensure your crew is fully conversant with the use and operation of the hook. If the boat has to be recovered when the hook (RFD) is in the 'cocked' position, for instance if a Sea Boat evolution is terminated after the boat has been lowered but before it has been launched, then the preventer must be hooked to the lifting sling ring before the boat is hoisted.

b.   **Recovery and care of a casualty.** The procedure for the recovery and care of a casualty when operating a RIB is given in Para 05084; this procedure, suitably modified for the type of boat being used, is applicable to any other boat being used as a Sea Boat.

c.   **Use of the boatrope.** When going alongside to hook on for hoisting or to conduct a transfer of stores or personnel a boatrope should be rigged. It is better to overshoot than undershoot the falls (or transfer position). If you overshoot, the boatrope can be recovered and secured, and the wind and sea will soon drop the boat astern.

However, if you undershoot, it can be difficult to regain the momentum necessary to get the boat forward into the correct position smoothly. Do not be afraid to use the engine to keep the boat correctly positioned until the boatrope is secured. See also Para 03072 in Chapter 3 regarding the use of a pilot/boarding ladder.

d. **Signals**. When away from your ship, keep an eye on her for signals; on your outward passage one member of the crew should be facing the ship to watch for flag, lamp or other signals. If you are to pick up a person or some other inconspicuous object, the ship may have to direct you to the position. In order to standardise light signals in this situation, the following indications are to be used (repeated in BR 45(6)):

Series of long flashes	Turn to starboard
Series of short flashes	Turn to port
Steady light	Go straight ahead
No light signals	Stop in your current position
Series of 'ROMEOs' (. — .)	Return to ship

e. **Suitability of transfer positions**. Should the Coxswain of a boat have doubts about the feasibility of conducting a transfer from a particular point on a ship's side because of prevailing weather conditions at that point, or for any other reason, he/ she should express their concerns to the CO of the ship concerned and request an alternative position.

05117. Assistance to ditched helicopters – introduction

a. **Foreword.** During flying operations, there is always the risk that an aircraft may ditch into the sea. The priority for ships and helicopters arriving on the scene is to locate and rescue aircrew and passengers. The crew of fixed-wing aircraft will normally eject from the aircraft before it ditches and may be found some distance from any aircraft wreckage. Helicopters that operate over the sea are usually fitted with flotation gear which inflates in the event of a ditching. The purpose of this flotation gear is to allow time for the escape and rescue of aircrew; their rescue is the only priority for ships and helicopters arriving on the scene. Even though ditched helicopters may float for a period of 20 minutes or more, experience has shown that they are prone to capsize or sudden sink. Deep water salvage techniques and capabilities have greatly improved, therefore upon completion of the rescue of survivors; the salvage of the aircraft is not to be considered. However, the marking of the aircraft and salvage area is to be attempted if time permits.

b. **Crash boat swimmer requirements.** All ships conducting flying operations should nominate at least two personnel who have undertaken the Swimmer of the Watch (SOW) training, as Crash Boat Surface Swimmers. They are to use swimming and recovery techniques and equipment as taught during SOW training. The swimmers must receive an aircraft familiarity exercise with special reference to the hazardous areas of the aircraft and the rescuing of survivors. This acquaint is to be repeated every 90 days.

c. **Flotation gear and escape panels**. The positions of the inflated flotation gear and escape panels (indicated by the shaded areas) for the Sea King, Lynx, Merlin and Apache AH Mk 1 helicopters are shown in Figs 5-62 to Fig 5-65.

Fig 5-62. Flotation gear and escape panels on the Sea King

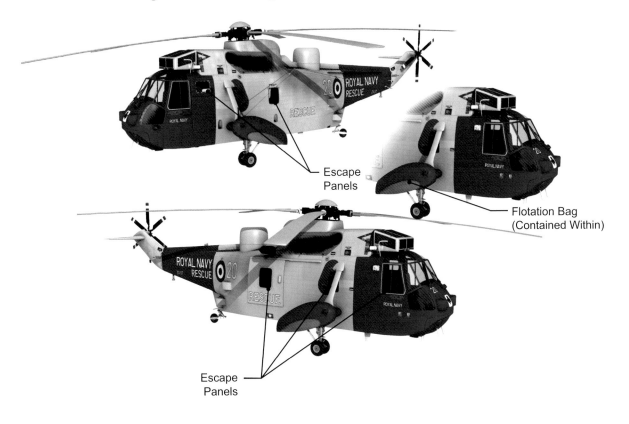

Fig 5-63. Flotation gear and escape panels on the Lynx

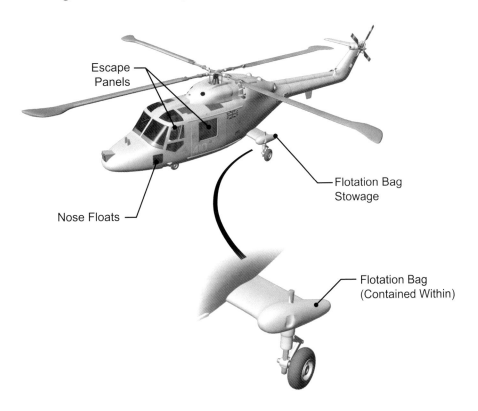

Fig 5-64. Flotation gear and escape panels on the Merlin

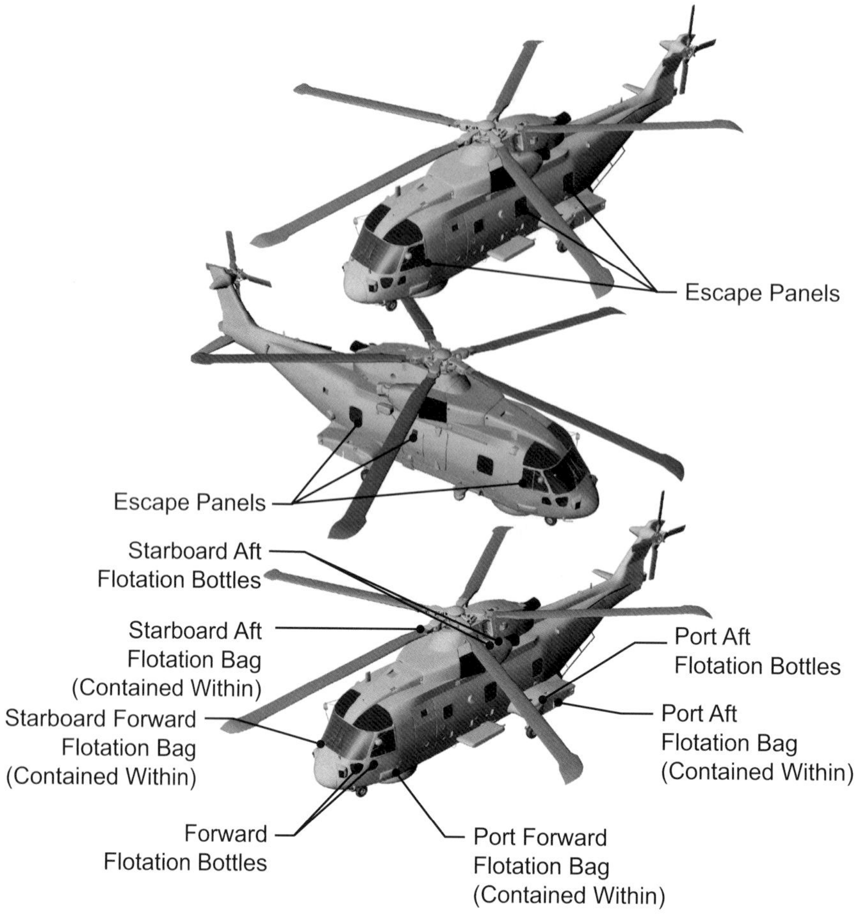

Escape Panels

Escape Panels

Starboard Aft Flotation Bottles

Starboard Aft Flotation Bag (Contained Within)

Starboard Forward Flotation Bag (Contained Within)

Forward Flotation Bottles

Port Aft Flotation Bottles

Port Aft Flotation Bag (Contained Within)

Port Forward Flotation Bag (Contained Within)

Fig 5-65. Escape panels on the Apache

Escape Route

05118. Assistance to ditched helicopters – crash boat – pescue of personnel

a.   **Crash boat.** Whenever flying operations are taking place, a Sea Boat is to be fitted with a crash bag and designated the ship's immediate on-call Crash Boat. The crash bag contains initial first aid equipment to assist in the immediate recovery of survivors and their immediate first aid.

b.   **Crash bag equipment**. (Approximate weight 25 kg)

   2 CNI Radio VHF (if other aircraft assisting)
   Basic first aid kit (Part of Boat bag)
   Two blankets (sealed in a polythene bag)
   Marker float with 100 metres of line
   Fireman's axe (0243/534-6513)
   DC lamp (unless Aldis lamp already carried)
   Rescue knife (0091/977-2081)
   Manual line Thrower (0472/781-0504)
   Swimmer Lifeline (50 metres x 8 mm polyethylene 0350/543-0141)

c.   **Manning the crash boat**. The crew of the crash boat consists of a Coxswain, Bowman and a Crash Boat Surface Swimmer.

Note.   *The rules for crew and passengers regarding the wearing of Boat Specific Lifejacket and Safety Helmets during boat operations (Para 05052) also apply to the Surface Swimmer who is to wear a Boat Specific Lifejacket whilst being deployed and recovered in the Crash Boat and then when at the scene of the incident before being deployed, changes to the SOW buoyancy aid.*

d.   **Preparation of the crash boat.** At 'Prepare for Flying' The Crash Boat Coxswain and Surface Swimmer are to confirm their equipment and report to the Flight Deck Officer (FDO)/FLYCO where they will then receive a full flying brief, on completion of which the OOW is then informed that a full Crash Boat briefing has been received and which boat is rigged as the Crash Boat.

e.   The FDO/FLYCO briefing is to include the following points:

   (1)   The type of aircraft/helicopter and its escape arrangements and flotation gear.

   (2)   The number of persons on board the aircraft.

   (3)   Any ordnance or under-slung load known to be attached to the aircraft.

   (4)   The risk of fire from fuel spillage.

f.   **Other seamanship preparations**. A Quick Reaction And Marker Buoy (QRAMB) should be at 30 minutes notice and the Quick Reaction Marker Buoy (QRMB) ready for immediate deployment.

05119. Assistance to ditched helicopters – approach phase

During the approach to the ditched helicopter, upon calling the Crash Boat away, the OOW over main broadcast is to brief the type of aircraft the number of persons on board (POB) and the aircraft's armament state. On-board preparations are to be made to receive casualties. A fully rigged QRAMB is to be prepared with the depth of mooring wire requirement supplied by the Navigator/OOW. Lashings (if fitted) are to be removed from the QRMB. A pilot/boarding ladder is also to be rigged but not deployed until required.

05120. Assistance to ditched helicopters – rescuing the aircrew

Aircrew close to the helicopter should be assisted by the Crash Boat Surface Swimmer operating from the crash boat. The considerable risks and potential hazards involved to the swimmer working below the rotor disk must be taken into account at all times. Survivors who are in the water, but clear of the helicopter, should be recovered as quickly as possible, followed by those in dinghies. The Crash Boat Surface Swimmer must wear a lifeline at all times, except in extreme circumstances where on balance, the removal of the lifeline, because of the danger of it becoming a snagging hazard, would directly lead to the saving of life.

CAUTIONS

1. IMPORTANT – Return of aircrew/casualties to the ship takes primacy over marking of the helicopter.

2. Marking the aircraft should only be carried out if time permits and a local risk assessment by the surface swimmer is carried out.

05121. Assistance to ditched helicopters – marking the helicopter

The line of the spherical float which is used as a marker buoy should be attached to the helicopter by the Crash Boat surface swimmer. A stick should be passed through the float and the line coiled round it in figure-of-eight turns. This ensures that the line has no loose bights to foul the surface swimmer or the helicopter and also that the line will run freely should the helicopter sink. If the helicopter has sunk, the position of ditching should be marked with a QRAMB or QRMB to serve as a datum for any subsequent search for the wreck.

05122. Assistance to ditched helicopters – specialist divers/swimmers

Only Clearance and Search and Rescue (SAR) divers may dive without a lifeline. The SAR diver is trained specifically for first-aid helicopter salvage, and when available, is the most suitable choice for this type of work. Work on the rotor head should only be conducted from above and clear of the rotor blades. Divers and surface swimmers on lifelines are not to work submerged under the helicopter on any account. Before they enter the water they must be thoroughly briefed on the procedure to be adopted and the task at hand. The combination of a damaged helicopter and a high sea state may make it inadvisable to attempt first-aid salvage or even the marking of the helicopter.

05123. Ceremonial in boats

a. The authoritative publications dealing with ceremonies in the Royal Navy are **BR 1834, Royal Naval Ceremonial and Drill**, and **BR2 Chapters 91 and 92** and these publications should be referred to when dealing with all but routine ceremonial procedures. The information given here is intended as a guide to boat coxswains.

b. **Wearing of ensigns**. The White Ensign (size 2 NSN 8345-99-571-3296) is to be worn by RN and RM boats and Tenders (power and sail) at all times unless operational circumstances dictate otherwise.

Note. *When the ensign is half-masted in HM ships, boats' ensigns should also be half-masted.*

c. **Flying of distinguishing flags or pennants**. Any of the persons authorised to fly a distinguishing flag or pennant may fly the appropriate flag (or pennant) in the bow of a boat when underway and proceeding on occasions of ceremony, such as official visits or inspections. If the person is other than a naval authority the boat also wears her ensign. The flag (or pennant) is to be flown only between the hours of 'Colours' and sunset. The masthead pennant is flown in a boat under similar circumstances by officers holding an appointment in command of one of HM ships, seagoing tenders, or shore establishments. The masthead pennant is also flown in a boat between the hours of 'Colours' and sunset if she is carrying members of a court-martial who are proceeding to or from the court. It is also flown by day and by night by a boat carrying the Officer of the Guard. A Queen's Harbour Master or his deputy may fly his flag in the bow of a boat or vessel when in the execution of his duty.

d. **Flag discs**. Flag discs (250mm in diameter) are displayed in boats on occasions when a distinguishing flag is not flown to denote the presence of senior officers. The following flag discs are authorised for this purpose when proceeding on duty:

The **red disc** denotes that the boat is carrying an officer entitled to fly a flag or broad pennant on a formal occasion, but that the full ceremonial due to his rank is not required.

The **blue disc** denotes that the boat is carrying on a formal occasion an officer of Flag rank or a Commodore not entitled to fly a flag or broad pennant, or Matron-in-Chief QARNNS. On such occasions the officer is received with the 'Alert'.

The **white disc** denotes that the boat is carrying an officer entitled to fly a flag or broad pennant on an informal occasion when only courtesy salutes are accorded

e. **Saluting of standards and distinguishing flags**. When a boat flying a standard or a distinguishing flag passes a ship at anchor, the ship should parade a guard and band and accord the appropriate salute unless orders to the contrary have been given. Should the ship be flying the flag or broad pennant of an officer senior to the officer in the boat, the guard and band are not paraded and the 'Alert' only is sounded. If the boat passes a ship underway, the ship should pipe the 'Still', and if her guard and band are paraded, the guard should come to the 'Shoulder' and no musical salute should be accorded. When a boat displaying the red or the blue disc passes a ship at anchor the ship should sound the 'Alert' only. A ship underway should pipe the 'Still'. When a boat displaying the white disc passes a ship at anchor, the Officer of the Watch (or in his absence the quartermaster) should salute from the gangway.

f. **Salutes and marks of respect**

(1) All officers when embarking or disembarking are saluted by the officer in charge of the boat or the Coxswain. The following rules govern the exchange of salutes between Service boats under way:

(a) The officer or Coxswain in charge of the boat will always salute, except that when he is in an inconspicuous position, one of the boat's crew will be detailed instead.

(b) The senior of the officers in the boat will also salute whenever this is practicable.

(c) The salute will be acknowledged by the officer being saluted, unless he details an officer or Coxswain to do so.

(d) No salutes are exchanged between boats carrying officers of equal rank.

(2) In boats other than service boats, whether alongside or underway, officers and men should pay and return salutes as indicated by courtesy, but only the officer or man in the most convenient position should salute. In addition to these salutes, special marks of respect are paid to royal and important personages and senior officers; these are shown in Table 5-2.

g. **Ceremonial boathook drill**. When coming alongside or leaving a jetty or ship during ceremonial occasions, Ceremonial Boathook Drill should be carried out. The drill should be performed when the boat is approximately 50 metres from its destination during berthing, and immediately the boat is clear of its berth during unberthing. The drill is shown in Fig 5-66.

h. **Boat hails**. At night, any boat approaching within hailing distance of a ship is challenged by the hail 'Boat ahoy'. If the boat is not calling alongside the hailing boat she will reply 'Passing'. If the boat is to call alongside, her reply will be governed by the rank or status of the person she is carrying, in accordance with Table 5-2.

Fig 5-66. Ceremonial boat hook drill (starboard side to)

Stage 1   Stage 2   Stage 3

Stage 4   Stage 5   Stage 6

Table 5-1. Special marks of respect to be paid in boats

Personage to whom, or occasion on which, marks of respect should be paid	Marks of respect by boats under way		Marks of respect by a boat alongside a landing place, an accommodation ladder, or made fast
	Power boat	Boat under sail	
1. The Sovereign; members of the Royal Family and equivalent personages in other nations; Ambassadors, Governors-General, and their equivalents in other nations. (Standard or appropriate flag is flown in the boat).	Stop the boat	Let-fly sheets	Crew called to attention (see Note 2 and Note 3)
2. Commanders-in-Chief, Flag Officers and Commodores, and their equivalents in other services and nations, when flying the appropriate flag of their command in their barges or boats.			
3. A boat containing a Service funeral party with the body. (Ensign at half-mast is worn by the boat).			
4. During the hoisting and lowering of colours in harbour, and during the firing of gun salutes			
5. Commanders-in-Chief, Flag Officers, Commodores, Commodores and above holding staff appointments, and officers or personages of equivalent rank in other Services or nations, when displaying a red or blue disc in the boat.	Reduce speed to slow		
6. Commanders-in-Chief, Flag Officers, Commodores, and officers of equivalent rank in uniform or plain clothes, when displaying a white disc in the boat.			
7. Any British or foreign naval officer flying a pennant in a boat.			

Notes:

1.   Marks of respect are paid in all boats on occasions (3) and (4); otherwise only in boats in which officers junior to the personage or officer passing are passengers.

2.   In decked-in boats, members of the crew who are not engaged in keeping the boat alongside, and all passengers, stand to attention and face in the direction of the personage or officer being saluted.

3.   In open boats of all types, members who are not engaged in keeping the boat alongside, and all passengers, sit at attention.

4.   It is the custom in the Royal Navy for a boat to avoid crossing close ahead of any boat which is carrying an important personage or a senior officer, even if the former boat has the right of way by the Rule of the Road.

Table 5-2. Boat hails

Person carried	Reply
A Royal Personage or Head of State	'Standard'
Commander-in-Chief	"Commander-in-Chief" and the "Name" of the ship he flies his flag
An officer of Flag rank or a Commodore entitled to fly his broad pennant	'Flag', followed by the name of his flagship when appropriate
A Chief-of-Staff or Chief Staff Officer (when no Chief-of-Staff is allowed)	'Staff' with the name of the flagship
Commanding Officer of a ship	Name of the ship which he commands
Other officers	'Ay, Ay'
Officer of the Guard	'Guard boat'
Ratings	'No, no'
A boat not coming to your ship	Passing

05124. Repair and replacement of ship's boats

a. **Introduction.** If a ship's boat is damaged or unserviceable to such an extent that it cannot be quickly repaired on board, in most cases this will require a ship's investigation as directed by NCHQ. A replacement boat must then be obtained. All replacement boats for the Fleet are allocated by the MOD Boat Manager at, Maritime Platform Systems – Maritime Spares – General Stores and Sea Survival (MPS-MS-GSS MOD Abbey Wood, Bristol, BS34 8JH, or by signal address DES Bath FAO MBM, SIC H5H/H4C. Paint punts are Naval Stores items and should be demanded from DGST (N).

b. **Rigid inflatable boats** Replacement policy. All RIBs in naval service are disposed of after 14 years service. All ships' RIBs, including those belonging to RFAs, are routinely replaced by new RIBs after eight years (short extensions can be granted via the MOD Boat Manager). These eight-year-old craft are refurbished and then reallocated to shore authorities and establishments. Ships under construction are not allocated new RIBs until shortly before acceptance; refurbished boats are made available for ship fitting purposes and contractors' Sea Trials. RIBs supplied to the ice patrol ship are specially constructed and are dealt with separately.

c. **Boat's logs.** The Power Boat Log is issued by the boat builder on first delivery, it is retained as Boat's Equipment **and should be transferred with every boat transaction.** The log format, which can be copied, is published at JSP 848 and is also available from Repair Yard Overseers or the MOD Boat Allocator at Maritime Platform Systems – Maritime Spares – General Stores and Sea Survival (MPS-MS-GSS). The aim of the log is to provide a complete history of the boat's operation from delivery, including a general synopsis of the maintenance and refits that the boat has received during its life. The information is required to enable staff to ascertain the potential life remaining in the hull and when it should be replaced. The Power Boat Log has been updated to improve its utility as a routine log and provide a more accurate record of the material state of the boat when transferring between the user and the repair authority. The update draws on experience from across the Fleet and represents current best practice.

d. **JSP 848**. The above information is a summary of the information contained in JSP 848 the MOD BOAT MANUAL. This publication should be referenced in all cases of boat procurement requests, refits, repair and disposal.

05125. Boat hanging pendants and anti-shock strops

Table 5-3 and Table 5-4 give details of hanging pendants and anti-shock strops for use with ship's displacement boats.

Table 5-3. SWR hanging pendants for boats (excluding RIBs)

SWR hanging pendants for boats (excluding RIBs)					
Type of boat	**SWR**	**Thimble**	**Bow shackle with pin**	**Spring hook**	**Straight shackle (with split pin)**
11.0m Work Boat	0235/523- 8652 32mm 6x41	0263/414- 9639	0263/ 414-9606	0263/414- 9773	0263/543 4535
13.1m LCVP	8656 36mm 6x41	9641	N/A	Straight Screw Shackle 0263/721-6097	4538

Table 5-4. Polyamide anti-shock strops for boats (excluding RIBs)

Polyamide anti-shock strops for boats (excluding RIBs)					
Type of boat	**Polyamide rope**	**Thimble**	**Bow shackle with Pin**	**Spring hook**	**Swivel ring shackle**
11.0m Work Boat	0350/923 7134 44mm	0263/414- 9642	0263/ 414-9606	0263/414- 9773	0263/543 9941
13.1m LCVP	7137 64mm	9645	N/A	Straight Screw Shackle 0263/721-6097	Straight Screw Shackle 0263/721-6097

SECTION 13 – MEXEFLOTE - ROYAL FLEET AUXILIARY

05126. General

This chapter gives an overview of operational factors of use to planning staffs when deploying MEXEFLOTEs from Landing Ship Dock (Auxiliary)s (LSD(A)s. Full details are in 'User Handbook for LSL and Harbour Pontoon Equipment (MEXEFLOTE)' Army Code No.14882.

Fig 5-67. Mexeflote in operation

05127. Description

a.   MEXEFLOTE is the name given to a series of linked pontoons which, when formed as an 18-cell raft, weighs approximately 93 tonnes. They are normally carried in the form of rafts on the side of LSD(A)s, to be lowered at the scene of amphibious operations, for use in ferrying personnel and equipment ashore, or as a causeway between ship and shore.

b.   The LSD(A) is capable of transporting two MEXEFLOTE rafts which are able to transfer all embarked vehicles including main battle tanks, palletised loads and personnel. The MEXEFLOTEs are transported with pontoons fully assembled but excluding ancillary equipment such as engines. This machinery is fitted once the MEXEFLOTE is in the water. Stowage of the MEXEFLOTE equipment is provided in a location accessible by the ship's cranes for this purpose.

c.   The standard MEXEFLOTE consists of three strings of pontoons, each with a bow pontoon, stern pontoon and four centre section pontoons. When stowed, MEXEFLOTEs are secured by hydraulic locking arrangements which prevent them being dislodged by wave action.

d.   MEXEFLOTEs can be launched and recovered in a controlled manner, using the MEXEFLOTE winches provided. The MEXEFLOTEs are capable of being launched with the ship in the docked-down condition without heeling the ship. Flying operations from the helicopter spot are not impeded or prevented by stowed MEXEFLOTEs; nor do the hoisting wires infringe stowage space on the vehicle deck when raising or lowering.

Note.   'MEXEFLOTE' is an acronym for **M**ilitary **EX**perimental **E**stablishment **FLOT**ation **E**quipment.

05128. Construction

Each MEXEFLOTE consists of bow, centre and stern cells. These can be connected side-to-side and end-to-end to form a floating platform. Centre and stern units have the same dimensions but the stern unit is modified to enable a propeller unit to be fitted. The bow unit incorporates a hydraulically operated ramp and is therefore larger.

05129. Propulsion

Currently, MEXEFLOTE rafts are powered by two 75hp Hydromaster propulsion units (although an upgrade is expected in the near future) and can achieve a maximum speed of 5.5 knots when fully laden in still water.

05130. Weights and dimensions

a.	Bow Unit:	7.92 metres (m) x 2.44 m x 1.45 m	Weight: 5896.8 kg
b.	Centre Unit:	6.10 m x 2.44 m x 1.45 m	Weight: 4644.9 kg
c.	Stern Unit:	6.10 m x 2.44 m x 1.45 m	Weight: 4409.0 kg
d.	1 x 38.42 m, fully assembled raft (complete with connectors, pivot posts, actuators and links but without propulsion units and other equipment loaded)		Weight: 93.0 t

05131. Draught

a. When fully laden with 610mm freeboard:

    (1)   Bow: 0.99 metres

    (2)   Stern: 1.75 metres (with propulsion unit which can be raised when beaching).

05132. Ramp

a. Effective length: 4.88 metres.

b. Raised: 0.45 metres above deck level.

c. Lowered: 0.38 metres below keel level.

05133. Usage

a. An LSD(A) normally side carries two 38.42 x 7.42 metre rafts which are usually operated as powered MEXEFLOTES. Alternatively, the two rafts can be joined end-to-end to form a 76.84 metre causeway. Additional unassembled units can be carried as deck cargo at the expense of normal cargo capacity.

b. Various configurations can be assembled to specific requirements. Some examples are:

    (1)   Powered raft.

    (2)   Tug.

    (3)   Helicopter landing platform.

    (4)   Staging platform (also known as RSP or Ramp Support Pontoon).

(5) Causeway.

(6) Jetty.

(7) RO RO.

05134. Capabilities and limitations

a. **Support (Afloat)**

(1) A 20.12 x 7.32 metre raft will support 55 tonnes distributed with 0.61-metre freeboard.

(2) A 38.42 x 7.32 metre raft will support 110 tonnes distributed (including Challenger MBT) with 0.61-metre freeboard.

b. **Support (dried out)**

(1) 20.12-metre rafts will support a full load if dried out on any reasonable bottom (i.e. one that will not penetrate the skin).

(2) 20.12-metre rafts will support their full load as suspended spans.

c. **Sea limitations.** The equipment is designed to:

(1) Be assembled in waves up to 0.61 metres.

(2) Operate in 1.22-metre waves.

(3) Survive unladen at moorings in 2.7 – 3.1 metre waves.

(4) Survive unladen in tow in 3.66-metre waves.

(5) Be recovered to the side stowed position in waves up to 0.61 metres. This procedure can be eased if the ship provides a lee.

05135. Launching and recovery procedure

a. The MEXEFLOTE rafts cannot be slipped from the vertical position but must first be lowered to the water. The ship must be in the fully docked condition before launching or recovery is attempted.

b. The MEXEFLOTE winches used to launch/recover the rafts are controlled by a single operator using a portable control panel and overlooking the rafts from positions on 1 and 2 Decks.

c. Responsibility for the actual lowering/raising of the MEXEFLOTE rests with the ship. The RLC Detachment is responsible for securing the mooring lines before lowering and the handling and fitting of the ancillary equipment after lowering. Similarly, during recovery, the RLC Detachment is responsible for manoeuvring the MEXEFLOTE alongside to a position where it can be engaged with the ship side lugs and reconnecting the hoisting wires to the lifting eyes on the raft prior to recovery.

d. The security of the MEXEFLOTE when carried is the responsibility of the ship's staff. However the raft crew are to maintain a continuous watch on the raft when at sea.

Fig 5-68. Mexeflote recovering

05136. Launch and recovery timings

a. **Ballasting/deballasting**

(1) Launching and recovery of the MEXEFLOTEs requires the ship to be ballasted from its sailing condition through a pre-docking standby condition (Pre-Action Standby State) to a pre-docking condition (Pre-Action State) and finally to a fully docked condition (Action State).

(2) In the **pre-action standby state,** the ship is ballasted down to a point where the waterline is coincident with the centre-line of the stern door hinge and the dock bottom is just above the waterline; the stern door remains closed and the dock dry.

(3) To achieve the **pre-action state,** further seawater is transferred to the dock itself. The stern door is gradually opened to equalise the water pressure on either side until the dock is flooded.

(4) In the **action state,** the stern door is fully open and the ship is trimmed to a level allowing the dock to flood and craft to operate from within.

(5) Deballasting from the **action state** to the sailing condition is the reverse of the above sequence.

Table 5-5. Typical timings for ballasting/deballasting.

Ballasting	Time taken
Draft 5.40 m (Trials Draft) to Draft 5.80 m (Load Draft).	1 h.
Draft 5.80 m to Pre-Action Standby State.	1 h.
Pre-Action Standby State to Pre-Action State.	20 min.
Pre-Action State to Action State (Draft 9.43m).	1 h 10 min.
Draft 5.40 m (Trials Draft) to Action State (Draft 9.43m)	3 h 30 min.
Deballasting	
Action State to Draft 5.40 m (Trials Draft).	2 h 40 min.

b. **MEXEFLOTE Operations**

Table 5-6. Typical timings for MEXEFLOTE operations.

Operation	Time Taken
To construct a 38.66 m x 7.42 m raft from readily accessible components (assuming the cells are pre-stowed ready for lift).	4 h.
To fit three engines after lowering.	30 min.
To lower a raft from ship's side	1 h.
To prepare to lift one raft from alongside (in ideal conditions).	15 min.

Note. *All these timings are approximations and are subject to the prevailing weather conditions.*

05137. Manoeuvrability

a. The Dynamic Positioning system is capable of holding the vessel's position, and heading to within +/- 2° (in conditions of at least Sea State 2 and 20 knots of wind from a direction +/- 10° from right ahead), with the vessel configured for deployment/ recovery of MEXEFLOTES.

b. The ship is able to make way at up to 15 knots while ballasting to the pre-docking condition.

c. The ship is able to make way at up to 4 knots while in the fully docked condition.

05138. Limiting weather conditions

a. **Responsibility.** The MEXEFLOTE Coxswain is solely responsible for the decision to sail and for the subsequent safety of his MEXEFLOTE, crew, passengers and cargo, bearing in mind at all times the limitations of the MEXEFLOTE as defined in the user handbook, which details weather, wind and sea limitations. The coxswain is also solely responsible for the ultimate decisions to side lift, lower, break or build a MEXEFLOTE or configurations thereof. The Coxswain should review his decision regularly, continuing with the task once conditions have improved.

b. **Fitting of engines**. The fitting of an engine to a MEXEFLOTE is a hazardous operation under even the best conditions. The movements affecting the fitting of the engine are the pendulum action of the engine on the crane sling, the rolling motion of the ship and the bouncing of the MEXEFLOTE. A 0.61-metre wave creates a physical limit for fitting an engine, but other movements may cause the physical limit to be reached in even smaller waves. The decision of the Coxswain whether to carry out the operation of fitting an engine must be considered as final. Pressure from Exercise Commanders to mount units and commence the disembarkation must not be allowed to influence the decision of the Coxswain.

c. **Side lifting and lowering of MEXEFLOTES.** The MEXEFLOTE Handbook instructs users that side lifts should be conducted only in calm sea conditions. It further states the limiting factor for lowering a raft as being Sea State 2 (the limit at which the engines can be fitted). Side lifts and lowering can however be achieved in unfavourable conditions when the LSD(A) can provide a lee. The decision to attempt side lifting or lowering of the MEXEFLOTE whilst the LSD(A) provides a lee, is one jointly taken by the CO, the XO, the I/C of the Port Operator Detachment and the MEXEFLOTE Coxswain.

d. **Weather refuge.** Unless weather forecasts are acted on (and MEXEFLOTEs are side lifted prior to the sea state precluding it), or due to a sudden deterioration in the weather conditions, it is possible they can be caught operating in unfavourable conditions. When the safe operating limits have been reached the MEXEFLOTE Coxswain has to find suitable shelter for his MEXEFLOTE and crew, options for which are:

(1) *Streaming.* The MEXEFLOTE streams astern of an LSD(A) or other large ship. It is the Coxswain's decision whether the crew stays on board the MEXEFLOTE.

(2) *Safe haven*. The MEXEFLOTE Coxswain identifies a safe berth, be it alongside in a harbour or port, moored to an Admiralty (or similar) mooring buoy or docked inside an LSD(A). He then secures the MEXEFLOTE until conditions abate.

05139. Crew

a. 17 Port and Maritime Regiment RLC hold MEXEFLOTE equipment and are also responsible for providing the crew.

b. The crew of six required to operate a powered raft consists of:

One Coxswain	(Cpl Mariner 2).
One Chief	(LCpl ME2).
One Mate	(LCpl Mariner 2).
One Engineer	(Pte ME3).
Two Seaman	(Pte Mariner 3).

c. When a MEXEFLOTE is carried by the LSD(A) the crew are embarked as part of the LSD(A) Detachment RLC.

d. For planning purposes one 38.42-metre MEXEFLOTE can carry:

1 x MBT or
15 x 0.75-tonne L/R or
18 x 0.5-tonne L/R (Wolf) or
12 x BVs or
12 x 0.75-tonne L/R with trailers or
6 x short wheelbase DROPS or
6 x long wheelbase DROPSs

05140. Communications

a. 17 Port and Maritime Regt RLC can provide VHF/HF radios for the raft if required.

b. Each Raft is scaled for 1 x BOWMAN Man Pack.

ANNEX 5A

GUIDANCE AND PROCEDURES FOR THE SAFE CONDUCT OF BOAT TRANSFERS TO RN/RFA SHIPS WHILST UNDERWAY

1.   The transfer of military and civilian personnel to RN/RFA vessels whilst underway is an essential element of operational capability that has become a subject of interest to the Maritime and Coastguard Agency (MCA) and the Marine Accident Investigation Branch (MAIB). Whilst RN activities, including the carriage of civilians on RN warships, are not regulated by the MCA, the transfer of civilian passengers from a civilian vessel to RN vessels and carriage of civilians using vessels contracted to the MOD that come under the Merchant Shipping Act (including SERCO boats), abut that jurisdiction and are, therefore, of interest. This interest has been raised by several incidents including a person falling overboard during an underway transfer with a civilian vessel that resulted in an RN and MAIB investigation. In addition, those operating in the Portsmouth area will be aware of limitations imposed by QHM Portsmouth on boat transfers whilst underway and making way which are linked to discussions with the MCA. It is therefore timely to provide additional guidance in order to demonstrate that the risks attendant upon RN underway transfers, particularly of civilians and when using commercial boats, are as low as reasonably practicable.

2.   This guidance is applicable worldwide and is designed to direct Command teams into identifying and allowing for the risks associated with different types of underway transfer involving transferees and coxswains of varying experience as early as practicable. It is also intended to be a reminder of some of the procedures already in place. **Where special instructions for the arrangement of boat transfers have been put in place by QHMs, they are to be used in place of instructions here. However, this guidance should still be consulted and elements used including the briefing process, the process for arranging DE&S staff transfers and the specific arrangements for the use of pilot/boarding ladders.**

3.   **Whilst primarily intended for underway transfers using a pilot/boarding ladder, this guidance should also be used as a framework to establish safe working practices for other forms of transfer where risk assessments and appropriate briefings do not already exist.** For transfers at buoys, at anchor or with boats when berthed, this framework will not normally be required, however, some conditions of wind and tidal stream may make adherence to elements of this framework appropriate at the discretion of the Commanding Officer. **It is recognised that this guidance is prescriptive, but it is important that an evolution that is conducted so regularly attracts consistent planning, preparation and execution.**

4.   Environmental conditions will clearly be a critical part of any risk assessment before and during an underway transfer. However, in order to provide a baseline of risk, the effects of environmental conditions form no part of this guidance and must be considered separately. The following types of transfer have therefore been categorised according to their own implicit risk in order that an appropriate level of assessment, planning, and mitigation can be applied to each:

a. **Cat A – transfers involving personnel inexperienced in underway transfers and unfamiliar boats:** This category includes the transfer of civilian (including the Press, affiliates, DE&S staff and contractors) or military personnel (including RN/RFA) whilst underway and/or making way, that have no experience of boat transfers, but are required to embark to support the moral component of operational capability, or for operational, maintenance or trials purposes. Also included in this category are any transfers where the coxswain is not experienced in underway transfers with warships, or the boat being used has not been the subject of a MOD safety study. As this category of transfer carries the highest predicted risk it requires the most preparation and assessment (See Para 14). **Important - This category of transfer should only be undertaken if all other methods of transfer have been ruled out as unreasonable in the operational context.**

b. **Cat B – Transfers involving personnel and boats teams with experience in underway transfers:** This category involves the transfer of military, DE&S, MOD approved (ie those cleared through the Fleet XO) and civilian personnel, including ship's personnel, visiting VIPs, FOST staff and training teams that have conducted the planned form of transfer previously and understand the associated risks (See Para 16 sub para a and sub para b). This category of transfer also requires the coxswain to hold the necessary qualifications to conduct the type of transfer and includes the use of RN/RFA RIBs, MIBS, LCVPs, LCUs and workboats. Transfers using SERCO boats in Devonport, Faslane, Portsmouth and the Kyle of Lochalsh fall into this category as they have been the subject of extensive safety case studies. Transfers to and from foreign warships are also included in this category (but see Para 15).

c. **Cat C – transfers involving MCA recognised seafarers using bespoke transfer boats:** The transfer of a designated Pilot, Harbourmaster or MCA surveyor that, through the nature of their work, has extensive experience of transfers to and from ships underway. This type of transfer must be with a bespoke boat used for pilot or other official transfers driven by an experienced coxswain (SERCO boats operating in Devonport, Faslane, Portsmouth and the Kyle of Lochalsh are included in this category when carrying the above personnel).

RESPONSIBILITIES

Commanding officer (CO)

5.   COs are to ensure that an assessment of the category of planned transfer is conducted as early as possible. Most transfers will be routine and will therefore fall into Cat B or C. However, a review of any additional hazards should be undertaken and added to the generic risk assessment which is already in place. For Cat A transfers COs are to nominate a Transfer Co-ordinator to ensure the appropriate assessments and exchange of information detailed in Para 14 and Para 30, Para 31, Para 32 and Para 33 below occur. For Cat B transfers, a Transfer Co-ordinator can be nominated if identified by a suitable and sufficient risk assessment. When there is a mix of experience amongst passengers, the Category is decided by the least experienced passenger.

a. **Embarking passengers:** The CO becomes responsible once the passenger has set foot on the brow or ladder. In the case of Cat A transfers the CO is to ensure that a briefing has been provided to passengers before the passengers disembark from the transfer boat, either by ensuring a briefing pack (Guidance is at Para 33) has been forwarded to all passengers and, whenever possible, by placing a member of his/her team onboard the transfer vessel (Referred to in Para 29 as the Responsible Person), who will be able to answer directly any questions or concerns.

b. Disembarking Passengers: The CO is responsible for the safe conduct of all passengers disembarking from his/her ship. This includes ensuring an assessment is made of the suitability of all passengers to undertake the transfer in terms of strength and mobility, particularly via pilot/boarding ladders and that all passengers requiring a brief receive one.

DE&S

6. **DG ships – ship visit safety guide Art 6.5** currently provides safety advice to DE&S personnel expecting to embark in RN/RFA ships. To provide more detailed guidance, DE&S line managers are being invited to ensure that the risks associated with any personnel they arrange to be transferred to RN/RFA ships via underway transfer have also been reviewed through the process at Para 32. This process includes forwarding details of boats they arrange (Using Para 31) and ensuring receipt of a briefing pack from the RN/RFA ship to be visited (Para 33). This process will require interaction between the Transfer Co-ordinator (RN/RFA) and the Visit Planning Officer (DE&S).

SERCO

7. SERCO masters are responsible for passengers up to the point that they step onto either the transfer ladder or brow. As part of their own assurance process, SERCO masters routinely ascertain the general suitability of their passengers for conducting underway transfers and will not allow any personnel they consider unable to conduct a certain type of transfer to continue. For Cat A transfers they will expect a member of the RN ship (or suitable person from ashore) as the nominated Responsible Person to provide an appropriate brief before the passengers embark upon the RN/RFA ship, or they will expect the passengers to have received an appropriate written briefing from the RN/RFA ship.

CIVILIAN PASSENGER TRANSFER VESSELS

8. Transfers with civilian passenger vessels are to be assumed to be Cat A unless there is assurance from the master or owner of the vessel that their boat and master/coxswain are competent and experienced in undertaking transfers with RN/RFA ships and their personnel are aware of the associated risks and procedures. COs of RN/RFA ships should also assume that they will need to ensure a nominated Responsible Person is made available to provide an appropriate brief before the passengers embark upon the RN/RFA ship, or provide a written brief in lieu.

ACTION BEFORE ALL TRANSFERS

9. Planned transfers are to be categorised as early as possible. For short notice transfers where no other practicable option exists, as much of the planning below is to be conducted in the time available to reduce the risk to As Low As Reasonably Practicable (ALARP). If a high risk remains it will be up to the CO or his delegated representative to accept the residual risk.

10. A briefing onboard the receiving ship is to be held for key personnel involved in the transfer including, as a minimum, the NO, OOW, CBM (Safety Officer) and I/C (LS(SEA)) of the evolution. Where the ship is conducting regular transfers, such as during OST, trials periods or within a WPP/Exercise Programme, the frequency of these briefings can be reduced to the minimum considered appropriate by the Command. Content should focus on, but not be limited to:

a. The number, experience and mobility of passengers to be transferred.

b. The type of boat being used and the resulting requirement for ropes (including consideration of securing points for the head rope or painter to ensure an appropriate lead) and fenders.

c. The designated side for transfer.

d. Any navigational/time constraints.

e. The expected weather.

f. Required clothing and lifesaving equipment for passengers and ship's team.

g. Type of ladder to be used and the associated safety requirements at the transfer point including use of manropes, rescue strop and hook lines.

h. Actions required in the event of a person falling overboard, including options for immediate observation and rapid deployment of swimmer or seaboat if required.

11. The brief need not be stand-alone and may be part of another planned brief such as the leaving/entering harbour brief.

12. When considering whether environmental conditions are suitable for the transfer, account must be taken of height of eye. Recent incidents have highlighted the considerable difference in perception of wave heights and swell when observed from differing heights of eye.

GUIDANCE ON THE ASSESSMENT OF SUITABILITY FOR TRANSFER

13. Much like the process of assessing the suitability of airline passengers to occupy emergency exit seats, individuals should be asked if they consider they have the strength and mobility to conduct a specific type of transfer. This question should be asked as early in the transfer process as possible, but the ultimate decision lies with the CO of the RN/RFA ship or coxswain of the transfer boat on the day of the transfer and if they consider a person is not physically capable or mobile enough they are not to be transferred.

ACTION BEFORE CAT A TRANSFERS

14. For Cat A transfers, to assist the risk assessment process, Para 30 is to be completed as far in advance of the transfer as practicable. The results of the assessment are to be briefed as part of the on-board briefing at Para 10. If early assessment is not operationally possible, an assessment using as much of the guidance at Para 30 as possible is to be conducted on VHF before the boat comes alongside and the details passed to those involved in the safe conduct of the transfer. Para 32 is to be used if DE&S or DE&S sponsored contractors are expected. If the boat company or the coxswain has not conducted a transfer with the class of warship before, Para 33 is to be completed by the RN/RFA ship and forwarded to the boat company before the transfer. The coxswain of the boat conducting the transfer is to be invited to confirm on VHF that he is aware of the intentions for the transfer, including the fendering and securing arrangements and the actions to be taken in an emergency.

a. For embarkation to RN/RFA vessels: Civilian passengers or non-MOD sponsored personnel are to be accompanied by one or more Service/RFA personnel experienced in the type of transfer (Responsible Person). The Responsible Person is to ensure passengers are briefed in accordance with the guidance at Para 29 before they set foot on the pilot/boarding ladder.

b. For disembarkation from RN/RFA vessels: A brief based on Para 29 is to be given by the Safety Officer with the person in charge of the transfer and onboard hosts in attendance in a benign environment where the briefing can be clearly understood. Passengers should then be invited to view the transfer position and ask questions if required.

Notes:

1.   *Where passenger transfers are arranged through Regional Officers, Attaches, Liaison Officers or MLS, ship's teams should consider obtaining as much information as possible towards the completion of Para 29 via them, noting that MLS has no contractual obligation to provide the information.*

2.   *This may also be forwarded via Regional Officers, Attaches, Liaison Officers or MLS.*

ACTION BEFORE CAT B TRANSFERS

15.   Where it is assessed that a Cat B transfer is programmed, the process at the Annexes and a formal assessment prior to transfer are required if any hazards remain a risk on top of the generic risk assessment (conducting a transfer with a foreign warship whose routines and capabilities are unknown is an instance where a formal assessment should be considered). However, existing instructions should be followed and the guidance at Para 10 used.

16.   Nothing in this guidance replaces the induction, safety briefings or training currently provided by RN/RFA/MOD organisations to prepare their staff for underway transfers.

a. For embarkation to RN/RFA vessels: Implicit within Cat B transfers is an expectation that the passengers are content in all respects, are fit and able, and consider themselves sufficiently experienced to conduct the transfer and that they have, either on this occasion or in the past 12 months, been briefed using similar guidance to that at Para 29. Furthermore, they fully understand the proposed sequence of events including the correct use of pilot/boarding ladder (or brow in the case of Swath vessels), appropriate dress, lifejacket policy and the optional use of the Marine Rescue Strop. For DE&S personnel the minimum requirement to fulfil Cat B status is to have attended the one-day sea survival course and previously conducted five or more underway transfers of the type planned.

b. For disembarkation from RN/RFA vessels: The Safety Officer for the evolution is to ensure the passengers fulfil the requirements of sub para a above.

ACTION BEFORE CAT C TRANSFERS

17.   Where it is assessed that a Cat C transfer is programmed, Para 29 to Para 33 need not be completed. However, guidance at Para 10 should be followed with respect to an onboard briefing. Notwithstanding the relaxation from using Para 29 to Para 33, both parties are to be absolutely clear about the intentions for the transfer and the safety issues involved whilst the boat is en route or in the waiting station, including recovery options should a person fall overboard. Should an individual for transfer request a briefing, this should be arranged either by VHF or by a member of the RN/RFA ship transferring to the boat.

ACTION DURING ALL TRANSFERS

18. During all transfers underway appropriate lifejackets are to be worn. The life-jacket is to be of an automatic operating type and preferably be SOLAS compliant, if available. If SOLAS compliant life-jackets are not available the Hazardous Duty type may be used. Use of lifejackets during other transfers (i.e. those using accommodation ladders whilst at anchor or at a buoy) is to be considered if the conditions dictate.

19. Early preparation of the transfer position is important and equipment IAW Chapter 3 para 03069 is to be correctly rigged before the boat makes its approach. If fenders are required, **they must not be tended by hand,** however they may be raised clear upon request of the transfer craft.

ACTION DURING TRANSFERS USING A PILOT/BOARDING LADDER

20. For Cat A & B transfers using a pilot/boarding ladder, the Marine Rescue Strop is to be offered IAW Chapter 3 para 03069. Use of the strop is to be considered as part of the risk assessment for those passengers, civilian or military that have no experience of boat transfers or, due to their physical strength or mobility, warrant this level of safety.

21. Chapter 3 para 03069 clearly states that the pilot/boarding ladder must never be placed within the guard rail/garden wall of the passenger boat. Neither should it be laid on the foredeck of pilot vessels or become trapped between the two vessels. Shortened pilot/ boarding ladders have been introduced into service and these are for use by passengers as well as pilots. If required the length of the shortened ladder is to be further adjusted, using a 1 Tonne SWL 0.5M round sling, so that it remains clear of the gunwale of the transfer vessel. Careful consideration also needs to be given to ensuring there is a safe area on boats for passengers to embark to/from and if there is a garden wall or the transfer vessel is large, sufficient fendering can be applied to prevent damage to either vessel or any risk of crushing of personnel between the two vessels.

22. An extra line/hook rope used for the recovery of the ladder **must not** be rigged or attached to the bottom of the ladder until all passengers have embarked or disembarked.

23. Personnel should never attempt to use a pilot/boarding ladder encumbered by any form of bag, laptop, etc. These items should be transferred separately using a hook rope.

24. A lifebuoy with man overboard marker is to be made available and at night the transfer area is to be illuminated.

25. The ladder is not to be used by personnel until all equipment is rigged correctly and the transfer craft is secured alongside. Under no circumstances should personnel be on the ladder while craft approaches. Only one person is allowed on the ladder at a time during the transfer.

26. Manropes must be provided.

ADMINISTRATION

27. A Cat A boat transfer scenario will be incorporated into the SARC 3 process for new build ships or those coming out of refit, and for those generating a Cat A serial will be included and assessed during OST and DCT.

28. During MASC, FOST staff will review records of Cat A transfers retained within the Seamanship Data Book.

29.   Boat Transfer Standard Briefing Form for Passengers (when completed, this page is to be retained within the Seamanship data Book for one year after the transfer.

This brief is to be given by the Safety Officer for the transfer or the Responsible Person in the transfer boat for Cat A transfers. On completion of the briefing process the Safety Officer/Responsible person is to:
a. Confirm with all transferees that they understand what is required of them and that they are content to carry on with transfer.
b. Sign the form.
The Safety/Responsible officer is to make a judgement as to whether the passengers are physically capable of conducting the transfer. Those not considered capable are not to be transferred.
Once all passengers are briefed and have agreed to transfer, the coxswain of the transfer boat and the bridge of the RN/RFA ship are to be informed and this form passed to/retained in the RN/RFA ship.

Date: **Time:** **Name of Transfer Boat:** **Transfer position:** **Method of Dis/Embarkation:**	

Dress:
    a. Foul Weather Clothing.
 	
    b. Footwear.
 	
    c. Personal baggage/shoulder bags (must **not** be carried/worn during pilot/boarding ladder transfers).
 	
    d. Gloves (remove).
 	
    e. Rings (remove or tape over if using a pilot/boarding ladder).	

Lifejacket:
    a. Type of life-jacket.
       What it is designed to do.
 	
    b. Demonstration of correct fitting.
Belt to be correctly tightened.
 	
    c. Understand how it works.
 	
    d. Red tell tales.
How to operate it/set it off,
Locate operating beaded handle as soon as lifejacket is fitted.
Demonstrate top up facility.	

Ladder:
    a. Description of ladder including manropes and their use.
 	
    b. Purpose of Marine Rescue strop and its use.
 	
    c. Procedures to be undertaken to safely ascend/descend the **ladder**.
 	
    d. Safe embarkation/disembarkation from passenger craft, (follow instructions from Safety Officer).
 	
    e. Position of ladder bottom relative to ship's side and boat.
	Signature of Safety Officer/Responsible Person

Any Questions? *Once all passengers are briefed, the bridges of the two vessels are to be informed and this form handed to, or retained by, the Safety Officer on the RN/RFA ship.*	

30. Boat Transfer Assessment Form

The Transfer Co-ordinator is to ensure an assessment of the possible risks associated with Cat A passenger transfers is completed as far ahead of the transfer as possible. This form is provided as a guide to the questions to be asked. A completed assessment for each Cat A transfer is to be retained onboard the RN/RFA ship (multiple transfers using the same boat can be entered on one form as long as dates/times are recorded).
IT IS TO BE USED IN ASSOCIATION WITH THE GENERIC RISK ASSESSMENT.

Date: **Time:**
Category of Transfer: **Transfer position on ship:**
Method of dis/embarkation:

Type of Boat for transfer:

    a. Length, beam and displacement, max speed (obtain a picture if possible).

    b. Requirement for fenders – size, number, position.

    c. Securing positions, likely lead, type of rope used, whether boat or ship's head rope will be supplied.

    d. Manning level of boat and whether coxswain has transferred to this type of vessel before? How long has the coxswain been driving?

    e. Transfer position, size and shape of transfer area and possible obstructions (Is there a garden wall/guardrail, is it a flat open deck?)

    f. Ability and method of recovering a person from the water.

Location for transfer:

    a. Consider likely prevailing weather, shelter and effect on a delay in the transfer to available shelter.

    b. Consider any navigational constraints including the effect of tidal stream.

General:

    a. VHF channel to be used.

    b. Preferred speed for transfer.

    c. RN/RFA vessel actions in the event of a person falling overboard.

31.   DE&S Arranged Boat Transfer Details

> *The DE&S Visit Planning Officer will use this form to give RN/RFA Ships details of boats they have booked/contracted to conduct transfers of their personnel.*

Date: **Time:**
Category of Transfer: **Transfer position on ship:**
Method of dis/embarkation:

Type of Boat for transfer:

    a.   Length, beam and displacement, max speed (obtain a picture if possible).

    b.   Requirement for fenders – size, number, position.

    c.   Securing positions, likely lead, type of rope used, whether boat or ship's head rope will be supplied.

    d.   Manning level of boat and whether coxswain has transferred to this type of vessel before? How long has the coxswain been driving?

    e.   Transfer position, size and shape of transfer area and possible obstructions (Is there a garden wall/guardrail, is it a flat open deck?)

    f.   Experience of visitors in undertaking underway transfers.

    g.   Ability and method of recovering a person from the water.

    h.   Likely number of crew to be embarked.

32. DES Boat Transfer Safe System of Work (see Note 1)

This safe system of work will be used by DES line managers whose non-seafaring personnel are involved in underway boat transfers to RN vessels while on official detached duty activities. This system of work is also to be forwarded to contractors employed by MoD to ensure their line managers have the opportunity to use it.

Boat transfers, can be extremely dangerous. No detached duty involving an underway transfer should take place without prior line management approval.

DE&S personnel conducting an underway transfer will be considered to be Cat A unless they hold a current sea survival training certificate and have conducted 5 or more transfers of the planned type before. (Contractors are not expected to hold this certification/experience, but must make this clear before the transfer in order that an immersion suit can be made available if the sea temperature is 15ºC or less).

Activity	Description	Activity Owner	Output
1	Requirement for Platform visit identified.	N/A	Request to visit platform
2	Confirm/decline visit pending health and safety/risk analysis.	Line Manager	Provisional visit approval.
3	Nominate Visit Planning Officer	Line Manager	Visit Planning Officer
4	Forward details of visitors and nominated transfer boat to RN vessel and request ship details (See Annex B2.)	Visit planning Officer	Visit Request Form
5	*Nominate a Transfer Co-ordinator.*	*CO of RN Vessel*	*Point of Contact onboard vessel.*
6	*Ensure hazards are identified, ensure an initial risk assessment and appropriate management actions are taken against risks identified and forward to Visit Planning Officer.*	*Transfer Co-ordinator*	*Briefing pack sent from Ship to Visit Planning officer*
7	Agree that all risks are being adequately mitigated to an acceptable level to allow the visit to continue.	Line Manager	Final Visit Approval
8	Nominate a Visit Lead Person for health and safety related decisions associated with the detached duty and underway transfer.	Line Manager	Visit Lead Person
9	Ensure risk management plan and list of those holding Sea Survival Certificates is forwarded to the ship to be visited.	Visit Planning Officer	ADVIS signal
10	Communicate health and safety risks and recommended mitigating action to all MoD personnel and contractors involved in the activity.	Visit Lead Person	Risk Management Plan
11	Visit the ship. Visit Lead Person to monitor and manage health and safety risks and issues for the duration of the visit. Provide feedback to DE&S.	Visit Lead Person	N/A

Notes:

1. *Drawn from the UWWIPT Business Procedure dated 20 Dec 05.*

2. *Actions in bold/italics refer to those undertaken by the ship to be visited. All other actions refer to those actions taken by DE&S.*

3. *Hazards include: Trips, Slips, falls and crushing, excessive vessel movement, possible back injury, enclosed spaces, vessel collision, grounding, sinking, fire, shock and drowning.*

33. Ship Transfer Briefing Pack.

A briefing pack/email is to be forwarded by RN/RFA ships for Cat A transfers to passengers that will not be briefed by a 'Responsible Person' and to boat coxswains for civilian vessels for which there has been no previous risk assessment/safety study. The following guide is designed to assist ships in producing this information. It is important that the information is forwarded for Cat A visits by DES staff and contractors as it forms part of their risk assessment process. The briefing should be amended depending on the target audience.

Dress:

a. Describe preferred dress including robust, slip free footwear, trousers for females, the need to take off gloves and remove or tape rings.

b. Describe the need to hand personal baggage for separate transfer and how that transfer will be achieved.

c. Remind passengers of the need to consider warm clothes and clothes over which SE equipment can easily be worn.

SE Equipment and Safety:

a. Explain that a lifejacket will need to be worn, the type of life-jacket, what it is designed to do and either how it works or that its use will be explained during a briefing.

b. Explain whether immersion suits may need to be worn and what this entails.

c. Explain the ship's man overboard procedures, what passengers should do in the event of entering the water and what to expect in terms of methods of recovery, and the role the transfer vessel is expected to play.

d. An indication of the briefing process (whether a member of the ship's company will transfer to the boat) and need for the transferee to agree to the transfer given the type of transfer and their physical abilities.

e. Explain the use of the Marine Rescue Strop and manropes if applicable.

RN/RFA Vessel Transfer Position/Ship Characteristics:

a. Forward a diagram of the ladder to be used.

b. Forward pictures of the transfer position rigged and ready for transfer from the deck and from sea level.

c. Forward pictures from sea level of rope and fender securing positions.

d. Forward details of securing and fendering arrangements and ascertain which vessel will be providing a headrope/painter.

e. Forward details about length, beam and displacement of RN/RFA ship and preferred speed for transfer

ANNEX 5B

BOAT SAFETY BRIEF FOR ALL PASSENGERS

The following brief must be given to all civilian and military personnel embarked in small boats.

All Coxswains must:

a.   Ensure all passengers are aware of the correct operation of their lifejacket and that they are wearing it correctly.

b.   Brief passengers on the conduct of the serial/task.

   (1) Duration.

   (2) Likely weather and sea conditions.

c.   Identify non-swimmers and weak swimmers and position them closest to the coxswain.

d.   Identify any passengers with medical problems/complaints and make an assessment as to whether the transit will aggravate and such complaints. **If this is judged to be the case they must not embark.**

e.   Brief passengers on the correct way to embark the craft and point out all the potential hazards.

f.   Ensure all passengers are seated correctly and remain seated at all times until directed otherwise by the coxswain. Passengers should remain physically flexible and ride the motion of the craft. The majority of the weight should be held on the legs and not the seat. Passengers should be invited to report any discomforts or injury to the coxswain.

g.   Brief passengers that should anyone experience problems or difficulties they are to make the coxswain aware immediately.

h.   Brief passengers on the Man Overboard Drill.

i.   Brief passengers on the Capsize Drill.

j.   Ask passengers if there are any final questions.

Note.   *The coxswain must take into account the age, physical condition and experience of passengers and the prevailing weather conditions and adjust speed accordingly in order to ensure a safe passage.*

ANNEX 5C

COXSWAIN'S OPERATIONAL BOAT SAFETY BRIEF

1.   **Briefing for boat operations.**
For all boat operations, the coxswain should ensure that he/she is fully briefed on the nature and purpose of the mission before leaving the ship. The brief should be tailored to the complexity of the mission noting that, with fitting as standard of the Xeres communications/ navigation system in most RIBs, boats often operate well beyond the visibility of the mother ship. Briefings can be divided as follows:

a. **Emergency** – When the boat is required as a Fast Rescue Craft, Helicopter Crash Boat or for other emergency tasking – this will be a simple verbal brief from the authorising officer/officer in charge of the lowering party.

b. **Planned** – Depending on the mission, the brief may be given by the Officer of the Watch, Navigating Officer or, if authorised, the Officer of the Day. It should include a weather forecast and tidal data, and should also highlight any navigational hazards. Particular care should be taken at night or in conditions of poor visibility. A standard boat's briefing format is provided at Annex 5B and should be used prior to all planned boat operations. It is to be authorised by the Commanding Officer or the XO or a formally delegated officer. In cases of recreational use or simple passenger transfer, when the mother ship is at anchor or alongside, the guidance at **BRd 9467 Fleet Administrative General Orders (FLAGOs) Chapter 8 paras 0801 to 0803** remains extant.

2.   **Limit exposure to vibration and shock**

a. **Safety**

(1) The coxswain is responsible for the safety of his boat, crew and passengers at all times, this includes minimising their exposure to shock and vibration.

(2) Personnel are to sit in designated seats. If this means sitting fore and aft then passengers are to limit the extent to which they twist to a minimum necessary to anticipate the movement of the boat.

(3) Personnel are to use toe straps (if fitted) whilst in transit.

(4) Personnel are to use hand/safety rails.

(5) The coxswain is to give a verbal warning prior to any alteration in course or speed.

(6) Passengers are to be encouraged by the coxswain to comment if they feel they are being subjected to unnecessary or excessive exposure to shock and vibration.

(7) All personnel are to be aware of the actions to be taken in the event of an emergency ie MOB, Fire etc.

(8) Passengers and crew are to be specifically asked after every boat journey whether they have suffered any injuries. Any reported injuries are to be fully recorded as part of the ongoing data capture process.

b. **Actions to reduce vibration and shock**

(1) Boats are subject to slamming if heading directly into the sea which places stress on a boat's structure and on the bodies of those in the boat.

(2) To reduce these stresses, speed and courses are to be carefully chosen. The aim is to ride comfortably over the waves and not to slam into the face of the waves. Speed and course should be adjusted, including an increase in speed if necessary, to achieve this. Where it is not possible to prevent slamming into the face of waves, the impact is to be minimised and consideration given to reducing or terminating the sortie if the operational/safety situation allows.

(3) A zig-zag course at 45° to the prevailing direction of the sea if most often the most comfortable.

(4) Passengers and crew are to adopt a posture whereby they raise and lower their body as they ride the sea to reduce shock/vibration to body in a similar way to balancing in the 'brace position'.

c. Operational boat safety brief

Date		
Period		
Serial		
SR		SS		MR		MS	

Weather		
	Actual	Forecast
Sea State		
Wind		
Visibility		
SS Temp		
Air Temp		
Wind Chill		
Survival Time		

Sea Boat	PORT	STBD
Crew Coxswain Bowman		
Dress		
Passengers		
Dress		

d. **Operational Boat Safety Brief cont:**

Comms	VHF Ch	
	Bowman	
	Harris Ch	
	Xeres	
Lost Comms		

Operating Areas	
Danger Areas	
Navigation Hazards	

Other Boat/ Flying Ops	

Conduct Vessel details Location Aims of mission Constraints ROE		

Timings		
	PORT	STBD
Away Sea boats		
Depart		
Recover		

Future Tasking

ANNEX 5D

PACIFIC 22 AND PACIFIC 24 RIB COLLAPSIBLE CRADLE ASSEMBLY INSTRUCTIONS

1.   **Introduction.** The collapsible cradle comprises a stern support frame and a bow support frame; both frames are heavy and weigh approximately 110kg each when stowed in their individual stowage bags. The cradle will require a minimum of two people to carry out the assembly procedure and a crane to re-stow the cradle components into the stowage bags. All personnel must wear appropriate personal protection equipment, ie. steel toe cap boots, safety helmets etc. On assembly, torque tighten all bolts to 17NM (for M12 threads) or 30NM (for M16 threads), as appropriate.

Fig 5D-1. Pacific 22 and Pacific 24 collapsible cradle complete

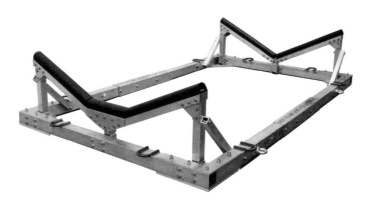

2.   **Assembly instructions**

    a. Open the stowage bag apertures at the top of the bag to reveal the lifting eyes (painted red).

    b. Using a suitable lifting appliance, rig the strops between the lifting appliance and the lifting eyes.

    c. Raise the frame to an upright position allowing enough space between the frame and the ground to remove the bag.

    d. Undo the bag buckles and pull the bag VELCRO® brand fasteners open then use the handles at the side of the bag to lower the bag as shown in Fig 5D-2.

Fig 5D-2. Stowage bag and lifting eyes

e. Lay the stern support frame out flat as shown in Fig 5D-3.

Fig 5d-3. Support frame laid out flat

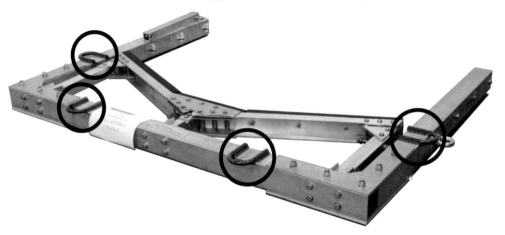

Note.   *The red tie down points shown circled on the framework must not be used for lifting the vessel in the cradle.*

f. Remove each transit bolt and ensure that the bolts and washers are retained.

Fig 5d-4. Bolts and washers being removed

g. Fit the support struts as shown circled and torque tighten the bolts to 30 NM.

Fig 5D-5. Support struts shown fitted

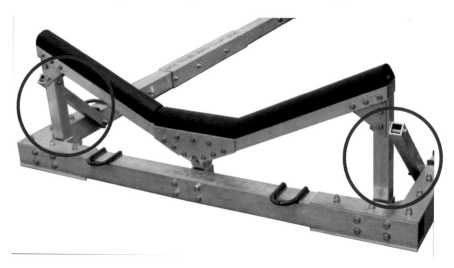

h.   Position the bow support frame in close proximity to the stern frame. Follow the same sequence as carried out for the stern frame to assemble the bow frame.

Fig 5D-6. Support frame in close proximity to the stern frame

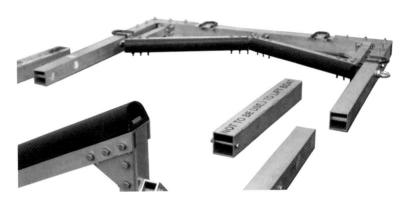

i.   Fit the two joint channels to the stern frame securing at the position marked for either the Pacific 22 or the Pacific 24, as appropriate. Torque tighten the bolts to 30 NM.

Fig 5D-7. Joint channels being fitted to the stern frame

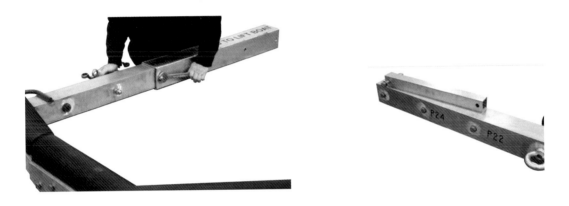

j.   Ensure all bolts are securely torque tightened (17NM for M12 threads and 30NM for M16 threads throughout the assembly. This completes the assembly procedure.

Fig 5D-8. Fully assembled cradle

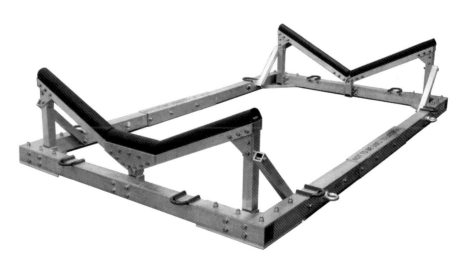

3.   **Dismantle procedure**

a.   To dismantle the cradle is a complete reversal of the assembly procedure.

CAUTION

When refitting the transit bolts, ensure that the washers are refitted (either side of the box section for the frame upright) and that each bolt protrudes into the box section of the bow and stern frames as indicated by the circled arrow below by a minimum of 25mm.

Fig 5D-9. Dismantling the cradle

b.   Rig the strops between the lifting appliance and the lifting eyes.

c.   Using a suitable lifting appliance raise the support frame to an upright position, allowing enough space between the frame and the deck to replace the bag.

d.   Undo the bag buckles and pull the bag VELCRO® brand fasteners open.

e.   Place the bag beneath the frame and use the handles at the side of the bag to slide the bag on and over the frame from the bottom of the frame.

f.   The frame must be stowed upright and securely lashed. Once the strops have been removed close the top of the bag (including the apertures for the lifting eyes) and reconnect the bag buckles.

Fig 5D-10. Re-stowing the bow and support frames in their bags

CHAPTER 6

ROYAL NAVAL WATER SAFETY

CONTENTS

Note. *Royal Fleet Auxiliary Sea Survival (Water Safety) Information is contained in BR 875 (5) Part 2 RFA* **SOLAS** *Training Manual.*

CHAPTER 6

ROYAL NAVAL WATER SAFETY

06001. Historical background

a.   During WWII, most Royal Navy shipwreck survivors were rescued within 12 hours of their ship sinking and in only a very few cases was rescue delayed for over 24 hours. Despite this timely response the death rate was extraordinarily high. It is estimated that two-thirds of all Royal Navy fatalities at sea abandoned ship successfully only to die in the water or on Carley Floats before rescue. The sinking of the aircraft carrier HMS Glorious is a frightening example of this point. Of the 1,000 or more ship's company who, it is estimated, abandoned ship, only about 400 were able to board the rafts and of these only 36 survived the two-and-a-half winter days in the North Sea before being rescued in a very poor physical condition. There were many contributing reasons for the high fatality rate but undoubtedly the major blame must lie with the life-saving equipment of the time. The equipment did little to reduce the excessive loss of body heat on immersion, even in subtropical waters, and when a survivor slowly became unconscious the flotation aid provided did not keep the wearer's mouth and nose above water. Analysis has shown without doubt that the greatest threat to shipwrecked survivors is the cold. The incidents on the graph (Fig 6-1) indicate the distribution of probable survival times for unprotected casualties immersed in water of various temperatures. The curve indicates the estimated time for which only 50% of unprotected casualties may expect to survive immersion at given water temperatures.

Fig 6-1. Curve of estimated time against water temperature for which 50% of unprotected casualties may expect to survive immersion

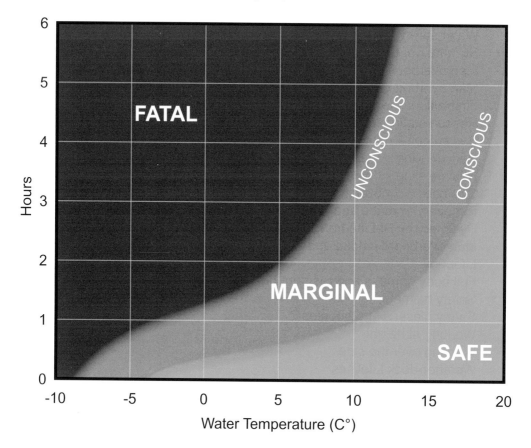

b.   Modern life-saving equipment has been designed specifically to counteract dangerous heat-loss from the body. Additionally, in the event of consciousness being lost, it should give the individual the best possible protection against drowning. Good knowledge of life-saving equipment, especially personal equipment, is essential in order to survive the rigours of a cold sea. Accounts of recent loss of life at sea, where modern equipment was available to men who did not know how to use it to the best advantage, reveal the importance of such knowledge and training. However remote the possibility of disaster from fire, collision, stranding or enemy action, seafarers should always be prepared to abandon ship when necessary and take to the liferafts. Every seafarer should also be prepared to rescue survivors from another ship. Preparation for such eventualities includes the provision of life-saving equipment and training in its use, but the best equipment is of little value without good organisation and high standards of discipline, leadership and morale. The chance of survival after shipwreck is better today than at any time in the past. A General Service lifejacket is designed to enable the wearer to jump safely into the sea from a considerable height and to keep his or her mouth and nose out of the water should they be unconscious or asleep. A survival suit keeps them dry, and an enclosed liferaft protects them from the elements and provides them with food and water until rescued. The prospects of rescue from liferafts have also been improved by radio beacons and other aids to detection. The following paragraphs give details of the water safety and general safety equipment used in the Royal Navy.

06002. The general service lifejacket Mk 4

a. **Introduction**. A General Service Lifejacket (GSLJ) (Fig 6-2), is supplied to every person in a ship; it should be carried at Emergency Stations, Action Stations and when the ship is in Defence Watches in wartime.

b. **Description**. The GSLJ is carried ready for use in a pouch attached to a waist belt. This is secured round the wearer's waist by an interlocking nylon buckle. There is a plastic nametag in a clear-view pocket on the pouch for showing the holder's name and official number (written in pencil). **This is the only method authorised for marking the GSLJ**. The lifejacket is used by removing it from its pouch (see Fig 6-2a), passing the head through the neck aperture of the stole and then adjusting the belt to a snug fit around the waist. Incorporated in the construction of the lifejacket is a hood with a transparent visor, a handling harness, a whistle, reflective patches, a lifeline and toggle and an alternative light fitting position on the hood.

c. **Operation**. The lifejacket has to be orally inflated by means of the oral inflation tube. Depression of the mouthpiece on the oral inflation tube when blowing opens a valve, which allows air to enter the stole. The valve is spring-loaded to the closed position and can also be turned to a locked closed position to prevent inadvertent deflation. If the valve cannot be depressed, rotate it one-half turn anti clockwise and then depress. **The lifejacket is only to be used fully inflated.**

Fig 6-2. General service lifejacket Mk 4

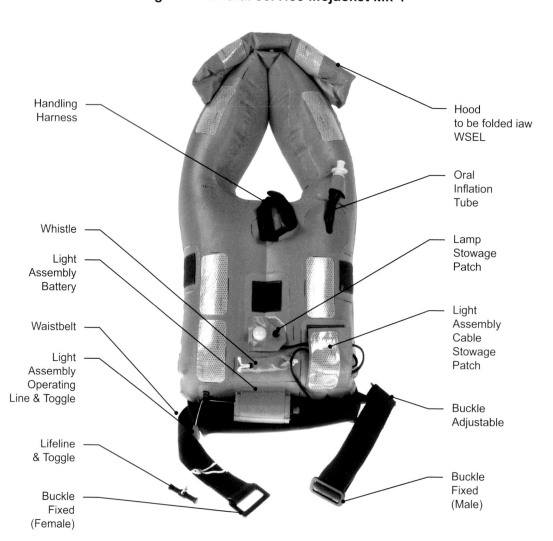

Fig 6-2a. Donning the general service lifejacket

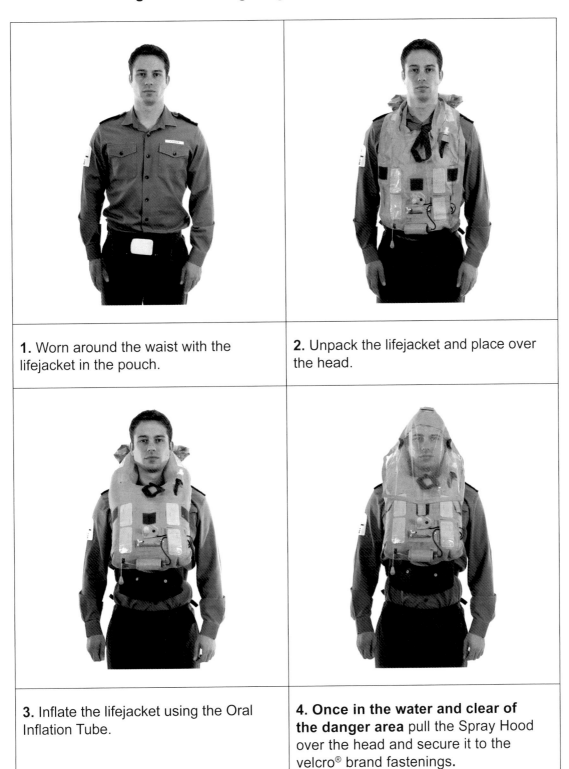

1. Worn around the waist with the lifejacket in the pouch.	**2.** Unpack the lifejacket and place over the head.
3. Inflate the lifejacket using the Oral Inflation Tube.	**4. Once in the water and clear of the danger area** pull the Spray Hood over the head and secure it to the velcro® brand fastenings.

d.   **Maintenance**. The GSLJ must be maintained and inspected in accordance with the schedules laid down in the Water Safety Equipment Log.

e.   **Allowances.** In addition to the GSLJs issued on personal loan to the ship's company, a further number equal to 50% of the ship's company are individually heat-sealed in plastic bags and stowed in Emergency Lifejacket boxes fitted on the upper deck adjacent to exits, escape and evacuation routes. A further quantity equal to 5% of the ship's company is held as spares by the Chief Bosun's Mate. In circumstances such as liberty men returning by boat, the OOW may authorise Emergency Lifejacket boxes to be placed in the boat. Coxswains of boats are to inform the ship's Water Safety Equipment Supervisor if any of the boxes have been opened. There is no separate allowance of GSLJs for boats.

f.   **Emergency lifejacket stowages**

(1)   As already mentioned, a quantity of GSLJs equal to 50% of the ship's company are carried in Emergency Lifejacket boxes fitted on the upper deck adjacent to exits, escape and evacuation routes. Where possible the boxes should be 'float-free'. The stowage boxes come in two sizes:

(A)   Emergency lifejacket box (large) stores no 4220-99-520-5493 for 25 jackets maximum.

(B)   Emergency lifejacket box (small) stores no 4220-99-758-2407 for ten jackets maximum.

(2)   Boxes must be clearly marked in red 25/50mm lettering **EMERGENCY LIFEJACKETS** stickers. The number of lifejackets contained in the box (10-25 maximum) is to be stencilled below in black lettering. Additionally, to assist in identification for maintenance purposes the boxes are marked with a local letter. To prevent tampering, the clips of each box cover are to be sealed with anti tamper tallies, which breaks easily on opening the box.

Fig 6-3. Weather-deck emergency lifejacket stowage (examples)

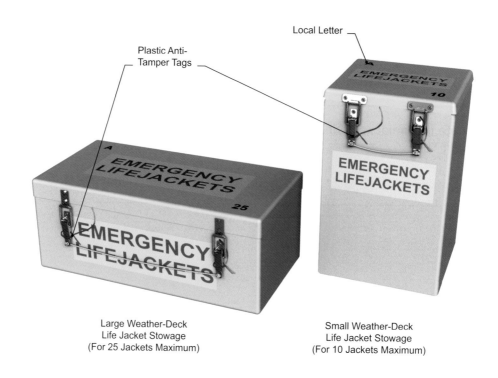

Local Letter

Plastic Anti-
Tamper Tags

Large Weather-Deck
Life Jacket Stowage
(For 25 Jackets Maximum)

Small Weather-Deck
Life Jacket Stowage
(For 10 Jackets Maximum)

06003. Hazardous duty lifejacket Mk 3

a. **Introduction**. The hazardous duty lifejacket (HDLJ) (Fig 6-4) is issued as and when required for use by personnel whose duty or work puts them at risk on the weather decks and in boats. It must not be worn in aircraft. A limited quantity is supplied to each ship, and these are used by personnel working in hazardous situations. The wearer is limited to 22.5kg of additional equipment.

b. **Description**. The lifejacket is contained in a blue halter-type valise and is fitted with an adjustable belt by which it is secured to the body of the wearer. It has a buoyancy of 192N. Incorporated in the construction of the lifejacket is a hood with a transparent visor which gives good spray protection to the face and is provided with effective location aids, a whistle, reflective patches, an LJ2 lamp assembly with alternative fitting positions for the light on the hood. The lifejacket is also fitted with a lifeline with toggle. On inflation of the jacket, the battery is activated automatically. It can be switched off when not required. Scarlet thread telltale ties are fastened through eyelets to both sides of the valise. These ties act as a guide to the user: if one or both of the threads are broken it must be assumed that the jacket has been inadvertently inflated and it must be returned to the Water Safety Equipment (WSE) rating for servicing. **It must not be used in this condition.**

Fig 6-4. Hazardous duty lifejacket Mk 3

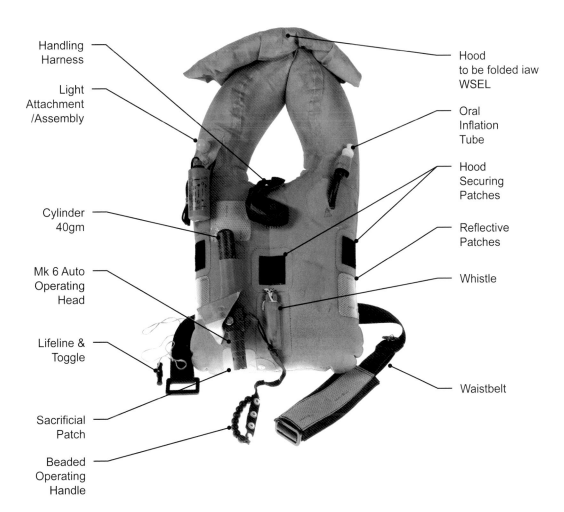

Handling Harness

Light Attachment /Assembly

Cylinder 40gm

Mk 6 Auto Operating Head

Lifeline & Toggle

Sacrificial Patch

Beaded Operating Handle

Hood to be folded iaw WSEL

Oral Inflation Tube

Hood Securing Patches

Reflective Patches

Whistle

Waistbelt

Fig 6-4a. Donning the hazardous duty lifejacket

1. Insert head through the neck aperture. Fasten the belt at the back and adjust to achieve a comfortable fit.	**2.** Pull down on the Beaded Operating Handle behind the valise to inflate.	**3. Once in the water and clear of the danger area** pull the Spray Hood over the head and secure to the VELCRO® brand fastenings.

c.　**Operation.** The lifejacket is designed to be inflated manually or automatically by CO_2 on immersion in water. The gas is contained in a replaceable cylinder attached to an operating head, which is an integral part of the lifejacket. On immersion in water when fitted with an automatic operating head the lifejacket will automatically inflate and burst from the valise within a few seconds and without any action by the wearer. However, the automatic mode of operation should be treated as a back-up system in case the wearer is unconscious or unable to inflate the lifejacket on immersion. A person falling overboard should, on entering the water, give a sharp downward pull on the beaded operating handle; if the manual and the automatic mechanism fail to function, the oral inflation tube should be used. Topping-up can be achieved with the oral inflation tube. **Orally inflated lifejackets should not subsequently be inflated by gas.**

d.　**Maintenance.** HDLJs must be maintained and inspected by the Water Safety Equipment Maintainer in accordance with the schedules laid down in the Water Safety Equipment Log.

e.　**Stowage.** HDLJs should only be stowed in the recently re-designed patternised locker NSN 4220-99-531-6921; these have the capacity for six lifejackets and should be sighted within the ship, near to weather deck accesses. Manual lifejacket lockers should be sighted within the ship near to weather deck accesses leading to boat bays for use by the boats crew in an emergency.

f.　**Allowances.** Allowances vary by class of ship but generally as follows: Minor War Vessels ten to 16; Frigates and Destroyers 57 to 67; Large Warships 67 to 102. The precise number, which appears on the ship's Consolidated Allowance List, is decided by the Ship's Platform Section in consultation with Navy Command.

g.   **Cold weather limitations**. The operating head does not quite meet the RN criteria for operation at the lower end of the temperature scale. Below minus 20°C, including wind chill factor, automatic inflation takes longer than the stipulated five seconds if the lifejacket has been exposed for long periods. In icy conditions, or if the temperature equivalent is minus 20°C or below, fresh lifejackets should be drawn when the watch changes over. In these conditions when not in use the lifejackets should be stowed between decks.

06004. Assault troop lifejacket Mk 4

a.   **Introduction**. The Assault Troop Lifejacket (ATLJ) (Fig 6-5) has a buoyancy of 414N. It is designed for use in amphibious operations, in conjunction with stretchers when transferring patients at sea, and when personnel (eg landing parties) are carrying heavy equipment attached to their person. The ATLJ may be used in aircraft as it is inflated by manual operation. It is neat and compact in the folded state and allows complete freedom of movement by the wearer when worn in this condition. Inflated it will support the wearer together with 47.5 kg of equipment in accordance with the Lifejacket Matrix. It is fitted with a quick-release clip so that it can be quickly discarded when no longer required. Discarding can be effected whilst on the move and can be achieved in three seconds with practice.

Fig 6-5. Assault troop lifejacket Mk 4

Fig 6-5a. Donning the assault troop lifejacket

1. Step through the Webbing Harness and place the Valise over the neck. Bring the crutch strap up between the legs and ensuring that the left hand short strap of the harness is placed over the swivel stud first followed by the right hand strap attach the webbing straps to the swivel stud.

2. Insert 'R' clip and cover with VELCRO® brand strap. Adjust straps until a secure and comfortable fit is achieved.

3. Once inflated the covert cover can be pulled down to prevent detection or left open to aid location, this will be dictated by the ships operational requirements.

4. Once in the water and clear of the danger area pull the Spray Hood over the head and secure the elasticated securing arrangement to each inflated lobe.

b.   **Description**. The lifejacket consists of an inflatable stole, an adjustable webbing harness and inflation equipment. The inflatable stole consists of a pillow section and two lobe sections. It is inflated from a nitrogen cylinder with a manually operated head. Pulling on the operating knob, which protrudes from the bottom of the left-hand lobe of the jacket, will cause the lifejacket to inflate. **There is no automatic inflation facility**. An oral inflation tube and valve are fitted to the left-hand lobe so that the valve is convenient to the mouth of the wearer, this may be pulled free by pulling the inflation valve release webbing lanyard. This facility is for emergency inflation and topping-up during long periods of flotation. The valve can be locked in the closed position by rotating it on the inflation tube. The stole is packed in a zipped outer cover, which will open on inflation. Each lobe has a reflective panel system, which can be opened or closed. A handling loop is fitted to each lobe and a light and whistle are provided. A spray hood is fitted with an alternate position for the light.

c.   **Allowances**. The lifejackets will be issued to personnel on an individual basis when appointed to an HM Ship in accordance with the current Matrix.

d.   **Maintenance**. ATLJs must be maintained and inspected by the Water Safety Equipment Maintainer (WSEM) in accordance with the schedules laid down in the Water Safety Equipment Log.

e.   **Stowage**. The ideal stowage to avoid damage and the possibility of premature inflation is a locker of sufficient size ventilated with warm dry air. The lifejackets should be hung on a supporting bar of not less than 25mm diameter. Space should be left between the lifejackets for air to circulate. ATLJs in their bags may be stowed in racks.

06005. Landing craft lifejacket Mk 3

a. **Introduction**. The landing craft lifejacket (LCLJ) (Fig 6-6) was originally developed for use by the crews of landing craft. This lifejacket is used for certain specific small boat operations and in accordance with the Matrix DIN. The lifejacket has 243N buoyancy, is light and comfortable to wear, and has an automatic inflation assembly with a manual override facility. The wearer is limited to 22.5 kg of additional equipment in accordance with the Lifejacket Matrix. **At present it is not cleared for use in aircraft, even when set to operate in the manual mode**.

Fig 6-6. Landing craft lifejacket Mk 3

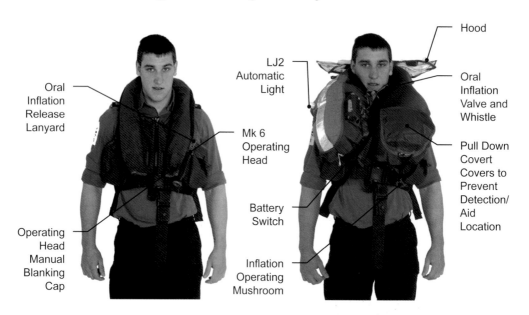

Fig 6-6a. Donning the landing craft lifejacket

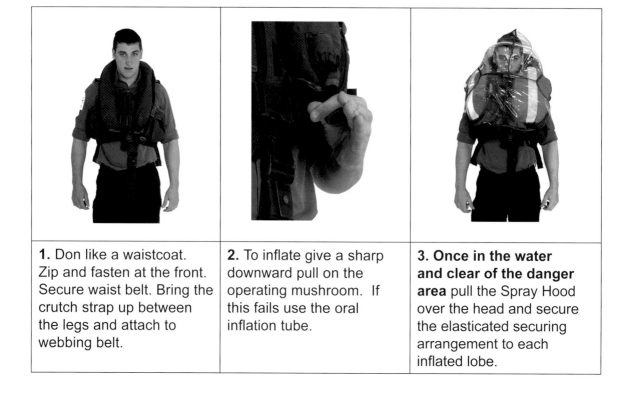

| 1. Don like a waistcoat. Zip and fasten at the front. Secure waist belt. Bring the crutch strap up between the legs and attach to webbing belt. | 2. To inflate give a sharp downward pull on the operating mushroom. If this fails use the oral inflation tube. | 3. **Once in the water and clear of the danger area** pull the Spray Hood over the head and secure the elasticated securing arrangement to each inflated lobe. |

b.   **Description**. The LCLJ comprises an adjustable waistcoat and an inflatable stole which is contained within a protective pouch by means of a fastener. Front closure of the waistcoat is achieved by means of a heavy-duty zip fastener and a large nylon buckle. The buckle is attached to a wide webbing belt which provides girth adjustment. An LJ2 battery and lamp assembly, attached to the stole, activates automatically upon lifejacket inflation. The battery is fitted with an on/off switch. A spray hood is attached to the pillow section of the stole, which is stowed in a folded condition and can be deployed quickly and simply. It is fitted with an alternate light position. Additional features include large-capacity pockets for the stowage of survival/location aids and a small pocket on the rear of the waistcoat which is intended to accommodate a chemical light stick and which is fitted with a facility to permit the light to be covered or exposed as required. Handling loops, a lifeline and a whistle are also fitted.

c.   **Operation**. The LCLJ is designed to be inflated automatically on immersion in water. The gas is contained in a replaceable cylinder attached to the operating head which is an integral part of the lifejacket. On immersion in water the lifejacket will automatically inflate and burst from the valise within a few seconds without any action by the wearer. However, the automatic mode of operation should be treated as a back-up system in case the wearer is unconscious or unable to inflate the lifejacket on immersion. A person falling into the water should give a sharp downward pull on the operating mushroom; if the manual and automatic mechanisms fail to function, the oral inflation tube should be used. If required, the automatic operating facility can be temporarily nullified by opening the valise at a point adjacent to the cylinder and placing the sealing cap over the cartridge. This practice is only necessary for certain operations conducted by Royal Marines.

d.   **Allowances**. Allowances are given in the ship or unit's consolidated allowance list (CAL) and the Matrix DIN.

e.   **Maintenance**. LCLJs must be maintained and inspected by the WSEM in accordance with the schedules laid down in the Water Safety Equipment Log.

f.   **Stowage**. The ideal stowage to avoid damage and the possibility of premature inflation is a locker of sufficient size ventilated with warm dry air. The lifejackets should be hung on a supporting bar of not less than 25mm diameter. Space should be left between the lifejackets for air to circulate.

06006. Crewsaver elite twin 275N lifejacket

a.   **Introduction**. This crewsaver elite twin chamber lifejacket (Fig 6-7) has a high buoyancy of 275N and is carried onboard solely for use by civilian personnel whilst onboard or in boats. It is easy to put on and move about in. The buoyancy of the lifejacket is provided by two chambers with a pressure relief valve, used to ensure the full buoyancy of 28kg is provided whether on single or double inflation. The high buoyancy ensures that the lifejacket is suitable when heavy clothing is worn. Inflation is achieved by either manual or automatic mechanisms.

Fig 6-7. Crewsaver elite twin 275N lifejacket

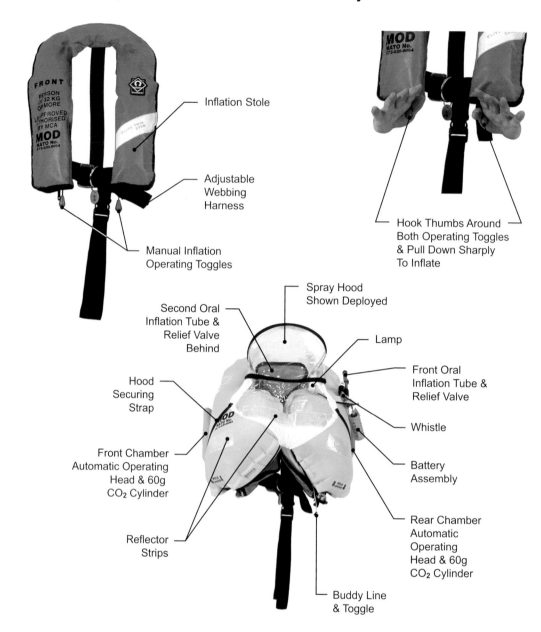

b.   **Description**. The lifejacket consists of an inflatable stole, adjustable webbing harness and an inflation system. It is neat and compact in its stowed state and allows complete freedom of movement by the wearer when worn in this condition. The lifejacket is inflated automatically on entry into water or manually by pulling on the two operating toggles, which protrude from the bottom of the left and right side of the stole of the jacket. An oral inflation tube and valve is fitted to the left hand side of the stole so that the valve is convenient to the mouth of the wearer. This facility is for emergency inflation and topping-up during long periods of flotation. Retro reflective tape is fitted on each chamber when inflated. A Safety Line is provided for use if required.

c.   **Maintenance.** Crewsaver lifejackets must be maintained and inspected by the Water Safety Equipment Maintainer (WSEM) in accordance with the schedules laid down in the Water Safety Equipment Log.

06007. Intrepid once-only survival suit (abandonment suit) (OOSS)

a. **Introduction.** This suit (Fig 6-8) meets the SOLAS requirement for Immersion Suits. It is military issue and as the name suggests is designed to be worn once-only in the event of an emergency. The suits are made of waterproof material in high-visibility red and are designed to be worn over warm clothing to enable survivors to reach liferafts dry-shod, and to prolong chances of survival in the sea. During the donning procedure it is important to ensure that all air is expelled from the suit, starting from the feet. Attached to the suit around the ankle and lower leg region are VELCRO® brand securing straps that must be secured once all the air has been expelled. Donning of the suit is to be carried out as shown below.

Fig 6-8. Donning the intrepid once-only survival suit

1. Kneel on one knee. Secure VELCRO® brand securing straps of the non-kneeling leg.	**2.** Repeat the process for the other leg.

3. Stand up, un-fasten the lifejacket belt from the waist and draw the suit up over the body. Re-fasten the lifejacket belt around the waist.	**4.** Place your arms in the sleeves. Remove the lifejacket from over the head. Pull the hood over the head and fasten the zip.

5. Place the lifejacket stole over the head and fully inflate the lifejacket.	**6. Once in the water and clear of the danger area** pull the spray hood of the lifejacket over the head and secure to the VELCRO® brand fastenings.

Note.   *For personnel who cannot reach liferafts immediately, the survival suit will give protection from cold in Winter/North Atlantic conditions for up to six hours.*

b.   **Allowances.**   2. OOSS "One size fits all" (NSN: O472/8415-99-279-8605) is the regular size issued to most ship staff, and the "Special Measure" OOSS (NSN:O472/8415-99-391-2083) is the larger size intended for taller members of ship's staff that are over 1.98m in height or with size 16 feet, which would not fit into the regular size.

c.   It has been identified that the regular "one size fits all" OOSS is not large enough for some personnel. When this has been identified a "special measure" size suit is to be demanded through naval stores separately and it becomes the sole responsibility of the user and is to be kept with their personal belongings. Personnel issued with this "special measure" size suit are to be aware that they may not be able to go and retrieve their suit in an evacuation situation.

d.   **Stowages.** To reduce the risk of taller personnel not having access to an OOSS "special measure" size, these suits have been included in multipack OOSS containers (Shown in Fig 6-9) as follows:

   (1)   50 man LR containers (NSN: O472/4220-99-839-3176) containing 130 OOSS consisting of 128 "one size fits all" and x 2 "special measure" OOSS.

   (2)   25 man LR containers (NSN: O472/4220-99-535-8441) containing 90 OOSS consisting of 89 "one size fits all" and x 1 "special measure" OOSS. Multipack OOSS have a servicing life of five years, so it will take 5 years for this change to be implemented completely. Any multipack containers that are returned to stores for servicing will be updated to the new standard.

e.   Tall members of ships staff are to request their own personal special measure size OOSS. The WSE Supervisor should identify and demand a special measures size suit when new tall personnel join a ship.

f. Special measure size OOSS are clearly marked with their NSN and "**SPECIAL MEASURE**" written on its labelling. The outer valise is also fluorescent YELLOW which differentiates them from the normal "one size fits all" suit which is in a BLUE outer valise. In addition, the special measure size OOSS will be at the top of all multipack containers making it immediately visible upon opening of the multipack for easy distribution.

g. **Maintenance**. Survival suit containers and survival suits on personal issue must be maintained, inspected and exchanged in accordance with the schedules laid down in the Water Safety Equipment Log.

Note.   *In Type 45s OOSSs are issued on a personal loan basis to each member of the ships company.*

Fig 6-9. Survival suit container

06008. 25 man Naval inflatable liferaft Mk1 (NLMk1) – general arrangements

a. **Introduction**. The 25 man NL Mk1 Liferaft (Fig 6-10) is fitted as standard equipment in most HM ships and is supplied on a scale to provide liferafts for a full war complement plus 100% total = 200%. The liferaft is supplied, packed in a weather-tight GRP container and is fitted in a weather deck stowage either singly or in pairs. The stowage is designed so that the liferaft(s) will fall unobstructed into the sea when released manually, or will release hydrostatically should the ship founder and sink. Contained within the liferaft are survival packs, which are described later.

b. **General description**. The liferafts are approximately 4.25 meters in diameter and 1.73 meters high, consists of two 12-sided buoyancy tubes to which are attached two canopy arches, a centre thwart, a seat and two boarding ramps, all of which are inflatable. The canopy is constructed from two separate layers, it incorporates two lookout ports, two entrances positioned immediately above the boarding ramps, and two rain water catchment points. Light reflector strips are fitted to the outer layer to assist in location by rescuers. Each entrance is fitted with two doors, an inner and outer. These can be closed during adverse weather conditions. The floor, which must be inflated manually by the bellows, adopts a quilted effect on inflation. When inflated the floor and seat tube promote comfort to the occupants and provide thermal insulation against cold rising from the sea. Water pockets are attached to the underside of the liferaft which provide stability and reduce drift. The pockets at either side of each entrance are fitted with trip lines which render them ineffective should it be necessary to manoeuvre the liferaft. Also fitted on the underside of the liferaft is an elasticated righting strap to enable the liferaft to be righted in the event of an inverted inflation/capsize. All inflatable sections (except the ramps and the thwart) have clearly marked topping up valves and deflation points.

c. **Inflating the liferaft**

(1) The liferaft is inflated by two gas cylinders attached to the underside of the liferaft. Each cylinder contains a mixture of CO_2 and nitrogen (the nitrogen content acting as an anti-freezing agent). Both cylinders are activated by pulling an operating cord. Pressure relief valves are fitted to the outside of the upper and lower buoyancy tubes; they are designed to release excess gas when the liferafts are inflated. They are **NOT** to be blocked off in any way to prevent the excess gas escaping.

(2) One gas cylinder inflates the upper buoyancy chamber, one roof arch, the roof cross member and the thwart. The other gas cylinder inflates the lower buoyancy chamber, the other roof arch, the seats and both boarding ramps. Due to non-return valves fitted in the buoyancy chambers, a defect in either buoyancy chamber will not affect the rest of the raft nor will it decrease the survivor carrying capacity. The operating cord consisting of 50 meters of braided polyester is secured to the wires of the gas cylinder operating heads and then to one of the two towing patches and faked inside the container during packing. The outboard end protrudes from the end of the GRP container. A weak link consisting of 3-4 mm of polyester is secured to end of the operating cord; the other end is secured to a strong point on the ship. Both ends are secured by either a stitched or taped bowline.

(3) The gas cylinders are activated manually by pulling the operating cord. If the ship sinks, the liferaft will release by hydrostatic action and inflate automatically. This is described later. Fig 6-11 and 6-12 show the general arrangement of the operating cord and how breaking is achieved should the ship sink.

Fig 6-10. 25 Man Naval inflatable liferaft Mk1 (NL Mk1)

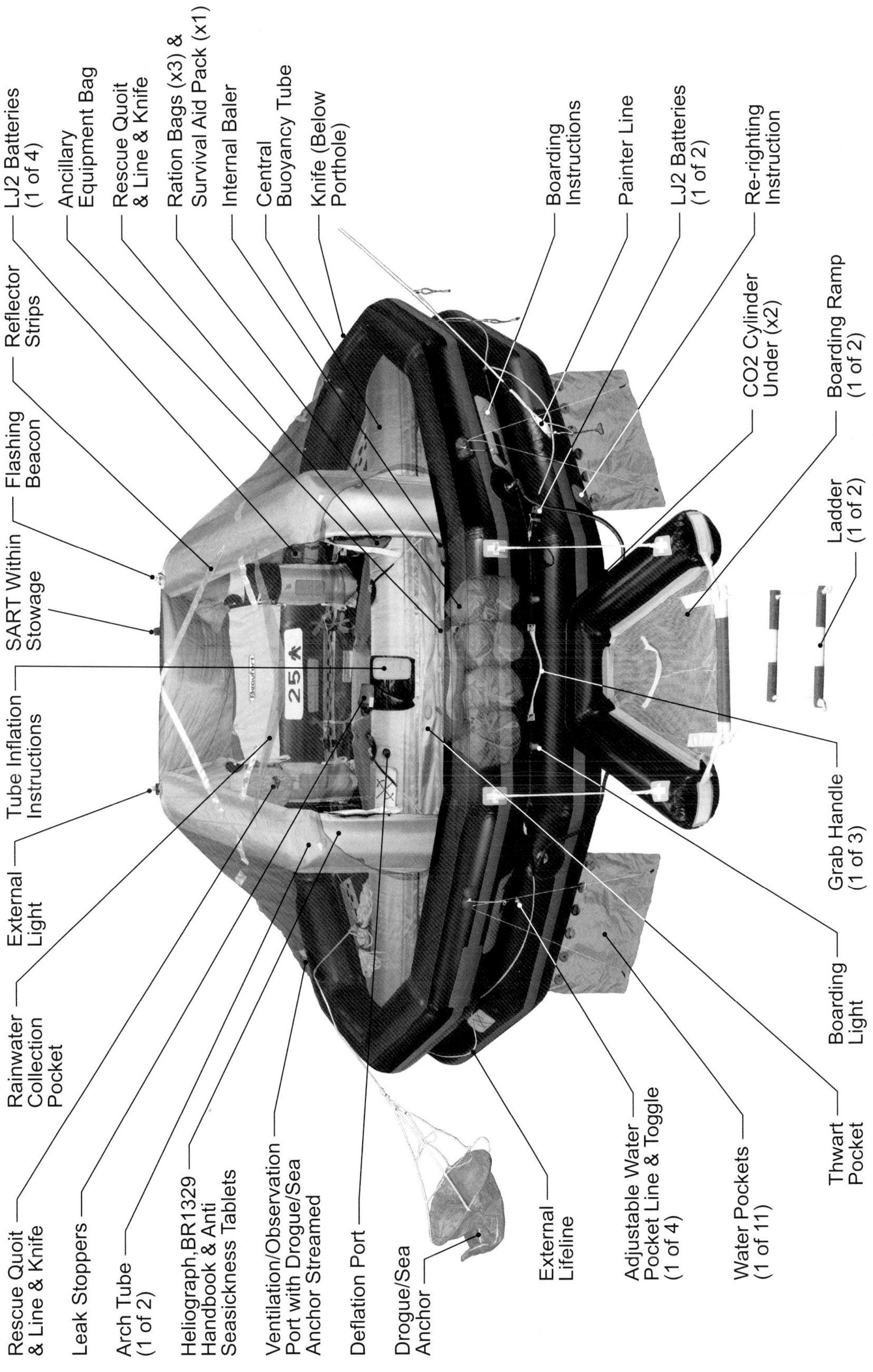

Labels (clockwise/around figure):

- LJ2 Batteries (1 of 4)
- Ancillary Equipment Bag
- Rescue Quoit & Line & Knife
- Ration Bags (x3) & Survival Aid Pack (x1)
- Internal Baler
- Central Buoyancy Tube
- Knife (Below Porthole)
- Boarding Instructions
- Painter Line
- LJ2 Batteries (1 of 2)
- Re-righting Instruction
- Reflector Strips
- Flashing Beacon
- SART Within Stowage
- Tube Inflation Instructions
- External Light
- Rainwater Collection Pocket
- Rescue Quoit & Line & Knife
- Leak Stoppers
- Arch Tube (1 of 2)
- Heliograph, BR1329 Handbook & Anti Seasickness Tablets
- Ventilation/Observation Port with Drogue/Sea Anchor Streamed
- Deflation Port
- Drogue/Sea Anchor
- External Lifeline
- Adjustable Water Pocket Line & Toggle (1 of 4)
- Water Pockets (1 of 11)
- Thwart Pocket
- Boarding Light
- Grab Handle (1 of 3)
- Ladder (1 of 2)
- Boarding Ramp (1 of 2)
- CO2 Cylinder Under (x2)

Fig 6-11. Liferaft manually launched – showing arrangement of operating cord

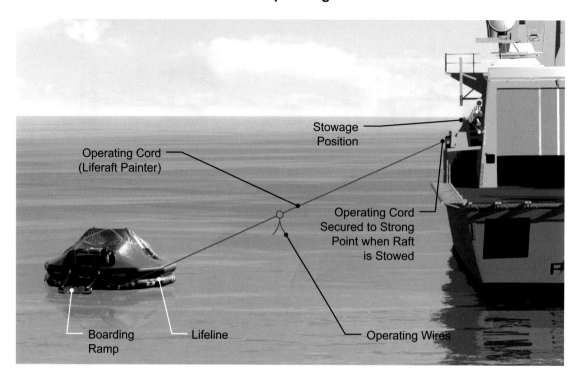

Stowage Position

Operating Cord (Liferaft Painter)

Operating Cord Secured to Strong Point when Raft is Stowed

Boarding Ramp

Lifeline

Operating Wires

Fig 6-12. Operation of hydrostatic release

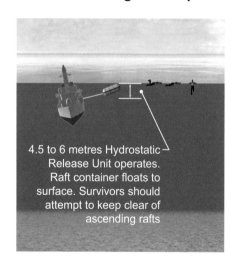

4.5 to 6 metres Hydrostatic Release Unit operates. Raft container floats to surface. Survivors should attempt to keep clear of ascending rafts

Ship sinks further. Operating cord pays out from liferaft container

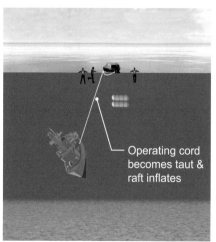

Operating cord becomes taut & raft inflates

Weak link will break after raft has inflated and ship has sunk

d.   **Stowage of liferafts**. Each liferaft is packed in a GRP container which is stowed on suitably designed platforms on the weatherdecks (Fig 6-13 and Fig 6-14). This method of stowage is essential to enable both containers to roll free of the stowage when released. The liferaft in its container is held securely in the stowage by two polyester webbing straps; the outboard ends of these straps are thoroughfooted to the stowage platform with attached stainless steel buckles and the inboard ends are secured to a 'coat hanger' arrangement as shown in Fig 6-15. A hydrostatic release mechanism is incorporated between the 'coat hanger' and the deck connection. Buckles are fitted in the straps to adjust their tension and ensure a secure stowage for the container. The end of the liferaft from which the operating cord protrudes must face aft to minimise water ingress; the operating cord is secured to a 'weak-link' line, which in turn is secured to a strong point in the ship.

Note.   *The NL Mk1 container and securing arrangements are shown in Fig 6-13, Fig 6-14 and Fig 6-15.*

Fig 6-13. Weather-deck single liferaft stowage

Fig 6-14. Weather-deck double liferaft stowage

Fig 6-15. Securing arrangement for the NL Mk1 liferaft container

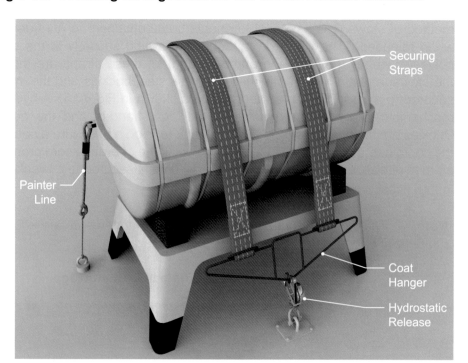

e.   **Hydrostatic release unit (Thanner)** (Fig 6-16). This mechanism is designed to release the liferaft containers should the ship founder. It is operated by the ingress of water through apertures in the body of the release. The pressure of the seawater at a depth of approximately six metres below the surface causes a diaphragm to trip the pawl of the hydrostatic release, thus releasing the 'coat hanger' from the jaws of the unit. The hydrostatic release **must not** be painted. Foreign matter and paint will block the apertures, preventing the mechanism from operating at the correct depth. The unit can be operated manually by removing the safety 'R' clip from the operating arm and pressing hard on the 'push to release' button.

Fig 6-16. Hydrostatic release unit – Thanner

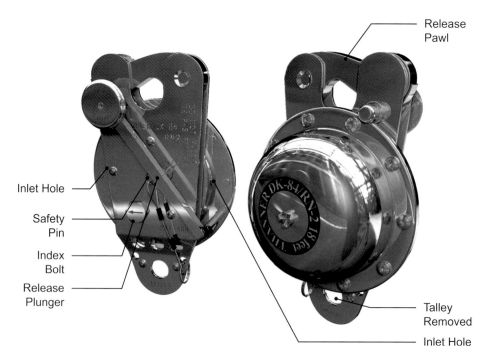

f. **Hydrostatic release unit (Hammar)** (Fig 6-17). The Hammar H20 Hydrostatic Release Unit is designed for liferafts from six to 150 persons. The Hammar H20 release unit consists of a double-looped white rope line, a release mechanism and a Red Weak Link Line (breaking strength 2.2± 0.4 kN). The white strong rope of the Hammar H20 is secured to the deck or liferaft cradle and attached to the liferaft lashing with a slip. If the ship sinks, the water pressure will, within four metres, activate the sharp knife within the hammar which cuts the white strong rope and the liferaft will float free. As the ship sinks, the liferaft painter line will be stretched and the liferaft will start to inflate. The Red Weak Link Line on the HRU breaks and the survivors will then be able to board the liferaft. The Hammar H20 needs no annual service, maintenance or spare parts, but has a two year in-service life with the expiry date marked on the unit by the user when installed.

Fig 6-17. Hydrostatic release unit – Hammar

g. **Handling liferaft containers**. The total weight of GRP containers and their contents is approximately 218 kg for 25 Man NL raft and approximately 132 kg for the Zodiac 16 man Liferaft. The use of a dockside crane is required when containers have to be removed, shipped or unshipped. Only round slings should be used for lifting the containers. The containers should not be rolled during shipment or stowage and care must be taken to avoid bumping, especially on deck projections. Containers are to be placed in their stowage with the operating cord facing aft.

h. **Marking of GRP containers**. Stuck on the top half of the container is a label, which gives details of packing date and place, details of manufacture and whether or not a SARBE beacon is installed. If a SARBE is fitted, the word SARBE is displayed in 30mm black lettering on the container.

i. **Maintenance**. Maintenance of the container and associated equipment is to be in accordance with the schedule given in the *Water Safety Equipment Log*. No work is to be carried out on the stowages and no welding or burning is to take place within a two-metre radius of a liferaft stowage whilst the rafts are *in situ*.

j. **Exchanging liferafts**. HM Ship's 25-Man liferafts run on a two-year cycle in accordance with the Water Safety Equipment Log.

k. **Liferaft equipment**. Items of essential equipment are either fitted to the liferaft or stowed inside the survival packs. They are as follows:

(1) *Topping-up valves*. These are yellow valves inside the liferaft to which the **topping-up pump** can be connected to top-up any part of the liferaft with air. They are clearly marked.

(2) *Deflation plugs.* These are fitted for **maintenance purposes only** and are identified by their slotted heads and identification labels. They are not to be removed.

(3) *Leakstoppers.* These are conical rubber plugs with serrated shanks, stowed in pockets on the thwart. The plugs are used as a temporary repair for holes. They are inserted by a gentle screwing action into the hole to be plugged. Care must be taken that the hole is not enlarged by the screwing action. Large tears can be repaired by using repair clamps from the survival pack.

(4) *Topping-up pump.* This is stowed in Ancillary Equipment Bag and is used to top-up any part of the liferaft with air, by inserting the tube into a topping-up valve.

(5) *Rescue quoit and lines.* These are stowed on the left-hand side (looking out of the raft) of both entrances, and consist of a rubber grommet and 18m of cordage.

(6) *Handbook for Survivors* (BR 1329). This handbook is stowed in a pocket on the right-hand arch looking out of the after entrance. It should be read as soon as possible by the person assuming command of the liferaft and in due course by all the occupants of the liferaft. All the information required for survival will be found in the handbook. Additional information, eg immediate action drill, is printed on large panels displayed on the underside of the canopy.

(7) *Heliograph.* This is used to attract the attention of ships and aircraft by reflecting the sun's rays in the required direction. It is stowed in the same pocket as the *Handbook for Survivors* also published by The Nautical Institute.

(8) *Hand bailers and sponges.* These are provided to dry out the inside of the liferaft and are stowed in the Survival Aids Pack.

(9) *Seasickness tablets.* These are stowed on an arch, in the same pocket as the *Handbook for Survivors* also published by The Nautical Institute. Tablets should be issued to all personnel as soon as possible - **whether they suffer from seasickness or not**. Extra tablets are provided in the Survival Aids Pack.

(10) *Floating knives.* These knives have blunt ends and two are supplied, each fitted with a lanyard. One is stowed on the left arch looking out of the aft entrance and the other is stowed by the starboard lookout port.

(11) *Bailing appliance.* Two manually operated bailing appliances (one in 16 and six man liferafts) are fitted into the floor of the liferaft. Each appliance is designed to drain the liferaft of water to the sea, through a non-return sleeve arrangement. The lip of the funnel is pushed beneath the level of water within the raft and then raised out of the water to its full extent. This action enables the water contained in the funnel to drain out through the sleeve fitted to the underside of the raft. The action is continued until the liferaft is drained. Hand bailers/sponges are then used to complete the drying out operation.

(12) *Water pockets*. To stabilise the liferaft and reduce drift from windage, eleven (eight in 16 man and five in six man liferafts) water pockets are fitted to the bottom of the raft. To increase the rate of drift of the raft the pocket either side of each entrance can be 'tripped' by pulling lines located at each entrance. The other seven pockets are not fitted with trip lines and therefore cannot be emptied.

(13) *Drogue or sea anchor*. This device (one or two may be supplied), which resembles a small parachute, is secured by 19 metres of cordage to the lower buoyancy tube below the port and starboard lookout ports. Its purpose is to slow the rate of drift and to assist in the stabilisation of the raft. It should therefore be streamed as soon as possible after boarding. The drogue also provides limited assistance in manoeuvring the liferaft in calm weather conditions. This is achieved by bunching up the drogue, throwing it in the required direction, and then pulling on the line to manoeuvre the raft towards the drogue. When manoeuvring in this manner the water pockets either side of each entrance should be tripped.

(14) *Distress signals*. The distress signals are stowed in the Survival Aids Pack. At the earliest opportunity they should be removed from the pack and fitted in their designated stowages on the top buoyancy tube at the entrances either side of the inflatable arch. Instructions for use are printed on a label attached to the body of the signal. The signals emit a bright flare light for night use and red smoke for day use, according to which end is operated. To simplify identification in the dark the **day** signal end is smooth and the **night** signal end has two ridges around it (knobbly for night is an easy *aide memoire*). On rare occasions, the smoke signal may produce a flame. Should this occur, immerse momentarily in water; smoke should then be emitted. On completion of burning, douse the signal in water and retain for use of the other signal end.

(15) *First-aid kit*. A first-aid kit is stowed in the Survival Aids Pack. Full instructions for the use of the contents are supplied with the kit. Additionally an inflatable arm and leg splint are supplied.

(16) *Survival suits and mittens*. Two spare survival suits and two pairs of mittens are stowed in the Survival Aids Pack. They are primarily for the use of lookouts but may be utilised as necessary.

(17) *Rations*. Rations of water and glucose biscuits as listed overleaf are provided in the three Survival Ration Packs. The policy for issue is explained fully in *Handbook for Survivors* also published by The Nautical Institute.

(18) *Lights*. All lights on the liferaft are run on LJ2 Batteries which are also called RB2 Batteries.

(19) *Thermal protection aid (TPAs)*. Three Thermal Protection Aids.

(20) *Miscellaneous items*. In addition to the items listed above the Survival Aids Pack contain playing cards, plastic beakers and a waterproof torch. Two paddles to assist in manoeuvring the raft are also carried in the Ancillary Equipment Bag.

Rations	Quantity
Water	25 x 1.5ltr sachets each containing 12 x 125ml sachets
Glucose biscuits	25 x biscuit blocks each containing 12 biscuits

06009. 16 man liferaft

a. **Introduction.** 16 Man Inflatable Liferafts (Fig 6-18a and Fig 6-18b) are fitted as standard equipment in Type 45 Destroyers and are supplied on a scale with the 25 man liferafts to provide liferafts for the full war complement. The liferafts are supplied flat packed in grey weather-tight GRP containers and are fitted in the enclosed forecastle, quarterdeck, boat bays and weather-deck stowages behind the breakwater in front of the 4.5 Gun. The 16 man liferafts situated on the upperdeck will release hydrostatically by a Hammar Hydrostatic Release Unit and the 16 man liferafts in enclosed stowages have to be manually operated.

Fig 6-18a. 16 man liferaft containers

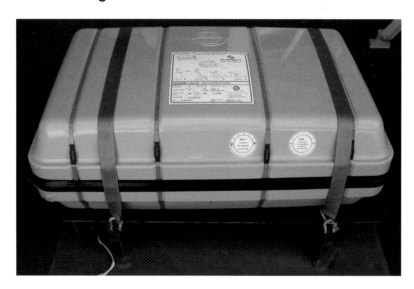

b. **Manual operation.** Manually operated liferafts are operated as follows:

(1)   Remove the securing straps, walk the container to the ship's side, secure the painter to a strong point then, throw overboard. The container is quite heavy so it will take three to four persons for the lift.

(2)   Pull Painter sharply to inflate.

(3)   Drag liferaft to a designated boarding position and board liferaft dry-shod.

(4)   Cut painter to release the liferaft.

c. **Liferaft equipment**. Items of essential equipment are either fitted to the liferaft or stowed inside the survival packs the same as previously explained for the 25 man liferaft.

Fig 6-18b. 16 man liferaft

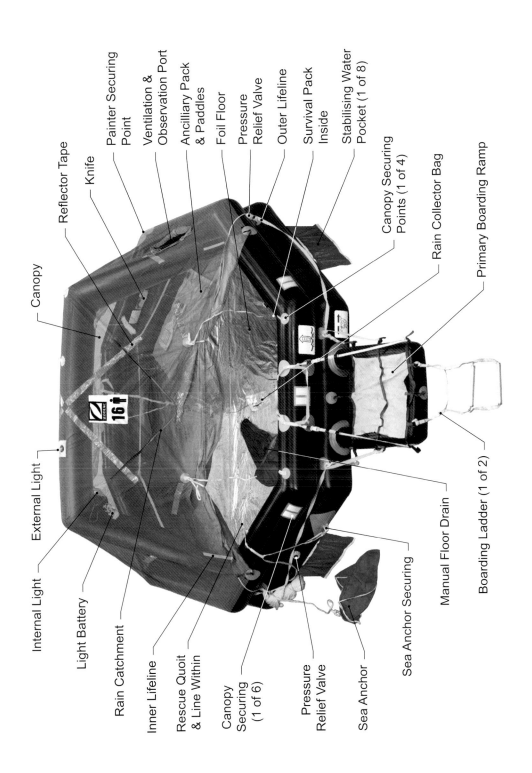

d.   **Maintenance**. Like the 25 man liferaft, containers these must also be maintained, inspected and exchanged in accordance with the schedules laid down in the Water Safety Equipment Log.

Note.   *Follow directions on the information sticker attched to the 16 man liferafts and do not jump in.*

06010. Typical global Maritime distress and safety system (GMDSS)

a.   All HM Ships are provided with Global Maritime Distress and Safety System (GMDSS) equipment to alert search and rescue services in the event of an emergency and to guide them to the position.   This equipment is maintained by the ET WE section in conjunction with the CIS department.   Various types of Emergency Position Indicating Radio Beacon (EPIRB) are available.   However, the principle of operation is the same for all types.   They are installed on the upper deck.   A crew member is delegated to retrieve this equipment and stow it aboard their liferaft. However, if the ship sinks or capsizes before the EPIRB can be manually removed from its stowage, a hydrostatic release system will ensure it automatically disengages and activates. If the EPIRB is seen floating (it will be emitting a powerful flashing light) every effort should be made to retrieve it and tether it to the liferaft.   It is designed to alert search and rescue services that your ship has sunk by transmitting a coded message on the 406MHz distress frequency.   This message is relayed via satellite to the nearest rescue co-ordination centre.   The satellite system can determine the position of your EPIRB as it makes the distress transmissions and it also recognises the unique number contained within the coded transmission.   This number is registered to the ship when the EPIRB is installed.   The EPIRB also transmits a 'homing' signal on the 121.5MHz international distress frequency which acts as a back-up for the 406MHz transmission and enables rescue vessels to 'home in' on the EPIRB during the final stages of the rescue.   Typical EPIRBs are illustrated in Fig 6-19.

Fig 6-19. Typical emergency position indicating radio beacons (EPIRBs)

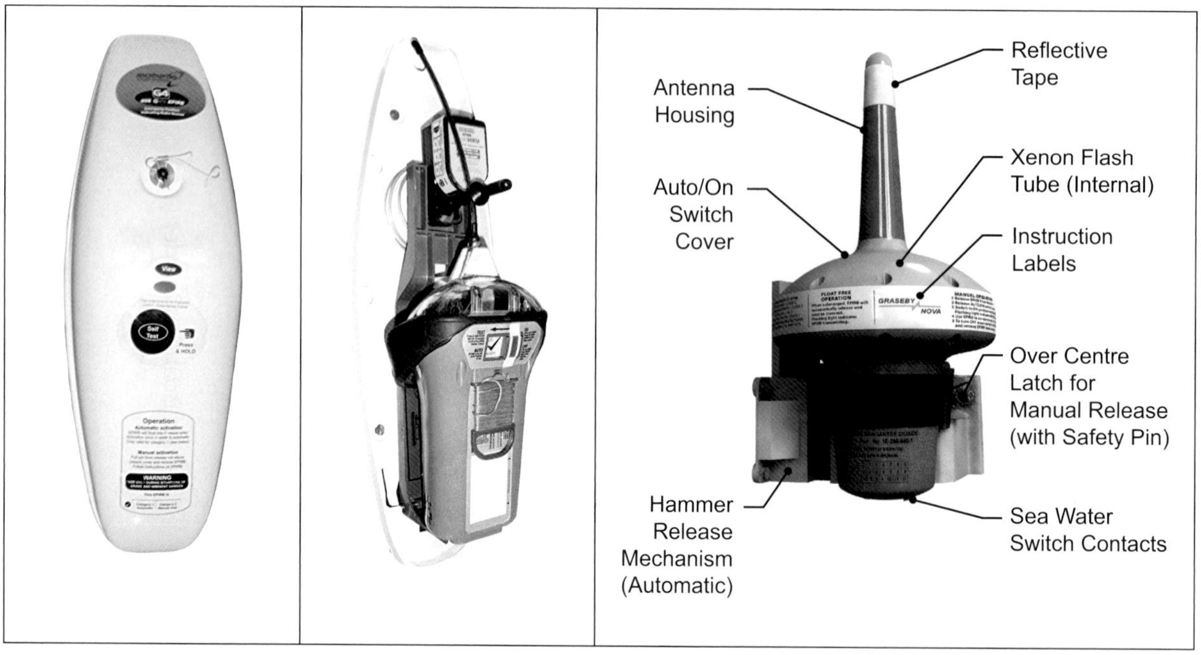

Note.   *Various types of EPIRB are issued with instruction leaflets which are to be kept within the EPRIB container should the need arise.*

b.   **Search and rescue radar transponder - SART**. All HM Ships carry at least two shipborne SARTs (Fig 6-20).   This equipment is maintained by the ET WE section in conjunction with the CIS Department.   Shipborne SARTs are stowed adjacent to escape routes and a crew member is delegated to retrieve it and stow it aboard their allocated liferaft in emergencies.   The SART is designed to help rescue services quickly locate the ship's position.   It is a radar transponder, which will operate with most maritime radars.

When the SART is switched on, it waits with its green light flashing until a radar signal is detected (usually at about 40 miles if the signal is from an aircraft, or five miles if it is from a ship) at which point it starts to transmit back. When it transmits back its red light will flash. The aircraft or vessel transmitting will see a line of dots on its radar screen, enabling the position of the liferaft to be pinpointed. (These SARTs are also carried in the Ancillary Bag of each NL Mk1 liferaft).

(1) *To operate the SART.* Remove the SART from its storage container. Slide the safety lock down and then turn the knurled ring clockwise to the ON position. Check that the green light is flashing.

(2) *Rigging the SART.* The SART must be raised at least one metre above the level of the sea for efficient operation. An extendable pole is supplied with the SART to cater for this. Screw the pole into the base of the SART, then undo the VELCRO® brand strap and extend the pole. Twist and pull hard across the pole joints to lock them. Tie the safety lanyard provided to the liferaft then push the SART through the SART port. The SART should be kept as near vertical as possible.

Fig 6-20. Typical SART

c.   **NAVICO portable waterproof VHF radio**. GMDSS requirements call for ships to carry two or three portable waterproof VHF radios (Fig 6-21). These radios are stowed in racks on board the ship and a crew member is delegated to retrieve them and stow them aboard their allocated liferaft when the ship is abandoned. The senior officer or rating must decide which rafts will carry the radios. The principal use of the radios is to provide a means of communication with other rafts and to liaise with rescue services as they approach. They can also be used to transmit MAYDAY broadcasts, monitor channel 16 for rescue activity and during Man Overboard recovery. As the batteries have a maximum life of twelve hours the radios must be used sparingly.

Fig 6-21. Portable waterproof NAVICO VHF radio with operating controls

(1) *To operate the radio.* The radio uses a combination of push buttons and rotary control. An audible 'beep' is emitted as confirmation whenever a button is pushed or the channel switch is rotated. The controls are illustrated in Fig 6-21 and described further as follows:

ON/OFF	This push button turns the radio on and off.
PTT	The *Press To Talk* button must be held down to make a voice transmission.
HI/LOW	This push button toggles the transmit power level between high (5W) and low (0.8W). The current level status is indicated by the TX indicator. See below.
SQUELCH	When pressed, this button defeats the squelch and can be used to set the squelch level.
VOLUME	This rotary control varies the loudspeaker listening level to suit ambient conditions.
CHANNEL SWITCH	This is a 16-position rotary switch.
LAMP	This push button illuminates the channel select dial to improve visibility.

(2) In addition to the listed controls, there are three indicator lamps with the following functions:

TX LAMP	Indicates either HI or LO power transmission.
BAT LAMP	Flashes when battery is nearly exhausted.
RX LAMP	Blinks to indicate the radio is squelched.

d.   **Portable waterproof SRH 50 VHF radio**

Fig 6-22. Portable waterproof SRH 50 VHF radio with operating controls

Pressing and holding certain keys will access additional functions. These are indicated by a double beep, or a triple beep if held for longer (see Table 6-1).

Table 6-1. Function table SRH 50 VHF radio

Key	1 x Press	2 x Press	Press & Hold Double Beep	Press & Hold Triple Beep	Hold During Power Up
VOL	Select Volume Mode Select Squelch Mode				Select secondary channel set*
SQ	**Standard Mode** Channel Up/Down				Disable/Enable First Key Beep
▲ **▼**	**Volume Mode** Volume Up/Down **Squelch Mode** Squelch Up/Down **Light Mode** Light Level Up/Down				
SCAN	Memory Scan	Add/Delete channel from memory scan	Scan all channels	Inhibit/Enable selected channel from scan	
D/W	Dual Watch		Tri Watch		
16	Select Channel 16		Select Personal Channel		
🔆	Select light Mode Backlight On/Off				
					* If available

e. **SAILOR SP3520 portable waterproof VHF radio**

Fig 6-23. SAILOR SP3520 portable waterproof VHF radio

Fig 6-24. SAILOR SP3520 portable waterproof VHF radio controls

(1) Pressing and holding certain keys gives access to additional functions shown in the table below.

Table 6-2. Function table SAILOR SP3520 portable waterproof VHF radio

Key	Short Press (1 beep)	Long Press (2 beeps)	Extra Long Press (3 beeps)
▲ / ▼	Show next available item in the list (up or down). Default: Channel election.	Run through available items, or select tagged channels **A** (▼) or **B** (▲).	Run through available items if an **A** or **B** channel is tagged.
SQ	Acitivate Squelch control (Adjust with up/down arrows).	Monitor function. Open Squelch completely.	
SCN	1 press: Activate/Terminate Dual/Triple watch. 2 presses: Activate memory scan.	Add/Delete channel from memory scan.	
Hi/Lo	Toggle between high and low transmitter power.		
16/C	Select channel 16.	Select programmed Call channel.	Program Call channel.

Fig 6-25. Function table SAILOR SP3520 portable waterproof VHF radio

(2)   The display above holds various fields of information, as explained below:

(a) Current working channel.

(b) Current channel mode.

(c) 'LO': Reduced transmitter power. Full transmitter power is not shown in display.

(d) Dual watch activated.

(e) Current working channel is marked for scanning.

(f) Keypad is locked.

(g) Battery level indicator.

(h) Transmitting (Tx)/Receiving (Rx).

(i) Accessory is connected.

(j) Service line for various purposes. In the example the volume level.

f.   **Search and rescue beacon** (SARBE). In selected liferafts a SARBE (Fig 6-26) is fitted. Although not part of the GMDSS kit, it is nevertheless a useful aid in survival situations. This lightweight radio operates automatically on an International Aviation UHF Distress Frequency and is also equipped with facilities for transmission and reception of speech on this frequency. Additionally, an auxiliary channel is incorporated which operates on an International Scene-of-Search frequency of 282.8 MHZ.

Fig 6-26. Typical SARBE locator beacon

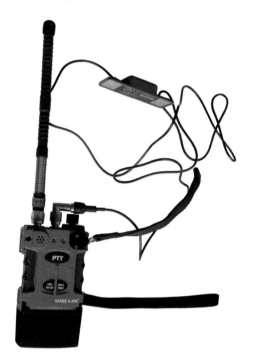

(1)   *Controls.* The Sarbe Locator Beacon is equipped with three controls which are simple to operate. It is emphasised, however, that these are mainly for two-way speech operation and do not control transmission of the distress frequency, which is automatic. The controls are:

(a)   *Press-to-talk/press-to-listen.* A rocker switch situated conveniently so that the voice receive/transmit facilities are easily selected when the beacon is held in the palm of the hand.

(b)   *Change channel.* This control, pre-set to the DISTRESS beacon transmission position on removal of the auto-activate pin, can be switched to either the AUXILIARY 'Scene-of-Search' channel or to 'OFF' as required.

(c)   *Volume.* This controls the level of all received signals and side tone and is continuously variable. It is inoperative in the transmission modes.

(2)   *Operation*

(a)   Transmission of the DISTRESS signal commences as soon as the operating lanyard is pulled and the 'auto-activate' pin is withdrawn from the top of the unit. Survivors should not normally touch the test lever. (The green/red lights are for pre-issue/packing checks only.) Survivor confidence check, in use, of the green indicator lamp situated adjacent to the selector switch will confirm that radio-frequency power of a satisfactory level is available at the aerial.

(b) Two-way speech is selected by operation of the press-to-talk/press-to-listen rocker switch located on the side of the unit.

(c) Once visual rescue contact has been established the selector switch should be turned to the AUXILIARY channel (to enable the DISTRESS channel frequency to be cleared for further search as required, at the same time allowing two-way communication to continue during the rescue operation).

(d) Should more than one Sarbe Locator Beacon be available in situations where liferafts are congregated and tied together, battery power should be conserved by the operation of one unit only.

(e) Instructions for the fitting of the SARBE Unit and aerial to the liferaft are in the polythene package containing the beacon.

Note.   *To avoid wasting the battery do not use the transmit/receive speech facility until such times as search aircraft or shipping have been located.*

06011. Emergency stations

a.   **Organisation and procedure.** In the Royal Navy the procedure for abandoning ship is part of the 'Emergency Stations' organisation. The word 'emergency' is used to avoid any confusion with the final 'Abandon Ship', which is ordered if necessary only after all available liferafts have been slipped and when the ship is about to founder. Emergency Stations are exercised regularly so that the ship's company is familiar with the organisation and order is maintained throughout. Emergency Stations have been developed over many years to provide a simple standard procedure that will bring a ship to a high state of personnel and material preparedness to deal with any hazardous situation in which Action Stations would not be appropriate. The routine thus evolved is a rapid and effective countermeasure, which will provide the command with an organisation capable of regaining the initiative in the event of:

   (1)   Fire.

   (2)   Collision or grounding.

   (3)   Aircraft or explosive incident.

   (4)   Flooding.

b.   The pipe 'Hands to Emergency Stations' should be made personally by the Executive Officer if the circumstances permit. It should always be preceded by the main broadcast alarm. The Officer of the Watch at sea has the authority (vested in them by the Commanding Officer) to pipe 'Emergency Stations'.

c.   Personnel not closed-up on watch, or not involved in first-aid measures as part of the fire-fighting or damage-control teams, are to act as ordered by the Command either to remain in their present positions or to proceed to stated muster points. The fire-fighting and damage control teams are not to be impeded. Hands are not to return to collect lifejackets from messdecks; however, lifejackets are to be carried, if to hand, when 'Emergency Stations' is broadcast. A more comprehensive explanation of Emergency Stations is described in **BRd 2170(1) CBRNDC Manual**. It is important to remember that Emergency Stations does not necessarily mean that the next step is Abandon Ship; however, should that situation arise, personnel are better prepared to abandon ship from Emergency Stations than they would otherwise have been.

d.   **Preparation and issue of water safety equipment**. Much will depend on the type of emergency and the material state of the equipment. However, the following points provide general guidelines:

(1)   Check the survival equipment and inform the Executive Officer/First Lt.

(2)   When ordered, break out and issue Emergency Lifejackets and Once-Only Suits. (Lay aside sufficient for personnel closed up).

(3)   Prepare for use scrambling nets, ladders, lifelines, boats and liferafts.

06012. Abandon ship

a.   **Introduction**. The order to Abandon Ship will be given by the Command, and the responsibility for deploying the liferafts/lifeboats when ordered rests with the senior officer or rating in the vicinity of a particular group of liferafts/lifeboats or personnel. It is likely, particularly after a collision or fire, that some liferafts/lifeboats will be unserviceable through damage; therefore it is not practical to detail individual members of the ship's company to particular liferafts/lifeboats from the Watch and Station Bill. An appraisal of the situation at the time of abandonment rests with the Executive Officer, who has to ensure that the ship's company is deployed to liferafts/lifeboats as the situation dictates.

b.   **Leaving the ship**. When the order 'abandon ship' is given, survival suits should be donned and general service lifejackets should be worn outside the suits. The lifejacket should be fully inflated, the hood and visor must be kept in the stowed position behind the neck, and the waist belt must be adjusted to a snug fit. The survival suit and general service lifejacket, and their method of use are described in Para 06002 and Para 06007. At the order 'Abandon Ship' board the raft as quickly as possible, if it is possible to climb down a ladder, scrambling net, rope line or hose and enter the raft dry-shod so much the better; do **not** attempt to jump directly on to liferafts or dive head first into the sea. If it is necessary to jump into the water this can be done quite safely from the upper deck or weatherdecks when wearing a fully inflated General Service lifejacket. Always jump feet first looking at the horizon. Keep feet together, place one arm over the front of the Lifejacket stole, grasping the opposite forearm or elbow and pinch the nostrils with the other hand. The elbows should be kept as close to the sides as possible. It is essential that the hood and face shield of the general service lifejacket are kept in the stowed position until you have entered the water and are clear of the danger area. This will ensure a safe drop into the water, prevent any undue movement of the lifejacket and prevent water being forced up the nose. Anyone left on the ship after the rafts have got away should abandon ship and swim as far as possible, to avoid being sucked down or entangled as the ship founders and to avoid being struck by wreckage which might subsequently rise to the surface with great force. The only efficient way to swim when wearing an inflated jacket is on the back using arms only.

c. **Points to remember**

(1)   If the ship is drifting, it is better to leave over the weather side; otherwise it may be difficult to swim clear. Jump well clear of the side and swim quickly away to avoid being washed back on board by the sea. If the ship has a list, abandon over the bows or stern if possible.

(2)   After launching, liferafts should be worked to the bow or stern, preferably while still in their GRP containers before inflation. In this way they are easier to move through the water and are unlikely to be abraded on the ship's side and easier to board. If you jump from the high side you may strike the bilge keel or propellers or injure your hands and feet on barnacles on the exposed part of the ship's bottom, and if you leave by the low side you may be struck by the superstructure, masts or funnels if the ship capsizes before you can swim clear.

(3)   If anti-submarine weapons are being fired or any underwater explosions appear imminent, swim on the back and lift the trunk as high as possible out of the water to avoid the pressure wave of the explosion.

(4)   When clear of the ship, swimmers should make for the nearest liferaft or, failing that, cling to any floating wreckage available and form themselves in compact groups to provide mutual support and encouragement. When possible, swimmers in a group should rope themselves together by means of the toggle and line on the lifejackets, preferably in a circle facing outwards, and they should avoid undue exertion. A group of swimmers stand a better chance of being rescued than do individuals.

(5)   Personnel have safely negotiated a patch of more than 100 metres of burning oil in the following manner. Deflate your lifejacket; take a deep breath and jump into the water feet first; swim under water for as long as possible, then spring above the flames and take another breath while pushing away the flames with a breast stroke; then sink and swim under water again.

d. **Submarine escape immersion equipment (SEIE)**

(1)   The SEIE (Fig 6-27, Fig 6-28 and Fig 6-29) is a British designed whole-body suit and one-man life raft that allows submariners to escape from a sunken submarine. The suit provides protection against hypothermia. The suit allows survivors to escape a disabled submarine at depths down to 183 metres (600 feet) at a rate of eight or more men per hour.

(2)   The SEIE is designed to enable a free ascent from a stricken submarine and to provide protection for the submariner on reaching the surface until rescued. The assembly comprises a submarine escape and immersion suit, an inner thermal liner, and a gas-inflated single-seat life raft, all contained in an outer protective stowage compartment.

(3)   The suit not only keeps the escapee dry and protected from the cold shock during escape, but also acts as a thermally efficient immersion suit on reaching the surface. Full protection is therefore provided while deploying and boarding the life raft. The suit provides sufficient lifting force to take the escapee from the submarine to the surface at a speed of approximately 2-3 metres per second.

Fig 6-27. Submarine escape immersion equipment suit

Fig 6-28. Submarine escape immersion equipment suit on the surface after escape

Fig 6-29. Submarine escape one-man liferaft

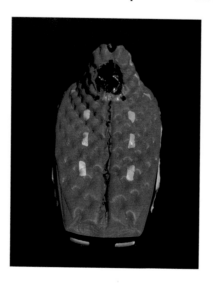

THE NAUTICAL INSTITUTE

06013. Mass evacuation system (MES)

a. Also referred to as Rapid Evacuation Systems (RES). Certain high-sided ships in service are fitted with a MES that permits the safe, fast and dry shod evacuation of a large number of personnel from the ship in an 'Abandon Ship' situation. Ships fitted with a MES are provided with the appropriate operating, training and maintenance documentation. There are two systems in use at present:

b. **The DBC system.** This consists of a steel housing containing a tubular fabric escape chute, an inflatable platform and fender. The equipment is deployed by removing two safety pins and operating the release lever. The Slide Away slides outboard on angled rails, a trap door on the bottom of the Slide Away opens allowing the chute and platform to drop into the water; the platform and fender automatically inflate. The platform is then bowsed into the ship's side using a manual winch. The liferafts are individually launched and retrieved one at a time via a retrieval line system. This enables the liferafts to be secured to the platform and inflated via their short-pull painter line.

Fig 6-30. Typical DBC - mass evacuation system

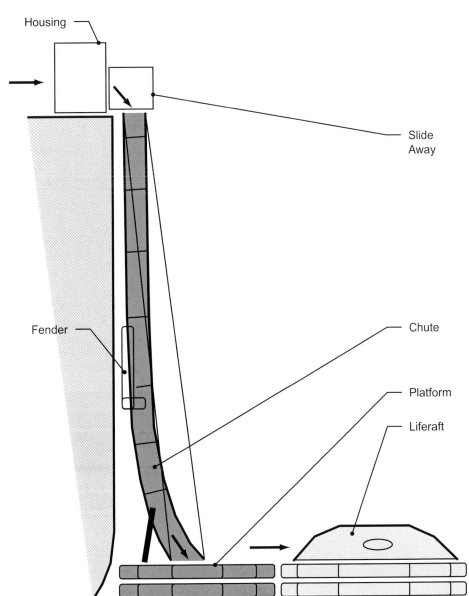

c.   **The MarinArk system.** This system consists of a GRP housing containing two tubular fabric escape chutes, and four inflatable liferafts (109 persons in each). The equipment is deployed by pulling a pump handle; the deployment is fully automatic (there are three other methods of deployment should the previous one fail). The platform is pushed automatically outboard on rails. At the end of the travel the platform tips over allowing the chutes and liferafts to drop into the water. The liferafts are inter-connected and inflate automatically. The liferafts are then bowsed into the ship's side via an electric winch with a manual override facility. The system is then ready for use.

Fig 6-31. Typical MarinArk – mass evacuation system

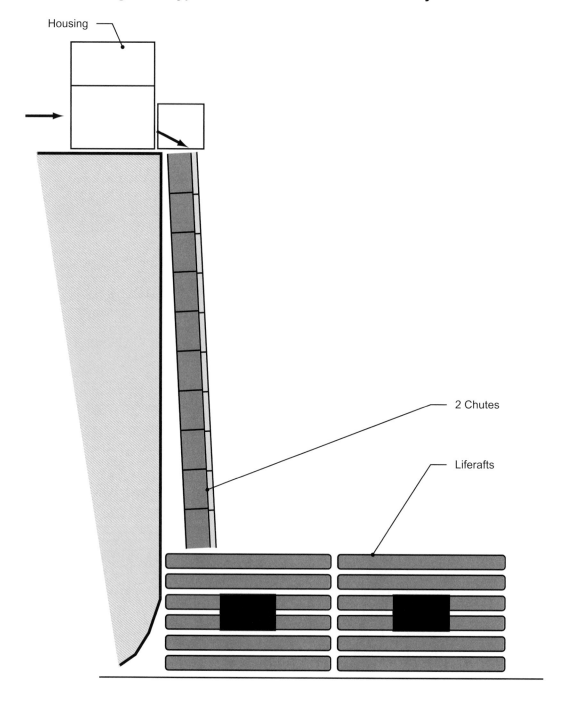

06014. Liferaft – immediate action on boarding

Cut, Stream, Close and Maintain.

a. **Search for survivors**. Listen for whistles; post lookouts to search for survivors, spot signalling lights and lights of other rafts, ships and aircraft during the hours of darkness. **Ensure the drogue** is streamed. In calm weather, limited assistance in manoeuvring the raft for short distances can be obtained by using the drogue and/or paddles. (See Para 06008(k) sub para (13). When there is a strong breeze blowing, the raft may drift faster than even good swimmers can swim; survivors may then be found to windward of the raft. The drogue will reduce the drift speed of the raft. If survivors are to leeward, speed downwind can be increased by tripping the drogue and water pockets.

b. **Examine the raft thoroughly for leaks**. CO_2 gas in concentrated form is dangerous. It is therefore important to make sure that there are no serious internal leaks when both entrances are closed. The gas cannot be detected by smell but its presence should be suspected if survivors are panting for breath and/or developing headaches. Immediately leakage of gas is suspected, first thoroughly ventilate the raft, then trace and deal with the cause. Instructions for repair are given in Para 06017 sub para g.

c. **Issue anti-seasickness tablets**. Anti-seasickness tablets are stowed in a pocket on the right-hand side of the after entrance looking out of the raft, and must be issued to everyone in the liferaft as soon as practical after boarding. Dosage instructions are printed on the outside of the packet and extra supplies of tablets are in the First Aid kit in the Survival Aids Pack. **Everyone** should take the tablets for the first 48 hours; even if personnel have never been seasick before they may become so in the raft, and a lot of body fluid can be lost by vomiting. After 48 hours personnel should be accustomed to the raft motion and need only take the tablets if actually suffering from seasickness. The tablets may make the mouth dry, and cause some minor visual disturbance or drowsiness but they will not cause any serious harm.

d. **Bail raft dry**. The liferaft is fitted with two integral bailers fitted to the floor of the raft, one either side of the centre thwart. After removing a bailer from its stowage bag, operation and subsequent draining of water from the liferaft is achieved by pushing the lip of the funnel beneath the level of water within the raft, raising the funnel out of the water to its full extent and allowing the water to drain out through the sleeve to the outside of the liferaft. Continue this action until the liferaft is drained of water. After use, to seal off the bailer opening and prevent ingress of water, the bailer should be wound around itself to form a spiral before it is stowed. Residual water in the liferaft can be mopped up using one of the sponges found in the Survival Aids Pack.

e. **Inflate the floor**. Inflate the floor by means of the topping-up pump as and when required.

f. **Treat injuries**. Even minor injuries should be treated at once. Instructions for using the First Aid kit are included with the kit, and instructions in First Aid are given in **BR 1329, Handbook for Survivors,** a copy of which is in each liferaft.

g. **Activate EPIRB and SART.** SARTs or EPIRBs must be activated. Instructions are printed on the side of the equipment.

h.   Gather wreckage. Gather any wreckage that may be considered to be useful either in the raft or on land. Containers of any type are valuable. Extra clothing is of vital and immediate importance in cold weather. Strip all belongings off the bodies of drowned personnel. Retain any similarly recovered Identity discs and personal gear. Be careful to stow metal containers and sharp objects where they will not wear and puncture the fabric of the raft.

i.   **Ventilate raft**. Adjust entrances and ports as required to reduce CO_2 content and foul air. In cold climates and/or high wind and sea states the CO_2 content can be lowered by opening a look-out port for five minutes every 30 minutes for 20 plus survivors, five minutes every 60 minutes for 10-20 survivors, or five minutes every 90 minutes if there are less than ten survivors in the raft.

j.   **Congregate rafts**. When the above instructions have been carried out all rafts should, if possible, congregate and be secured to each other by means of long lines tied to the towing patches. Apart from the ability to transfer personnel and stores, such a collection of rafts is better for morale and is far easier to spot from the air than isolated rafts.

06015. Liferaft – subsequent actions on boarding

a.   **Designate command**. When the rafts are congregated and secured, the senior officer or rating fit to do so should assume command of the flotilla and appoint a leader in each raft.

b.   **Muster survivors**. A muster of survivors is to be taken. In warm climates, transfers of personnel from one raft to another to equalise the numbers may be carried out immediately (the fewer personnel in each raft the cooler they will be). In the Arctic, bring rafts up to full complement for mutual warmth, and secure any empty rafts by lines approximately ten metres in length attached to Painter Line/Towing Patches.

Note.   *In a cold environment where the liferaft is completely closed down, entrances and ports must be adjusted for the ventilation of CO_2 from the occupants' respiration.*

c.   **Organise a duty roster**. A roster should be started as soon as possible, and the personnel in each raft detailed for domestic and other duties. It is most important that the minds of survivors be kept occupied, whilst keeping physical exertions to a minimum.

d.   **Detail lookouts**. Lookout duties should be kept to a maximum of 30 minutes on watch dependent on weather conditions. In hot climates, shirt sleeves must be rolled down, and heads covered to give protection from sunburn, sunstroke etc. In cold inclement weather it is important that lookouts are suitably clothed in survival suits, lifejackets and survival mittens when carrying out their duties. Ensure signalling aids are immediately to hand, particularly at night or during poor visibility. Prevent damage to the raft. No sharp-edged pieces of hard material must be allowed to lie about the raft. Unsheathed knives, jagged tins, the sharp points of the tongues of buckles on overalls, sandals etc., may cause leaks which are difficult to trace, and endanger personal safety.

e.   **Share stores and equipment**. When all stores, equipment and spare clothing in each raft has been mustered, it should be shared out equally amongst the flotilla. In the Arctic this procedure should be delayed until the personnel are re-warmed.

f.   **Adapting to conditions**. Personnel should now settle down to life on the raft, familiarise themselves with the raft and its equipment, read **BR 1329** and take its advice. Personnel will appreciate that every situation cannot be allowed for; common sense and initiative must prevail to deal with unexpected situations.

06016. Liferaft – food and water

a.   **Introduction.** Survivors can live for weeks without food provided they have water. It is for this reason that as much water has been supplied as can be stowed in the rafts. The food ration, consisting of glucose biscuits, has been found by experiment to be the kind of diet most suitable for survivors. These biscuits are to be eaten every six hours. This quantity has been designed to give sufficient energy to keep personnel fit for the period you may expect to be adrift. The diet contains no meat foods, which would make personnel pass more urine than does the sugar of your ration, and, therefore, it helps to conserve body water. The ability to survive can be increased by avoiding vomiting and sweating which result in loss of liquid from the body.

b.   **Water.** Drinking water is supplied in sachets stowed in the Survival Aids Pack. There are rations for 25 persons for three days. Do not issue any water during the first 24 hours. A person's body is already full of water – if you put more into it during the first 24 hours it will be wasted in the form of urine. After 24 hours the body will be drier and will absorb any water you drink, just as a dry sponge will hold water but a wet sponge will not hold any more. The only exception is for a casualty who has severe external wounds. If a casualty has obviously bled a lot, or if he or she has been badly burned, their water ration must start immediately if they are conscious.

c.   **Daily water ration**. The daily ration of water per person is four x 125ml sachets. To ensure that rules regarding rationing and drinking of water are adhered to, the raft commander should oversee the water usage. Resist the temptation to cut down the ration below this level. If you do, you are going to get weak very quickly and your chance of survival is lessened. However, when you are left with your last day's ration is it permissible to half the ration to provide water for the next day.

d.   **Sea water**. **It is fatal to drink seawater**. Numerous lives were lost from this cause during the last war. Madness and death follow very quickly after drinking seawater. (It is useless, and may actually be harmful, to try to introduce seawater into the back passage). It is better not to use seawater for the dry and cracked lips, which are particularly liable to occur in the tropics. Forcibly restrain anyone who tries to drink seawater.

e.   **Urine**. Since personnel are drinking less water than you normally do, less urine will be passed. It will be more concentrated and will, therefore, appear dark coloured. It may even cause a burning sensation when you pass it, which you will do much less frequently than is your normal habit. This is nothing to worry about. You may have experienced the same sort of thing after sweating a lot in the tropics. **Urine should not be drunk**; it is of no benefit, and can be harmful.

f.   **Saving Drinking Water.** In the tropics carry out the following instructions to reduce the need for water:

(1)   Keep out of the sun and try to prevent the sun's rays shining directly into the liferaft.

(2)   Align the drogue with an entrance and adjust entrances and ports to allow as much breeze as possible to blow through the raft. If the floor has been inflated, deflate it during the day to enable the floor area to be kept cool by the outside seawater. Inflate again at night.

(3)   To help reduce the temperature inside the raft keep the outside of the canopy wet with sea water throughout the heat of the day, but avoid the rain water catchments on the canopy. Detail individuals for spells of dousing duty of not more than ten minutes each in turn.

(4)   Keep your clothing wet during the day by immersing your shirt in the sea and putting it on soaking wet, even if you are not feeling hot. Rinse your clothes before sundown and squeeze it out to get rid of any accumulated salt. Your clothing and the floor of the raft should be dried before sundown.

(5)   Don't go swimming. Swimming wastes energy and will increase your thirst. Your food ration is not enough to allow for wasted energy. Swimming is dangerous in that the raft may be drifting faster than you can swim. Also remember sharks.

g.   **Supplementing water rations**

(1)   You must make every effort to add to your water rations, by the collection of rainwater. In the Tropics, storms can be very heavy and may be frequent at certain seasons. With care and common sense, large quantities of rainwater may be collected and stored and with lives saved. It is, therefore, important that a night look-out should be detailed, not only to look for rescuing craft, but to rouse companions should rain occur. Rain-water may be collected and stored by the following methods:

(a)   The roof of the canopy has two rainwater catchments. Drain tubes from these catchments allow for the filling of water containers. Ensure the water is free from salt before starting to collect it in containers.

(b)   Fill every container that you can find, such as water bags, empty water cans, lifejackets and even boots and shoes. The end of the rainwater drain tube fits snugly over the mouthpiece of the lifejacket. Press the valve down to allow the water to pass into the lifejacket.

(c)   The entrance closure sleeves and lookout ports of the raft can be arranged to collect rainwater if weather conditions permit.

(2)   When all possible containers are filled, then drink your fill of the rain that follows. Once the rain stops, carry on your normal ration routine, but remember to use the stored rainwater first. Water will condense on the inner lining of the canopy. Collect this if possible, but take care that it is not contaminated with seawater from the raft floor. In the Arctic, water can be obtained from sheltered pools in blue icebergs (i.e. old icebergs) and from the ice of those bergs. New icebergs are milky-grey in colour; their ice is salty and must **not** be used for drinking water. Do not suck ice. First let it melt and then drink the water only if it is not salty.

h.   **Food.** Each liferaft carries biscuit rations for a three-day period.   These should be eaten every six hours.   Each biscuit package should be distributed among the liferafts complement of survivors prior to the first day's water ration.   It may be left to each person's discretion at what time they actually eat the biscuit, but each person must eat their daily ration.   As the food does not leave any useless residue there is nothing for your bowels to pass on. You will, therefore, appear to be constipated. This need not worry you; in fact, it is beneficial since the less your bowels work the less water you are wasting.

i.   **Supplementing the food ration with seafood**.   Many varieties of fish will be seen from a quietly floating raft, particularly in tropical waters.   These will range from flying fish, crabs or octopus-like animals to barracuda, turtles, porpoises, giant rays, sharks and whales.   You must not eat fish flesh unless you have, the same day, been able to drink at least 20 fluid ounces of rain-water over and above your ration; that is about 50 fluid ounces in all.   The reason is that when such fish or animal flesh is eaten, the body has to make urine to get rid of the waste products of flesh digestion.   The water for this urine comes out of the water stored in your body.   You cannot afford to waste this amount of water if you are on your ration only.   (It is important to remember that water is of more value to you than food).

Note.   Sharks, porpoises, giant rays and whales will not deliberately attack the raft if they are left alone.   Never try to catch a shark from a raft; never bathe or dangle arms or legs in the water for amusement, nor trail anything to attract sharks.   Sharks may lurk in the shade underneath the raft out of your vision, showing a somewhat unnerving desire to sometimes buffet the raft, either in an attempt to brush parasites from the body or to catch the numerous suckerfish that may cling to the underside of the liferaft.

06017.   Liferaft – general raftsmanship

a.   **Control and command**.   Keep rafts congregated and secured to each other. This will assist morale, and provide mutual aid as well as presenting a bigger target for searchers to spot.   The senior officer or rating will take charge of the flotilla and appoint a leader in each raft.   A daily routine should be worked out and the leader of each raft should see that this routine is carried out.   The person in charge of the flotilla should draw up a schedule on the use of distress flares, bearing in mind the need to spread supplies over five days.   The search will start at the place where your ship was lost, due allowances being made for wind and current drift.   You should stream the drogue and ensure the water pockets are untripped at all times to cut down wind and drift.   If the drogue is carried away a spare can be found in the Ancillary Bag with the end attached to the starboard side of the raft.   The search for the rafts may be made by either aircraft or ships, or both combined.

b.   **Navigating the raft**.   In relatively calm conditions and if the need arises it is possible to manoeuvre the raft for short distances by working the drogue.   To navigate with the drogue, haul the raft up to the drogue, take the drogue out of the water, bunch it and throw in the direction required.   Pull the raft up to it and repeat as necessary.   To throw the drogue to its full length of line and to achieve a faster sink rate, tie a weight such as a spare shoe or boot to it.   Liferafts are supplied with two paddles to assist manoeuvring.   When manoeuvring the raft, trip the water pockets either side of each entrance by means of the trip lines. Speed downwind is increased by tripping the drogue and the water pockets.   Navigation against a wind of any strength will not be possible, so navigation should always be across the wind or downwind.   When rafts are congregating, progress should be made towards those downwind; those furthest downwind should stream their drogue to reduce the rate of drift.

c.   **Boarding the liferaft and distributing weight**. The normal method of boarding is by the boarding ramps situated at each entrance. As soon as one person is aboard they should assist others. On boarding, survivors should occupy the windward side of the liferaft first to minimise the danger of capsizing in strong winds. In a partially occupied liferaft, survivors should always occupy the windward side. Once aboard, the raft survivors not involved in rescuing others should avoid congestion around the entrance unless assisting other survivors to board.

d.   **Raft capsizing**. If there is danger of your raft capsizing, everyone should don lifejackets, and inflate them. If the raft capsizes do not panic; the raft will float upside down and you will be able to vacate it through either of the entrances. The raft should then be righted and boarded again by the survivors. Take care that the liferaft - when upside down and empty of survivors - does not blow away.

e.   **Righting a capsized raft** (Fig 6-32). Righting of the liferaft can be carried out by one person. However, two or more persons may be required to carry out this operation on the NL MK1 using the procedure as follows.

   (1)   The liferaft should be manoeuvred so the topside/canopy of the liferaft is facing upwind as the wind can assist the righting process.

   (2)   Using the white lifeline secured around the liferaft, the righting persons should manoeuvre themselves to a position close to the gas cylinders.

   (3)   Using the ladder under the boarding ramp place their feet in the bottom rung and kick backwards with their legs to enable them to reach the straps on the CO_2 cylinders.

   (4)   Next, climb on to the cylinders and stand on the outboard cylinder shoulder to shoulder with inner feet on the cylinder and outer feet on the bottom tube of the raft (this will help them keep the liferaft square as it comes over).

   (5)   Form a semi-crouch position and pull in the re-righting straps until taut (they are elasticated so work in the straps) and take as high a grip as is possible making sure both persons are holding the same position on the straps (this will also help in keeping the raft square as it comes over).

   (6)   There may be surface tension between the canopy of the liferaft and the water, so bounce at the same time to help break the surface tension. Then both persons begin to lean straight back remaining shoulder to shoulder.

   (7)   As the liferaft is pulled over gather the righting straps using inner hands, at the same time make a fist with your other hands and put them in the air to await the floor of the liferaft to touch them, this will give you an air pocket underneath the liferaft. As soon as your hands touch the floor of the liferaft bring them straight back down again; otherwise both persons will be pushed under the water.

   (8)   While underneath the liferaft relax on your back and let your feet float up to the surface of the water. At the same time begin to slide to the outside of the liferaft maintaining a point of contact with the straps underneath to avoid being caught up in them.

(9)   Once the liferaft is fully righted reach out with the free hand and get a firm grip of the lifeline, or the bottom of the tube and pull yourself out at 90° to the straps.

Note.   *Due to the large diameter of the liferaft it will be necessary to be submerged for a few seconds before swimming from under.*

(10) When on the outside of the liferaft hold onto the lifeline and replace your visor. It is important to ensure that both persons are out from underneath before taking hold of the lifeline or boarding

Fig 6-32. A typical example of righting a lifeRaft

f.   **Hauling an injured person into a raft.** The following procedures assume the injured person is incapable of assisting the rescuers.

(1)   *Two-person routine.* If an injured survivor is floating some distance away, one person should swim to them with the rescue quoit and line, the other end of which is secured on board. Both can then be hauled towards the raft. The injured person should be brought close alongside with their back to the raft and then, if possible, seated in the boarding ramp. Removal of the injured person from the water into the liferaft is best carried out by two people sitting astride the buoyancy chamber facing each other, with their backs against the arches. In this position the rescuers reach outboard and, while holding the safety straps on the arch tube with one hand, clasp the survivor under the armpits, or their clothing at the shoulders, and ease them onto the boarding ramp and then into the raft. Other personnel in the raft should assist as necessary.

(2)   *One-person routine.* If only one person is available for carrying out the recovery of the survivor, the rescuer should stand with feet fairly close together and legs pressed hard against the buoyancy chamber. Reaching outboard, the rescuer should, if possible, pass their hands under the armpits of the injured person and clasp them together on the injured person's chest. If this is not possible, firmly grasp the clothing on the survivor's shoulders. Push them downward first before starting the upward pull, when the rescuer's arms and body should be straightened and the weight thrown backwards.

By thus employing the full length of the body as a lever against the weight of the injured person, the latter will more easily be hauled inboard.

g.   **Maintaining and repairing the raft**. Your raft is designed not only to keep you afloat but also to surround you with a layer of still air, which will insulate you against extremes of temperature.

(1)   *Inflating the floor*. Inflate the floor by means of the topping-up pump and use it to keep the raft topped up.

(2)   *Examining the raft for damage*. One of the first actions on boarding the raft is to examine it thoroughly for damage. Pay particular attention to buoyancy chamber and arch pressures; flabbiness may indicate leakage from unsuspected or minor sources.

(a)   Examine the topping-up valves and deflation plugs (The deflation plugs have a slotted head and if loose should be tightened with the back of the blade of the J knife).

(b)   Examine the fabric parts of the raft.

(3)   *Repairing a small hole or tear*. If a small hole or tear is found, plug it at once with the smallest leak stopper that can be used. Care must be exercised in using the stopper. A slight screwing motion may be necessary to seat it correctly, but do not keep on screwing, as this will enlarge the hole.

(4)   *Repairing large holes*. Four repair clamps are provided for this purpose. Instructions for their use are as follows:

(a)   Unscrew the butterfly nut fully from thread.

(b)   Separate the oval-shaped metal plates.

(c)   Insert the metal plate with rubber washer through the hole or tear and turn into a position whereby the damaged area is covered.

(d)   Place the second plate over the exterior of damaged area and mate up with plate in sub para (c).

(e)   Screw the butterfly nut on to the thread and fully tighten up to ensure an airtight and watertight seal.

06018. Liferaft – raftsmanship in the Arctic
In the Arctic, first close the outer cover and inner sleeve at both entrances, and inflate the floor. Make sure there are no leaks of CO_2 gas into the raft.

a.   **Closing the outer cover**

(1)   Do up the zips.

(2)   Close the inner sleeve by doing up the zips.

b.   **Dealing with chilled survivors.** If there are survivors in your raft chilled from immersion and shivering uncontrollably, warm them and ensure they have their once-only survival suits on. Three Thermal Protection Aids can be found in the Survival Aids Bags.

Huddle everybody together, ensuring that any persons without survival suits are situated between those people wearing suits. In a partially occupied liferaft survivors should always occupy the windward side.

c.   **Maintaining a comfortable environment.** When personnel are warm and the atmosphere in the raft is heavy and uncomfortable, survival suits may be removed to prevent sweating and to distribute body heat equally throughout the raft. If necessary, open the entrance ports slightly at each end to provide ventilation, adjusting as required to suit conditions. Then:

(1)   Keep as dry and warm as possible.

(2)   Mop up the floor of the raft and keep it as dry as you can at all times.

(3)   Huddle together - the closer you huddle together the warmer it will be.

(4)   Cover yourselves with all the spare clothing that has been salvaged.

Notes:

1.   *It is particularly important that feet are kept warm. Keep moving toes, fingers, hands and feet, clench fists and stretch limbs. This provides a little warmth and will keep the circulation going in the hands and feet.*

2.   *Avoid exposure to the cold. Remember the face, ears and hands are quickly affected by frostbite. Lookouts should be well wrapped up, and monitored for signs of imminent frostbite and cold as the persons themselves may be unaware.*

06019. Liferaft – raftsmanship in the tropics
In the Tropics instructions are designed to preserve body water. Water is lost from the body in the breath, in the urine, in bowel motions and most of all by evaporation from the skin. Obviously personnel lose water when they sweat, but personnel are also losing water if their skin feels dry. Keep out of the sun; wet shirts with seawater by day, and take turns to douse the raft; align the drogue onto a position on the raft, which will allow as much breeze as possible to blow through the entrances. It will be cooler by day if the floor of the raft is deflated, but inflate it at night, and ensure any clothing used for dousing of the raft in the day is dry by nightfall, as tropical nights can be cold. Lookouts must be well protected from the sun.

06020. Liferaft – organising watches
Ideally, personnel in each raft should be divided into five watches; each watch should do a two-hour turn of duty. Such arrangements may not be practicable and circumstances will dictate the precise organisation.

a.   **Duties.** The following duties must be carried out, and personnel in each watch should be detailed to carry out the tasks.

(1)   Inspection of raft hourly; baling and drying out; topping up the buoyancy tube and repairs.

(2)   Collection of rainwater; in tropics, dousing outside of liferaft with seawater.

(3)   Care of injured personnel, distribution of rations at morning, noon and night.

(4)   Signalling (using distress flares, heliograph, Sarbe Locator Beacon and GMDSS where fitted).

(5)   Look-out duty - ideally not longer than 30 minutes on watch; less, if weather conditions dictate.

b.   **Keeping a log**. The raft leader should keep a log recording incidents of weather, morale, and conditions within the raft. The log should also contain issue of rations, condition of injured personnel. Remember, valuable information can be gathered from a log, which will greatly assist the raft designer and medical authorities. Blank pages are provided at the back of **BR 1329** for the keeping of such a log.

06021. Land survival

a.   **Making for land**. Although you are advised not to attempt to navigate your liferaft away from the scene of a sinking in mid-ocean, you should attempt to reach land if such is in sight or is known to be in the immediate vicinity. There are numerous islands in certain tropical seas. It is possible to locate a tropical island, although not directly visible, by:

(1)   Noticing the presence of low cloud, which does not alter its position, in an otherwise clear sky.

(2)   Watching the flight of birds. Where birds are seen in numbers flying in a fixed direction in the evening, they are flying towards land. The presence of occasional birds at sea does not mean land is near.

(3)   Noticing a localised green haze in the sky caused by reflection from lagoons.

b.   **Reefs**. Tropical islands are usually surrounded by coral reefs. Such coral is sharp and causes quite severe wounds, which often become infected and ulcerate very easily. Coral reefs are often covered by dangerous surf and by breaking seas. A smooth break in the line of surf will indicate a passage through the reef. Always try to make for this smooth patch. The chances are that your raft will be badly damaged by the coral. Before reaching such a reef you must:

(1)   Don and inflate your life jacket.

(2)   Put on boots and protect your hands with strips of cloth or similar material.

(3)   Get outside the canopy - so that you are not trapped if the liferaft strikes, or in case you capsize in the breakers.

Note.   *All these points are equally applicable when approaching any rocky, rough type of coastline.*

c.   **Salvaging equipment**. The liferaft and equipment are valuable items for survival on land. Attempts should be made to salvage all available items of equipment. Where conditions permit, exercise patience and navigate the raft so as to get the most favourable approach for landing.

d. **Survival on land in the Tropics**

(1) *Obtaining water.* If you land on a tropical island your problem will be that of a water supply. If the island is inhabited, water must be available and your problems are over. It may, however, be small and uninhabited. Even so, water can still be found or made. If no stream can be found, dig in the sand above the high water mark. As soon as you strike damp sand stop digging and let water accumulate in the sandpit. It will taste salty or brackish. Continue such diggings farther away from the sea until you find water, which is drinkable. Water may be obtained from:

    (a) Vines and Rattan (not with red sap).

    (b) Bamboo.

    (c) Coconuts.

    (d) Palms.

    (e) Natural pools and ponds.

    (f) Pitcher plants.

(2) *Boiling Water.* Water should be boiled for five minutes before being used for drinking whenever the island is inhabited by natives or where pollution of a stream is suspected. It is possible to boil water in the stems of bamboo trees. Cut off a suitable length just below a cross partition; fill the hollow stem with water and lay it across a fire at an angle of 45°. The water will boil before the wood burns.

(3) *Wading.* Do not wade in the lagoons. There are dangerous fish, which inhabit the sand and hollows in the reefs. Beware at all times of sharp coral.

e. **Survival in the arctic snow or ice.** In the winter your main problem is to keep warm and find food. Water should not be difficult to obtain from snow and ice and in summer from freshwater pools on ice floes.

(1) *Shelter.* If your liferaft is intact it will provide you with a shelter - it will be as effective on land as afloat. Place your liferaft in a sheltered spot, and if possible keep it off the snow or ice by putting mosses, lichens or other soft vegetation under the floor. The inside of the liferaft will be even warmer if you can cover the tent with light vegetation to increase the insulation. Should your liferaft be destroyed, it is possible to build a shelter from snow-blocks, igloo fashion, or a shelter may be provided by a dugout in the snow.

(2) *Warmth.* If you are able to build a fire, build it just outside the entrance to the raft/shelter, far enough away to avoid the risk of burning your raft, which is flammable. A screen of logs behind the fire will reflect heat towards the liferaft/ shelter. Brush off all snow from clothing before entering the shelter; otherwise the snow will thaw with the warmth inside and freeze when you go out again, when it cannot be easily got rid of. Boots and socks should be carefully dried out at night, in order to guard against frostbite and help preserve the footwear. Footwear is a vital part of your clothing, which you may not be able to replace. Do not leave it unattended near a fire.

f.   **Rescue hints – all climates.** Always keep dry material ready for use as a signal fire should rescue aircraft or ships appear. If possible, a large SOS sign should be made on any beach or open ground - using coloured/contrasting materials such as dark soil, stones, seaweed, lifejackets etc on a sandy beach or on snow. Make the letters as large as possible with the materials available. You should make actual letters, rather than the Morse dots and dashes (which may be mistaken for natural markings). If you have any matches, hoard them for use as a signal emergency - when you will need a light urgently. Keep dry material under nearby shelter, so that a signal fire can be started at a moment's notice. When once ablaze make smoke with damp vegetation. You will now appreciate the reason for gathering as much wreckage, clothing and personal effects as possible at the time of abandoning ship. Even trivial things like pins, bits of string, wrist watches and the like, may provide the materials you will require if compelled to survive on land.

06022. Training and familiarisation

a.   **Introduction**. Training prepares the individual psychologically for an emergency and reduces the mental and emotional shock caused by fear. This is attributable partly to familiarity with the procedure or drill, and partly to knowledge gained of the dangers to be faced and of the capabilities of the equipment provided. The passengers of a liner, for example, are less likely to panic when ordered to their boat station in emergency if they have already attended several boat drills. In the Royal Navy everyone must have a thorough knowledge of the life-saving equipment and should be drilled in its use.

b.   **Training for service personnel**

(1)   *Basic sea safety course (BSSC).* Before joining a ship all personnel have to complete a BSSC at the Royal Naval Sea Safety Training Centre. This course is valid for four years.

(2)   *Intermediate sea safety course (ISSC).* This course is to be completed by all personnel after the four year period from the BSSC. This course like the BSSC is only valid for four years.

(3)   *Embarked forces sea safety course (EFSSC).* Embarked forces (EF) that are required to serve on a ship for a period no longer than 28 days are to complete an EFSSC.

Note.   *EF cannot perform ship fire fighting or damage control duties. If they are to remain onboard longer than 28 days a BSSC or ISSC is to be completed.*

(4)   On the first occasion of joining a ship personnel should be briefed on the general Safety and Water Safety equipment carried by the ship, and provided with a diagram of the ship showing the disposition of the equipment and the action to be taken in the event of hands being ordered to Emergency Stations. Thereafter continuation training should be in accordance with BRd 9274.

c.   **Training and familiarisation for casual visitors**. There are many occasions when a ship embarks casual visitors: these may be service or civilian. On joining a ship that is at or going to sea, such visitors should, when practicable, be briefed on the Safety and Water Safety equipment carried by the ship. In any event they should be provided with a diagram of the ship showing the disposition of the equipment, and the action to be taken in the event of hands being ordered to Emergency Stations. When the number of visitors is small, the spare capacity in the number of lifejackets carried by the ship can be utilised in accordance with the Matrix DIN. For large numbers of visitors see sub para d.

d. **Provision of lifejackets for large numbers of civilian visitors**. Maritime Coastguard Agency (MCA) lifejackets must be embarked for such occasions. The procedure for demanding (and returning) these lifejackets, details of briefs and demonstrations that must be given prior to the ship sailing are laid down in **BRd 9467 Fleet Administration and General Orders.**

e. **Water safety equipment location diagram**. In all HM ships diagrams are to be sited in prominent positions throughout the ship showing the stowage positions of life-saving equipment. An example is shown in Fig 6-33.

f. **Instructional illustrations**. The following Water safety Life Saving posters are available from the Navy Graphics Centre, Building 159, Whale Island. Portsmouth, Hants PO2 8BY by emailing NPGO-GRAPHICS MAIL BOX and requesting which poster and how many are required. The number of posters per class of ship is controlled by NAVY SSM-AW SEA WO1 (RN) and NAVY-NLM PERS RFA XS CPOC (RFA).

Hazardous Duty Lifejacket Mk3	Navy graphics centre 10/091/01
General Service Lifejacket Mk 4	Navy graphics centre 10/091/02
Assault Troop Lifejacket Mk4	Navy graphics centre 10/091/03
Landing Craft Lifejacket Mk3	Navy graphics centre 10/091/04
COSALT Premier Lifejacket	Navy graphics centre 10/091/05
Intrepid OOS Suit with GSLJ	Navy graphics centre 10/091/06
Intrepid OOS Suit with COSALT LJ	Navy graphics centre 10/091/07
COSALT Premier LJ Dressing Procedure	Navy graphics centre 10/091/08
Crewsaver Elite Twin Chamber LJ	Navy graphics centre 10/091/09
Crewsaver 275N Yachting Lifejacket – MOD	Navy graphics centre 10/091/10
Crewsaver 275N Yachting Lifejacket – MOD	
Dressing Procedure	Navy graphics centre 10/091/11
50 Man Liferaft	Navy graphics centre 11/488
16 Man liferaft	Navy graphics centre 11/488.01
6 Man liferaft	Navy graphics centre 11/488/01
25 Man Liferaft (NL Mk1)	Navy graphics centre 14/698
Davit Launched Liferaft	RN S3274

06023. Maintenance of water safety equipment

All ratings of the Seaman Specialist branch are qualified in the use and maintenance of life-saving equipment. HM ships not complemented with a Seaman Specialist carry at least one rating specially trained in the use and maintenance of life-saving equipment; they are designated the title Water Safety Equipment Maintainer (WSEM). Courses on the Maintenance of Water Safety Equipment are given by the Royal Naval Water Safety Equipment School HMS SULTAN and by the Royal Naval School of Seamanship HMS RALEIGH. Equipment must be maintained in accordance with the procedures and schedules laid down in the **Water Safety Equipment Log**, which is part of the ship's Maintenance System. All maintenance carried out is to be supervised by a suitably qualified person.

Fig 6-33. Typical stowage for water safety equipment (example)

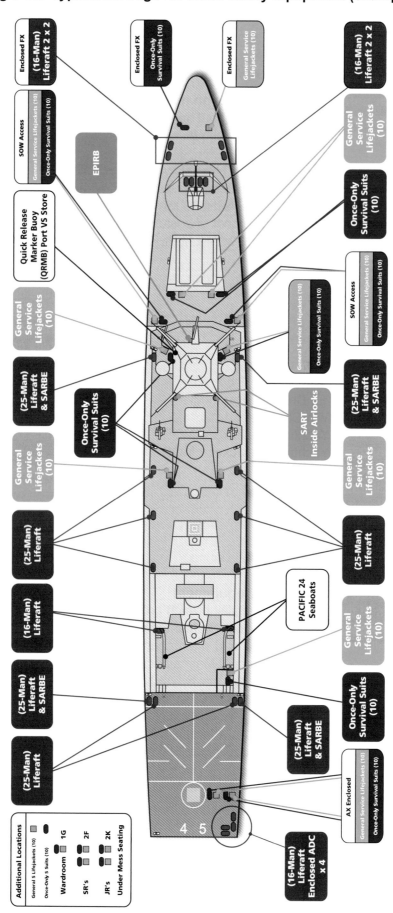

06024. Water safety equipment log (WSEL)

This log forms part of a ship's Maintenance System and is used to plan and record the servicing tests and inspections called for on a ship's outfit of water safety equipment. Details of the criteria regarding the qualifications necessary for Water Safety Equipment Maintainers and Water safety Equipment Supervisors are given in the foreword of the WSEL.

06025. Swimmer of the watch recovery rig

a.   **Introduction**. The Swimmer of the Watch (SOW) rig (Fig 6-34) is a very effective method of recovering a person from the water, particularly when rough seas or other circumstances preclude the safe use of a boat. Before assuming the duties of SOW the person must be fully trained and endorsed competent by the CBM/Bosun/ Seamanship Safety Officer in all aspects of the drills, maintenance of equipment, and ability to function effectively in the water.

Fig 6-34. Swimmer of the watch recovery rig

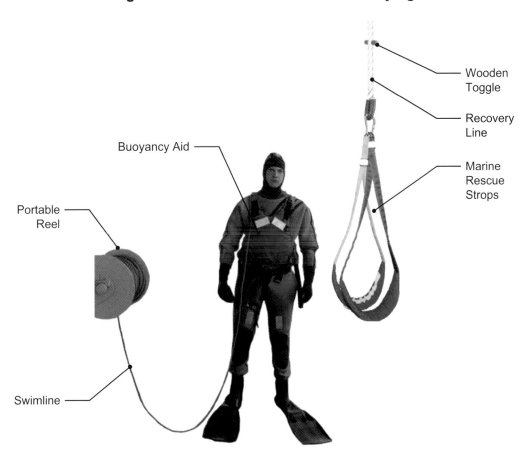

b.   **Training.** All AB Seaman Specialists are trained as SOW. Where non Seaman Specialists are borne, HMS RALEIGH can provide training to nominated personnel. On completion of initial training, a locally produced Certificate of Competency Record Card is to be made up (see example overleaf) as proof that the SOW is safe to conduct the required tasks involved. The certificate is to be retained within the Seamanship Data Book and is to be used to record each task that the SOW undertakes. The Remarks Column should be used to record the duration of the task and any other relevant information.

CERTIFICATE OF COMPETENCE

SWIMMER OF THE WATCH

SHIP/UNIT....................................

NAME...RATE..................................

DATE OF TRAINING/QUALIFIED AS COMPETENT...

SIGNED...NOMINATED OFFICER.

RECORD OF SOW TASKS				
Date	Sea Conditions	Serial No	Remarks	Supervisors Signature

c. **Equipment required – surface ship**

SOW Recovery Gantry	Rigged in accordance with Ships Drawings	
Recovery Line 16mm Polypropylene, length to suit, stowed on a portable reel, SDN 004515659. End fitted with soft eye 4" or 10cm long with leather chaffing piece: Wooden toggle	0350/075-0861 5340-99-924-4520 Local manufacture	The toggle is to be fitted to stop the splice being pulled into the block. Its precise position is optional, as it can be used to indicate the 'high enough' position for the recovery of the casualty or swimmer.
Swimline 8mm Polyethylene	4020-99-543-0141	110 metres, stowed on a portable reel with both ends whipped and heat sealed.
Blocks	3940-99-521-2797	SRBF block with swivel, oval eye and becket.
Shackles for Blocks Straight screw Bow screw	4030-99-721-6090 4030-99-721-6105	Straight shackle - straight pull. Bow shackle - angled pull.
Man Overboard Recovery Stretcher(MORS) Karabiner hook	2090-99-974-9030 8465-99-770-7551	3 x legged Sling
For'ard steadying line for MORS Polypropylene line Karabiner hook	0350/075-0861 8465-99-770-7551	Forward steadying line for MORS. Made from 16mm Polypropylene, length to suit. Fitted with a Karabiner hook at one end to be attached to the MORS at the reception area to ensure that it is tended when deployed from fwd.
Rescue Strop Assemblies Yellow (upper) 2 in number Blue (lower) 1 in number Karabiner hook 2 in number	4220-99-904-0115 4220-99-904-0116 8465-99-770-7551	The strops are to be provided at the recovery point to recover the Swimmer of the Watch. See details of preparing the rig on following page.
Swimmer's Equipment SOW Suit dry, Buoyancy Aid, AQ98 Light Neoprene hood, Neoprene gloves, Split fins, Divers knife, Belt divers,	4220-99-333-0107 (S) 4220-99-212-9985 (M) 4220-99-734-4983 (L) 4220-99-255-1620 (XL) 4220-99-912-9544 (S/M) 4220-99-724-6643 (L/XL) 4220-99-607-3900 4220-99-549-6837 (M) 4220-99-693-0503 (L) 4220-99-362-7024 (M) 4220-99-192-4777 (L) 4220-99-480-7975 4220-99-052-0629 4220-99924-1407	The suit that comes in four sizes must be a good fit, gloves are optional, as is the hood if water is clean and above 15° Celsius, where the duration of the immersion is expected to be below 15 minutes. The knife, which can be strapped to the swimmer's leg if preferred, must be secured to the scabbard with a line long enough to allow the swimmer to be able to work at arm's length. The knife should be used should the swimmer get into difficulties or the requirement exists to cut any lines preventing the safe recovery of the MOB.
Directional Pointers	Local Manufacture	One for daylight and one for darkness

d. **Personnel**

(1)   OIC as detailed by CBM. (OIC to wear a HDLJ and a white safety helmet).

(2)   Swimmer.

(3)   Swimline tender.

(4)   Minimum of six hands to man recovery line.

(5)   Swimmer director (Carrying the appropriate pointer).

(6)   Hand (wearing a HDLJ) to operate top guardrail and assist swimmer/casualty.

(7)   Medical Team (with stretcher for transportation of casualties if required).

(8)   Safety Officer.

Note.   *The team is to be dressed to suit weather conditions. Dress is to be specified in the initial broadcast.*

e.   **Preparing the rig**. On proceeding to sea the SOW recovery gantry/davit is to be rigged (out in readiness) in accordance with ship's drawings ready for immediate use at all times whilst at sea (see Note). Reeve the Recovery Line from outboard through the leading block(s) and on to the Portable Reel. Reel the swimline onto a locally manufactured portable reel and place this close to the rescue station. Check the Man Overboard Recovery Stretcher (MORS) (see Para 06026) is correct and ready for immediate use with steadying line available. Ensure both single and double strop assemblies are available and that all karabiners are fully operational.

Note.   *The only exception to the ruling above is that should the SOW gantry/davit interfere with any shipboard evolutions the gantry/davit can be stowed in the **UP** position temporarily until completion.*

f.   **Care of equipment**. Maintenance, testing and replacement of equipment should be in accordance with the MMS and WSEL. For management purposes the Double Strop Assembly and the Single Strop Assembly are to be retained as unique assemblies and identified with a local ID number. Strops used for SOW must not be used for any other purpose.

g.   **Actions on closing up**

(1)   Swimmer dresses and is checked by the OIC.

(2)   The swimline is attached to the 'D' ring on the back of the buoyancy aid by means of a bowline ensuring that at least three inches of the tail of the swimline is protruding (see Note). The swimline is then draped across the shoulder of the swimmer and placed between the VELCRO® brand tabs on the right hand shoulder strap of the buoyancy aid and a further VELCRO® brand tab situated at chest level. The swimline tender now pulls from the reel a bight of swimline sufficient to reach the waterline and either leads it over the ship's side or coils it neatly in one hand free for running. (The swimline reel should be sited so that the bight of swimline is well clear of the swimmer's entry position).

Note.   *Any member of the recovery team can tie the bowline, it must however, be proved to the OIC/Safety Officer prior to the swimmer's deployment.*

(3)   The recovery team takes the MORS from its stowage, removes the recovery line from its reel and hooks the outboard end of the recovery line to the slings of the MORS. The recovery line is then manned by the recovery team. (To ease confusion on deck, this task may be completed once the swimmer has been deployed).

(4)   The swimmer director is to be positioned as ordered by the OIC. Once the swimmer is deployed however, the director must ensure that he is within sight of the swimmer at all times and when within earshot encourages the swimmer throughout.

(5)   The medical team is to be sited in a convenient position so that they can be quickly brought in to remove the casualty, but not hamper the recovery. They must provide a stretcher ready for immediate use. If there is more than one casualty an additional stretcher provided by the medical team to remove casualties as they are brought inboard (see drills for operating the rig).

h.   **Operating the rig – surface ship**

ORDER	ACTION	SIGNAL
Swimmer ready (OIC)		
Carry on with the swimmer (OOW)	Lower the top guardrail. The swimmer positions himself at the deck edge, looks to the horizon and steps off. Set up the top guardrail. When the swimmer surfaces he vents his suit and checks the swimline is clear.	Thumbs up by the swimmer.
Swimmer is directed to the casualty by pointer	Swimmer swims on his back to the casualty, directed by the pointer. The swimmer reassures the casualty if conscious, then manoeuvres into position before grasping the casualty securely from behind. After checking the swimline is clear, he indicates he is ready to return.	Thumbs up by the swimmer.
Check away recovery line (OIC)	As soon as the swimmer is clear the for'ard steadying line is hooked to the MORS and the MORS is hoisted outboard and lowered into the water.	
Haul away swimline (OIC)	Swimline is hauled in to assist the swimmer's return to the recovery position. Care is to be taken not to haul away too quickly as this may cause the swimmer and casualty to be dragged beneath the surface.	
Avast hauling on the swimline (OIC)	This order is given when the swimmer is beneath the recovery position.	
Insert the casualty into the stretcher (OIC)	The swimmer, working from aft of the MORS, manoeuvres the casualty, upper torso first, into the MORS.	Thumbs up by the swimmer.
Swimmer swim clear (OIC)	Swimmer swims clear of the casualty, checking that his swimline is not fouled.	Thumbs up by the swimmer.
Walk away recovery line (OIC)	The recovery team walk away with the recovery line, taking care the MORS is hoisted smoothly without jerking.	
Avast recovery line (OIC)	The recovery team stop walking away and hold on to the recovery line.	

ORDER	ACTION	SIGNAL
Recover MORS inboard (OIC)	Bring the MORS inboard by grasping the inboard rungs of the stretcher and hauling it over the top guardrail.	
Walk back recovery line (OIC)	The recovery team carefully walk back with the recovery line in hand, allowing the MORS to be lowered to the deck. Unhook the MORS.	
Medical team in (OIC)	The medical team enter the recovery position and, using the MORS, quickly remove the casualty for treatment. If there is more than one casualty to be recovered the first casualty can be transferred to the spare stretcher supplied by the medical team. The MORS is then reattached to the recovery line and the rescue procedure repeated. Alternatively the *Double Strop recovery procedure remains an alternative method of recovering a casualty(s) from the water should the MORS become unfit for purpose. The* OIC can decide to use the double strop method if required.	
Prepare the recovery line for swimmer recovery (OIC)	Once the MORS has been removed, hook the single upper recovery strop to the recovery line and lower it to the swimmer, who places it over his head and tightens the becket. If the swimmer appears fatigued, or requests it, the double strop should be passed and the SOW secures himself into the double strop, the upper strop under the armpits, the lower strop behind the knees. The toggles of both strops are then tightened and the SOW is hoisted inboard as described for the MORS. However, if using the single strop, once the SOW is at deck-edge level the upper guard-wire must be lowered so the SOW can be assisted inboard and lowered to the deck. Immediately the SOW is inboard the top guard-wire must be re-set	Thumbs up by the swimmer when ready to be hoisted.
Swimmer inboard (OIC)	Set up the top guardrail (if necessary). Check on the swimmer's well-being, and then send him to report to the medical team or sickbay.	
Secure the recovery position. (OOW)	Secure the recovery position. Carry out 'After use' routines on all equipment. Ensure all gear is ready for immediate use.	

i.   **Equipment required – submarine**

Swimline 8mm Polyethylene	4020-99-543-0141	To be made up in accordance with sub para j below..
Knotted Recovery Line Polypropylene line (16mm). Karabiner Hook.	0350/075-0861 8465-99-770-7551	This is a multi-purpose line and during man overboard it is used by the recovery team to assist/haul the casualty and swimmer from the water onto the casing. It is made of 16mm polypropylene, 15min length with a soft eye spliced in both ends. One eye is to be protected by a chaffing piece and must be large enough to allow attachment of a karabiner hook. The line is to be knotted at 0.5m intervals.
Rescue Strop Assemblies Yellow (upper) 2 in number Blue (lower) 1 in number Karabiner hook 2 in number	4220-99-904-0115 4220-99-904-0116 8465-99-770-7551	The strops are to be provided at the recovery point to recover the Swimmer of the Watch. See details of preparing the rig on following page.
Swimmer's Equipment SOW Suit dry, Buoyancy Aid, AQ98 Light Neoprene hood, Neoprene gloves, Split fins, Divers knife, Belt divers,	4220-99-333-0107 (S) 4220-99-212-9985 (M) 4220-99-724-6643 (L) 4220-99-255-1620 (XL) 4220-99-912-9544 (S/M) 4220-99-724-6643 (L/XL) 4220-99-607-3900 4220-99-549-6837 (M) 4220-99-693-0503 (L) 4220-99-362-7024 (M) 4220-99-192-4777 (L) 4220-99-480-7975 4220-99-052-0629 4220-99-924-1407	The suit that comes in four sizes must be a good fit, gloves are optional, as is the hood if water is clean and above 15° Celsius, where the duration of the immersion is expected to be below 15 minutes. The knife, which can be strapped to the swimmer's leg if preferred, must be secured to the scabbard with a line long enough to allow the swimmer to be able to work at arm's length. The knife should be used should the swimmer get into difficulties or the requirement exists to cut any lines preventing the safe recovery of the MOB.
Directional Pointers	Local Manufacture	One for daylight and one for darkness

j.   **General equipment – submarine (Fig 6-35 and Fig 6-36)**

(1)   *Man overboard reel.* Made up from a design in the Rigging Warrant the MOB Reel is constructed from aluminium. On a SSN the reel is mounted on the fin handrail. On a SSBN it is fitted with a spigot that permits it to be fitted over a guardrail stanchion. This reel holds the swimline, which is attached to the reel by an eye splice. The basic design is similar but the fixing point can vary. The reel is fitted with a handle to facilitate winding. The swimline is made up from 110 metres of 8 mm polyethylene MMFC. NSN 4020-99-543-0141. An additional 15 metres length is spliced into the swimline at the outboard end to provide a two-legged arrangement. A karabiner hook (NSN 8465-99-770-7551) is fitted at the end of each spur by the use of a soft eye splice.

CAUTION

With the swimline attached the reel is quite heavy, requiring a two-man lift when transferring it to/from and around the casing.

Fig 6-35. Submarine man overboard reel

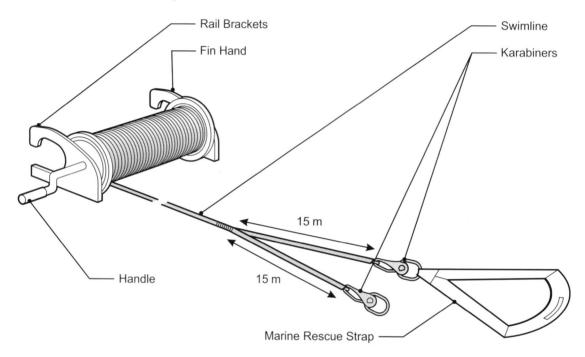

(2) *Knotted recovery lines.* This is a multi-purpose line which, during man overboard, is used by the recovery team to assist/haul the casualty and swimmer from the water onto the casing. It is a 15-metre length of 16mm polypropylene with a soft eye spiced in both ends. One eye is to be protected by a chafing piece and must be large enough to allow attachment of a karabiner hook. The line is to be knotted at 0.5-metre intervals.

Fig 6-36. Knotted recovery line

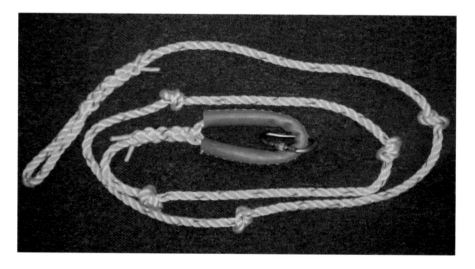

06026. Man Overboard Recovery Stretcher (MORS)

a. **Introduction.** The Man Overboard Recovery Stretcher (MORS), (Fig 6-37) NSN 2090-99-974-9030 allows the horizontal recovery of casualties from the water; it replaces the Single and Twin Marine Rescue strop Assemblies as the principle means of recovering casualties from the water via the SOW rig. The MORS is a floating stretcher made up of plastic rungs (similar to the Jason's cradle fitted in RN rescue boats) and is supported in the water by two attached floatation tubes. Operating instructions are supplied with the MORS and servicing and maintenance procedures are given in the WSEL. Recovery of Man Overboard drills and procedures when using the MORS are given in Para 06026 of this Chapter. When not in use the MORS is to be stowed in the PVC bag supplied in accordance with the instructions supplied with the equipment.

b. **Standard operating procedures**. When fitted on the upperdeck the MORS is to be situated in the vicinity of the SOW gantry and secured to fixed guardrails or other suitable fixtures depending on class of ship. Where there is a shortage of stowage space at the recovery station, alternative stowage arrangements can be used provided reaction times are not compromised.

c. The MORS is to be attached to the SOW recovery line and the stretcher raised to ensure there is clearance between the MORS and the top guardrail. If the MORS fails to clear the guardrail, reposition the toggle to allow adequate clearance.

d. A forward steadying line fitted with a Karabiner hook (8465-99-770-7551) is to be manufactured from 16mm polypropylene, length to suit. The steadying line is to be available with the MORS and is to be attached to the forward inboard end of the stretcher and led forward in the ship prior to the MORS being lowered. This line is to be used to steady the stretcher at all times during recovery operations.

Fig 6-37. Man overboard recovery stretcher (MORS)

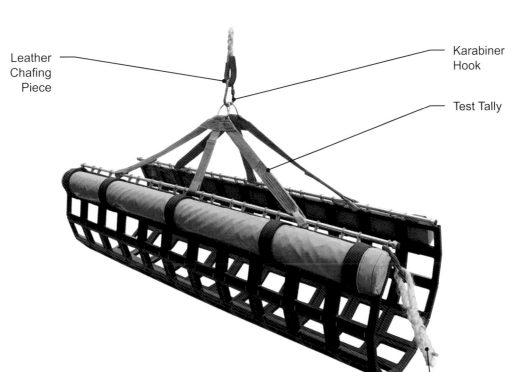

Leather Chafing Piece

Karabiner Hook

Test Tally

Steadying Line

06027. Man overboard dummy (RUTH)

A 40kg waterproof life-saving dummy (6910-99-783-7372) complete with orange overalls is allocated to give realism to man overboard exercises. It is filled with aggregate and has legs supported using plastic strips. It is lighter than the previous dummy (FRED) and therefore no lifejacket is required. The dry weight of RUTH is 40kg and the wet weight is 70kg. Cylume stick holders x 6 and a LJ2 light pocket are fitted.

06028. First-aid for the apparently drowned

The type of first-aid needed for a person who is apparently drowned depends upon their condition. Fig 6-38 indicates the type of first-aid treatment required for different states of rescued person at various stages of the rescue. The coxswain of the seaboat and the swimmer of the watch must assess the condition of the casualty in the water when they reach them and be prepared to give the necessary first-aid treatment while they are being returned to the ship.

Fig 6-38. Flow chart showing recovery and first-aid treatment

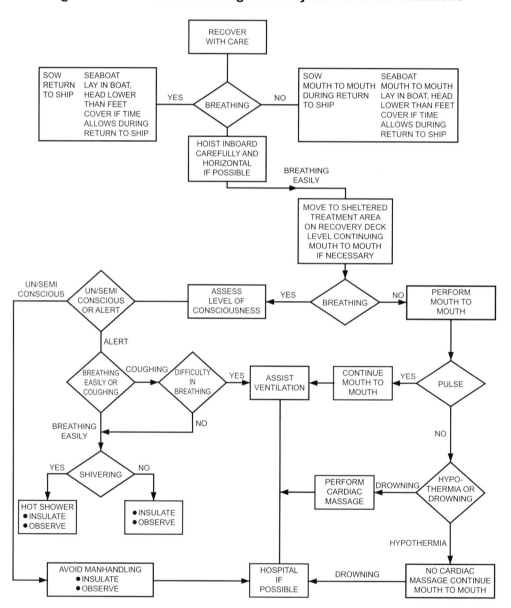

- OBSERVE FOR EARLY SIGNS OF RESPIRATORY DISTRESS.

- IF WATER INHALATION WAS MINIMAL, THE PATIENT MAY BE DISCHARGED AFTER REWARMING.

- CUT OFF LOOSE CLOTHING, PLACE IN BED AND WARM SLOWLY.

06029. Rescue stations

a.   **Introduction.** The Swimmer of the Watch (SOW) rig is ideal for rescuing and recovering a single casualty from the water. However, each ship should have its own internal organisation for rescuing survivors in the event of a shipwreck or other major disaster when large numbers of personnel may require rescue. The organisation should provide for rescuing as quickly as possible as many survivors as the ship can carry; hoisting inboard the sick and wounded; feeding, clothing and accommodating the survivors on board; and giving medical care and treatment to the sick, injured or wounded and to those suffering from shock and exposure.

b.   **Seamanship equipment preparations**. Much will depend on the nature of the rescue to be undertaken and the prevailing weather. In addition to preparing the SOW recovery rig(s) some or all of the following preparations may be appropriate:

(1)   *Boats*. These may be used to recover or assist personnel in the water. Boats' davits or cranes may be used to hoist casualty's inboard by rigging them as additional SOW recovery rigs.

(2)   *Liferafts*. These can be launched to provide shelter for personnel waiting to be recovered from the water.

(3)   *Means of recovery raft (MOR)*. Carried in Type 45 Destroyers and stowed on the mezzanine deck in the hanger. When required it is transferred to the boat bay nominated for its use. It is used in conjunction with a Rescue Craft (Seaboat), and is deployed from the same davit as the Seaboat. The raft can only be launched when the Seaboat has been deployed. However, should a situation arise where there is a requirement to launch the MOR at short notice and due to the length of time and logistics involved in preparing the MOR, then it is acceptable at the discretion of the Commanding Officer to deploy the 16-man liferaft stowed in the boat bay in place of the MOR. In a planned rescue though, that has a reasonable timeframe for preparations, every effort should be made to utilise and deploy the MOR.

(4)   *Swimmers*. Qualified Swimmers of the Watch should be available to render assistance to survivors in the water as directed by the OIC. Reliefs for swimmers must be provided at regular intervals.

(5)   *Ladders and scrambling nets*. In favourable conditions, active survivors may be able to board a ship by ladder or scrambling net, but as a general rule the physical effort required will be beyond them. However, such equipment is likely to prove useful for swimmers and divers, and it gives survivors something to cling to prevent them from drifting away from the rescue ship, until they can be hoisted or assisted on board.

(6)   *Heaving lines and lifelines*. Heaving lines and a plentiful supply of 16mm polypropylene lifelines should be provided. A 24mm polypropylene hawser can be bent to a buoy and fitted at intervals of one metre with long beckets. It is streamed astern so that survivors can grasp the line and put the beckets either round their waists or through the beckets of their lifejackets. The inboard bight of the hawser is snatched into a block well forward; the survivors can then be hauled alongside.

(7)   *Gangway safety nets or cargo nets*. It may be possible to rig these from a davit or crane. They can then lowered beneath the surface and used to hoist a number of survivors at a time.

(8)   A *lightweight transport stretcher* or some form of stretcher with slings, which can be submerged sufficiently for an injured survivor to be floated over it and then hoisted on board should be prepared.

(9)   *A line-throwing rifle* can be used to pass a line to a conscious isolated survivor.

c.   **Recovery of personnel in rafts**. The recovery of personnel in rafts is affected by the ship drifting down to the raft and making a lee for it. If the survivors are active and the conditions are favourable, they may be able to board the rescue ship by scrambling net or ladder. If the survivors are distressed, or conditions are unfavourable, recovery should be made by the SOW recovery rig. If survivors are not able to help one another the rescue ship should put two fit people on board the raft to assist.

d.   **Recovering a liferaft**. If it is required to recover the raft, trip the water pockets and remove all loose gear to reduce the weight. Pass two lengths of webbing or rope at right angles to each other under the raft, and then connect them together centrally above the canopy to form a sling for hoisting the raft by crane or derrick.

e.   **Recovery of personnel from the water**. Survivors will probably have little or no reserve of energy, and they will either be unable to help themselves or will expend their remaining energy in trying to climb out of the water. In the past many survivors have been lost while floating alongside a rescue ship because they were unable to climb up her scrambling nets or ladders, or even bend lifelines round themselves. Whenever possible, persons swimming should be hoisted on board, not assisted up scrambling nets or ladders, because the latter method wastes their rescuers' time and energy. When a ship is rolling there is considerable surge close alongside, particularly on the lee side, which tends to draw a swimmer under the ship.

f.   **Means of rescue raft (MOR).** The MOR Raft (Fig 6-39) is carried on board as a means of rescue for survivors since the demise of the Scrambling Nets previously carried by all RN ships for this purpose. The MOR Raft is stowed on a purpose built stowage sited on the port side forward of the mezzanine deck within the hangar.

(1)   *Removal and Preparation of the MOR*

(a) Remove the raft from the stowage port side forward mezzanine deck and move to the gantry position for lowering to the hanger deck.

(b) Open the soft patch on the raft to reveal the lifting arrangement. Temporarily remove the spring hook.

(c) Remove the temporary guardrail on the mezzanine deck. Attach the raft to the gantry hook by the shackle in the MOR and lower to the hangar deck.

(d) Unhook the raft from the gantry, replace the spring hook to the MOR and manually carry the MOR to the designated boat bay.

(e) Launch the Seaboat.

(2)   *Deploying the MOR.* Once the Seaboat has been launched, the procedure for deploying the MOR is as follows and as shown in Fig 6-39:

(a)   Clear the area and position the raft under the davit head. Prepare the raft for deployment.

(b)   Pull out the inflation Red Painter (red bag) 3-4 metres and secure to a strong point. Pull out 3-4 metres of the fore and aft steadying lines (blue bags) and secure them to strong points.

(c)   Attach the MOR to the boat's fall and hoist the MOR clear of the guardrails.

(d)   Slew the MOR outboard and lower to the ship's side. Inflate the MOR by pulling out the entire inflation lanyard.

(e)   Once the MOR has inflated, recover the container shells inboard using the red inflation lanyard. Slew the MOR hard against the ship's side and take up the slack in the fore and aft steadying lines.

(f)   Embark nominated ships crew (normally two). Lower the MOR to the water line, ensuring that the steadying lines are tended at all times.

(g)   Switch the davit control to 'wave compensator' so that the davit wire maintains constant tension with the rise and fall of the sea (see manufacturer's instructions).

(h)   Personnel crewing the MOR are to assist survivors into the MOR. The Seaboat is to assist in the rescue by ferrying survivors to, or towing liferafts alongside, the MOR.

(i)   On completion of the rescue operation prepare the boat bay for recovery of the MOR.

(j)   On completion recover the Seaboat inboard and secure the boat bay.

(k)   Report the state of the Seaboat and boat bay to the Bridge/OOW.

Fig 6-39. Inflatable means of rescue raft – type 45

Inflatable means of rescue raft – type 45 (Cont'd)

(vii)

(viii)

(ix)

(x)

(xi)

(xii)

06030. Balcan bell – manual line thrower

a. **Introduction.** The Balcan Emergency Life Line (BELL) (4220-99-781-0504) (Fig 6-40) comprises of a bright coloured, plastic capsule which contains a specially wound cop of buoyant, high quality braided polypropylene line of either 25m or 40m. This emergency line is made to tight engineering tolerances so is exceptionally strong for its size with the breaking strength of the line being 260lbs (118kgs). When the BELL is thrown and lands on the water both the line and the capsule float and can be easily seen.

b. **Operation.** To use the BELL, the blue cap is removed and the grip held whilst a few feet of the line are pulled out. The capsule is then thrown over or under arm towards and past the victim who either grabs the capsule or the line whilst being hauled back to safety.

Fig 6 - 40. Typical balcan emergency life line (BELL)

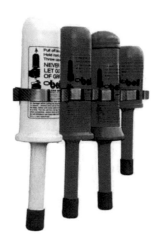

06031. Rescue sling – manual line thrower

a. The Rescue Sling (Fig 6-41) is used to assist in the safe rescue of personnel who have fallen into the water from a ship alongside, at anchor or secured to a buoy.

Fig 6-41. Gangway rescue sling – manual line thrower – sited and ready for use

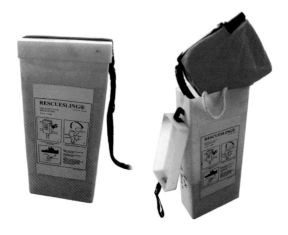

b.   **Stores. -** Each ship is to carry the following equipment:

(1)   Man overboard inflatable Rescue Sling with a 70ft line 4220-99-676-4518.

(2)   4 x Mk 6 Auto head service kit   4220-99-573-6823.

(3)   4 x Disposable CO2 cylinder 18g   6830-99-131-4419.

c.   **Ship's allowances**

LPD/LPH	3 per ship
DD/FF	2 per ship
MCMV	1 per ship
NI/FI/GIB/Cyprus	1 per ship
River Class	1 per ship
P2000	1 per ship
Survey Squadron	1 per ship
Trafalgar/Astute Class Submarines	2 per ship
Vanguard Class Submarine	2 per ship
RFA Units	2 per ship
HMS Bristol	1 only
HMS Raleigh/Sultan	two per establishment (for training purposes only)

d.   **Instructions for use.** The Rescue Sling Manual Line Thrower is stored in a box and is to be sited on the gangway alongside or at anchor/buoy. It comprises of a small fabric bag housing an automatic inflatable ring, which is attached to approximately 70ft of floating cordage. One end of the cordage is attached to a strong point on the vessel and the bag is thrown to the MOB. On contact with the water the ring will inflate automatically and can be donned. Once the MOB is recovered to the water's edge or ship's side using the attached line, he/she can then be recovered using whatever means are available. Operational instructions are clearly displayed on the side of the storage container.

e.   **Care and maintenance**

(1)   On surface ships, the CBM is responsible for the safe storing and maintenance of the equipment at sea. Maintenance is to be carried out in accordance with the relevant instructions in the Water Safety Equipment Log. Servicing and maintenance must only be carried out by a qualified WSEM.

(2)   On submarines, the Second Coxswain is responsible for the safe storage and maintenance of the equipment at sea. Servicing and maintenance must only be carried out by a qualified WSEM.

Note.   *All members of the ship's company are to be fully conversant with the operation and use of this equipment.*

06032. Rescue sling – Jon buoy

a.   Like the Manual Line Thrower Rescue Sling the Jon Buoy Rescue Sling (4220-99-377-5540) is used to assist in the safe rescue of personnel who have fallen into the water from a ship alongside, at anchor or secured to a buoy.

b.   **Instructions for use.** The Rescue Sling (Fig 6-42) is stowed within an orange/white container and like the Line Thrower Rescue Sling is to be attached to a strong point on the vessel in accordance with the outer cover instruction label. It is fitted with an automatic Mk 6 operating head and an AQ98 light.

The inflatable sling has an oral inflation tube and is connected to 30-metre of floating line. The sling will automatically inflate on entering the water where it is then to be donned. Once the MOB is recovered to the water's edge or ship's side using the attached line, he/she can then be recovered using whatever means are available. Operational instructions are clearly displayed on the side of the storage container.

Fig 6-42. Gangway rescue sling – Jon buoy

c.   **Care and maintenance.** The WSE maintainer is responsible for the safe storing and maintenance of the equipment at sea. Maintenance is to be carried out in accordance with the relevant instructions in the Water Safety Equipment Log.

Note.   *All members of the ship's company are to be fully conversant with the operation and use of this equipment.*

06033. Stretcher – lightweight transport stretcher and harness

a.   This outfit, (Fig 6-43) comprising a stretcher, harness and sling is provided in ships and air stations for the movement of patients by helicopter or jackstay.

b.   **The stretcher**. This consists of a rectangular tubular-steel frame fitted with a sheet-metal floor. The stretcher is supported by four tubular-steel skids on the underside and four lifting-eyes are fitted to the upper side of the frame. Metal rings are fitted at suitable points to attach the harness. On completion of load testing the head and foot rails are to be painted yellow.

c.   **The harness.** This is designed to restrain movement of the patient, thus ensuring, as far as possible, protection from aggravation of injuries by violent movement during flight or transfer. The harness consists of a set of upper straps designed to fit over the patient's shoulders, lower straps which pass across the legs and abdomen and a waist strap which passes across the patient. The upper and lower straps connect into a quick-release fitting secured to the waist strap. The harness is attached to the metal rings of the stretcher by spring hooks which are fitted to the ends of the straps. Buckles are fitted to the upper, longer lower and waist straps to permit adjustment of the harness and enable the waist strap and quick-release fitting to be positioned clear of the patient's injuries.

d.   **The sling**. A four-legged polyamide webbing bridle is secured to a metal D-ring, which forms the lifting point. Spring hooks are fitted to the ends of each leg by which the sling is attached to rings shackled to the lifting-eyes of the stretcher. When used to transfer a casualty by light jackstay, a 4030-99-721-6103 bow shackle is to be used to attach the D-ring to the jackstay traveller. The sling has a ten-year life from the date of manufacture found on the sling.

Fig 6-43. Lightweight transport stretcher, harness and sling rigged for transfer by helicopter or light jackstay

e.   **Associated equipment.** The following items are used in conjunction with the stretcher:

(1)   *Assault troop lifejacket*. The Assault Troop Lifejacket (see Para 06004) is worn by the patient to enable both him/her and the stretcher to remain afloat should he/she become disengaged from the aircraft winch wire or the jackstay traveller. The lifejacket is to be inflated **before** the patient is transferred by light jackstay or boat but **not before** being winched into a helicopter. Further advice on the transfer of stretcher patients by helicopter is given in **BRd 766, Helicopter Operating Handbook.**

(2)   *Head cushion*. The cushion is attached to the head of the stretcher by two straps, fastened with press-studs, to form a headrest.

f.   **Equipping the stretcher.** The harness and cushion are fitted as follows:

(1)   Position the harness on the stretcher with the adjusting buckles and quick-release fitting uppermost.

(2)   Clip the spring hooks at the ends of the upper, lower and waist straps to the metal rings at the head, foot and sides of the stretcher.

(3)   Place the cushion at the head of the stretcher and secure the two straps by the press-studs.

g.   **Strapping the patient in the stretcher.** The patient is strapped-in by the following method:

(1)   Fit the Assault Troop Lifejacket to the patient, ensuring that the crutch strap is adjusted to a loose fit with the patient lying down.

(2)   Lay the patient on the stretcher with his head on the headrest. The patient should be as near the head end of the stretcher as possible without actually touching the end bar.

(3)   Position the quick-release fitting in the centre of the patient's abdomen, clear of the ribs and hips, ie. approximately over the navel.

(4)   Ensure that the harness upper straps are passed under the lobes of the lifejacket.

(5)   The position of the waist strap is dependent upon the size of the patient. Position it so that it is transversely at right angles to the patient when tightened, with the quick-release fitting in the correct position.

(6)   Tighten all the harness straps, ensuring that the quick-release fitting remains in the correct position and the patient's arms are free and clear of the harness.

(7)   Clip the sling to the rings at the lifting eyes of the stretcher. Ensure slings are attached correctly ie. Head to head and foot to foot of the stretcher.

06034.   Recovery from the sea by helicopter

a.   If a helicopter rescue of survivors in a lifeboat/liferaft is to be achieved, the following procedures should be followed;

b.   The sea anchor/drogue should be streamed to hold the craft head to wind, this assists the pilot in assessing the surface wind direction and also increases the wind speed over the boat/raft, making flying easier.

c.   The rescue will usually be achieved using a strop or sling. If practicable the helicopter crewman will descend to assist in securing the strop. However, if this is not possible, the strop should be fitted under the arms with the toggle drawn tightly down to the chest. The hands must be kept by the side until the survivor is in the aircraft. On nearing the aircraft, the survivor should not attempt to try to board; the aircrew man will issue instructions that must be followed.

d.   If the survivor is injured, it may be necessary to use a stretcher, in which case an aircrew man will be lowered to assist in the rescue.

e.   When helicopters are hovering, the downdraft caused by the rotors is very great, and it is imperative that all loose equipment and clothing should be properly secured before the arrival of the helicopter. All small gear should be stowed in the lockers provided, and all headgear correctly secured or removed. If a large-scale rescue of persons by helicopter is to be achieved, it should be noted that rescue from lifeboats is much easier than rescue from liferafts. It may therefore be prudent to transfer survivors to lifeboats before they are winched into the helicopter.

f.   In air/sea rescue operations, it should be noted that the number of survivors capable of being rescued at any one time by a single helicopter depends upon its distance from its base and the amount of fuel it has to carry.

g.   Helicopters dedicated to air/sea rescue are fitted with VHF Channel 16 and should be contacted on that channel.

Note.   *Fig 6-44 and Fig 6-45 show the correct use of upper body helicopter strops prior to recovery.*

Fig 6-44. Correct use of a helicopter strop

Fig 6-45. Double strop when sssisted by the helicopter crewman

06035. Recovery by Hi-Line transfer (Fig 6-46 and Fig 6-47)

WARNING

THE HEAVING LINE OR ANY POINT OF THE WINCH WIRE MUST NEVER BE SECURED TO THE VESSEL. CARE MUST ALSO BE TAKEN TO ENSURE THAT THE WEAK LINK IS PLACED INTO THE WINCH HOOK BEFORE ANY STROPS OR SLINGS.

---

a.   The Hi-Line transfer is a procedure employed when normal winching would be hazardous. Conditions under which it might be used are as follows:

b.   When the winching area is confined or obstructed such that there is a risk of the winched load or man striking or snagging obstructions.

c.   The vessel is too small or the winching area located such that the pilot cannot maintain visual contact whilst hovering, eg. a submarine's fin.

d.   When ship movement is a hazard to the helicopter hovering at the height for a normal winch transfer.

e.   When normal winching areas are unusable for any reason, eg. weather conditions, damage.

f.   Where possible the transfer should be carried out aft, with the wind on the ship's port bow although other combinations may be acceptable at the pilot's discretion. The aircraft comes to a high hover, clear of all obstructions, and a weighted heaving line attached to the aircraft winch hook by a weak link, is lowered to the ship. When the weighted bag is in hand the aircraft moves to the left, clear of the ship, and descends to a height of 6 to 10 metres above the water.

    (1)   For transfers to the ship, the winch cable is paid out while the deck party keep the heaving line slack and free from obstructions. The aircraft climbs slowly while the person in the strop (or the load) is lowered until at the same horizontal level as the transfer point. At a signal from air crew, the person is hauled towards the transfer point by the deck party with the heaving line. When on deck he/she is released from the strop and the thumbs-up is given on completion.

    (2)   For transfers from the ship, the winch cable is paid out to the ship from the low hover. The deck party secure the strop to the person or load to be transferred, giving thumbs up on completion. The aircraft climbs slowly as the deck party check away on the heaving line easing the person over the guardrails until the winch wire is plumb. The aircraft then descends slowly recovering the person and during this part of the recovery the heaving line must remain slack.

g.   Throughout the transfer, the winch cable should be kept as near vertical as possible. The heaving line is used to guide the winch hook to/from the transfer area using minimum force and there should never by any tension in the heaving line unless it is very nearly at right angles to the winch wire. A direct tug-of-war between the deck party and the aircraft could part the weak link connecting the winch wire to the heaving line.

Fig 6-46. Hi-Line arrangements

(i) Hi-Line

(ii) Warning Pennant

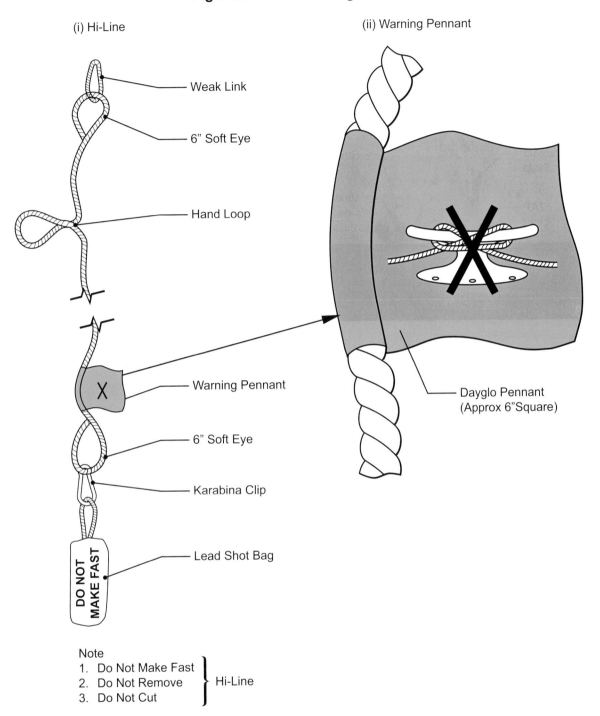

Weak Link

6" Soft Eye

Hand Loop

Warning Pennant

6" Soft Eye

Karabina Clip

Lead Shot Bag

DO NOT MAKE FAST

Dayglo Pennant
(Approx 6" Square)

Note
1. Do Not Make Fast
2. Do Not Remove   } Hi-Line
3. Do Not Cut

Fig 6-47. Winch wire hook on arrangements

1.

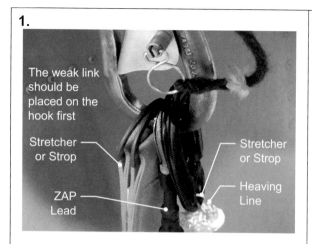

The weak link should be placed on the hook first

Stretcher or Strop

Stretcher or Strop

ZAP Lead

Heaving Line

2.

Transfer to a Vessel. Lower the Hi-line to the vessel. Under no circumstances should the Hi-line be attached to the vessel.

3.

Helicopter reduces height and moves left to a reasonable hover position alongside the vessel. The winch is then lowered to the level of the transfer area.

4.

Helicopter climbs and closes, lowering the hoist. Deck party haul at a signal from the helicopter aircrew.

5.

Transfer from a Vessel. Hi-Line/equipment is passed as before:
Then: Deck party check away on signal from helicopter until cable is plumb. Helicopter moves down and left while raising the hoist.

6.

Hi-Line is held in hand until a signal is given by the aircrew to release. The Hi-Line should be passed clear of the vessel side.

06036. Man overboard smoke and light marker

a. **Introduction.** The man overboard smoke and light marker (Marker Man Overboard Y402) illustrated in Fig 6-48 with a lifebuoy attached is carried in all HM ships. The marker is secured to the lifebuoy by four metres of 4mm of polyethylene cordage. At the top of the marker is a black ring to which one end of the polyethylene cordage is secured with a taped bowline, the other end being secured similarly to the lifebuoy. For tidiness the line is made up into a hank and tucked behind the marker.

Fig 6-48. Marker man overboard Y402

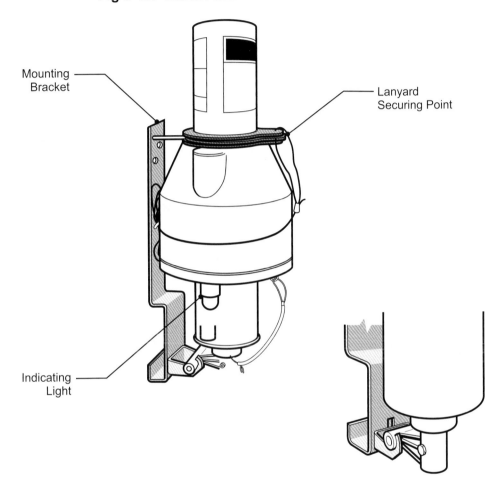

b. The marker is mounted in such a position that it can be released from its stowage to fall unobstructed into the sea, or can be easily cast into the sea to give a seamark by day or night for a man overboard casualty. Markers are sited on both bridge wings and on both sides in the after part of the ship; certain large warships may carry additional markers amidships (port and starboard). The marker is secured in a spring clip, from which it is pulled by the weight of the lifebuoy when it is released or thrown. When activated, the marker gives off a dense orange-coloured non-toxic smoke for approximately fifteen minutes and shows two white lights for a minimum of two hours thus having a day and night location facility. The smoke is produced by the action of two strikers igniting a composition in the body of the marker, the strikers being activated when the weakened black plastic "T" bar moulding breaks off during release. The lights are activated by the plastic lanyard attached to the "T" bar pulling out the rubber plug in the float section.

c. **Stowage**

(1) *Automatic and manual release stowage's.* The stowage is sited at least five metres above the waterline to enable the lifebuoy to pull the marker out of its retaining clip before reaching the sea. There are two types of release stowage; Fig 6-49(i) shows a stowage operated by a lifebuoy release toggle; Fig 6-49(ii) shows a stowage operated either by remote control from the bridge, or by a push button control at the site of the stowage. In the event of a power failure at the latter type of stowage the marker and lifebuoy can be released manually by disconnecting the two Inglefield clips incorporated in the lifebuoy-retaining loop.

(2) *Hand operated stowage.* In ships where the five-metre requirement cannot be met, a typical stowage for this arrangement is shown in Fig 6-50. The marker must be pulled by hand from its stowage bracket and then cast over the side with the lifebuoy as illustrated in Fig 6-51 in the following manner;

(a) Remove the storm clip if fitted.

(b) Pull the marker down and away from the bracket to break the "T" bar. Pull striker lanyards out of the marker.

(c) Hold downwind until the smoke commences then throw the marker and lifebuoy into the water.

Where manual operation of markers is required, ship's personnel must be briefed, and a warning sign (yellow background/black letters) reading 'Hand Operated' must be provided at each position.

Note. *A rubber storm clip (Fig 6-51) is available from stores. Users must be aware that fitting the clip will prevent automatic or manual release until the clip is removed. Clips are therefore only to be fitted to marker stowages where it is deemed acceptable to prevent accidental detachment due to adverse weather conditions or vibrations. A warning sign reading **storm clip fitted – remove before operating** must be provided on the Bridge and at each marker position.*

Fig 6-49. Marker man overboard Y402 – release stowage

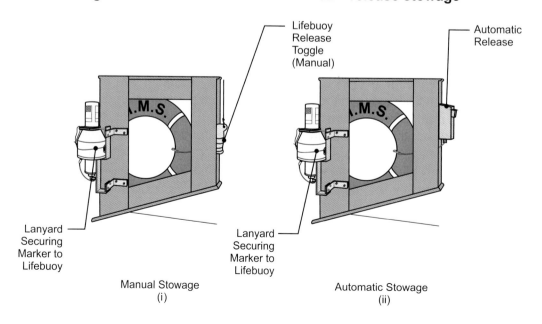

Fig 6-50. Marker man overboard Y402 – hand operated stowage

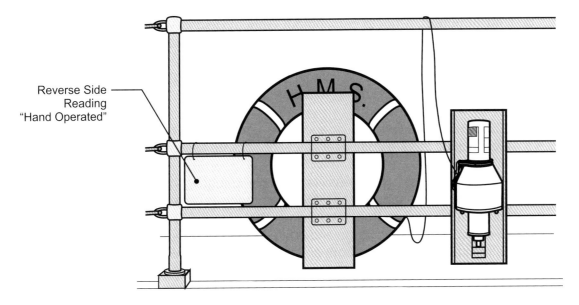

Reverse Side
Reading
"Hand Operated"

Fig 6-51. Marker man overboard Y402 – hand operation

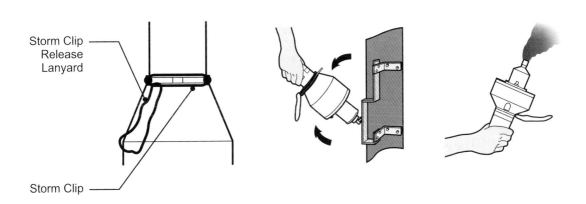

Storm Clip
Release
Lanyard

Storm Clip

    d. **Maintenance.** Smoke and Light Markers, associated lifebuoy and stowage
release mechanisms are to be maintained, inspected and exchanged in accordance
with the procedures laid down in the WSEL.

06037. Lifebuoy

    The standard lifebuoy in service with the Royal Navy is constructed of polyurethane
foam with a covering of flame-orange polyvinyl chloride. Lifebuoys used for general purpose
should not be painted, except for the ship's name in 50mm black lettering. Those required for
ceremonial use should be painted white using the appropriate two-pack polyurethane paint.

WARNING

THE 30" DIAMETER LIFEBUOY IS AVAILABLE COMMERCIALLY IN 2 WEIGHTS, 2.5KG
& 4KG. THE 4KG LIFEBUOY (0472/4220-99-521-3363) <u>MUST BE USED</u> IN AUTOMATIC
RELEASE STOWAGES TO ENSURE THE MARKER PULLS OUT OF THE BRACKET
AND ACTIVATES.

06038. Full body harness and restraint belts

a.   **Introduction.** Prior to carrying out Work at Height (WaH), careful consideration should be given to ensure that the safest possible fall protection solution is chosen:

(1)   *Work restraint.* This category of work restricts the movement of the user to prevent them approaching fall hazards.

(2)   *Work position.* Suspends the user at height; however, work position techniques require additional safety or back up system.

(3)   *Fall arrest.* Fall arrest is the only category that actually allows a fall to take place. The fall arrest system then reacts by arresting the fall in a controlled manner. The Full Body Harness (FBH) (Fig 6-52) is supplied in three sizes: Small, Standard and Large and is fitted with a work-positioning belt (with two side attachment links) and a front and rear attachment links. It enables the wearer to be connected to fall arrest, rescue, work restraint and work positioning system. It is not suitable for use in personal suspension systems.

(4)   *The restraint (Excel) belt.* This belt is fitted with two side and one rear attachment links. It enables the wearer to attach a work restraint lanyard only to either of the attachment links. Under no circumstances can the restraint belt be used with a fall arrest/suspension system.

b.   **Full body harness – selection of appropriate attachment points**

(1)   Anatomically the human frame has a greater capacity to withstand an arrest force at the dorsal (upper back) position than any other point. Consequently it is the preferred attachment point for fall arrest use (rescue and a restraint lanyard). The thoracic (front chest) attachment point is the next best.

(2)   The side position attachment links are strictly for work positioning and work restraint use only and not for fall arrest (or rescue). Fall arrest forces applied to a worker when connected at the side position are likely to produce serious if not fatal injuries. This is because the effect is like falling whilst wearing a waist belt; the shoulder and leg straps become totally ineffective. The fall victim would experience jack-knifing with a high probability of causing internal injury through flexion or extension of the body. Further guidance on the use of WaH Personal Protective Equipment and WAH can be found in JSP 569.

(3)   The range of WaH PPE supplied by the WaH Support Cell can be found in JSP 569 and Water Safety Equipment Log PMS 1-5986-0000.

Fig 6-52. Full body harness

THE NAUTICAL INSTITUTE

06039. Safety helmets

a.   A safety helmet (Fig 6-53) is to be worn by personnel employed in areas where there is a danger of being struck on the head. The tough shell provides protection against penetration by sharp objects whilst the cradle will minimise the shock loading and crushing effect of the impact. It is essential that the cradle is kept in position and that the designed gap between the cradle and the top of the shell is maintained for the helmet to perform effectively. Chin stays are to be fitted at all times. There are four colours available; white, blue orange and red. White helmets are worn by Safety Officers and OICs of evolutions; red by gunline firers, orange by crane controllers and blue by all other personnel. The pattern numbers are as follows:

Red	8415-99-920-0977	White	8415-99-132-1013
Blue	8415-99-132-1014	Orange	8415-99-132-1015

Fig 6-53. Safety helmet

b.   Rules for the care of safety helmets are as follows:

(1)   The date of issue and a local number is to be marked with a ball-point pen on the manufacturer's label inside the helmet.

(2)   Helmets must not be left for long periods in strong sunlight.

(3)   Helmets must not be painted, nor have adhesive stickers applied as these actions may disguise cracks or other damage to the helmet.

(4)   Helmets should not be washed in strong detergent.

(5)   If a helmet is struck by a falling object or otherwise suffers a heavy impact it should be discarded.

(6)   Helmets should be checked regularly by the wearer for cracking or other damage and should be replaced if any faults are found.

(7)   Irrespective of appearance or condition, helmets must be replaced in accordance with the manufacturer's instructions. For most manufacturers this period is five years. However, the literature that accompanies each hat must be read to ascertain the precise period recommended.

Note.   The adjustable headband and chinstrap (which can be used alternatively as a back strap) should be adjusted to ensure that the helmet is held firmly in position on the head.

06040. Safety glasses and goggles

Many of the seaman's tasks, such as hammering a lead pellet into a shackle involve a risk of eye injury. Anyone engaged in such work must take precautions to protect their own eyes and also ensure that the eyesight of other people nearby is not endangered. Wherever work constituting an eyesight hazard is taking place, the officer or rating in charge must make certain that the appropriate visors or goggles are made available and worn. Personnel having to work in the neighbourhood must also protect their eyes, but other persons should be forbidden to enter the area. Information on the protection of eyesight, together with a table of processes for which appropriate eye protection appliances are supplied, is given in **BRd 167 Safety, Health and Environment Manual for HM Ships and Submarines.**

06041. Working at height

a. **Introduction**. Personnel working aloft on masts, funnels or other high points are at risk unless they follow the correct procedures given in BRd 167 and BRd 167 for working at height form. The accidents that could occur include:

    (1)   Falling due to:

        (a) Ship movement.

        (b) The movement of an aerial.

        (c) Loose clothing catching.

        (d) Uncertain foothold on wet or greasy rigging.

        (e) The reaction to electric shock arising from current induced into the rigging by radio transmissions.

        (f) The reaction to the unexpected sounding of sirens or noisy discharges from funnels.

        (g) Being overcome by funnel gases.

    (2)   *Suffering from exposure.* The wind, where there is no shelter, will lower the effective temperature below the ambient temperature at deck level.

    (3)   Radiation from microwave transmissions, eg. from radar aerials.

    (4)   Injury from falling tools and equipment either to those already aloft or to those on the weather decks below.

b. **Precautions before proceeding aloft**. Before going aloft personnel concerned are to:

    (1)   Obtain permission of the OOW/OOD. (Permit to Work).

    (2)   Complete the ship hazard board in accordance with **BR 2924** (A.25).

    (3)   Inform Machinery Control Room.

    (4)   Dress in overalls or No 4s with trousers tucked into socks and with nonslip heeled footwear securely fastened.

    (5)   Wear industrial safety helmet.

(6)   Wear a full body harness.

(7)   Ensure there are no loose or heavy articles in their pockets.

(8)   Secure all tools by line to the person or in a full body harness tool bag or to a halyard.

Note.   *The rescuer is to draw the SHARK Rescue Kit/Safety Harness before the climb commences and the items are to be placed at the base of the climb in the event a rescue is required.*

c.   **Ships alongside**. Where there is another ship alongside that could irradiate the mast or produce a discharge from its funnel the hazard state board for that ship is to be completed and her OOW and Machinery Control Room informed.

d.   **Tending a person working at height**. A responsible person is to be in attendance at all times on men working aloft, keeping them in view at all times and warning personnel in the area of work in progress above.

e.   **Completion of work**. The OOW/OOD is to be informed and the ship returned to the normal Radhaz state as soon as work aloft is completed.

06042. Working over the side

a.   **General precautions**. The following precautions must be taken by personnel working over the side.

(1)   Permission must be obtained from The OOD/OOW.

(2)   When working over the side in order that ships passing do so at a slow speed the flag hoist 'Code Romeo Yankee' (Fig 6-54) must be hoisted at the yardarm on the side the work is to take place.

Fig 6-54. Code Romeo Yankee as shown

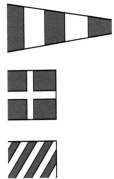

(3)   All personnel working over the side must wear a HDLJ and appropriate WaH PPE as explained in para 06038).

b.   **Paint catamarans**. These catamarans are platforms for use when painting the ship's side. Personnel working from a paint catamaran should wear an HDLJ. Alternatively they may wear a safety harness. The catamaran securing lines must be tended from inboard of the ship's guardrails, and breast ropes should be used to bowse the catamaran close in to the ship's side before work commences. Code Romeo Yankee should also be hoisted.

06043. Weather-deck lifelines

> **WARNING**
>
> PERSONNEL REQUIRED TO PROCEED ON TO THE WEATHER DECKS IN INCLEMENT WEATHER ARE TO WEAR A RESTRAINT BELT AND TWO RESTRAINT LANYARDS; HOWEVER, IF THERE IS A RISK OF A FALL THEN A FULL BODY HARNESS AND APPROPRIATE FALL ARREST LANYARDS ARE TO BE WORN.

Before adverse weather is encountered, weather deck lifelines must be rigged on all the weather decks. This enables the wearer to traverse the lifeline shackles or change from one section of lifeline to another by securing one restraint/fall arrest lanyard before releasing the other. Weather-deck lifelines are rigged at the discretion of the Commanding Officer, who will give due consideration to the time and difficulty involved and the prevailing and forecast weather conditions.

06044. Working on deck in heavy weather

a. There is a risk to personnel working on the upper deck in rough weather with high seas running. An unexpected wave may wash over the upper deck or an awkward movement of the ship may throw people off balance. To minimise such hazards the Command should take the following precautions whenever it is necessary to send personnel on the upper deck in bad weather:

(1) Brief the team formally on the task.

(2) Keep the team as small as sensibly possible.

(3) Obtain permission from the OOW and ensure good communication between the bridge and the upper deck in order to be able to warn the team of changes in sea and weather.

(4) Ensure that everyone going on the upper deck wears lifejackets, safety helmets and restraint belt/full body harness. The latter must be clipped to the weatherdeck lifelines at all times by means of a restraint lanyard/fall arrest lanyard.

(5) Select the course and speed that gives most protection from the wind and sea.

(6) A responsible person is to be in attendance at the exit/entry point whilst personnel are on the upper deck, monitoring wherever possible.

06045. General onboard safety considerations

a. **Clothing and footwear**

(1) For safety and comfort, a seaman must be appropriately dressed and equipped when working on the upper deck. Number 4's and/or overalls, beret, woollen pullover and DMS boots are the basic requirements, and a knife and spike should always be carried. In cold or inclement weather, foul-weather gear is worn, and personnel in very exposed areas should don Immersion suits. The loss of body heat through wind chill can easily be underestimated; even off the south coast of England in summer this can be a problem. To retain body heat, several layers of loose fitting clothing should be worn under the outer garments.

(2)   Wearing gloves whilst handling wires and ropes carries certain risks, for example if they snag on a broken strand in a wire, or become trapped in turns on a capstan or winch. However, in certain conditions these risks are outweighed by other dangers, eg. frostbite in very cold weather or the inability to grip with bare hands a greasy wire hawser. Therefore the wearing of gloves is left to the discretion of the OIC, who must take account of the prevailing conditions.

Note.   *Gloves PVC fabric 8415-99-978-4507/9 are supplied for use by personnel working on the upper deck.*

b.   **Guardrail safety**. The following points apply to guardrail safety:

(1)   Guardrails must be set up taut, and all shackles should be moused. Additionally, before entering a dry dock, all guardrail 'R' clips must be moused in position.

(2)   Whenever guardrails are broken, for example to allow a brow into a ship, personnel are to wear HDLJ, restraint belt, lanyard and safety helmet. The gap must be roped off as soon as possible using 12mm Polyester. (See also Para 03073).

c.   **Submarine guardrail safety.** Guardrails should be rigged on arrival alongside. At least one side is to be rigged on the outboard side, if the time alongside is expected to be sufficiently long, both sides are to be rigged from Aft of the Fin.

WARNING

**IT IS DANGEROUS AND UNSEAMANLIKE TO LEAN OR STAND
ON GUARDRAILS.**

---

d.   **Flight-deck and weapon-deck safety nets**. Guardwires are not appropriate around flight decks and certain weapon-decks where there is a frequent requirement to lower stanchions in order to operate equipment safely. In such areas, nets are laced between the stanchions so that when the stanchions are lowered outboard, a degree of protection in the form of a safety net is provided to personnel working in the area. The nets must be installed in accordance with the relevant ship's drawing, and they should be checked regularly to ensure that they remain properly secured. Stanchions must be 'toed-in' at all times whenever the nets are not lowered for use.

e.   **Guarding of hatches and edges**. Any opening, open hatchway or dangerous edge into, through or over which a person may fall are to be fitted with secure guards or fencing. Guard-chains fitted with a shackle/spring hook are to be rigged at accommodation ladder gangways, around hatches and at the top of vertical screen ladders. Where an opening affords a permanent means of transit about the ship, the chain offering access to the opening may be stopped back. The chain should be re-rigged in the event of foul weather, removal of the ladder or where the safety of personnel is at risk.

06046. Health and safety at work

a.   The Health and Safety at Work Act (HSWA), and its implications for service personnel, is fully covered in JSP 375 – Application of the Health and Safety at Work Act, which is the authoritative publication on the subject.   The duties of personnel aboard ships are summarised as follows:

b.   The duty of Commanding Officers and all superiors at all levels to:

(1)   Ensure that compartments and access thereto are kept in a safe condition.

(2)   Ensure that equipment and machinery can be safely operated.

(3)   Inform personnel who may be at risk of the existence of hazards and the precautions to be taken.

(4)   Ensure that material used can be handled and stowed safely.

(5)   Provide sufficient training and supervision to maintain safe conditions.

c.   The duty of all officers and ratings to:

(1)   Take care of themselves and those with whom they work.

(2)   Co-operate with others in health and safety matters eg by obeying lawful orders.

d.   The duty of suppliers of materials to ships or installers of equipment to:

(1)   Check that materials and equipment have been tested and are safe.

(2)   Inform possible users of any hazards that could arise from material or equipment and of the safety precautions and procedures.

06047. Lifejackets and safety aids – what to wear and when

Details of the policy of water safety equipment can be found in the Water Safety Equipment Management Defence Instruction and Notice (DIN) published on an annual basis by Maritime Platform Systems – Maritime Spares – General Stores and Water Safety (MPS-MS-GSS).

APPENDIX 1

GLOSSARY

Terms and expressions which have been explained in the text of this manual are not included here unless they have other meanings or interpretations. Slang terms, and proper terms with a slang version, are printed in *italics*.

A1 – first class, the best. The highest classification at Lloyd's Register of a vessel's seaworthiness. (The letter refers to the hull and the number to the equipment.)

AB – able-bodied seafarer. It denotes a person who is technically qualified and fit to carry out a seafarer's duties, both aloft and on deck.

Adrift – absent, or late for muster or an appointment.

AHOY! – the seafarer's hail to call attention.

All at sea – confused, at a loss.

ALL STANDING – to bring up any thing or person all standing is to bring it or him to a sudden and unexpected stop.

AMAIN – suddenly.

Andrew Miller, or ***the Andrew*** – the Royal Navy. Andrew Miller was a zealous press-gang officer who impressed so many men into the King's Naval Service during the Napoleonic wars that he was said to own the Royal Navy.

ARISINGS – pieces of material or metal left over from a job which are of value. They are collected and may be sold, melted or made up again.

As AND As – alterations and additions to the structure, rigging and equipment of a warship.

ATHWART – across, as in 'athwart the hawse', 'athwart the tide'.

AWASH – level with the surface of the sea.

BAGGYWRINKLE – the service on standing or running rigging to prevent chafing where one rope crosses another. See *bolster* and *scotchman*.

BAR – a shoal or spit formed by the action of the tides at the mouth of a river or harbour.

Bare Navy – members of a mess are said to live on 'bare navy' when they feed solely on Service rations.

BARE POLES – a sailing vessel is said to be under bare poles when she is under-way and has no sails set.

BARGE – a cargo-carrying coastal sailing vessel. In the Royal Navy, the boat of a Flag Officer.

Barrack Stanchion – a person who has served for a long period in a Naval barracks or shore establishment.

BARRATRY – fraudulent claim for compensation, as when a ship is deliberately wrecked or *scuttled* (which see) to obtain her insurance money.

BARREL – a measurement of volume for liquids particularly in the petroleum industry; one barrel equals 0.152 cubic metres.

BATTEN DOWN – to close all openings in the weather decks or superstructure of a ship, or to close all openings in one of her compartments.

Beach, on the beach – retired from sea service. See *swallow the anchor*.

BEAM ENDS – a ship is said to be on her beam ends when she is lying over on her side, with her beams and decks perpendicular. The expression is used colloquially to describe a precarious position.

BEAR A HAND – an order to hasten, or to do something smartly, quickly.

BELAY – colloquially, to countermand an order. See *wash out*.

BELOW THERE! – a hail from someone aloft to anyone below him.

BERTH – the allotted place or position for a ship or a person. 'To give a wide berth' is to keep well clear of anything. 'To shift berth' is to change position.

BETWEEN DECKS – a general term applied to the space or the decks between the upper deck and the lowest deck of a ship.

Bilge – rubbish, nonsense.

BILL – a certificate or a written agreement, such as a 'Bill of Health', 'Bill of Lading' or 'Bill of Exchange'.

BITTER END – the inboard length of a ship's cable. (The cables of ships at anchor used to be belayed to specially fitted centre-line bollards called 'bitts'.)

BLEED – to drain a buoy of water. To *bleed the monkey* – to extract the contents of a rum barricoe by boring a small hole in it.

BLOCK AND BLOCK, TWO-BLOCKS – these terms describe the state of a tackle when it's standing and moving blocks are hauled close together. Colloquially they are used to describe the position of two objects which are close together. See *chock-a-block*.

BLOW THE GAFF – to divulge information you have learnt confidentially, to give away a secret. Its origin probably lies in a ship revealing her identity by hoisting her colours at the peak of her gaff.

BLUE-JACKET – a seafarer of the Royal Navy (from the short blue jacket that was worn).

BLUFF – a headland with a broad, perpendicular face. Hence, 'bluff-bowed' – a ship with broad perpendicular bows.

BOARD (1) – the old name for the side of a ship from which the following terms also are derived: 'to go on board' – to enter a ship; 'to board' – to enter a ship by force or authority; 'boarders' or 'boarding party' – a body of men detailed to board a ship; 'inboard' – between the sides of a ship; outboard' – outside the ship; 'on board' – anywhere in the ship; 'to go by the board' – to fall over the ship's side; 'board and board' – alongside, side by side and touching; 'close aboard' – close to the ship's side; 'star-board' – the side on which the steering oar or 'steer-board' was formerly shipped (the right hand side when the ship or boat was facing forward); 'larboard' – the opposite side to starboard, over or through which the cargo was embarked or disembarked (originally spelt 'ladeboard').

BOARD (2) – the distance made good by a sailing vessel between two successive tacks when beating towards windward.

BOBSTAY – properly the stay leading down from the nose of a sailing vessel's bowsprit to her stem near the waterline, but also applied to any stay used in a similar fashion. See *martingale*.

BOLSTER – a pad or cushion of canvass or leather used to prevent chafe between ropes, or a piece of wood or metal used to give a fair lead to, or prevent a bad nip in, a rope. See *scotchman* and *baggywrinkle*.

Bone – to scrounge, pilfer or steal. Derived from a boatswain of that name who served in the flagship of Admiral Cornwallis and was notorious for acquiring ship's stores from other ships to make good deficits or provide a surplus in his own ship. When the boatswain was leaving the ship the Admiral is said to have remarked: 'I trust, Mr Bone, you will leave me my bower anchors'.

BONNET – any small cover or hood, of canvas or metal, used to cover or protect a small fitting or opening.

BOOMKIN, **BUMPKIN** – a small boom.

BOOT-TOPPING – properly the operation of scraping marine growths from the waterline, but also the name for the painted band, one to one-and-a-half metres wide in a large ship, extending from stem to stern of the ship along her waterline; the paint is usually of a different colour from that of the sides and bottom, and is of special composition designed to prevent the growth of marine organisms, which otherwise always form between wind and water.

Bottle – a reproof or admonishment (contracted from *a dose from the foretop-man's bottle*, which was a cure for all evils).

BOTTOMRY – a system of pledging the hull of a ship as security for a loan.

BOUND (1) – restrained, tied, fettered, as in 'weather-bound', 'wind-bound', 'tide-bound'; and 'iron-bound coast' used to describe a rocky and dangerous coast with no shelter.

BOUND (2) – ready to go to a destination, or on the way to a destination, as in 'outward bound', 'homeward bound'.

BOWSE – to haul on a rope; 'bowse down' – to tauten a rope or a lashing.

BREAK BULK – to start unloading a full hold.

Break surface – to wake up or come to life (has its origin in a submarine 'breaking surface' after being submerged).

Brick – a gun projectile or shell.
BRIGHT-WORK – polished metal fittings.

BROACH – to break into, or open for the first time, a cask, package or similar receptacle.

BROACH-TO – when applied to a vessel running before the sea, is to slew round inadvertently broadside-on in the trough of a wave.

BROKEN WATER – surf caused by breaking waves.

Bull a cask – formerly the practice of putting a small quantity of water in an empty rum cask and leaving it until it became grog.

Bullocks – the name formally given to members of the Royal Marine Artillery because of their magnificent physique. See *jollies*, *turkeys*, *pongos* and *grabbies*.

BULLROPE – a rope led from the ring of a buoy to the nose of the bowsprit of a sailing vessel, or to the stem head of a clipper-bowed ship, to prevent the buoy from bumping the bows at slack water.

BULLSEYE (1) – a light built into a bulkhead between adjacent compartments so that it illuminates both.

BULLSEYE (2) – a thimble made of hardwood and usually inserted in the end of a lizard, or used as a small leading block. See *deadeye*.

BUM-BOAT – a shore boat carrying fresh provisions or small merchandise for sale to ships in a harbour. 'Bum-boatmen' – the owner of such a boat, or of her stock in trade.

Bundleman – a married man. (Originates from the days when men could buy ship's provisions for their families, and the married men could then be distinguished when going ashore by the bundle of provisions he carried.)

BUNT – the belly of a sail and the middle of a yard.

Bunts – a signalman (derived from bunting).

BURDEN – the carrying capacity of a merchant vessel expressed in tons of cubic capacity, ie the net register tonnage.

Burgoo – the seafarer's name for oatmeal porridge.

BUTT-END – the largest end of a spar or any similarly shaped object.

Buzz – rumour. See *galley-packet*.

BY-AND-LARGE – under all conditions, generally speaking. (Derived from the sailing terms 'by the wind' meaning close-hauled, and 'sailing large' meaning running or sailing free.) See *large*.

BY THE HEAD – a vessel trimmed more deeply forward than aft.

BY THE STERN – a vessel trimmed more deeply aft than forward.

Cag – to discuss, to argue.

CAMEL – a tank secured to the hull of a ship to provide her with extra buoyancy, used mainly in salvage work.

CANT – to incline from the perpendicular.

CAPFUL OF WIND – a puff of wind on a calm day, but of sufficient strength to fill a vessel's sails. See *catspaw*.

CAPSIZE – to overturn, to turn bottom upwards.

CARRY AWAY – to break away, or to part.

CAST – to pay a vessel's head off on a course, or on a new tack.

CAT, CAT-O'NINE TAILS – a former instrument of punishment in the Navy. It was originally made of nine lengths of cord, with three knots at the end of each, spliced to a short length of thick rope to form a handle. *No room to swing a cat* means that there is insufficient space in which to wield a cat-o'nine tails.

CATSPAW – a light puff of wind on a calm day, just strong enough to ruffle the surface of the water; usually the forerunner of a sailing breeze.

CAULK – to drive oakum or other similar caulking material into the seams of planking to make them watertight; after caulking the seams are 'paid' by pouring molten pitch into them to preserve the caulking. Also, colloquially, to lie down and snatch some sleep, which has its origin in the fact that a someone who had just taken a *caulk* on a hot deck could be identified by the marks of pitch on their clothing.

Charlie Noble – the funnel of a galley or a stove when sheathed in brass and polished.

CHATHAM CHEST – a fund established by Queen Elizabeth I, after the Armada, for the care of wounded and infirm seamen. It was supported by contributions from the men, which were kept in a special chest at Chatham. This chest is now in the National Maritime Museum, Greenwich.

Chats – Chatham.

Chippy chap – shipwright.

CHOCK-A-BLOCK – full up (from 'choking' the luff of a block). *Chock-a-block* and *chocker* – slang terms for bored or 'fed-up'.

CHOKED – a block is said to be choked if its fall jams in the swallow. 'To choke the luff' is to choke the block of a tackle by leading the bight of the hauling part across the swallow of the block and jamming it between the swallow and the hauling parts, thus preventing the tackle from overhauling.

CHOPPY SEA – a short, steep and usually confused sea.

CHOPS OF THE CHANNEL – the entrance to the English Channel (derived from 'chap' or 'chop', meaning jaws).

Chummy ships – ships whose respective officers and men are on particularly friendly terms.

CLAP ON – an order to man a fall or a halyard. To attach one tackle to another or to a rope.

CLENCH, CLINCH (1) – to join a rope to a fitting or to another rope by a half hitch with the end seized to its own part. This method was formerly used to join one end of a ship's hempen cable to her anchor, and the other end to the housing of her mainmast. A 'clench', nowadays, is a strong fitting securely attached to a deck or the hull structure, to which the end of a cable or hawser is shackled. A cable or rope is said to be 'out to a clinch' when it has all run out, or been paid out, but its end is secured inboard.

CLENCH, CLINCH (2) – to fasten two pieces of wood together by driving nails through both and turning their ends over (as in 'clinker'-, or 'clencher'- built boats), or to hammer over the end of a bolt to prevent it from withdrawing from its hole (as in a 'clenched shackle').

CLEAN (1) – to dress in the 'rig' (suit of clothing ordered), or to change from night clothing or working rig into a clean rig.

CLEAN (2) – or white. Descriptive of the cargo of a tanker carrying refined oil products, namely aviation spirit, motor spirit, kerosenes and some grades of gas oil.

CLEAR (1) – good visibility, as in 'clear weather', or as in a 'clear sky', meaning that it is cloudless; free from shipping or obstructions, as in 'clear horizon' and 'clear channel'.

CLEAR (2) – to free, the reverse of to *foul* (which see); to make free (a rope clear for running, to clear a block); to put in order, to tidy (to clear up decks); to pass an obstruction safely (to clear a point of land); to empty (to clear a hold or a lighter); to pay port or Customs dues and complete port formalities (to clear quarantine, or to clear Customs).

COASTER – a vessel which plies between the harbours of a particular coast or adjacent coasts, usually in pilotage waters and seldom out of sight of land.

A'COCK-BILL – an anchor is said to be a'cock-bill when it is hung up-and-down, ready for letting go. Yards are said to be a'cock-bill when they are topped at an angle with the horizontal. See *scandalise*.

COME UP! – an order to slack off rope.

COME UP WITH A VESSEL – to overtake her.

COMMANDER – a large mallet used in rigging work, or a hammer or specially shaped striker stowed adjacent to an important slip to ensure there is always an implement available to release the slip.

COMPANION LADDER – a ladder or staircase leading from the poop or upper deck of a merchant ship to the saloon or main cabin.

COMPLAIN – a block is said to complain when its sheave squeaks.

Copper-bottomed – well found, reputable. (The bottoms of wooden ships were sheathed with copper to protect them from marine parasites; but, being very expensive, this was done only to ships whose owners were of substance and repute.)

CRAB – a small hand capstan.

CRACK ON – to set more sail, to increase speed.

CRANK – a ship is said to be crank when she heels readily to one side or the other and returns sluggishly to the upright. See *tender* and *stiff*.

CREEPER – *grapnel* (which see) used for sweeping or dragging for objects lost overboard. (See *drag* and *sweep*.)

CROWFOOT, CROW'S FOOT – three or more lines or small ropes radiating from the end of a whip or pendant, so that its support or pull is spread and divided between them. The lines are kept apart by a *euphroe* (which see).

CROW'S NEST – a small shelter for the masthead lookout.

Crusher – a member of the ship's police.

CUDDY – the Master's cabin in sailing vessels, and the slang term for the Admiral's or Captain's cabin.

Cut and run – to escape or quit. (Derived from the days when a ship cut her hemp cable and left her anchor on the bottom to enable her to put to sea quickly in emergency; also, in similar circumstances, when she set her sails by cutting their gaskets, so unfurling them at the run.)

CUT-WATER – the stem of a ship. In sailing vessels with bluff bows it was a false stem.

CUT OF HER (OR HIS) JIB – the general appearance of a ship or person.

DAVY JONES'S LOCKER – bottom of the sea. The origin of the term is obscure, but it may have originated in a pirate of that name who made his prisoners walk the plank.

D.D. – the letters inserted in the ship's ledger against the name of a deceased officer or seaferer to denote the closing of their account and signifying that they have been 'discharged dead'.

DEADEYE – a block of hardwood with one or more holes drilled in it to take a rope or ropes or the fall of a simple purchase; the earliest form of block. Now used for standing rigging only.

Dead marine – an empty bottle, which 'has done its duty and is ready to do it again'.

Dead men – stray ropes' ends hanging from aloft. See *Irish pendant* and *hanging Judas*.

DEEP (1) – a depression in the sea bed.

DEEP (2) – the intervening metres between the marked metres on a lead line, eg 'Deep six'.

DEMURRAGE – the time, and its financial compensation, which a merchant vessel is delayed in port beyond the *lay time* (which see).

DERELICT – a ship afloat but abandoned by her crew.

DEVIL – in wooden ships a large seam near the gunwale. 'Between the devil and the deep sea' – between the gunwale and the waterline; any precarious position.

Dhobeying – washing clothes (derived from the Indian word 'dhobey', a washerman).

DIP – to lower partially and temporarily. As slang this is used for disrating, forfeiting a good conduct badge, or failing an exam.

DIRTY (black) – descriptive term applied to the cargo of a tanker carrying crude oils, fuel oil and some grades of gas oil.

Ditch – the sea. 'To ditch' is to throw overboard.

DITTY BOX – a small wooden box which was issued to seamen as a receptacle for their small personal effects. In 1938 it was replaced by an attaché case but this is not now issued.

DIVISION – two or more warships of a squadron or a flotilla under one command. See *squadron* and *flotilla*.

Dodge Pompey – to evade doing a job of work.

DODGER – a canvas screen laced to guardrails to provide shelter from wind or spray. In the Royal Navy a slang term for a messdeck sweeper.

DOG – to twist a rope round a spar or another rope to obtain a grip on it.

Doggie – a midshipman detailed to attend on a senior officer.

DOG-VANE – a small wind-vane of bunting secured to the weather shrouds of a sailing vessel. See *wind-vane*.

DONKEY – a prefix given to any small mechanical contrivance for saving labour, such as the 'donkey engine' used for working winches or small capstans and the 'sailmaker's donkey' or sewing machine.

DORY – a flat-bottomed boat carried by fishing vessels.

DOWSE – to lower or slacken suddenly, to extinguish, '*Dowse that glim*' – to put out the light. See *glim*.

DRAG – to haul a grapnel (which see) or some similar instrument along the sea bed to recover something lost. See *sweep*.

DRAW – a sail is said to draw when it is filled by the wind. A ship is said to draw so many metres (in draught). A ship is said to draw ahead of you if her position relative to yours advances, and to draw astern if she drops back.

DREDGE – to deepen a channel by excavating it.

Drip – to grumble or grouse.

DROWN – to drench or immerse. To drown a boat is to fill her with water by removing her plug when she is afloat, and is done to swell her planks and make her seams tight.

DUNNAGE – pieces of wood, matting, old rope, old canvas or similar material used to prevent cargo coming into contact with the ship's structure or other cargo and thereby suffering damage or contamination.

EASY! – go or haul carefully, slowly, or less vigorously.

EDDY – a swirl in the water made by a fast-moving current passing over a rock or a hollow in the bottom; the swirl made by a current on the lee side of rock or the buttress of a bridge, and the backwash of a current at the sides of a channel. Also a circular movement of the air.

END FOR END – to turn anything end for end is to reverse its position.

EUPHROE OR UVROE – a circular or oblong piece of wood, bored with holes and used to separate the parts of a *crow's foot* (which see).

FAG – to separate or tease out the strands of a rope ('fag-end' is the very end of anything).

FAIR – favourable, unobstructed, the reverse of *foul* (which see); as in 'fair wind', 'fairlead' and 'fairway'.

Fairweather friend – one who is a friend only for so long as it suits their own ends.

FAKE – a coil in a coiled rope.

Fanny – a cylindrical mess tin holding nearly five litres. The introduction of tinned meat into the Navy was not popular and coincided approximately with the murder and dismemberment, in 1867, of a child called Fanny Adams. The tins in which the meat was packed were then used as mess utensils throughout the Service.

FIDDLE – a bar of metal or wood holding a number of sheaves in line, and used chiefly for signal halyards or the halyards of wireless aerials. Also, battens fitted over a mess table to keep the mess traps in place in rough weather. *Working a fiddle* is to act dishonestly.

FIT OUT – to rig and provide a ship with her complete equipment of gear, stores and provisions.

Flannel – a term describing a long-winded or meaningless speech; also applied to nonsense or rubbish.

FLAT – a flat surface shoal or bank usually close inshore, which may or may not uncover at low water.

FLEET (1) – 'The fleet' is a general name given to the Royal Navy as a whole; a fleet is a number of men-of-war under one overall command, and it can be sub-divided into squadrons, flotillas and *divisions* (which see).

FLEET (2) – shallow tidal waters eg Benfleet, Purfleet.

FLEET (3) – the span or scope of a rope or tackle; the distance to which an object can be moved in one haul by a rope or tackle. 'To fleet' anything is to haul it along in a series of fleets, and to fleet a tackle is to overhaul a tackle which is block and block to its full scope. 'Fleet along', 'Fleet aft', 'Fleet forward', are orders to a body of men to move carefully in the required direction.

FLEET (4) – the area covered by a stage when painting a ship's side.

FLOTILLA – formerly a number of small warships under one command but nowadays the name applied to the main grouping of ships in the Fleet.

FLOTSAM – floating cargo, stores or equipment, freed from a wreck or cast overboard to lighten a ship. It is the property of the owners, and if not claimed it becomes the property of the Crown. See *jetsam* and *ligan*.

FLYING DUTCHMAN – the ghost of a sailing vessel which is said to haunt the waters off the Cape of Good Hope. The sighting of it is supposed to portend disaster.

FORE-AND-AFT RIG (1) – a ship rigged with fore-and-aft sails only, as in a schooner.

Fore-and-Aft Rig (2) – a slang term for the dress of Royal Naval Warrant Officers, Chief Petty Officers and Petty Officers.

FORE-FOOT – the lower end of the stem where it meets the keel.

FORE-PEAK – the compartment or space between decks in the bows of a ship.

FORESHORE – the beach below high-water mark.

FOUL – entangled, obstructed, or dirty.

FOUL ANCHOR – the badge of the Royal Navy, consisting of an Admiralty pattern anchor with a rope fouling its stock, shank and arms; it originated in the badge of Lord Howard of Effingham, who held office as Lord High Admiral in the reign of Queen Elizabeth I.

FOUNDER – to sink.

FRAP – to bind with lashing; to pass a rope round a sail or over an awning to keep it from breaking loose.

FREE – unobstructed, unencumbered, clear for running.

FRESHEN, or **FRESHEN THE NIP** – to shift the position at which a rope is being chafed (by a fairlead, for example), by paying it out or hauling it in by a short length.

FULL DUE – to do anything 'for a full due' means to do it permanently, eg to secure a rope or a fitting 'for a full due'.

FURL – to fold up or roll up and stop a sail or an awning.

Gadget or gilguy – a small mechanical fitting or contrivance, a dodge or device.

GALLEY – a single banked, six-oared pulling boat, properly called a 'gig', which was provided for the use of the captain of a ship.

Galley-packet – a rumour, usually unfounded (so-called because such rumours originated in the ship's galley or cook-house).

GANGWAY – any recognised entrance to, or passageway or traffic route within, a ship. Also used as an order or warning to make way.

GARLAND – a strop or rope sling round a mast or spar with which to lift or hoist it.

Gash – any refuse, remnants of a meal, leavings and pickings.

GASKET – a stop used for lashing up a furled sail or awning.

GHOSTING – a sailing vessel or boat is said to be ghosting, or ghosting along, when she is making good way in a very light breeze.

GIG – see *galley*.

Gilguy – see *gadget*.

GINGERBREAD-WORK – the ornate guilt carving with which the sterns of former men-of-war were decorated. The term is derived from the gingerbread sweetmeats formerly sold at fairs; they were made of treacle or honey and gilded over.

GIRT OR GIRDED – bound. A vessel is said to be girt when she is moored so tautly that she is prevented from swinging to wind or tide by fouling her cables as she swings round. Also said of a tug when she is inadvertently hauled broadside on her towrope, in which position she is powerless and must slip the tow or be capsized. To 'under-girt' is to bind the hull of a vessel with ropes or chains to strengthen it (see *swift*).

Glim – a light. See *dowse*.

Goffer or *gopher* – a non-alcoholic fruit drink or mineral water.

Grabbies – soldiers. See *pongos*.

GRAIN – the line of water ahead of a vessel along which she will pass; the opposite to *wake* (which see).

GRAPNEL – a small boat's anchor with three or four arms; used also for dragging, and for grappling a floating object. 'Grapnel-rope' is an old term for a boat's cable. See *drag*, *sweep* and *creeper*.

GREEN SEA – an unbroken wave. A vessel is said to be 'shipping it green' when unbroken water is driven aboard.

GROG – rum diluted with water; until 1970, when the issue of rum ceased in the Royal Navy, the regulation mixture was two parts water to one of rum. A 'nor'-wester' was a mixture of one part water to one of rum; the more northerly the direction, the stronger the grog. Watered rum was introduced in 1740 by Admiral Vernon, who was known as 'Old Grog' because he habitually wore clothing made of material called grogram. See *tot*.

Grog-blossom – a red nose or pimple.

GROUND SWELL – a heavy swell caused by a distant storm or by one that has passed; it may also be caused by a submarine earthquake.

GUEST WARP – corruption of guess warp – a rope running from the accommodation ladder to the lower boom, for the assistance of boats coming alongside. Its purpose is now served by the gangway boatrope. Also a rope having one end secured to a buoy or quay and the other end kept handy on board so that a boat can be hauled along it.

Guzz – the Naval Base of Devonport, adjoining Plymouth. GUZZ was a wartime signal letter group from the port's callsign.

HALF-TIDE ROCK – a rock which uncovers at half-ebb.

Hanging Judas – a fall, whip or halyard which is not properly secured aloft, or not properly belayed, or hanging loose from aloft. See *dead men* and *Irish pendants*.

Hard tack – ship's biscuits, which used to be very hard and tough. See *soft tack*.

Harry Freeman – free of charge, a gift, or something obtained for nothing. The origin of this term is obscure.

HEADS – a ship's latrines. The 'heads' of a sailing man-of-war were platforms on each side of the stem which were used as latrines by the men.)
HEAVER – a level, handspike.

HOG OUT – to scrub out thoroughly. A hog was a stiff brush used for scrubbing the ship's bottom.

HOLIDAY – a gap left in a row or line; an unpainted patch in paintwork.

HOLYSTONES – blocks of sandstone that were used for scrubbing decks, so-called because their use entailed kneeling down. Medium-sized holystones were called *bibles*, and small ones *prayer books*.

Hookie – the nickname of any Leading Rating, derived from the single anchor he wears as a distinguishing badge.

Hook-rope party – a party of men detailed to give the decks a final clear-up just before an inspection.

HORSE LATITUDES – a belt of light and variable winds, between the Westerlies and the Trade Winds in the northern and southern hemispheres, in which sailing vessels were often becalmed for some time. The name had its origin in the middle of the nineteenth century, when numerous horses were transported from Europe to America and the West Indies, and dead horses could often be seen floating within this belt of the North Atlantic.

HULK – a vessel condemned as unfit for sea service, and used in harbour for some purpose such as a store ship or an accommodation ship.

HULL A SHIP – to penetrate the hull of a ship with shot or shell.

In everybody's mess, but nobody's watch – a phrase applied to a plausible, work-shy person.

Irish pendants – rope yarns, or stray rope's ends hanging in the rigging, or flags with frayed flies. See *dead men* and *hanging Judas*.

JETSAM – sunken cargo which has been cast overboard to lighten a ship. If recovered it is the property of the owners, but if not claimed it is the property of the Crown. See *flotsan* and *ligan*.

JETTISON – to cast overboard.

Jollies – Royal Marines. See *bullocks* and *turkeys*.

Jonah – a bringer of bad luck.

Joss – luck (Chinese).

JUNK – old rope set aside for picking. See *rounding* and *rumbo*.

JURY – a prefix meaning temporary, as in 'jury-mast', for example, which is a mast specially made and rigged temporarily in place of a damaged one.

KEG – a small cask.

Ki – cocoa (the origin of this term is obscure).

KID – a small tub. See *spitkid*.

KILLICK – a small anchor. A slang term for a Leading Rating, because they wear an anchor as a distinguishing badge.

LABOUR – a ship is said to labour when she pitches and rolls heavily in rough weather.

LANDFALL – first sight of land after a passage in the open sea.

LAND-LOCKED – surrounded by land.

LARGE – a ship is sailing large when she is sailing free with the wind abaft her beam; 'an offender at large' is one who is not under constraint. See *by and large*.

LAY UP – to take a ship out of service. To twist the strands of a rope together.

LAY TIME – the time allocated to the charterer of a merchant vessel for the purpose of loading or discharging cargo. See *demurrage*.

LEAGUE – an obsolete sea measurement of distance equivalent to three nautical miles.

LEE-BOARD – a board lowered down into the water on the lee side of a sailing vessel to prevent her making lee-way when close-hauled or reaching.

LEE-SHORE – a shore towards which the wind is blowing.

LEE-TIDE – a tidal stream running in the same direction as the wind. See *weather-tide*.

LET FLY – to let go instantly; usually applied to the sheets of a sailing vessel.

LET RUN – to let go a rope, chain or other flexible object so that it runs out of its own accord.

LIBERTY – leave of less than 24 hours.

LIGAN – sunken cargo or gear which has been cast overboard and buoyed. It is the property of the owners, but if unclaimed becomes the property of the Crown. See *flotsam* and *jetsam*.

Lights – an extension of the regulation time for 'lights out', which may be granted on certain occasions.

Lurk – to impose upon someone else's kindness, eg to persuade someone to take your trick or watch.

Lush up – to stand treat. Lush is sometimes used to mean abundant liquor, or the condition of being drunk.

MAKING – tides are said to be 'making' during the period between neaps and springs when their height progressively increases. See *take-off*.

MANIFEST – an official inventory of all cargo carried by a merchant vessel.

MARTINGALE – a stay leading from the nose of the jib-boom of a sailing vessel to her stern; in some ships it is passed through the head of a dolphin striker to give it a better downward pull on the jib-boom. Any stay which prevents a boom, spar or strut from topping up (lifting higher than the rigged position) is also called a martingale. See *bobstay*.

MASTER – the Captain of a merchant vessel.

MASTER-OF-THE-FLEET – the title accorded to the Navigating Officer in a flagship, when the Flag Officer and staff are embarked, who is charged with the navigation of the *flotilla* (which see) as a whole.

Maties – dockyard workmen.

MESS TRAPS – food utensils for a naval officers' mess.

MESS UTENSILS – food utensils for a naval ratings' mess.

Money for old rope – something for nothing, simple.

MONKEY – a prefix meaning small eg 'monkey's island', 'monkey jacket', 'monkey boom', 'monkey block'.

Mother Cary's chickens – small sea birds otherwise known as stormy petrels. The origin of the term is legendary; it was well known among English seamen in the days of Captain Cook.

MUFFLE – to muffle the oars is to parcel their looms with canvas where they pass through the rowlocks or crutches to prevent them from creaking.

MULCT – a fine imposed as a punishment; 'to mulct' is to fine.

Mundungus – untidy rubbish. Derived from the Spanish 'mondongo', meaning tripe.

Mungy – food. Derived from the French 'manger', to eat.

MUZZLER – a gale blowing from right ahead.

NEAPED OR BENEAPED – a vessel which cannot leave harbour except at spring tides is said to be neaped; the term also describes a vessel grounded at the height of a spring tide which cannot be refloated until the next spring tide.

Neaters – prior to the cessation of rum issue, the slang term for neat rum which was issued to Chief Petty Officers and Petty Officers.

Nicknames in general use afloat – 'Granny' Anderson and Henderson; 'Dinger' or 'Daisy' Bell; 'Wiggy' Bennet; 'Ginger' Casey; 'Nobby' Clark; 'Jumper' Collins or Short; 'Bandy' Evans; 'Harry' Freeman; 'Jimmy' Green; 'Tosh' Gilbert; 'Chats' Harris; 'Cosher' Hinds; 'Jerry' King; 'Bogie' Knight; 'Dodger' Long; 'Pincher' Martin; 'Dusty' Miller; 'Pony' Moore; 'Spud' Murphy; 'Nosey' Parker; 'Spike' Sullivan; 'Buck' Taylor; 'Hookey' Walker; 'Sharkey' Ward; 'Knocker' White; 'Slinger' Woods; 'Shiner' Wright.

NIPPER – a stop or strop used temporarily to seize two ropes together.

NORTHERN LIGHTS – the Aurora Borealis, seen occasionally in the northern sky when in high latitudes at night. The similar Aurora Australis or Southern lights are seen in high southern latitudes.

Nor'-easter – the same as *not entitled* (which see). A North-easterly wind is an unpopular one, particularly in winter.

Nor'-wester – see *grog*.

NOT ENTITLED – a report at a naval pay table signifying that a person is not due for any pay.

OFFING – that vaguely defined part of the sea which lies between the entrance to a harbour, or the shoal water of a coast, and the horizon.

Oppo – a friend in the same, or in another, ship.

Opposite number – a person having the same station or duties as your own; eg the opposite number of a person in the port watch is the person in the starboard watch who carries out the same duties.

OVERHAUL (1) – to overtake.

OVERHAUL (2) – to examine carefully and repair where necessary.

OVERHAUL (3) – to haul the blocks of a tackle apart to the full scope of the fall.

PASS THE WORD – to relay an order or a summons.

PAY – to give a coating to a surface.

PAY A SEAM – to pour molten pitch into a seam.

PAY AWAY – to slacken a rope.

PAY OFF – to fall away from the wind. Also to place a ship out of commission (in former times the ship's company were then paid their wages and discharged).

PAY OUT – to ease out by hand.

PEAK – fore peak – the space immediately abaft the stem of a ship; after peak – the space immediately before her stern post. These spaces are often used in merchant ships for storage of fresh water in what are known as 'peak tanks'.

Perks – perquisites, ie allowance in cash or kind appertaining to a particular office or employment.

Pier-head jump – joining a ship just as she is about to sail.

PIPE DOWN – the last routine of the day, after which silence is maintained throughout the messdecks until the hands are called. May also be given verbally as an order to stop talking, arguing or skylarking.

Plushers – the residue, particularly of food or drink, caused by over-issue or by the distribution of short measures. Previously applicable to the residue of the grog ration of a mess.

Pompey – Portsmouth.

Pongo – soldier. See *grabbies*.

PORT – a square or rectangular hole cut in a ship's side as an entrance for embarking passengers or cargo, or for light and ventilation.

PREVENTER – any rope, chain or fitting backing up or limiting the movement of rigging, spars, cable, etc.

Private ship – any ship, other than a flagship, commanded by an officer of Captain's rank.

PROUD – projecting from an otherwise flat surface, such as the head of a rivet which is not countersunk. The term is also applied to a wooden shore which is cut slightly longer than the space into which it is to fit, so that it has to be driven home when set up and so be jammed in place.

PUDDING – a rope fender, cylindrical in shape and sometimes with the ends tapered; generally used on the bows of tugs and harbour launches, also on the griping spar of radial davits.

PURSER – the officer in a merchant ship responsible to the Master for the catering and accommodation of passengers. Formerly the officer in a ship of the Royal Navy charged with her provisions and clothing stores was called the purser.

Pusser – colloquial derivative of 'purser' – the Supply Officer of a warship. 'Pusser's dip' – a candle; 'pusser's dirk' – a clasp knife; 'pusser's crabs' – shoes; 'pusser's medal' – a food stain on clothing.

Putty – the shallow seabed. 'On the putty' – to run aground.

Queen's hard bargain – a lazy, incompetent person.

Quiet number – see *soft number*.

Rabbit – any article made or converted from ship's stores for private use.

Raggie – friend or chum. Formally seamen provided their own cleaning gear, and if two men shared their cleaning rags it was a sign of trust and friendship. 'To part brass rags' is to dissolve a friendship.

RAKE – to lean or incline from the perpendicular; to fire into a ship along her length. The term 'rakish' is applied to a ship with an appearance of force and speed.

RANGE – to lay out (usually applied to rope or cable).

Rattle – to be *'in the rattle'* is to be on the list of defaulters, or in the 'report'.

REFIT – to repair, put in order, recondition.

RELIEF – the person who relieves another of their watch, trick or other specific duty.

RELIEVING TACKLES – tackles or ropes secured to the tiller of a vessel to assist her steering in a heavy sea.

RIGOL – a curved metal fitting above a side scuttle to prevent water running down the ship's side from entering the scuttle.

ROAD, ROADSTEAD – an exposed or offshore anchorage.

Rockie – an officer or person of the Royal Naval Reserve.

Rogue's salute – the gun fired on the morning of the day appointed for a Court Martial.

ROGUE'S YARN – a coloured yarn laid up in a strand or strands of a fibre rope. It was formerly used to distinguish Service cordage from commercial cordage to prevent misappropriation of the former, but it is now used to distinguish one type of cordage, whether service or commercial, from another. Service cordage, however, can still be distinguished from commercial cordage by the colour and the number of strands containing the rogue's yarn.

ROUNDING – condemned rope of under 32mm diameter. Also any service on a rope or spar. See *junk* and *rumbo*.

ROUND UP – to haul together the two blocks of a tackle to a convenient scope for stowage.

RUMBO – condemned cordage. See *junk* and *rounding*.

RUMBO LINE – rope made from old rope, such as stage lashing.

RUN (1) – the distance sailed (steamed) by a ship.

RUN (2) – the note made in the ship's ledger against the name of a deserter. 'To run' is to desert.

RUN DOWN – to ram a vessel, either on purpose or by accident.

RUNNERS – smugglers.

SCANDALISE – to settle the halyards of a gaff in order to spill the wind out of its sail (see *a'cock-bill*). Yards are said to be 'scandalised' when they are not squared.

SCANTLINGS – standard dimensions for the various parts of a ship's structure; they vary with the type or class of ship.

SCEND – the scend of a sea is the vertical movement of its waves. A ship is said to scend when she rises and falls bodily on the crests and in the troughs of heavy seas; it is different from pitching, in which the bows and stern of a vessel are alternately raised and lowered. See *surge*.

SCOTCHMAN – any piece of metal, wood, leather, canvas or other material used to prevent chafe or wear. See *baggywrinkle* and *bolster*.

Scran – food. A 'scran-bag' was formerly used as a receptacle for the remains of a meal but then became the stowage for personal gear, such as clothing, which had been left lying about. It was customary to pay a forfeit of a bar of soap to reclaim any item from the scran-bag.

SCRATCHER – The second coxswain of a submarine who is the subject matter expert for all seamanship matters.

SCUD – low, fast-moving clouds. A sailing ship is sometimes said to be scudding before a gale when she is running before it.

Sculling – to leave something sculling is to leave it lying about or unattended.

SCUPPER – to sink, to founder (from water flooding aboard through the scuppers). 'I'm scuppered' – an expression of defeat or resignation.

SCUTTLE – to cut a hole in a ship's bottom, or to open her seacocks, for the purpose of sinking her.

Sea-daddy – an experienced seafarer detailed to instruct youngsters; sometimes applied to the officer in charge of the midshipmen. See *Snotties' nurse*.

Sea-lawyer – an argumentative person; one more given to questioning orders than readily obeying them, and to talking rather than working.

Sea-legs – people are said to have got their sea-legs when they can move about their ship without losing their balance when she rolls or pitches heavily.

SEWED – (pronounced 'sued') – a ship is said to be sewed when she has been grounded on a falling tide, either intentionally or accidentally, and can only be refloated by the rising tide; the difference between the actual level of the water and the level to which it must rise to refloat her is the distance by which she is sewed. She can also be described as being sewed to a certain point, eg if the water was level with the bilge keel she would be 'sewed to the bilge keel'. The term is also used to describe the condition of a ship in this respect during the operations of docking and undocking in a dry dock. This term derives from the old verb 'to sew', meaning to drain.

SHAKE – to cast off fastenings; to take to pieces (a cask or a packing case, for example).

SHEER PLAN – a drawing showing the longitudinal cross-section of a vessel through her keel.

SHIP'S COMPANY – all personnel of a warship other than her officers. The synonymous term in the Merchant Navy is 'crew'.

SHIVER – to break in numerous pieces, to shatter.

SHIPSHAPE – seamanlike in appearance.

SHOT MAT – a heavy rope mat used to protect anything, especially the deck, from heavy weights dropped on it (originally to protect the deck in the event of cannon shot being dropped on it). Now known as a paunch mat.

Shove in your oar – to break into a conversation; to interrupt or interfere.

SICK BAY – the ship's hospital.

SISTER SHIPS – ships built to the same design.

Skate – a person always in trouble or mischief.

SKIPPER – Master of a fishing vessel or of a small trading vessel.

SKULK – to avoid duty.

SLOPS – articles of uniform clothing made for the Crown and issued on repayment to officers and men of the Royal Navy.

Snob – a shoemaker.

SNOTTER – a strop supporting the heel of a swinging boom, derrick or *sprit* (which see). A rope or chain stopper used to hold the lifts of derricks. A type of rope or chain sling.

Snottie – a midshipman.

Snotties' nurse – the officer in charge of midshipmen.

Snowball hitch (slippery hitch) – a hitch that will slip under strain.

SNUB – when applied to a rope or a cable, means to stop suddenly.

SNUG – properly secured; 'snugged down' – prepared to meet a gale.

Soft number – an easy job or duty; a sinecure.

Soft tack – bread. See *hard tack*.

SPEAK – to communicate at sea with another vessel or a shore signal station by visual signalling.

SPELL – a period of continuous work, such as 'a spell at the pumps'; or a period of leisure, such as 'a spell on deck'. 'Spell ho!' is sometimes used as the call for a relief.

SPINDRIFT – spray blown from the crests of waves.

Spithead pheasant – the bluejacket's term for a kipper.

SPITKID – a small tub or other receptacle, placed on the decks during smoking hours, for cigarette ends, pipe dottles and waste paper.

SPLINTER MAT – a rope mat, with one side smooth and the other thrummed (or tufted), used for stopping small leaks in the hull of a vessel. See *thrums*.

SPRING (1) – to splinter or crack. A 'spring' is a crack in a spar, and a sprung spar is one which is weakened by splits or by cracks. When a vessel makes water through straining her hull she is said to 'spring a leak'.

SPRING (2) – A spring is a hawser laid out to slew a vessel, or point her in some required direction. 'To spring a boat ahead' is to haul her ahead on a guest warp or a boatrope.

SPRING-PIPE – A short pipe running through bulwarks and used as a fairlead for hawsers.

SPRIT – a boom used for supporting and extending the mainsail of a sailing vessel; it extends from the tack to the peak, and its heel is supported by a *snotter* (which see).

SPURNWATER – a wooden or metal beading, or low coaming, round the edges of decks or waterways to prevent wash-deck water spilling over and soiling the ship's side. The term is also applied to the breakwater on a ship's forecastle.

SQUADRON – a number of similar warships under one command. See *division* and *flotilla*.

Square one's own yard-arm – to put oneself in the right, usually with a superior without regard for others; to observe the letter of the law (or of regulations or instructions) with the object of avoiding possible blame.

SQUARE RIG – the rig of a ship whose sails are set on yards athwart her masts. A slang term for the uniform of most ratings of the Royal Navy below the rate of Petty Officer. See *fore-and-aft rig*.

Square yards (with anyone) – is to agree with, or to enter into agreement with them.

SQUEEGEE – a form of broom with a rubber edge, used for sweeping water from a deck.

STAND – to sail in a certain widely defined direction, eg 'to stand in to the shore', 'to stand southward'.

STANDING – a term denoting anything fixed or permanent, eg 'standing rigging', 'standing guy', 'standing orders' and 'standing number' (ie a permanent job).

START – to move from rest, to loosen, to break out, or to allow to move from rest as in starting a boat's falls.

STATION (1) – a person's place or post for a specific duty, eg 'station for leaving harbour'; or the allotted position of a ship at sea with a fleet, squadron or flotilla. 'To station' is to allot a place or duty to a person or a ship.

STATION (2) – formerly an area of land and sea placed under the naval jurisdiction of a Commander-in-Chief.

STAVE – to break in a plank or a stave, eg of a cask; 'to stave in' – to hole anything or break into it; 'stove in' – holed, eg the bows or side of a vessel which has been in collision.

STEVEDORE – strictly the person who contracts for the handling of cargo into or from a vessel. Now applied to those actually handling the cargo.

STIFF – very stable, the opposite of 'crank'. Such a ship will return quickly to the upright when heeled over. See *crank* and *tender*.

Stone frigate – a naval shore establishment.

THE STRAITS – the Strait of Gibraltar.

STRIKE (1) – A ship is said to strike when she hits the bottom. A ship on an ocean passage and approaching land is said to 'strike soundings' when she reaches water sufficiently shallow for taking soundings.

STRIKE (2) – To lower from aloft; 'to strike the colours' is to haul them down in token of surrender. 'Strike down' is to lower anything into the hold of a ship or between decks.

STRIP TO A GANTLINE – to strip a ship of all her rigging, leaving one gantline rove to the masthead with which to begin refitting the rigging when required.

Strongers – a strong solution of soda and water used to dissolve dirt on decks.

SULLAGE – garbage, rubbish. 'Sullage lighter' – the lighter which, in some ports, is sent to ships to collect their sullage so that it is not *ditched* overboard, thus preventing pollution of the harbour. See *gash*.

SURGE – the lateral movement of a stationary vehicle caused by a swell or the wash of a passing ship. See *scend*.

Swallow the anchor – to retire from sea service.

SWASH-WAY – a channel across or between shoals or spits.

SWEAT – moisture, on bulkheads, decks, deckheads and sides of a ship, due to condensation.

SWEAT UP – to give an extra hard pull on a rope to take down every vestige of slack in it.

SWEEP – to drag the bight of a wire or chain along the bottom to locate or recover a sunken object. See *drag*.

SWEEPER – In the Royal Navy, a person charged with the cleanliness of a compartment or a flat. See *dodger*.

SWEEPS – large oars used to propel lighters, barges and small sailing vessels.

SWIFT – to tauten, to bind, to stay; shrouds are swifted when the slack in them is taken down; a shaky vessel is swifted (or 'under girded') when her hull is bound round with hawsers or chains (see *girt*); the outer ends of capstan bars are swifted to keep the bars shipped in the capstan-head.

SWIG OFF – to haul out on the bight of a taut rope at right-angles to its lead in order to take up the last vestige of slack in its span (usually applied to halyards and lashings).

Swing the lead – to avoid duty by feigning illness, to malinger. See *skulk*.

TAFFRAIL – the top rail round the stern of a ship from quarter to quarter.

TAIL ON – to clap on to a rope. See *clap on*.

TAKE CHARGE – an inanimate object, such as a rope or a cable, takes charge when it gets out of control and runs out by its own momentum.

TAKE OFF – the tides are said to be taking off when they decrease progressively between springs and neaps. See *making*.

TAKE UP – to tauten, to absorb, to swell; to 'take up the slack' (of a rope or nut, for example); when a dry boat is placed in water her planking will gradually take up and become tight; when applied to *slops* which see, it means to buy.

TAKEN ABACK – surprised; a sailing vessel is said to be taken aback when the wind strikes her sails on the wrong side.

TALLY – a label or the name of a person or an article. 'To tally' – to keep a record (of stores or cargo being embarked or disembarked, for example).

Tanky – the midshipman assisting the Navigating Officer; a seaman attached to the Supply department for special victualling duties.

Tar, or *Jack Tar* – name formerly applied to a seaman of the Royal Navy (from his tarpaulin hat and tarry trousers).

TARPAULIN – a heavy canvas cover tarred or painted; usually used to cover hatches to make them watertight.

TELL-OFF – to detail men for work.

Tell that to the Marines – a seafarer's repartee to an improbable story.

TENDER (1) – a small vessel employed to attend on a larger vessel, for duties such as ferrying, store-carrying or training. She is under the direct command of, and her accounts are kept by, her parent ship.

TENDER (2) – a term applied to a ship having poor stability; one which rolls easily and recovers slowly, the same as 'crank' and the opposite of *stiff* (which see).

THRUMS – short rope yarns forming the tufted surface of a mat. See *splinter mat*.

Ticklers – service tobacco issued in tins. The term originated in the tinned jam which was first supplied to the Navy in 1908 by a manufacturer of the name of Tickler.

Tiddie-oggie – the bluejacket's term for a small flat meat pie of oval shape, called in the West Country a Cornish pasty.

Tiddley – neat, smart.

TIDE RACE – a fast moving, turbulent stretch of water, often with eddies and whirls in it, caused by a strong current meeting a tidal stream or a heavy sea or swell, or passing over a sharply uneven bottom.

TIDE RODE – a vessel at anchor in tidal waters is said to be tide-rode when she is lying swung to the tidal stream rather than to the wind. See *wind-rode*.

TIGHT – watertight.

TINGLE – a small patch, usually of copper sheet with a waterproof lining, applied as a temporary repair to a small hole in the hull of a boat.

TIMONOGUY – a gut fitted to a projecting fitting to prevent a rope from fouling it.

TOMBOLA – a game, similar to a lottery, played on board HM ships; other names of the game are 'House' or 'Bingo'.

TOP-HAMPER – top weight, ie any weight carried, either temporarily or permanently, above the upper deck; superstructures, masts, funnels and deck cargo are examples.

TOT – one-eighth of a pint. Prior to 1970 the ration of rum issued to ratings of the Royal Navy. Issued neat to Chief Petty Officers and Petty Officers and as grog (which see) to all other ratings.

TRIATIC STAY – a stay led from the head of the mainmast to the head of the foremast. It was formerly used for staying the mainmast.

TRICK – a short spell of special duty involving continuous work or alertness. Tricks are carried out in turn by men of the watch on deck, and their length depends upon the nature of the duty; lookouts do from half an hour to an hour, helmsmen one hour.

TRINITY HOUSE – a corporation which is the General Lighthouse Authority (GLA) for England, Wales, the Channel Islands and Gibraltar. It is the principal pilotage authority for the London and Isle of Wight districts as well as thirty-nine other districts in the United Kingdom. It was granted its first charter by Henry the Eighth in 1514. The Board of the Corporation comprises Master Mariners, who are known as 'Elder Brethren'. The Corporation also administers certain charitable trusts for the relief of elderly and distressed Master Mariners and their dependants.

Turkeys – the name formally given to men of the Royal Marine Light Infantry because of the red tunics they wore. See *jollies* and *bullocks*.

TWO BLOCKS – see *block-and-block*.

Uckers – the sailor's name for the game of Ludo; a game of skill and chance played with counters and dice.

ULLAGE – *the quantity a cask, case or tank lacks of being full.*

ULOEING – a Chinese method of sculling with a single oar shipped over the stern of a boat. The oar is pivoted about a round-headed pin on the transom, and its loom is secured to the bottom of the boat by a martingale of rope or chain.

UNSTABLE – a ship is said to be unstable when she is top-heavy and so is unable to recover when heeled over by wind or sea. See *crank*, *stiff* and *tender*.

UVROE – see *euphroe*.

WAKE – the strip of water astern of a vessel through which she has passed. The opposite of *grain* which see).

WALL-SIDED – said of a ship with perpendicular sides and high freeboard.

Warm the bell – to act or arrive before the appointed time; to be early.

WARP – any rope or hawser used to haul a vessel from one position to another; 'to warp' is to move a vessel by this means. Also a lengthwise thread in the weave of canvas.

WASH – the disturbance in the water made by the movement of a vessel through it.

Wash out – to countermand an instruction or an order. Derived from the days when signalmen recorded messages on a slate and expunged them before recording new ones. See *belay*.

WATER-LOGGED – a vessel is water-logged when she is full of water but still floating.

WEATHER-BOUND – unable to put to sea owing to the weather.

WEATHER-TIDE – a tidal stream flowing in the opposite direction to the wind. See *lee-tide*.

WEEP – to leak slightly; a weeping cask, or joint in a pipe, for example.

Wet – stupid. *Wet as a scrubber* – extremely stupid.

WHARF – a loading-place for shipping.

WIND-RODE – a vessel at anchor in tidal water is said to be wind-rode when she is swung to the wind rather than to the tidal stream. See *tide-rode*.

WIND-VANE – a thin strip of metal mounted on a vertical pivot on the head of a mast, or other suitable place aloft, so that it will indicate the direction of the wind in relation to the ship's course and speed.

WINDSAIL – a ventilation trunk of canvas slung from aloft with its mouth set to catch the wind and its foot led below to the space to be ventilated.

WORK UP – to train the officers and ship's company of a newly-commissioned ship to an efficient state.

Royal Navy Authorship

The 2014 edition of the Royal Naval *Admiralty Manual of Seamanship* has a pedigree with earlier published editions dating back to 1908. These hardback editions reflected the requirements of the Royal Navy of that era taking into account changing technology and techniques as they developed. The 1995 edition has been in general use to this day with annual changes keeping it up to date with the latest equipment and procedures. This authoritative publication is widely available within the Royal Navy, Royal Fleet Auxiliary, training establishments, NATO, UK sea cadet forces and many other nations around the world.

This 2014 edition brings together seamanship equipment, procedures and methodology of the modern Royal Navy Surface and Subsurface Fleet and the Royal Fleet Auxiliary Service. It covers general sea terms, anchors and cables, towing ships/submarines, boatwork, general rigging and slinging, replenishment at sea, water safety, targets and markers and tactical communications.

This *Admiralty Manual of Seamanship* has been produced by the Royal Navy and is published by The Nautical Institute. Whether on Naval ships, commercial vessels or leisure craft, this leading seamanship publication will benefit all mariners.

Current Author

The current author of *The Admiralty Manual of Seamanship* is Mr Vic Vance, a retired Royal Navy Warrant Officer Seaman Specialist. Mr Vance was educated at Hundred of Hoo Secondary School Nr Rochester Kent and entered the Royal Navy as a Junior Seaman in 1965. He served in a variety of ships from Antarctic Survey to frontline Frigates/Destroyers with three years as the Hong Kong Patrol Squadron Seamanship Officer. On promotion to Warrant Officer Seaman Specialist, Mr Vance became part of the Flag Officer Surface Flotilla Staff where he was responsible for Seamanship procedural policy making and ship inspections for all surface ships of the Royal Navy; he retired from uniformed service in1999.

On retirement Mr Vance joined the Civil Service as a Warship Support Agency Desk Officer and focal point for Replenishment at Sea equipment and general seamanship. In 2004 Mr Vance was promoted and took up the appointment of the Royal Navy's Staff Author for *The Admiralty Manual of Seamanship*, the *Royal Marines Landing Craft and Small Craft Operations Manuals*, the *Sailmakers Handbook* and the *Survivors Handbook*. The latter two publications are published in collaboration with The Nautical Institute.